If it's APRIL 2007
and you are still using this Directory,
it's time to order the NEW Edition.

Please visit our website

www.cabells.com

or contact us at

Cabell Publishing, Inc.

Box 5428, Beaumont, Texas 77726-5428
(409) 898-0575
Fax (409) 866-9554
Email: publish@cabells.com

Cabell's Directory Of Publishing Opportunities In Psychology

VOLUME I   A thru J of A
FIRST EDITION 2005-2006

David W. E. Cabell, Editor
McNeese State University
Lake Charles, Louisiana

Deborah L. English, Editor
Twyla J. George, Assistant Editor
Lacey E. Earle, Assistant Editor

To order additional copies
visit our web site
www.cabells.com

or contact us at

Box 5428 Beaumont, Texas 77726-5428
(409) 898-0575 Fax (409) 866-9554

$99.95 U.S. for addresses in United States
Price includes shipping and handling for U.S.
Add $50 for surface mail to countries outside U.S.
Add $100 for airmail to countries outside U.S.

ISBN # 0-911753-21-4

TABLE OF CONTENTS

ii

vi

Preface

The objective of *Cabell's Directory of Publishing Opportunities in Psychology* is to help you publish your ideas.

The *Directory* contains the editor's name(s), address(es), phone and fax number(s), and e-mail and web address(es) for over 315 journals.

To help you in selecting those journals that are most likely to publish your manuscripts the **Index** classifies the journals into thirty-nine different topic areas. In addition, the Index provides information on the journal's type of review process, number of external reviewers and acceptance rate.

To further assist you in organizing and preparing your manuscripts, the *Directory* includes extensive information on the style and format of most journals. If a journal has its own set of manuscript guidelines, a copy of these guidelines is published in the *Directory*. Also, each entry indicates the use of a standard set of publication guidelines by a journal. For example, some journals use the *Chicago Manual of Style* or the *Publication Manual of the American Psychological Association*.

Furthermore, the *Directory* describes the type of review process used by the editor(s) of a journal, type of review, number of reviewers, acceptance rate, time required for review, availability of reviewers comments, fees charged to review or publish the manuscript, copies required and manuscript topics. Information on the journal's circulation, readership and subscription prices are also provided.

Although this *Directory* focuses on journals in the specialized area of **Psychology**, other directories focus on **Educational Psychology and Administration** and **Educational Curriculum and Methods**. The division of education journals into these two directories more appropriately meets the researcher's need for publishing in his area of specialization.

The decision to place journals in this directory is based on the manuscript topics selected by the editor as well as the journals' guidelines for authors.

The *Directory* includes a section titled **"What is a Refereed Article?"** which tends to emphasize the value of a blind review process and use of external reviewers. However, this section cautions individuals using these criteria to also consider a journal's reputation for quality. Additionally, it indicates that differences in acceptance rates may be the result of different methods used to calculate these percentages and the number of people associated with a particular area of specialization.

How To Use the Directory

TABLE OF CONTENTS
Table of Contents provides over 315 journals to help your locate a publication.

INDEX
Index classifies the journals according to thirty-nine (39) different manuscript topics. It also includes information on the type of review, number of external reviewers, acceptance rate and page number of each journal.

ADDRESS FOR SUBMISSION
Address for Submission provides: the Editor's Name(s), Mailing Address(es), Telephone and Fax numbers(s), and E-mail and Web address(es).

PUBLICATION GUIDELINES
Manuscript Length refers to the length of the manuscript in terms of the number of double-spaced typescript pages.

Copies Required indicates the number of manuscript copies you should submit to the editor.

Computer Submission indicates whether the journal prefers hardcopy (paper) or electronic submissions such as disk, e-mail attachment, or a combination of methods.

Format refers to the type of word processing programs or computer programs the journal requires for reviewing the manuscript. Some examples of these programs are Microsoft Word, WordPerfect, PDF, or RTF.

Fees to Review refers to whether the journal charges a fee to review the manuscript. Knowing this item permits the author to send the required funds with the manuscript.

Manuscript Style refers to the overall style guide the journal uses for text, references within the text and the bibliography. This is usually either the *Chicago Manual of Style* or the *Publication Manual of the American Psychological Association (APA)*.

REVIEW INFORMATION
Type of Review specifies blind, editorial, or optional review methods. A blind review indicates the reviewer(s) does not know who wrote the manuscript. An editorial review indicates the reviewer knows who wrote the manuscript. The term "optional" indicates the author may choose either one of these types of review.

No. of External Reviewers and *No. of In House Reviewers*
These two items refer to the number of reviewers who review the manuscript prior to making a decision regarding the publication of the manuscript. Although the editor attempted to determine whether the reviewers were on the staff of the journal or were outside reviewers, many of the respondents had trouble distinguishing between internal and external reviewers. Thus it may be more accurate to add these two categories and determine the total number of reviewers.

Acceptance Rate refers to the number of manuscripts accepted for publication relative to the number of manuscripts submitted within the last year. The method of calculating acceptance rates varies among journals.

Time to Review indicates the amount of time that passes between the submission of a manuscript and notification to the author regarding the results of the review process.

Reviewer's Comments indicates whether the author can obtain a copy of the reviewer's comments. In some cases, the author needs to request that the editor send these remarks.

Invited Articles indicates the percentage of articles for which the editor requests an individual to write specifically for publication in the journal. The percentage is the number of invited articles relative to the total number of articles that appeared in a journal within the past year.

Fees to Publish refers to whether the journal charges a fee to publish the manuscript. Knowing this item assists the author in his decision to place the manuscript into the review process.

CIRCULATION DATA
Reader indicates the predominant type of reader the publication seeks to attract. These are divided into a group designated as practitioners or another group referred to as researchers and academics in the psychology discipline.

Frequency of Issue indicates the number of times a journal will be published in a year.

Copies per Issue indicates the number of copies the journal distributes per issue.

Sponsor/Publisher indicates the journal's affiliation with a professional association, educational institution, governmental agency, and/or publishing company.

Subscribe Price indicates the cost to order a year's subscription unless otherwise indicated.

MANUSCRIPT TOPICS
Manuscript Topics indicates those subjects the journal emphasizes.

MANUSCRIPT GUIDELINES/COMMENTS
Manuscript Guidelines/Comments provides information on the journal's objectives, style and format for references and footnotes that the editor expects the author to follow in preparing his manuscript for submission.

How the Directory Helps You Publish

Although individuals must communicate their ideas in writing, the *Directory* helps the author determine which journal will most likely accept the manuscript. In making this decision, it is important to compare the characteristics of your manuscript and the needs of each journal. The following table provides a framework for making this comparison.

Information Provided by the Directory for Each Journal	Manuscript Characteristics
Topic(s) of Articles Manuscript Guidelines	Theme
Acceptance Rate Percentage of Invited Articles	Significance of Theme
Type of Reader	Methodology and Style
Circulation Review Process	Prestige
Number of Reviewers Availability of Reviewers Comments Time Required for Reviewer	Results of Review

This framework will help the author determine a small number of journals that will be interested in publishing the manuscript. The *Directory* can assist the author in determining these journals, yet a set of unwritten and written laws prevent simultaneous submission of a manuscript to more than one journal. However, a manuscript can be sent to another journal in the event of a rejection by any one publication.

Furthermore, copyright laws and editorial policy of a given publication often require the author to choose only one journal. Consequently, some journals will require the author to sign a statement indicating the manuscript is not presently under review by another publication.

Publication of the manuscript in the proceedings of a professional association does not prevent the author from sending it to a journal, however there usually are some restrictions attached. Most professional associations require that the author acknowledge the presentation of the manuscript at the associate meeting.

Since the author is limited to submission of a manuscript to only one journal and the review process for each journal requires a long period of time, a "query" letter may help the author determine the journal most likely to publish the manuscript.

The query letter contains the following information:

- Topic, major idea or conclusion of the manuscript
- The subject sample, research setting conceptual framework, methodology type of organization or location
- The reasons why the author thinks the journal's readers would be interested in your proposed article
- Asks the editor to make comments or suggestions on the usefulness of this type of article to the journal

While the query letter is helpful in selecting a journal that will be likely to publish the manuscript, the author could use the *Directory* and the framework presented to develop a set of journals which would be likely to publish the manuscript. With this number of possible journals, it makes the sending of a query letter more feasible and tends to achieve the objective of finding the journal most likely to publish the manuscript.

Relating the Theme of the Manuscript to the Topics of Articles Published by Each Journal

To begin the process of choosing the journals to receive the "query" letter and, at some future time, the manuscript, the author needs to examine the similarity between the theme of the manuscript and the editor's needs. The *Directory* describes these needs by listing the topics each publication considers important and the manuscript guidelines. To find those journals that publish manuscripts in any particular area, refer to the topic index.

In attempting to classify the theme, the author should limit his choice to a single discipline. With the increasing specialization in the academic world, it is unlikely that reviewers, editors, or readers will understand an article that requires knowledge of two different disciplines. If these groups do not understand a manuscript, the journal will reject it.

If a manuscript emphasizes an interdisciplinary approach, it is important to decide who will be reading the article. The approach should be to explain the theoretical concepts of one discipline to the specialist in another discipline. The author should not attempt to resolve theoretical issues present in his discipline and explain their implications for specialists in another discipline.

Although the discipline classifications indicate the number of journals interested in your manuscript topic, the manuscript guidelines help the author determine the journals that will most likely have the greatest interest in the manuscript. The manuscript guidelines provide a detailed statement of the criteria for judging manuscripts, the editorial objectives, the readership and the journal's content and approach. This information makes it possible to determine more precisely the congruence between the manuscript and the type of articles the journal publishes. **The *Directory* contains the manuscript guidelines for a large number of journals.**

The Relationship Between the Journal's Acceptance Rate and Significance of the Theme of the Manuscript

In addition to determining the similarity between the topic of the manuscript and the topic of articles published by the journal, an examination of the significance of the theme to the discipline is also an important criterion in selecting a journal. The journals with the lowest acceptance rate will tend to publish those manuscripts that make the most significant contributions to the advancement of the discipline. Since these journals receive a large number of manuscripts, the editors distinguish those manuscripts likely to make a significant contribution to the reader's knowledge.

Defining newness or the contribution of any one study to the understanding of a discipline is difficult. However, it is possible to gain some insights into this definition by asking the following questions:

1. Is the author stating the existence of a variable, trend or problem, not previously recognized by the literature?

2. Is the author testing the interactions of a different set of variables or events?

3. Is the author presenting a new technique to cope with a problem or test an idea not previously presented in the literature?

4. Is the author using a subject sample with different characteristics than previously presented in the literature?

If the manuscript does not satisfy one of the first two categories, it is unlikely that a journal with a low acceptance rate will accept it for publication. Thus, the author should send the manuscript to those journals where the acceptance rate is higher.

Although the *Directory* provides the acceptance rates of manuscripts for many different journals, it is important to examine the data on percentage of invited articles for each journal. A high acceptance rate may result because the editor has asked leaders in the discipline to write articles on a particular subject. These invited articles are usually accepted. Since the author of an unsolicited manuscript competes with the leaders in the discipline, the manuscript will have to make a significant contribution to receive the editor's approval.

The Relationship of the Manuscript's Style and
Methodology to the Journal's Readership

Another factor in selecting the journal to receive the manuscript is the journal's readership. The readers of each journal include either, practitioners and professionals, academics and researchers in psychology, or a combination of these groups.

Since the most important goal for an author is to publish the manuscript, the author should consider the prestige of the journal only after the manuscript has a relatively high probability of being published by more than one journal. This probability is determined by the responses the author received to his query letter and the similarity between the finished manuscript and the needs of the journal.

The method of determining the prestige of a journal varies depending on its readership and the goals of the author. If the readership is primarily administrators or practicing professionals and the goal of the author is to improve the author's image and that of the institution, the journal's circulation would probably be the best indicator of prestige.

In contrast, the author whose goal is to become known among the author's colleagues might consider the type of review process the journal uses as well as its circulation. With a few exceptions, the most prestigious journals with academic readership use a refereed review process.

The Possible Results of the Review Process and the
Selection of a Journal to Receive the Manuscript

Despite the fact that a journal with lower prestige would most likely publish the article, the author might be willing to take a chance on a journal with a greater amount of prestige. Since this will decrease the chances of manuscript acceptance, the author should also consider the consequences of rejection. The consequences include the knowledge the author will gain from having his manuscript rejected.

To determine the amount of knowledge the author is likely to gain requires consideration of the number of reviewers the journal uses in the review process, the availability of the reviewer's comments and the time required for the review process. If the journal makes the reviewer's comments available to the author, this provides a great learning opportunity. Also, the more people that review the manuscript, the greater the author's knowledge will be concerning how to improve the present manuscript. Hopefully, the author will transfer the knowledge gained from writing this manuscript to future manuscripts.

Should the review process take a small amount of time relative to a long period of time, the author is provided with a greater opportunity to use this knowledge to revise the manuscript. To assist the author in determining those journals that provide a suitable learning opportunity, each journal in the *Directory* includes information on the number of reviewers, availability of reviewer's comments to the author and time required for review.

Sending the Manuscript

Before sending the manuscript to an editor, the author should write a cover letter, make sure the manuscript is correctly typed, the format conforms to the journal's guidelines and the necessary copies have been included. **The author should always keep a copy of the manuscript.**

The cover letter that is sent with the manuscript makes it easy for the editor to select reviewers and monitor the manuscript while it is in the review process. This letter should include the title of the manuscript, the author name(s), mailing address(es) phone and fax number(s) and e-mail addresses. In addition, this letter should provide a brief description of the manuscript theme, its applicability and significance to the journal's readership. Finally it should request a copy of the reviewer's comments regardless of whether the manuscript is accepted or rejected.

Receipt of the Reviewer's Comments

The reviewers may still reject the article although the author may have followed this procedure and taken every precaution to avoid rejection. When this occurs, the author's attitude should be focused on making those changes that would make the manuscript more understandable to the next editor, and/or reviewer. These changes may include providing additional information and/or presenting the topic in a more concise manner. Also, the author needs to determine whether some error occurred in selecting the journal to receive the manuscript. Regardless of the source of the errors, the author needs to make those changes that will improve the manuscript's chances of being accepted by the next journal to receive it.

Unless the journal specifically requests the author to revise the manuscript for publication, the author should not send the manuscript to the journal that first rejected it. In rejecting the manuscript, the reviewers implied that it could not be revised to meet their standards for publication. Thus, sending it back to them would not improve the likelihood that the manuscript will be accepted.

If your manuscript is accepted, go out and celebrate but write another one very quickly. When you find you're doing something right, keep doing it so you won't forget.

"What is a Refereed Article?"

With some exceptions a refereed article is one that is blind reviewed and has at least two external reviewers. The blind review requirement and the use of external reviewers are consistent with the research criteria of objectivity and of knowledge.

The use of a blind review process means that the author of the manuscript is not made known to the reviewer. With the large number of reviewers and journals, it is also likely that the name of the reviewers for a particular manuscript is not made known to the author. Thus, creating a double blind review process. Since the author and reviewers are frequently unknown, the manuscript is judged on its merits rather than on the reputation of the author and/or the author's influence on the reviewers.

The use of two (2) or more reviewers permits specialists familiar with research similar to that presented in the paper to judge whether the paper makes a contribution to the advancement of knowledge. When two reviewers are used it provides a broader perspective for evaluating the research. This perspective is further widened by the discussion between the editor and reviewers in seeking to reconcile these perspectives.

In contrast to these criteria, some journals that have attained a reputation for quality do not use either a blind review process or external reviewers. The most notable is *Review of General Psychology* that uses an editorial review process. Its reputation for quality results from its readership whose continual subscription attests to its quality.

In addition to these criteria, some researchers include the journal's acceptance rate in their definition of a refereed journal. However, the method of calculating acceptance rates varies among journals. Some journals use all manuscripts received as a base for computing this rate. Other journals allow the editor to choose which papers are sent to reviewers and calculate the acceptance rate on those that are reviewed that is less than the total manuscripts received. Also, many editors do not maintain accurate records on this data and provide only a rough estimate.

Furthermore, the number of people associated with a particular area of specialization influences the acceptance rate. If only a few people can write papers in an area, it tends to increase the journal's acceptance rate.

Although the type of review process and use of external reviewers is one possible definition of a refereed article, it is not the only criteria. Judging the usefulness of a journal to the advancement of knowledge requires the reader to be familiar with many journals in their specialization and make their own evaluation.

Academic Psychiatry

ADDRESS FOR SUBMISSION:

Laura W. Roberts, Editor-in-Chief
Academic Psychiatry
American Psychiatric Publishing, Inc.
1000 Wlison Boulevard, Suite 1825
Arlington, VA 22209-3901
USA
Phone: 703-907-7889
Fax:
E-Mail: bjones@psych.org
Web: See Guidelines
Address May Change:

PUBLICATION GUIDELINES:

Manuscript Length: 11-15
Copies Required: Four
Computer Submission: Yes Disk & Email
Format: Any - excluding PDF
Fees to Review: 0.00 US$

Manuscript Style:
, American Journal of Psychiatry

CIRCULATION DATA:

Reader: Academics
Frequency of Issue: Quarterly
Copies per Issue: Less than 1,000
Sponsor/Publisher: AADPRT & AAP (See
  Guidelines)
Subscribe Price: 120.00 US$ Individual
  209.00 US$ Institution
  43.50 US$ Student

REVIEW INFORMATION:

Type of Review: Editorial Review
No. of External Reviewers: 3+
No. of In House Reviewers: 1
Acceptance Rate: 50%
Time to Review: 2 - 3 Months
Reviewers Comments: Yes
Invited Articles: 6-10%
Fees to Publish: 0.00 US$

MANUSCRIPT TOPICS:
Counseling Process; Psychiatric Residency Training; Psychiatry

MANUSCRIPT GUIDELINES/COMMENTS:

Instructions for Authors
Academic Psychiatry is the premier peer-reviewed journal focused on psychiatric education and professional development in academic psychiatry. The American Association of Directors of Psychiatric Residency Training, the Association for Academic Psychiatry, and the Association of Directors of Medical Student Education in Psychiatry have joined together to sponsor *Academic Psychiatry*, which is published quarterly by American Psychiatric Publishing, Inc. Formerly the *Journal of Psychiatric Education*, *Academic Psychiatry* is dedicated to the publication of work concerning educational and professional development efforts by and for psychiatrists. Articles that address teaching, research, administrative, clinical, organizational, and economic issues relevant to the academic missions of departments of psychiatry are welcomed by the journal. The Editors invite high-quality submissions that further knowledge in psychiatric education, stimulate improvements in academic psychiatry, and foster professional development of academic psychiatrists at every career stage.

Peer Review

All submissions are reviewed by at least two experts to determine the originality, validity, and importance to the field of their content and conclusions. Authors will be sent reviewer comments that are judged to be useful to them. *Academic Psychiatry* has initiated a rapid review procedure, and authors can expect to receive notification of the Editor's decision regarding their submission *within three months* of receipt of the submission by the journal office. To foster rapid publication, any required revisions are expected to be accomplished by the authors within an additional two-month period.

Manuscript Specifications

Manuscripts must be prepared according to the manuscript specifications of *The American Journal of Psychiatry*. All manuscripts will be edited for clarity, conciseness, and conformity to journal style. For instructions see **http://ajp.psychiatryonline.org/misc/ifora.shtml**. (Please note, however, that *Academic Psychiatry* does not publish color figures.) Empirical reports of data derived from studies with human participants should briefly but explicitly describe in the methods section what ethical safeguards were in place in the study, e.g., IRB approval, confidentiality protections, informed consent, conflict of interest disclosure, etc.

Manuscripts submitted to *Academic Psychiatry* should include a structured abstract. All submissions, except letters, require abstracts. The abstract of a Brief Report should be no more than 40 words. All other abstracts should be structured and no more than 150 words. Authors should use the active voice and third person. The structured abstract should include information under the following headings: Objective: the primary purpose of the article; Methods: subjects, design, setting, interventions if any, measurements, data analysis; or, for review articles, data sources, study selection, data extraction; Results: key findings; and Conclusions: potential implications, future directions.

Below the abstract, authors should provide, and identify as such, 3 to 5 keywords or short phrases that will assist indexers in cross-indexing the article and that may be published with the abstract. Terms from the medical subject headings (MeSH) list of *Index Medicus* should be used; if suitable MeSH terms are not yet available for recently introduced terms, present terms may be used.

Types of Articles

Original reports of empirical research or critical analyses of important topics in psychiatric education or academic psychiatry may be submitted in one of the following formats. **Special Articles** are overview articles that bring together important information on a topic of general interest to academic psychiatrists. Authors who wish to write a Special Article are advised to check with the Editor to ensure that a similar work has not already been submitted or invited. Special Articles may not exceed 6,000 words (24 double-spaced pages) including any tables, figures, and appendices, a structured abstract of no more than 150 words, and no more than 100 references. **Original Articles** may not exceed 3,500 words (14 double-spaced pages) including references and any tables, figures, and appendices, and a structured abstract of no more than 150 words. Original Articles may be conceptually or empirically oriented. **Brief Reports** may not exceed 1,750 words (7 double-spaced pages), with up to 10 references, 2 tables or figures, and an abstract of no more than 40 words. Brief Reports may be conceptually or empirically oriented.

For all articles, any tables, figures, and appendices should be included in the total word count. A table or figure that fills one-half of a vertical manuscript page equals 150 words of text; one that fills one-half of a horizontal page equals 300 words of text; an appendix equals two-thirds of its actual word count.

Commentary

Submissions for the Commentary section should be tightly reasoned opinion pieces not exceeding 2,500 words (10 double-spaced pages) that address an important issue in psychiatric education, professional development, or academic psychiatry more broadly.

Other Communications

Brief letters not exceeding 1,000 words (4 double-spaced pages) will be considered if they include the notation *for publication*. Editorials and pertinent notices and official actions of the sponsoring organizations will also be published.

Submission Procedure

Academic Psychiatry has recently adopted a new electronic manuscript submission and peer review system called "Manuscript Central." This system allows authors and peer reviewers to upload and access information online, creating a virtually paperless process. Authors upload an electronic file of their paper, peer reviewers read and respond to papers online, and all communications regarding each paper, including letters about interim and final decisions, occur via e-mail. To submit a manuscript for consideration, go to appi.manuscriptcentral.com and either create an account or use your existing account. Then follow the instructions to upload your manuscript in the Author Submission Center. The journal staff and the technicians at Manuscript Central have worked hard to make the process as user-friendly as possible. Help information is available within the site including links to a comprehensive question and answer database, a contact e-mail address for online customer service and technical support phone numbers for national and international callers.

Because the journal's peer review process is blind, please ensure that the title page of the file you upload does not contain any author information. Check the acknowledgements section and delete any author-identifying information. Do not use running heads with author names.

Manuscript Central is convenient, easy to use for editors, authors, and reviewers, and dramatically decreases the length of the peer review process.

For further information regarding the online submission process or the requirements for submission to *Academic Psychiatry*, contact Angela Moore at (703) 907-7856 or e-mail **amoore@psych.org**.

Accident Analysis & Prevention

ADDRESS FOR SUBMISSION:

Rune Elvik & Karl Kim, Editors
Accident Analysis & Prevention
PO Box 6110, Etterstad, N-0602
Olso,
Norway
Phone:
Fax:
E-Mail: rune.elvik@toi.no
Web:
Address May Change:

PUBLICATION GUIDELINES:

Manuscript Length: 5,000 words max
Copies Required: Four
Computer Submission: Yes Prefer Email
Format: Word - Most other formats
Fees to Review: 0.00 US$

Manuscript Style:
    American Psychological Association

CIRCULATION DATA:

Reader: Practitioners
Frequency of Issue: 6 Times/Year
Copies per Issue: No Reply
Sponsor/Publisher: Elsevier Science
    Publishing Co.
Subscribe Price:

REVIEW INFORMATION:

Type of Review: No Reply
No. of External Reviewers: 3
No. of In House Reviewers: 0
Acceptance Rate: 45%
Time to Review: 2 - 3 Months
Reviewers Comments: Yes
Invited Articles: 0-5%
Fees to Publish: 0.00 US$

MANUSCRIPT TOPICS:
Decision Making Theory; Human Relations; Transportation/Safety/Psychology

MANUSCRIPT GUIDELINES/COMMENTS:

Description
Accident Analysis & Prevention provides wide coverage of the general areas relating to accidental injury and damage, including the pre-injury and immediate post-injury phases. Published papers deal with medical, legal, economic, educational, behavioral, theoretical or empirical aspects of transportation accidents, as well as with accidents at other sites. Selected topics within the scope of the Journal may include: studies of human, environmental and vehicular factors influencing the occurrence, type and severity of accidents and injury; the design, implementation and evaluation of countermeasures; biomechanics of impact and human tolerance limits to injury; modelling and statistical analysis of accident data; policy, planning and decision-making in safety.

Audience
Regional planners, research scientists, civil engineers, trauma physicians, psychologists, public health planners.

Objective
Accident Analysis and Prevention is intended to advance understanding of accident causes, and means of their prevention, through presentation of research findings.

SUBMISSION OF ARTICLES
General
Authors are to submit their papers electronically, preferably by e-mail attachment in Word to one of the Editors or Associate Editors:

R. Elvik (Epidemiological studies, evaluation studies, cost-benefit analyses), Institute of Transport Economics, PO Box 6110 Etterstad, N-0602, Oslo 6, Norway, email:
rune.elvik@toi.no

Jeremy Broughton, Traansport Research Laboratory, Old Wokingham Rd., Crowthorne, Berkshire RG11, UK email: **jbroughton@trl.couk**

L. Hakamies-Blomqvist (Psychology and social psychology of traffic; older road users), Swedish National Road and Transport Research Institute S-581 95 Linkoping, Sweden Email:
liisa.hakamies-blomqvist@vti.se

K. Kim University of Hawaii at Manoa, 242 Maile Way, Honolulu, HI 96822, USA email
karlk@hawaii.edu

A.J.McKnight, (Driver behavior and related counter-measures; performance measurement; problem identification; program evaluation), Transportation Research Associates, 78 Farragut Rd., Annapolis, MD 21403, USA, email: **ajamesmcknight@comcast.net**

H. Moskowitz (Effect of acute or chronic stress on skill performance; program evaluation; human capacity limitations), 4138 Royal Crest Place, Encino, CA 91436, USA, email:
herbmosk@ucla.edu

To allow the fullest use of the journal as a means of communicating research findings, articles must be made as concise as possible. Papers should be limited to 5,000 words in length except as approved by the Editor.

Submission of an article implies that the work described has not been published previously (except in the form of an abstract or as part of a published lecture or academic thesis), that it is not under consideration for publication elsewhere, that its publication is approved by all authors and tacitly or explicitly by the responsible authorities where the work was carried out, and that, if accepted, it will not be published elsewhere in the same form, in English or in any other language, without the written consent of the Publisher.

It is essential to give a fax number and e-mail address when submitting a manuscript. Articles must be written in good English.

Upon acceptance of an article, authors will be asked to transfer copyright (for more information on copyright see http://authors.elsevier.com). This transfer will ensure the widest possible dissemination of information. A letter will be sent to the corresponding author confirming receipt of the manuscript. A form facilitating transfer of copyright will be provided.

If excerpts from other copyrighted works are included, the author(s) must obtain written permission from the copyright owners and credit the source(s) in the article. Elsevier has preprinted forms for use by authors in these cases: contact ES Global Rights Department, P.O. Box 800, Oxford, OX5 1DX, UK; phone: (+44) 1865 843830, fax: (+44) 1865 853333, email: permissions@elsevier.com

Electronic format requirements for accepted articles

We accept most word-processing formats, but Word, WordPerfect or LaTeX is preferred. An electronic version of the text should be submitted together with the final hardcopy of the manuscript. The electronic version must match the hardcopy exactly. Always keep a backup copy of the electronic file for reference and safety. Label storage media with your name, journal title, and software used. Save your files using the default extension of the program used. No changes to the accepted version are permissible without the explicit approval of the Editor. Electronic files can be stored on 3 inch diskette, ZIP-disk or CD (either MS-DOS or Macintosh).

Although Elsevier can process most word processor file formats, should your electronic file prove to be unusable, the article will be typeset from the hardcopy printout.

PREPARATION OF TEXT

Presentation of manuscript

Please write your text in good English (American or British usage is accepted, but not a mixture of these). Italics are not to be used for expressions of Latin origin, for example, in vivo, et al., per se. Use decimal points (not commas); use a space for thousands (10 000 and above).

Authors in Japan kindly note that, upon request, Elsevier Japan will provide a list of people who can check and improve the English of an article before submission. Contact our Tokyo office: Elsevier K.K., Editorial Service, 1-9-15 Higashi Azabu, Minato-ku, Tokyo 106-0044, Japan; tel.: +81-3-5561-5032; fax: +81-3-5561-5045; e-mail: info@elsevier.co.jp

Print the entire manuscript on one side of the paper only, using double spacing and wide (3 cm) margins. (Avoid full justification, i.e., do not use a constant right-hand margin.) Ensure that each new paragraph is clearly indicated. Present tables and figure legends on separate pages at the end of the manuscript. If possible, consult a recent issue of the journal to become familiar with layout and conventions. Number all pages consecutively.

Provide the following data on the title page (in the order given).

Title. Concise and informative. Titles are often used in information-retrieval systems. Avoid abbreviations and formulae where possible.

Author names and affiliations. Where the family name may be ambiguous (e.g., a double name), please indicate this clearly. Present the authors' affiliation addresses (where the actual work was done) below the names. Indicate all affiliations with a lower-case superscript letter immediately after the author's name and in front of the appropriate address. Provide the full postal address of each affiliation, including the country name, and, if available, the e-mail address of each author.

Corresponding author. Clearly indicate who is willing to handle correspondence at all stages of refereeing and publication, also post-publication. Ensure that telephone and fax numbers (with country and area code) are provided in addition to the e-mail address and the complete postal address.

Present/permanent address. If an author has moved since the work described in the article was done, or was visiting at the time, a 'Present address' (or 'Permanent address') may be indicated as a footnote to that author's name. The address at which the author actually did the work must be retained as the main, affiliation address. Superscript Arabic numerals are used for such footnotes.

Abstract. A concise and factual abstract is required (maximum length 200 words). The abstract should state briefly the purpose of the research, the principal results and major conclusions. An abstract is often presented separate from the article, so it must be able to stand alone. References should therefore be avoided, but if essential, they must be cited in full, without reference to the reference list.

Keywords. Immediately after the abstract, provide a maximum of 6 keywords, avoiding general and plural terms and multiple concepts (avoid, for example, 'and', 'of'). Be sparing with abbreviations: only abbreviations firmly established in the field may be eligible. These keywords will be used for indexing purposes.

N.B. Acknowledgements. Collate acknowledgements in a separate section at the end of the article and do not, therefore, include them on the title page, as a footnote to the title or otherwise.

ARRANGEMENT OF THE ARTICLE
Subdivision of the article. Divide your article into clearly defined and numbered sections. Subsections should be numbered 1.1 (then 1.1.1, 1.1.2, ?), 1.2, etc. (the abstract is not included in section numbering). Use this numbering also for internal cross-referencing: do not just refer to 'the text.' Any subsection may be given a brief heading. Each heading should appear on its own separate line.

Introduction. State the objectives of the work and provide an adequate background, avoiding a detailed literature survey or a summary of the results.

Figure legends, tables, figures, schemes. Present these, in this order, at the end of the article. They are described in more detail below. If you are working with LaTeX and have such features embedded in the text, these can be left, but such embedding should not be done

8

specifically for publishing purposes. Further, high-resolution graphics files must be provided separately (see Preparation of illustrations).

Appendices. If there is more than one appendix, they should be identified as A, B, etc. Formulae and equations in appendices should be given separate numbering: (Eq. A.1), (Eq. A.2), etc.; in a subsequent appendix, (Eq. B.1) and so forth.

Acknowledgements. Place acknowledgements, including information on grants received, before the references, in a separate section, and not as a footnote on the title page.

References. See separate section, below.

Units. Authors are seriously recommended to use SI (metric) units in their manuscripts, with optional English equivalents in parentheses.

Mathematical formulae. Present simple formulae in the line of normal text where possible. In principle, variables are to be presented in italics. Use the solidus (/) instead of a horizontal line,

e.g., Xp/Ym rather than

Powers of e are often more conveniently denoted by exp. Number consecutively any equations that have to be displayed separate from the text (if referred to explicitly in the text).

Footnotes. Footnotes should be used sparingly. Number them consecutively throughout the article, using superscript Arabic numbers. Many word processors build footnotes into the text, and this feature may be used. Should this not be the case, indicate the position of footnotes in the text and present the footnotes themselves on a separate sheet at the end of the article. Do not include footnotes in the Reference list. Table footnotes. Indicate each footnote in a table with a superscript lowercase letter.

Tables. Number tables consecutively in accordance with their appearance in the text. Place footnotes to tables below the table body and indicate them with superscript lowercase letters. Avoid vertical rules. Be sparing in the use of tables and ensure that the data presented in tables do not duplicate results described elsewhere in the article.

References
Responsibility for the accuracy of bibliographic citations lies entirely with the authors.

Citations in the text. Please ensure that every reference cited in the text is also present in the reference list (and vice versa). Any references cited in the abstract must be given in full. Unpublished results and personal communications should not be in the reference list, but may be mentioned in the text. Citation of a reference as 'in press' implies that the item has been accepted for publication.

Citing and listing of web references. As a minimum, the full URL should be given. Any further information, if known (author names, dates, reference to a source publication, etc.), should also be given. Web references can be listed separately (e.g., after the reference list) under a different heading if desired, or can be included in the reference list.

Text: All citations in the text should refer to:
1. Single author: the author's name (without initials, unless there is ambiguity) and the year of publication;
2. Two authors: both authors' names and the year of publication; 3. Three or more authors: first author's name followed by 'et al.' and the year of publication.
Citations may be made directly (or parenthetically). Groups of references should be listed first alphabetically, then chronologically.

Examples: "as demonstrated (Allan, 1996a, 1996b, 1999; Allan and Jones, 1995). Kramer et al. (2000) have recently shown ...."

List: References should be arranged first alphabetically and then further sorted chronologically if necessary. More than one reference from the same author(s) in the same year must be identified by the letters "a", "b", "c", etc., placed after the year of publication.

Examples:
Davis, G.A., Yihong, G., 1993. Statistical methods to support induced exposure analysis of traffic accident data. Transportation Research Record 1404 (1), 43-49.

Fleming, T.R., Harrington, D.P., 1990. Counting Process and Survival Analysis. John Wiley, New York.

Watanabe, K., Yamaguchi, T., 1989. Analysis of factors affecting dummy readings in side impact tests. In: Proceedings of the 12th International Technical Conference on ESV, Gothenburg, pp.1104-1114.

American Hospital Association, 1991. American Hospital Association Hospital Statistics, 1990-91 Edition, American Hospital Association, Chicago, IL, Table 5c, p.135.

PREPARATION OF ILLUSTRATIONS
Preparation of electronic illustrations
Submitting your artwork in an electronic format helps us to produce your work to the best possible standards, ensuring accuracy, clarity and a high level of detail.

General points
- Always supply high-quality printouts of your artwork, in case conversion of the electronic artwork is problematic.
- Make sure you use uniform lettering and sizing of your original artwork.
- Save text in illustrations as "graphics" or enclose the font.
- Only use the following fonts in your illustrations: Arial, Courier, Helvetica, Times, Symbol.
- Number the illustrations according to their sequence in the text.

- Use a logical naming convention for your artwork files, and supply a separate listing of the files and the software used.
- Provide all illustrations as separate files and as hardcopy printouts on separate sheets.
- Provide captions to illustrations separately. ? Produce images near to the desired size of the printed version.

Files can be stored on 3 inch diskette, ZIP-disk or CD (either MS-DOS or Macintosh).A detailed guide on electronic artwork is available on our website:
    http://authors.elsevier.com/artwork

You are urged to visit this site; some excerpts from the detailed information are given here.

Formats
Regardless of the application used, when your electronic artwork is finalised, please "save as" or convert the images to one of the following formats (Note the resolution requirements for line drawings, halftones, and line/halftone combinations given below.):
EPS: Vector drawings. Embed the font or save the text as "graphics".
TIFF: Colour or greyscale photographs (halftones): always use a minimum of 300 dpi.
TIFF: Bitmapped line drawings: use a minimum of 1000 dpi.
TIFF: Combinations bitmapped line/half-tone (colour or greyscale): a minimum of 500 dpi is required.
DOC, XLS or PPT: If your electronic artwork is created in any of these Microsoft Office applications please supply "as is".

Please do not:
- Supply embedded graphics in your wordprocessor (spreadsheet, presentation) document;
- Supply files that are optimised for screen use (like GIF, BMP, PICT, WPG); the resolution is too low;
- Supply files that are too low in resolution;
- Submit graphics that are disproportionately large for the content.

Non-electronic illustrations. Provide all illustrations as high-quality printouts, suitable for reproduction (which may include reduction) without retouching. Number illustrations consecutively in the order in which they are referred to in the text. They should accompany the manuscript, but should not be included within the text. Clearly mark all illustrations on the back (or - in case of line drawings - on the lower front side) with the figure number and the author's name and, in cases of ambiguity, the correct orientation.

Mark the appropriate position of a figure in the article.

Captions. Ensure that each illustration has a caption. Supply captions on a separate sheet, not attached to the figure. A caption should comprise a brief title (not on the figure itself) and a description of the illustration. Keep text in the illustrations themselves to a minimum but explain all symbols and abbreviations used.

Line drawings. Supply high-quality printouts on white paper produced with black ink. The lettering and symbols, as well as other details, should have proportionate dimensions, so as not to become illegible or unclear after possible reduction; in general, the figures should be designed for a reduction factor of two to three. The degree of reduction will be determined by the Publisher. Illustrations will not be enlarged. Consider the page format of the journal when designing the illustrations.

Photocopies are not suitable for reproduction. Do not use any type of shading on computer-generated illustrations.

Photographs (halftones). Please supply original photographs for reproduction, printed on glossy paper, very sharp and with good contrast. Remove non-essential areas of a photograph. Do not mount photographs unless they form part of a composite figure. Where necessary, insert a scale bar in the illustration (not below it), as opposed to giving a magnification factor in the legend.

Note that photocopies of photographs are not acceptable.

Colour illustrations. Submit colour illustrations as original photographs, high-quality computer prints or transparencies, close to the size expected in publication, or as 35 mm slides. Polaroid colour prints are not suitable.

Further information concerning colour illustrations and costs is available from Author Support (authorsupport@elsevier.com)

Submit colour illustrations as original photographs, high-quality computer prints or transparencies, close to the size expected in publication, or as 35 mm slides. Polaroid colour prints are not suitable. If, together with your accepted article, you submit usable colour figures then Elsevier will ensure, at no additional charge, that these figures will appear in colour on the web (e.g., ScienceDirect and other sites) regardless of whether or not these illustrations are reproduced in colour in the printed version. For colour reproduction in print, you will receive information regarding the costs from Elsevier after receipt of your accepted article. For further information on the preparation of electronic artwork, please see
    http://authors.elsevier.com/artwork.

Please note: Because of technical complications which can arise by converting colour figures to 'grey scale' (for the printed version should you not opt for colour in print) please submit in addition usable black and white prints corresponding to all the colour illustrations.

Preparation of supplementary data. Elsevier now accepts electronic supplementary material to support and enhance your scientific research. Supplementary files offer the author additional possibilities to publish supporting applications, movies, animation sequences, high-resolution images, background datasets, sound clips and more. Supplementary files supplied will be published online alongside the electronic version of your article in Elsevier web products, including ScienceDirect: http://www.sciencedirect.com. In order to ensure that your submitted material is directly usable, please ensure that data is provided in one of our recommended file formats. Authors should submit the material in electronic format together with the article and supply a concise and descriptive caption for each file. For more detailed instructions please visit our Author Gateway at http://authors.elsevier.com.

Files can be stored on 3 inch diskette, ZIP-disk or CD (either MS-DOS or Macintosh).

Proofs. When your manuscript is received by the Publisher it is considered to be in its final form. Proofs are not to be regarded as 'drafts'.

One set of page proofs in PDF format will be sent by e-mail to the corresponding author, to be checked for typesetting/editing. No changes in, or additions to, the accepted (and subsequently edited) manuscript will be allowed at this stage. Proofreading is solely your responsibility.

A form with queries from the copyeditor may accompany your proofs. Please answer all queries and make any corrections or additions required.

Elsevier will do everything possible to get your article corrected and published as quickly and accurately as possible. In order to do this we need your help. When you receive the (PDF) proof of your article for correction, it is important to ensure that all of your corrections are sent back to us in one communication. Subsequent corrections will not be possible, so please ensure your first sending is complete. Note that this does not mean you have any less time to make your corrections, just that only one set of corrections will be accepted.

Offprints. Twenty-five offprints will be supplied free of charge. Additional offprints and copies of the issue can be ordered at a specially reduced rate using the order form sent to the corresponding author after the manuscript has been accepted. Orders for reprints (produced after publication of an article) will incur a 50% surcharge.

Enquiries. Authors can keep a track on the progress of their accepted article, and set up e-mail alerts informing them of changes to their manuscript's status, by using the "Track a Paper" feature of Elsevier's Author Gateway http://authors.elsevier.com. For privacy, information on each article is password-protected. The author should key in the "Our Reference" code (which is in the letter of acknowledgement sent by the publisher on receipt of the accepted article) and the name of the corresponding author. In case of problems or questions, authors may contact the Author Support Department, E-mail: authorsupport@elsevier.com.

Addiction

ADDRESS FOR SUBMISSION:

Professor Griffith Edwards, Editor
Addiction
Head Office
National Addiction Centre
4 Windsor Walk
London, SE5 8AF
UK
Phone: +44 (0) 20 78480452
Fax: +44 (0) 20 77035787
E-Mail: spjepad@iop.kcl.ac.uk
Web: www.blackwell-science.com
Address May Change:

PUBLICATION GUIDELINES:

Manuscript Length: No Reply
Copies Required: One
Computer Submission: Yes Disk or Email
Format: No Reply
Fees to Review: 0.00 US$

Manuscript Style:
    See Manuscript Guidelines

CIRCULATION DATA:

Reader: , Multidisciplinary
Frequency of Issue: Monthly
Copies per Issue: 1,001 - 2,000
Sponsor/Publisher: Society for the Study of
    Addiction / Blackwell Publishers, Inc.
Subscribe Price:
    See Website

REVIEW INFORMATION:

Type of Review: Peer Review
No. of External Reviewers: 2-3
No. of In House Reviewers: 0
Acceptance Rate: 21-30%
Time to Review: 1-3 Months
Reviewers Comments: Yes
Invited Articles: No Reply
Fees to Publish: 0.00 US$

MANUSCRIPT TOPICS:
Alcoholism & Drug Addiction; Illicit Drugs & Tobacco

MANUSCRIPT GUIDELINES/COMMENTS:

Aims and Scope
Addiction is a prestigious monthly international peer-reviewed journal, publishing nearly 2000 pages every year. In continuous publication since the Society for the Study of Addiction was founded in 1884, it features original research on alcohol, illicit drugs and tobacco.

Addiction publishes peer-reviewed research reports on alcohol, tobacco and other drugs and brings together research conducted within many different disciplines. The journal is truly international in scope and read in over 60 countries worldwide.

In addition to original research, the journal features editorials, commentaries, reviews, historical articles, interviews with leading figures in the addictions, letters, news and a comprehensive book review section, with listings in collaboration with SALIS. The journal

14

supports the ethical principles enshrined in the Farmington Consensus (Addiction, 92(12) pp 1617-1618).

Instructions for Authors
The Journal fully supports the 'Farmington Consensus' [*Addiction* (1997) **92**: 1617-1618]. The editorial staff would be most grateful for your assistance in relation to the matters listed below. Please follow these guidelines carefully when preparing a submission.

Submissions and editorial correspondence
All submissions from the USA, Canada, Central and South America and the Caribbean should be addressed to the Regional Editor for the Americas. All submissions from Australia and New Zealand should be addressed to the Regional Editor for Australasia. All other submissions and communications, including books for review, should be addressed to the Editor at the Head Office:

Griffith Edwards,
Head Office, National Addiction Centre,
4 Windsor Walk, London SE5 8AF, UK
Tel: +44 (0) 20 7848 0452/0853
Fax: +44 (0) 20 7703 5787

Ethical standards
Manuscripts are accepted on the understanding that they are subject to editorial revision. Submissions must be accompanied by a signed statement from all authors saying that: (a) the material has not been published in whole or in part elsewhere; (b) the paper is not currently being considered for publication elsewhere; (c) all authors have been personally and actively involved in substantive work leading to the report, and will hold themselves jointly and individually responsible for its content; (d) all relevant ethical safeguards have been met in relation to patient or subject protection, or animal experimentation. This statement must also declare sources of funding, direct or indirect, and any connection with the tobacco, alcohol or pharmaceutical industries. With regard to points (a) and (b): if data from the same study are reported in more than one publication, this should be stated in the manuscript and/or covering letter to the Editor, along with a clear explanation as to how the submitted manuscript differs, and copies of closely related manuscripts reporting these data should be enclosed. If at any stage during the handling of their submission, authors decide to withdraw it, we ask them to notify the Editor.

Length
We ask authors to be as concise as possible and will negotiate with you personally and sympathetically if we feel shortening would improve communication. Case reports are welcomed but should not be more than 6 pages long. Letters should not be more than 2 pages long.

Language
Addiction's expectation is that when the authors of a paper do not have English as a first language, they will have their text checked before submission.

Submission and layout
Addiction welcomes submissions in either hard copy or electronic form. For hard-copy submissions, please send one paper copy plus a Word disk version. They should be typed on one side of the paper, double-spaced, with margins of at least 25 mm. The first sheet should contain the title of the paper, a short title not exceeding 45 characters, a total page and word count, names of authors, the address where the work was carried out, and the **full postal and email** addresses of the author who will check proofs and receive correspondence and off-prints. Any Conflict of Interest declaration should be included on this page. The second sheet should contain only the title, names of authors and an abstract. Please state any sources of funding in the Acknowledgments section. The entire manuscript, including all references, tables, figures and any other material, should be numbered in one sequence from the title page onwards. Footnotes to the text should be avoided where possible.

Electronic submissions
For electronic submissions by email (other than for the following areas) and Letters to the Editor, please send to Pat Davis at **p.davis@iop.kcl.ac.uk**

Electronic submissions from the USA, Canada, Central and South America and the Caribbean should be sent to Debbie Talamini at **talamini@up.uchc.edu**

Electronic submissions from Australia and New Zealand should be sent to Margaret Eagers at **ndarc21@unsw.edu.au**

Authors should also send two paper copies of their submission to the appropriate Regional office, together with their signed ethical statement. When sending a final, revised version of an *accepted* article, it is essential that the hard copy exactly matches the material on disk. Save all files on a standard 3.5 inch high-density disk. We prefer to receive disks in Microsoft Word in a PC format, but can translate from most other common word-processing programs, as well as Macs. Please specify which program you have used. Do not save your files as 'text only' or 'read only'.

Abstract
In the case of research reports, abstracts should use the following headings: Aims, Design, Setting, Participants, Intervention (experimental trials only), Measurements, Findings and Conclusions. The findings should be clearly listed because it is these that will form the main basis for the editorial decision. Abstracts should normally be no more than 250 words long. Please include keywords.

References
The reference list should not be needlessly profligate and should include only items that are retrievable through standard bibliographic sources. The Harvard system should be followed. References should be indicated in the typescript by giving the author's name, with the year of publication in parentheses, e.g. Smith (1984); if there are three authors Smith, Green & Jones (1984) on the first citation and Smith *et al.* (1984) subsequently; or if there are more than three authors Smith *et al.* (1984) throughout. If several papers from the same authors and from the same year are cited, (a), (b), (c), etc. should be put after the year of publication. References should be listed at the end of the paper in alphabetical order. All authors should be included.

Journal titles should not be abbreviated. Please include first and last pages of book chapters. Where foreign language papers or books are cited, the title in English needs to be included in brackets after the foreign language version. Examples are:

Abrams, D. B. & Wilson, G. T. (1979) Effects of alcohol on social anxiety in women: cognitive versus physiological processes. *Journal of Abnormal Psychology*, 88, 161-173.

Blane, H. T. & Leonard, K. E. (1987) *Psychological Theories of Drinking and Alcoholism.* New York: Guilford Press.

Illustrations
These should not be inserted in the text but each provided separately and numbered on the back with Figure numbers, title of paper and name of author. All photographs, graphs and diagrams should be referred to as Figures in the text and should be numbered consecutively in Arabic numerals (e.g. Fig. 3). A list of legends for the figures should be submitted on a separate sheet; legends should include keys to any symbols.

Tables
These should be typed on separate sheets and should be cited in the text. Words or numerals should be repeated on successive lines - 'ditto' or 'do' should not be used. Tables should not be ruled.

Authors' checklist
Further advice to authors on the preparation and presentation of their papers can be found in the checklist.

Page proofs. Proofs will be sent via e-mail as an Acrobat PDF (portable document format) file. The e-mail server must be able to accept attachments up to 4 MB in size. Acrobat Reader will be required in order to read this file. This software can be downloaded (free of charge) from the following Web site: www.adobe.com/products/acrobat/readstep2.html

This will enable the file to be opened, read on screen, and printed out in order for any corrections to be added. Further instructions will be sent with the proof. Proofs will be posted if no email address is available; in your absence, please arrange for a colleague to access your email to retrieve the proofs.

Refereeing policy. Papers will normally be sent by the Regional Editor for review to an Assistant Editor, who will solicit referees' reports and make a recommendation to the Regional Editor. The Regional Editor will make a decision on the paper and communicate this with the authors. The Regional Editor or the Assistant Editor may return a paper unrefereed if in their judgment it is not suitable for the Journal.

Copyright. It is a condition of publication that authors vest copyright in their articles, including abstracts, in the Society for the Study of Addiction to Alcohol and Other Drugs. Authors are themselves responsible for obtaining permission to reproduce copyright material from other sources.

Addictive Behaviors

ADDRESS FOR SUBMISSION:

Peter M. Miller, Editor
Addictive Behaviors
Medical University of South Carolina
Prevention and Wellness Program
ONLINE SUBMISSIONS ONLY
114 Doughty St., Room 113, Box 250772
Charleston, SC 29425
USA
Phone: 843-792-4241
Fax: 843-876-1905
E-Mail: millerpm@musc.edu
Web: See Guidelines
Address May Change:

PUBLICATION GUIDELINES:

Manuscript Length: 21-25
Copies Required: Electronic
Computer Submission: Yes Required
Format:
Fees to Review: 0.00 US$

Manuscript Style:
    American Psychological Association

CIRCULATION DATA:

Reader: Academics
Frequency of Issue: 6 Times/Year
Copies per Issue: 5,001 - 10,000
Sponsor/Publisher: Elsevier Science
    Publishing Co.
Subscribe Price:

REVIEW INFORMATION:

Type of Review: Editorial Review
No. of External Reviewers: 2
No. of In House Reviewers: 1
Acceptance Rate: 60%
Time to Review: 2 - 3 Months
Reviewers Comments: Yes
Invited Articles: 11-20%
Fees to Publish: 0.00 US$

MANUSCRIPT TOPICS:
Alcoholism & Drug Addiction; Alcoholism & Drug Addiction; Psychiatry; Smoking

MANUSCRIPT GUIDELINES/COMMENTS:

Description
Addictive Behaviors is an international scientific journal publishing research on substance abuse. The journal specifically focuses on studies related to the abuse of alcohol drugs and nicotine. Articles represent interdisciplinary endeavors with research in such fields as psychology, psychiatry, epidemiology, medicine, pharmacology and neuroscience. While theoretical orientations are diverse, the emphasis of the journal is primarily empirical. That is, sound experimental design combined with valid, reliable assessment and evaluation procedures are a requisite for acceptance. Uncontrolled clinical demonstrations and case studies are not accepted for publication. Priority is given to the publication of research that evaluates behavioral and/or pharmacological treatment or prevention interventions. In addition, studies of the functional relationships between substance use and any one of a combination of social, emotional, cognitive, environmental, and attitudinal factors are

18

encouraged. Studies that clearly contribute to current knowledge of the etiology, prevention and/or treatment of substance abuse are given priority. Research on the epidemiology of substance use is also published. A limited number of reviews are published.

Audience. Psychiatrists, psychologists, pharmacologists, sociologists, social workers.

Guide For Authors
Manuscript Requirements. All manuscripts must be submitted online via the Elsevier Author Gateway page at http://authors.elsevier.com/journal/addictbeh. Authors, reviewers and editors send and receive all correspondence by e-mail and no paper correspondence is necessary. Detailed information about this electronic submission process and specific instructions on how to submit manuscripts can be found at the Author Gateway page which is also linked from the main journal homepage at **http://www.elsevier.com/locate/addictbeh**. Problems encountered while submitting online can be resolved by emailing authorsupport@elsevier.com Questions about the appropriateness of a manuscript for *Addictive Behaviours* should be directed (prior to submission) to the Editor-in-Chief, Dr. Peter Miller, at **millerpm@musc.edu**.

Articles submitted must contain original material which has not been published and which is not being considered for publication elsewhere. Papers accepted by the journal may not be published elsewhere in any language without the consent of the Publisher.

Style. Manuscripts must adhere to the instructions on references, preparation of tables and figures, abstracts, manuscripts format, etc. as described in the *Publication Manual of the American Psychological Association,* 5th edition. Manuscripts that do not conform to the style set forth in this Manual will not be accepted for submission and will not be reviewed. The title of the paper, the author's name and full postal address should be included and the name and address of the organization where the work was conducted should be indicated on the cover sheet of the paper. Please supply the corresponding author's telephone/fax number and E-mail address.

Tables and Figures. All tables and figures should be numbered separately using Arabic numerals, and grouped together at the end of the manuscript. Clearly visible notes within the text should indicate their approximate placement. Figures must be camera-ready; photocopies, blue ink, or pencil are not acceptable. Use black India ink, and type figure legends on a separate sheet. Write the article title and figure number lightly in pencil on the back of each.

Abstracts. An abstract for a research paper should be 100-175 words; one for a review or theoretical article, 75-100 words. General style should be the same as that of the article.

Keywords. Authors should include up to six keywords with their manuscript. Keywords should be selected from the APA list of index descriptors, unless otherwise agreed with the Editor.

Short Communications. In an effort to utilize our journal space more fully, articles that can be condensed to a maximum of 6 double space typewritten pages will be published as short communications. Manuscripts may be submitted as short communications or the editors may suggest that a longer manuscript be modified for inclusion in this section.

Author Enquiries. For enquiries relating to the submission of articles please visit the Author Gateway from Elsevier at http://authors.elsevier.com. The Author Gateway also provides the facility to track accepted articles and set up e-mail alerts to inform you of when an article's status has changed, as well as detailed artwork guidelines, copyright information, frequently asked questions and more.

Administrative Science Quarterly

ADDRESS FOR SUBMISSION:

Donald Palmer, Editor
Administrative Science Quarterly
Cornell University
20 Thornwood Drive, Suite 100
Ithaca, NY 14850-1265
USA
Phone: 607-254-8304
Fax: 607-254-7100
E-Mail: ASQ-Journal@cornell.edu
Web: See Guidelines
Address May Change:

PUBLICATION GUIDELINES:

Manuscript Length: 30+
Copies Required: Five
Computer Submission: No
Format:
Fees to Review: 0.00 US$

Manuscript Style:
    Chicago Manual of Style

CIRCULATION DATA:

Reader: Academics
Frequency of Issue: Quarterly
Copies per Issue: 4000
Sponsor/Publisher: Cornell Johnson
    Graduate School of Management
Subscribe Price: 70.00 US$ Individual
    190.00 US$ Institution
    30.00 US$ Student, $59 Assoc. Member

REVIEW INFORMATION:

Type of Review: Blind Review
No. of External Reviewers: 3
No. of In House Reviewers: 0
Acceptance Rate: 9-11%
Time to Review: 2-3 Months
Reviewers Comments: Yes
Invited Articles: 0-5%
Fees to Publish: 0.00 US$

MANUSCRIPT TOPICS:
Decision Making Theory; Group Dynamics; Industry & Organization; Motivation;
Negotiating Process; Organizational Behavior & Theory

MANUSCRIPT GUIDELINES/COMMENTS:

Website. http://www.johnson.cornell.edu/publications/asq

Notice to Contributors
The *ASQ* logo reads, "Dedicated to advancing the understanding of administration through empirical investigation and theoretical analysis." The editors interpret that statement to contain three components that affect editorial decisions. About any manuscript they ask, does this work (1) advance understanding, (2) address administration, (3) have mutual relevance for empirical investigation and theoretical analysis? Theory is how we move to further research and improved practice. If manuscripts contain no theory, their value is suspect. Ungrounded theory, however, is no more helpful than are atheoretical data. We are receptive to multiple forms of grounding but not to a complete avoidance of grounding.

Normal science, replication, synthesis, and systematic extension are all appropriate submissions for *ASQ*, but people submitting such work should articulate what has been learned that we did not know before. That it has been done before is no reason that it should be done again. There are topics within organizational studies that have become stagnant, repetitious, and closed. Standard work that simply repeats the blind spots of the past does not advance understanding even though work like it has been published before.

ASQ asks, "What's interesting here?" But we take pains not to confuse interesting work with work that contains mere novelties, clever turns of phrase, or other substitutes for insight. We try to identify those ideas that disconfirm assumptions by people who do and study administration. Building a coherent, cumulative body of knowledge typically requires work that suggests syntheses, themes, causal sequences, patterns, and propositions that people have not seen before. Interesting work should accelerate development.

We attach no priorities to subjects for study, nor do we attach greater significance to one methodological style than another. For these reasons, we view all our papers as high-quality contributions to the literature and present them as equals to our readers. The first paper in each issue is not viewed by the editors as the best of those appearing in the issue. Our readers will decide for themselves which of the papers is exceptionally valuable.

We refrain from listing explicit topics in which we are interested. *ASQ should* publish things the editors have never thought of, and we encourage that by being vague about preferences. Authors should look at what *ASQ* has published over the last 10 years, see if there are any precedents for the proposed submission, and, if there is even a glimmer of precedent, submit the work to *ASQ*. Manuscripts that are inappropriate will be returned promptly.

We are interested in compact presentations of theory and research, suspecting that manuscripts with over 35 pages of text contain an unclear line of argument, multiple arguments, or no argument at all. Each manuscript should contain one key point, which the author should be able to state in one sentence. Digressions from one key point are common when authors cite more literature than is necessary to frame and justify an argument.

We are interested in good writing and use poor writing as a reason to reject manuscripts. We're looking for manuscripts that are well argued and well written. By well argued, we mean that the argument is clear and logical; by well written we mean that the argument is accessible and well phrased. Clear writing is not an adornment but a basic proof of grasp.

The basic flaw common to rejected manuscripts is that authors are unable to evaluate critically their own work and seem to make insufficient use of colleagues before the work is submitted. All work has alternative explanations. All work contains flaws. The best way to recognize flaws is to discard the discussion section, ask what was learned and what is wrong with it, and frame the discussion in terms of these discoveries. To do this is to anticipate reviewers and improve the probability of acceptance.

Preparation of Manuscripts. Send five copies of manuscripts for review to the Editor, ASQ, Cornell University, 20 Thornwood Drive, Suite 100, Ithaca, NY 14850. Prepare manuscripts according to the following guidelines:

1. Type all copy (including footnotes, references, or appendices) double-spaced, on one side only.

2. To permit anonymity, the author's name should not appear on the manuscript proper. Instead, attach a cover page giving the title of the article and the name and affiliation of each author. The title of the manuscript should be typed on the first page of the paper.

3. Include an informative abstract of less than 100 words with each copy of the paper.

Format of References in the Text

Use footnotes sparingly. Important material should be incorporated into the text; material having weak relevance should be deleted. References to articles, books, and other sources should be cited in the text by noting in parentheses the last name of the author, the year of publication, and page numbers when appropriate. Do not use "ibid.," "op. cit.," or "loc. cit."; specify subsequent citations to the same source in the same way as the first citation. Examples follow:

1. If the author's name is in the text, follow it with the year in parentheses. ["...Perrow, (1986) described...."] If the author's name is not in the text, insert it and the year in parentheses ["...institutional theory (Tolbert and Zucker, 1996)...."] Multiple references are listed chronologically in parentheses, separated by semicolons. ["(e.g., Thompson, 1967; Perrow, 1986)."]

2. In the case of two or three authors, give all the authors' last names; if there are four or more authors, give only the first author's name followed by "et al." ["...(Dutton et al., 1997)"].

3. Page numbers, to indicate a passage of special relevance or to give the source of a quotation, follow the year and are preceded by a colon. ["Zbaracki (1998: 615) explained...."]

4. If there is more than one reference to the same author in the same year, postscript the date with "a, b, c..." ["Miller and Friesen (1980a)...."]

The List of References in Appendix

Alphabetize by author, and for each author list in chronological sequence. List the authors' last name and initials. Use no italics or abbreviations. See examples:

References

Glaser, B.
1992 Basics of Grounded Theory Analysis. Mill Valley, CA: Sociology Press.

Miller, D., and P. Friesen
1980a "Archetypes of organizational transitions." Administrative Science Quarterly, 25: 268-299. 1980b "Momentum and revolution in organizational adaptation." Academy of Management Journal, 22: 591-614.

Perlow, L. A.
1998 "Boundary control: The social ordering of work and family in a high-tech corporation." Administrative Science Quarterly, 43: 328-357.

Perrow, C
1986 Complex Organizations: A Critical Essay, 3rd ed. New York Random House.

Stuart, T. E.
1995 "Technological positions, strategic alliances, and the rate of innovation in the worldwide semiconductor industry." Unpublished Ph.D. thesis, Stanford University.

Tolbert, P. S., and L. G. Zucker
1996 "The institutionalization of institutional theory." In S. Clegg, C. Hardy, and W. R. Nord (eds.), Handbook of Organizational Studies: 175-190. London: Sage.

Zbaracki, M. J.
1998 "The rhetoric and reality of total quality management." Administrative Science Quarterly, 43: 602-636.

Style Checklist For Submissions

Length and Format. The recommended length of manuscripts is 35 pages of double-spaced text in 12-point font, excluding references, tables, figures, and appendixes.

Typing. Type in block form; do not indent for paragraphs. Type everything, except tables, double-spaced, including footnotes, references, and appendices; quadriple-space between paragraphs. Type tables, figures, footnotes, references, and appendix each on separate pages, with footnotes following the last page of text.

Style Format

- *Quotation marks*--use only for direct quotations.
- *Italics*--omit unless absolutely necessary.
- *Parentheses*--avoid in textual material.
- *Abbreviations*--use only those that are known by the general public; spell out an abbreviated term when first used.
- *Numbers*--spell out those that begin a sentence and numbers from one to nine.

Graphic Material

Figures and tables should be directly pertinent to the discussion; delete extraneous material. Present graphic material so that the meaning is immediately clear; include a title on each figure. Do not confuse figures with tables: Tables present numbers for words; figures display diagrams and graphs.

Abstract. Be sure to supply an informative abstract of less than 100 words. Do not mistake an introduction or summary for an abstract. Abstract only the material presented in the paper.

Review of Literature. Discuss only literature that pertains directly to the thesis or research of the paper. Cite a representative set of references when there is a large literature; do not discuss it in detail.

References Cited. List every reference that has been cited in the paper. Do not list a reference that has not been cited in the text. Cite the authors' names exactly as they appear in the work cited. Make certain that every item in the references cited is accurate--author, title, volume number, pages, etc. See *ASQ* "Notice to Contributors" for details in citing references.

Footnotes. Incorporate these into the text, except where it is impossible to do so.

Headings. Organize the paper by using primary, secondary, and tertiary headings (check a recent issue of *ASQ* for format).

Terminology
Define a term (or mathematical symbol) accurately and use it consistently with that meaning throughout. Use the same term (or mathematical symbol) for the same concept throughout the paper.

Tense. Use the past tense for discussing earlier studies or presenting methods, samples, data, findings, results, conclusions, etc.

Antecedents. Make these clear, explicit, and closely precede pronouns.

Writing. Do not repeat the same idea in different words; find out the best way to say it. Do not use a clause where a phrase will do or a phrase where a word will do. Avoid jargon; do not mistake it for technical terminology. Don't begin a sentence or a paragraph with "However," or "Indeed."

Avoid the following and similar words and phrases:

matter	the manner in which	in this respect	in summary
nature	in this fashion	on the part of	the area of
situation	a process of	with regard to	indeed
condition	in the direction of	act to modify	concerning
fashion	an important concern	by no means	in this case
manner	operates to elicit	in brief	on this basis

"Data" is a plural noun; "Management," "Staff," and "Faculty" are singular.

Use the active voice whenever possible and avoid using strings of nouns to modify a final noun.

Avoid using words ending with "-tion" followed by a preposition. **Example**: "...move beyond exploration of product possibilities to implementation of product design..." should be rewritten as "move beyond exploring the possibilities of a product to implementing a design."

Adolescence

ADDRESS FOR SUBMISSION:

Editor
Adolescence
Libra Publishers, Inc.
3089C Clairmont Drive, PMB 383
San Diego, CA 92117
USA
Phone: 858-571-1414
Fax: 858-571-1414
E-Mail:
Web:
Address May Change:

PUBLICATION GUIDELINES:

Manuscript Length: Any up to 40
Copies Required: Two
Computer Submission: No
Format: N/A
Fees to Review: 0.00 US$

Manuscript Style:
   American Psychological Association

CIRCULATION DATA:

Reader: Academics
Frequency of Issue: Quarterly
Copies per Issue: 2,001 - 3,000
Sponsor/Publisher: Libra Publishers, Inc.
Subscribe Price: 100.00 US$ Individual
   143.00 US$ Institution

REVIEW INFORMATION:

Type of Review: Blind Review
No. of External Reviewers: 2
No. of In House Reviewers: 2
Acceptance Rate: 11-20%
Time to Review: 2 - 3 Months
Reviewers Comments: No
Invited Articles: 0-5%
Fees to Publish: 1.00 US$
   18.00 US$ Opt/Early Publication

MANUSCRIPT TOPICS:

Abnormal Psychology; Adolescent Psychology; Alcoholism & Drug Addiction; Behavior Modification; Child Psychology; Counseling Process; Developmental Psychology; Educational Psychology; Experimental Psychology; Family Counseling & Therapy; Neuropsychology; Personality; Physiological Psychology; Psychiatry; Psychobiology; Psychological Testing; Psychopathology; Social Psychology

MANUSCRIPT GUIDELINES/COMMENTS:

General Policy
Adolescence is not dominated by a single point of view and wishes to present as many views as possible. It relies for its contents mainly on solicited material, but ideas and suggestions will be welcomed by the editor. Authors should not submit manuscripts; they should write to us about them and furnish short abstracts first. Material submitted should be accompanied by a stamped, self- addressed envelope to insure safe return.

Manuscripts, References, and Reprints
Manuscripts must be typewritten, double-spaced, on one side of the page, and in duplicate. Footnotes, charts, tables, graphs, etc., should be kept to a minimum and submitted in the

original, camera-ready copy. (We prefer that when practical, the information contained in this material be incorporated into the text instead.) References to books and articles should follow the *APA* style.

Authors will be furnished galley proofs which must be returned to the editor within two days. Corrections should be kept to a minimum. A schedule of reprint costs and order blanks for reprints will be sent with galley proofs.

Book Reviews

Adolescence contains a substantial book review section. In each issue, a large number of books will be described in abstract form. More space may be devoted to some books deemed to warrant extensive review, but this will not be done at the expense of the larger number of brief reviews.

Publishers are invited to send copies of books they would like us to review. Naturally, we cannot promise that all books submitted will be reviewed. Book reviews appear in alphabetical order by names of authors.

Aggressive Behavior

ADDRESS FOR SUBMISSION:

Ronald Baenninger, Editor-in-Chief
Aggressive Behavior
Temple University
Psychology Department
Philadelphia, PA 19122
USA
Phone: 215-204-7314
Fax: 215-204-5539
E-Mail: baenning.r@temple.edu
Web: www.interscience.wiley.com
Address May Change:

PUBLICATION GUIDELINES:

Manuscript Length: 16-20
Copies Required: Three
Computer Submission: No
Format: N/A
Fees to Review: 0.00 US$

Manuscript Style:
    Chicago Manual of Style

CIRCULATION DATA:

Reader: Academics
Frequency of Issue: Bi-Monthly
Copies per Issue: Less than 1,000
Sponsor/Publisher: International Society for
    Research on Aggression
Subscribe Price: 75.00 US$ Individual
    1200.00 US$ Library

REVIEW INFORMATION:

Type of Review: Blind Review
No. of External Reviewers: 2
No. of In House Reviewers: 1
Acceptance Rate: 50%
Time to Review: 2 - 3 Months
Reviewers Comments: Yes
Invited Articles: 0-5%
Fees to Publish: 0.00 US$

MANUSCRIPT TOPICS:
Aggression and Violence; Experimental Psychology; Group Dynamics; Psychiatry;
Psychobiology; Social Psychology

MANUSCRIPT GUIDELINES/COMMENTS:

Aims and Scope
Aggressive Behavior will consider manuscripts in the English language concerning the fields of Animal Behavior, Anthropology, Ethology, Psychiatry, Psychobiology, Psychology, and Sociology which relate to either overt or implied conflict behaviors. Papers concerning mechanisms underlying or influencing behaviors generally regarded as aggressive and the physiological and/or behavioral consequences of being subject to such behaviors will fall within the scope of the journal. Review articles will be considered as well as empirical and theoretical articles.

Disk Submission Instructions
1. Manuscripts must be typewritten, double-spaced. Spelling should follow *Webster's Dictionary* (American) or the *Shorter Oxford English Dictionary* (English). A first sheet should contain the title of the paper and the name(s) and place(s) of work of the author(s)

together with a short running title, a list of up to 6 key index terms, and the name and address of the author to whom correspondence and reprint requests should be sent. An abstract of the work and results, limited to 500 words, should be included. The second page should contain the title of the paper and the abstract without the name(s) of the author(s). The author's name(s) should not appear in the manuscript itself since the review of the papers will be done without knowledge of the author's identity. Tables (the minimum number) should be typed on separate sheets, each with a title. Tables should be numbered in sequence with Roman numerals. Brevity will be considered to be an asset. Two carbon or photocopies of each manuscript must accompany the original.

2. Illustrations must be submitted in triplicate. One set should bear a number and the author's name on the reverse (the others should have the number only). Illustrations should be either good quality photographs or standard artwork (eg, India ink on tracing paper). The type area on the printed page will be 4 ½ x 7 inches; Illustrations should be planned with these proportions in mind, and lettering size should be chosen to be legible without being too big after the necessary reduction.

Illustrations should be numbered in a single Arabic-numeral sequence. All figures should have a descriptive legend (even though brief) and these legends should be given in a list at the end of the paper. Where applicable, magnifications, etc, should be indicated.

3. All abbreviations must be defined initially and, where possible, standard tests should be used. Units should conform to the centimeter, gram, second system.

4. References should be cited as [Pellegrini, 1988] in the text. For more than two authors, the first author's name followed by et al. may be used. The reference list at the end of the paper should be in alphabetical order by authors' names and should include author's initials, full titles of articles and inclusive page numbers. Journal titles should not be abbreviated. References to books should include chapter title, date and edition number, place of publication, publisher's name and editor's name.

Follow these examples:
Connell A, Farrington DF. 1997. The reliability and validity of resident, staff and peer reports of bullying in young offender institutions. Psychol Crime Law 3:287-300.

Farrington D. 1992. Understanding and preventing bullying. In: Tonry M, Morris N, editors. Crime and justice: An annual review of research, Vol. 17. Chicago: University of Chicago Press. p. 75-90

It is expected that only essential references will be quoted. Papers by the same author(s) in the same year may carry a suffix, eg, 1987a, 1987b

5. Short communications reporting new techniques or small but complete investigations may be published but they should not exceed 1000 words and two tables.

6. Submission of a paper will be held to imply that it is unpublished work which is not being considered for publication elsewhere. If accepted, it is expected that the paper will not be published in another journal or book in either the same or another format or language.

7. Contributors will be requested to sign an agreement transferring copyright to the publisher, Wiley-Liss, Inc. Permission to publish articles in their entirety or in part elsewhere must be sought from the publisher and from the editorial board.

8. Authors will receive proofs for correction. Order forms for reprints will be sent with the proofs. No page charges are levied.

9. Manuscripts should be sent to the Editor-in-Chief: Ronald Baenninger, Psychology Department, Temple University, Philadelphia, PA 19122; Phone: (215) 204-7314; Fax: (215) 204-5539. European manuscripts should be sent to Paul Brain, Editor for Europe, University College of Swansea, Singleton Park, Swansea SA2 8PP, Wales.

DISK SUBMISSION INSTRUCTIONS
Please return your final, revised manuscript on disk as well as hard copy. The hard copy must match the disk.

The *Journal* strongly encourages authors to deliver the final, revised version of their accepted manuscripts (text, tables, and, if possible, illustrations) on disk. Given the near-universal use of computer word-processing for manuscript preparation, we anticipate that providing a disk will be convenient for you, and it carries the added advantages of maintaining the integrity of your keystrokes and expediting typesetting. Please return the disk submission slip below with your manuscript and labeled disk(s).

GUIDELINES FOR ELECTRONIC SUBMISSION
Text
Storage medium. 3 ½" high-density disk in IBM MS-DOS, Windows, or Macintosh format.

Software and format. Microsoft Word 6.0 is preferred, although manuscripts prepared with any other microcomputer word processor are acceptable. Refrain from complex formatting; the Publisher will style your manuscript according to the Journal design specifications. Do not use desktop publishing software such as Aldus PageMaker or Quark XPress. If you prepared your manuscript with one of these programs, export the text to a word processing format. Please make sure your word processing program's "fast save" feature is turned off. Please do not deliver files that contain hidden text: for example, do not use your word processor's automated features to create footnotes or reference lists.

File names. Submit the text and tables of each manuscript as a single file. Name each file with your last name (up to eight letters). Text files should be given the three-letter extension that identifies the file format. Macintosh users should maintain the MS-DOS "eight dot three" file-naming convention.

Labels. Label all disks with your name, the file name, and the word processing program and version used.

Illustrations

All print reproduction requires files for full color images to be in a CMYK color space. If possible, ICC or ColorSync profiles of your output device should accompany all digital image submissions.

Storage medium. Submit as separate files from text files, on separate disks or cartridges. If feasible, full color files should be submitted on separate disks from other image files. 3 ½" high-density disks, CD, Iomega Zip, and 5 ¼" 44- or 88-MB SyQuest cartridges can be submitted. At authors' request, cartridges and disks will be returned after publication.

Software and format. All illustration files should be in TIFF or EPS (with preview) formats. Do not submit native application formats.

Resolution. Journal quality reproduction will require grayscale and color files at resolutions yielding approximately 300 ppi. Bitmapped line art should be submitted at resolutions yielding 600-1200 ppi. These resolutions refer to the output size of the file; if you anticipate that your images will be enlarged or reduced, resolutions should be adjusted accordingly.

File names. Illustration files should be given the 2- or 3-letter extension that identifies the file format used (i.e., .tif, .eps).

Labels. Label all disks and cartridges with your name, the file names, formats, and compression schemes (if any) used. Hard copy output must accompany all files.

Print and return with labeled diskette(s)

Corresponding author's name:	E-mail address:	Telephone:
Manuscript number:	Type of computer:	Program(s) & version(s) used:
Miscellaneous:		

I certify that the material on the enclosed diskette(s) is identical in both word and content to the printed copy herewith enclosed.
Signature: _____ **Date:** _____

Aging, Neuropsychology and Cognition

ADDRESS FOR SUBMISSION:

L. A. Bieliauskas, M. Sliwinski, Editors
Aging, Neuropsychology and Cognition
 ONLINE SUBMISSIONS ONLY
Phone:
Fax:
E-Mail: See Guidelines
Web: http://www.tandf.co.uk/journals
Address May Change:

CIRCULATION DATA:

Reader: Academics
Frequency of Issue: Quarterly
Copies per Issue:
Sponsor/Publisher: Taylor & Francis
Subscribe Price: 160.00 US$ Individual
    496.00 US$ Institution

PUBLICATION GUIDELINES:

Manuscript Length:
Copies Required:
Computer Submission: Yes Email
Format: MS Word or WordPerfect
Fees to Review: 0.00 US$

Manuscript Style:
    American Psychological Association

REVIEW INFORMATION:

Type of Review:
No. of External Reviewers: 2-3
No. of In House Reviewers:
Acceptance Rate:
Time to Review: 2-6 Months
Reviewers Comments: Yes
Invited Articles:
Fees to Publish: 0.00 US$

MANUSCRIPT TOPICS:
Adulthood; Gerontology; Neuropsychology

MANUSCRIPT GUIDELINES/COMMENTS:

Aims & Scope. The purposes of *Aging, Neuropsychology, and Cognition* are to (a) publish research on both the normal and dysfunctional aspects of cognitive development in adulthood and aging, and (b) promote the integration of theories, methods, and research findings between the fields of cognitive gerontology and neuropsychology.

The primary emphasis of the journal is to publish original empirical research. Emphases of interest include information processing mechanisms, intellectual abilities, the impact of injury or disease on performance, cognitive training, cognitive and pharmacological approaches to treatment and rehabilitation, metacognition, and the social and personal aspects of cognitive functioning. Articles on both normal and dysfunctional development that are relevant to the interface between cognitive gerontology and neuropsychology are particularly welcome.

Submission of Manuscripts. Manuscripts must be submitted through the journal's Scholar One website: **http:// neuropsychology.manuscriptcentral.com**. Questions for the editor may be addressed to: **linas@med.umich.edu** or **mjsliwin@psych.syr.edu**. Only original papers will be considered. Manuscripts are accepted for review with the understanding that the same work has not been published, that it is not under consideration for publication elsewhere, and

32

that its submission for publication has been approved by all of the authors and by the institution where the work was performed and that any person cited as a source of personal communications has approved such citation.

Preparation of Manuscripts. The manuscript should be prepared using MS Word or WordPerfect. Authors are responsible for obtaining permission to reproduce copyrighted material from other sources and are required to sign an agreement for the transfer of copyright to the publisher. All accepted manuscripts, artwork, and photographs become the property of the publisher.

All parts of the manuscript should be double-spaced, with margins of at least one inch on all sides. Number manuscript pages consecutively throughout the paper. The title page must include the title, authors' names and addresses, and the phone and fax numbers and e-mail address of the corresponding author. Authors should also supply a shortened version of the title suitable for the running head, not exceeding 50 character spaces, an abstract of not more than 150 words. Avoid abbreviations, diagrams, and references to the text in the abstract.

Acknowledgments. Acknowledgments should be gathered into a brief statement at the end of the text. All sources of financial sponsorship are to be acknowledged, including the names of private and public sector sponsors. This includes government grants, corporate funding, trade associations and contracts.

References. References should be formatted in APA style (as indicated in the *APA Publication Manual* 5th Ed.) and cited in the text by author and date (Smith & Jones, 1983). Multiple references within one set of parentheses should be set off by semi-colon.

Examples:
Journal: Marsh, R.L., & Bryan, E.S. (1999). The activation of unrelated and cancelled intentions. *Memory and Cognition*, 27, 320--327.

Book: Wechsler, D. (1981). *Manual for the Wechsler Adult Intelligence Scale -- Revised*. New York, Psychological Corporation.

Chapter in Book: Craik, F.I.M., & Jennings, J.M. (1992). Human memory. In F.I.M. Craik & T.A. Salthouse (Eds.), *The handbook of aging and cognition* (pp. 409--422). Amsterdam: Elsevier.

Tables and Figures. Tables and figures should not be embedded in the text, but should be included as separate files. A short descriptive title should appear above each table with a clear legend and any footnotes suitable identified below. Figures should be completely labelled, taking into account necessary size reduction. For highest quality reproduction authors should follow these guidelines:
- 300 dpi or higher
- sized to fit on journal page
- EPS, TIFF, or PSD format only
- submitted as separate files - not embedded in text files.

Color illustrations will be considered for publication; however, the author will be required to bear the full cost involved in their printing and publication. The charge for the first page with color is $900.00. The next three pages with color are $450.00 each. A custom quote will be provided for color art totaling more than 4 journal pages. Good-quality color prints or files should be provided in their final size. The publisher has the right to refuse publication of color prints deemed unacceptable.

Proofs. Page proofs will be sent to the designated corresponding author using the electronic Taylor & Francis EProof system. They should be checked and returned within 48 hours of receipt.

Offprints. The corresponding author of each article will receive a complimentary copy of the issue in which the article appears. Offprints of an article may be ordered from Taylor & Francis. Use the offprint order form included with page proofs. Up to 10 additional issue copies may also be ordered. If offprints are not ordered by the required date, reprint pricing goes into effect, and issue copies may not be ordered.

Alcohol and Alcoholism

ADDRESS FOR SUBMISSION:

J. Chick & P. de Witte, Chief Editors
Alcohol and Alcoholism
35 Morningside Park
Edinburgh, EH10 5HD
UK
Phone: +44 131 537 6442
Fax: +44 131 537 6866
E-Mail: jchick@compuserve.com
Web:
Address May Change:

PUBLICATION GUIDELINES:

Manuscript Length: 16-25 See Guidelines
Copies Required: Electronic
Computer Submission: Yes Email only
Format: MS Word
Fees to Review: 0.00 US$

Manuscript Style:
     See Manuscript Guidelines

CIRCULATION DATA:

Reader: Academics, Practitioners
Frequency of Issue: Bi-Monthly
Copies per Issue: Less than 1,000
Sponsor/Publisher: Medical Council on
     Alcohol (U.K.) / Oxford University Press
Subscribe Price: 605.00 US$ Institution
     150.00 US$ ISBRA, RSA, ESBRA,
     JAS, BRA

REVIEW INFORMATION:

Type of Review: Editorial Review
No. of External Reviewers: 2-3
No. of In House Reviewers: 3
Acceptance Rate: 40%
Time to Review: 1 - 2 Months See
     Guidelines
Reviewers Comments: Yes
Invited Articles: 0-5%
Fees to Publish: 0.00 US$

MANUSCRIPT TOPICS:
Alcoholism & Drug Addiction; Behavior Modification; Clinical and Biomedical Aspects; Experimental Psychology; Neuropsychology; Personality; Physiological Psychology; Psychiatry; Psychobiology; Psychological Testing; Research Methods & Statistics; Thinking & Cognition

MANUSCRIPT GUIDELINES/COMMENTS:

Alcohol and Alcoholsim - The International Journal of the Medical Council on Alcohol and The Journal of the European Society for Biomedical Research on Alcoholism

Aims and Scope
Alcohol and Alcoholism publishes papers in English on biomedical, psychological and sociological aspects of alcoholism and alcohol research, provided that they make a new and significant contribution to knowledge in the field and areas thereof concerned. Papers may include new results obtained experimentally, descriptions of new experimental (including clinical) methods of importance to the field of alcohol research and treatment, or new interpretations of existing results. Theoretical contributions will be considered equally with

papers dealing with experimental work provided that they are not of a largely speculative or philosophical nature.

Submission of Typescripts. Contributors should submit in Microsoft WORD by email or by disk to either Chief Editor (Dr J Chick or Professor P de Witte) at the following Editorial Office addresses. All submissions will be subjected to peer review and must be prepared in accordance with the following Instructions to Authors.

Jonathan Chick, Editor, Alcohol and Alcoholism, 35 Morningside Park, Edinburgh EH10 5DX, U.K. Phone: +44 131 537 6442; Fax +44131 537 6866
Email: **jchick@compuserve.com**

Prof. Ph. De Witte, Lab. Biologie du Comportement, UCL - Place Croix du Sud 1 - box 10, B-1348 Louvain-la-Neuve; Phone: 00 32 10 474017; Fax: 00 32 10 474094
Email: **Dewitte@bani.ucl.ac.be**

INSTRUCTIONS TO AUTHORS
Organization
The following items will be included in the Journal:
1. **Full-length papers.** These should be written in the style described below, their length being the minimum required for precision in describing the experiments and clarity in interpreting them. A concise well-written paper tends to be published more rapidly.

To meet increased demand on pages because of continually rising submissions, and despite printing the Journal in the larger (A4) format, the size of a full length paper is now restricted to six printed pages of the Journal, or 5000 words in total, including space for Tables and Figures. The Editors, therefore, strongly urge authors to be concise and to submit their work to occupy the smallest possible space. The shorter the papers are, the more that could be accommodated in an issue and the quicker they could be published in this bi-monthly journal. Authors should ensure that no data are presented in both tabular and graphical forms and that the content of a small table could easily be described in the text, without loss of clarity, especially when there are many other Tables and/or Figures in the paper. Methods should not be described in detail if previously published and the 'Discussion' section should have the minimum of speculation and not be excessively long, ideally occupying no more than 25% of the length of the text excluding the references. Authors must also avoid excessive referencing.

2. **Rapid Communications.** All appropriate papers describing important novel, unusual and/or exciting findings, and which can be accommodated in up to four printed pages of the Journal (including Figures and/or Tables) will be treated as Rapid Communications. They will receive priority treatment and it is hoped that they will be published within 12-16 weeks from date of receipt provided they do not require major revision. Criteria for acceptance and method of preparation of Rapid Communications are not regarded as preliminary communications but as complete and final accounts. Authors are discouraged from attempting to take advantage of this rapid handling procedure to divide a substantial piece of work into smaller submissions.

The Abstract of a Rapid Communication must not exceed 80 words. The total size of the text (excluding the title, authors, addresses and Abstract) should not exceed 3000 words, which should include references and any Figures and/or Tables. Figures and Tables must be of reproducible quality and not require redrawing, since this will delay publication. Authors should therefore assess the approximate space required for Figures and/or Tables and reduce the size of the text accordingly. Papers exceeding these specifications (and therefore likely to occupy more than four printed pages of the Journal) will not be given priority handling but will be treated as full-length submissions.

To expedite the publication of Rapid Communications, proofs will be faxed or sent by e-mail to authors, who will be given 48 hours to fax or e-mail back their corrected proofs.

3. **Letters to the Editors**. These are intended to provide an opportunity to discuss or expand particular points made in published work, to comment on or criticize work previously published in *Alcohol and Alcoholism*, or to present a new hypothesis. They should not contain extensive new data (which would best be placed in a regular paper), nor be used as a vehicle for publication of preliminary results. If a letter is polemical in nature, a reply may be solicited from other interested parties before publication.

4. **Reviews**. Review articles will usually be solicited, although unsolicited reviews will be considered for publication. However, prospective writers of reviews should first consult the Chief Editors of the Journal.

5. **Commentaries**. These now replace Editorials and Annotations, which were important features of the Journal before volume 18. Commentaries should provide succinct, comprehensive and up-to-date accounts of topical issues in alcohol and alcoholism research and treatment, where either rapid progress is being made or the need for a brief review is both timely and warranted. Another important aim of a Commentary is stimulation of debate. A Commentary may or may not be solicited and can be between 1000 and 4000 words (occupying no more than five printed pages). As with unsolicited Reviews, prospective writers of Commentaries should first consult the Chief Editors.

6. **Book Reviews**. Publishers, agents and other distributors of books are urged to send review copies direct to the Book Review Editor, Dr Brian D. Hore, at the following address: 22 Handforth Road, Wilmslow, Cheshire SK9 2LU, UK. Books are reviewed by experts in their fields and a copy of the review is sent to the publisher/distributor soon after its appearance.

Editors, Advisors and Independent Referees. Normally a paper is read by the handling Editor and two other persons, who may be Editorial Advisors, independent referees or both. The main task of the advisors and referees is to make recommendations on the acceptability of a paper. If rejection of a paper is recommended or if there is any serious disagreement between those who have red the paper, the final decision is made by the Editor or Editors. Normally each paper is handled throughout by an Editor who will, if the paper is acceptable, make amendments and will request revision or shortening. Once the Editor(s) is satisfied, the paper is then prepared for press by an in-house sub-editor. In this final process, attention is paid to grammar and the detailed conventions of the Journal.

Submission of Papers. Submission of a paper implies that it has been approved by all the named authors (who should all sign a statement to this effect), and that it reports unpublished work, that it is not under consideration for publication in whole or in part elsewhere, and that, if accepted by *Alcohol and Alcoholism*, it will not be published elsewhere in the same form, either in English or in any other language, without the consent of the Editors.

Papers that are scientifically acceptable but need revision because they are not clear and concise or do not conform sufficiently to the conventions of *Alcohol and Alcoholism* will be returned to the authors for amendment.

Authors should submit by email or 3.5" HD/DD disk in Microsoft WORD. (1) Include the text file and separate Table and illustration files. (2) The file should follow the general instructions on style/arrangement and, in particular, the reference style of this journal as given in the Instructions to Authors. (3) The file should be single-spaced and should use the wrap-around end-of-line feature, i.e. not returns at the end of each line. All textual elements should begin flush left; no paragraph indents. Place two returns after every element such as title, headings, paragraphs, Figure and Table call-outs. (4) Keep a back-up disk for reference and safety. It is essential that, when your paper has been refereed, revised if necessary and accepted, send a disk or email containing the final version.

Reprints and permissions. All communications about reprints should be addressed to the Publisher, Oxford University Press, Great Clarendon Street, Oxford OX2 6DP, UK. Authors will receive 25 offprints of their published work free of charge. Additional copies can be purchased by using the order form sent with the proofs of the paper. Requests for consent for reproduction of material from the Journal should be addressed to the Publisher.

Quotations of personal communications. When such a quotation is made the authors should provide written evidence of permissions from the person(s) concerned to be quoted. Such reference to personal communications should be made only in the text, not in the list of references.

Copies of submitted papers. The original typescript plus three copies should be submitted to either Chief Editor together with a letter signed by all the authors giving consent for publication in the Journal including the following statement: 'This paper has not been, nor will be, published in whole or in part by any other journal'. The senior author may, for reasons of convenience, submit a written and signed authorization by another co-author(s) for him(her) to sign on his(her) behalf, if such a co-author(s) is likely to be absent during the week of submission. In submitting illustrations or photographs, only one original is required, four photocopies should be enclosed with the four copies of the paper. The original manuscript and figures will be discarded one month after publication unless the Publisher is requested to return original material to the author(s).

Title Page. The title of the paper should be given in full, together with the name(s) of the author(s), address(es) of the Laboratory or Unit(s) in which the work was performed, the address, telephone, fax and e-mail numbers of the author to whom correspondence concerning the handling of the paper should be sent. A running title for the paper and a list of no more than six key words should also be provided. A copy of the *Journal* should be consulted for the *Journal* style.

Abstract. An Abstract of between 3 and 5% of the total length of the paper (60 words for Rapid Communications) should precede the text. It should be structured as: Aims, Methods, Results, Conclusions. Do not include introductory material. Include salient data with statistical comparisons if appropriate

Style of Papers. Typing should be on one side of white paper of uniform size, no smaller than quarto, double-spaced and with wide margins on either side of the typed text.

Spelling should conform to that of the *Oxford English Dictionary*. Full stops are not allowed in contractions or abbreviations: ATP, 11 g/dl, etc.

Tables. Each Table should be typed on a separate sheet and should be supplied with a heading and an explanatory legend. The heading and legend should make the general meaning comprehensible without reference to the text. The heading, which should precede the Table details, must be short but informative, and must not include any details of any kind. Conditions specific to the particular experiment should be stated in the legend, which should be placed at the bottom of the Table. Reference to the text for general experimental methods is permissible provided that there is no ambiguity. Footnotes should be as few as possible. The units in which the results are expressed, e.g. g/dl, should be given at the top of each column, and not repeated on each line of the Table. Words or numerals should be repeated on successive lines: 'ditto' or " are not to be used. The approximate positions of the Tables should be indicated in pencil in the margin of the text.

Illustrations. Each illustration should be on a separate sheet and packed flat; each should bear the author's name, the title (abbreviated if necessary) of the paper and the Figure number on the back. All photographs, diagrams and charts (both line and half-tone) should be referred to as Figures, given Arabic numerals numbered consecutively in the order in which they are referred to in the text. The approximate position of each Figure in the text should be indicated in pencil in the margin of the text. Figure legends must be typed on a separate sheet at the end of the paper. Each Figure should be supplied with a heading and legend which should make the general meaning comprehensible without reference to the text. The heading must be short but informative and must not contain any details of any kind nor be merged with the legend. The legend should then be started on a separate line and should include details specific to the particular experiment. Reference to the text for general experimental details is permissible provided that there is not ambiguity.

Illustrations must be of good quality, unmounted, glossy prints (not negatives or transparencies) proportionate to 17 cm wide and 20 cm deep. They should not be smaller than half that size. Line drawings, graphs and charts must be arranged to the same proportionate dimensions and should be drawn in black Indian ink on heavy white paper or card. Line diagrams that are submitted in a form unsuitable for direct reproduction, for any reason, will be redrawn by the Publisher's draughtsman, with consequent delay.

Reproduction of Half-tone Illustrations (Photographs). Glossy prints are required for these. The magnification, if any, is to be indicated; this is best done by adding a bar representing a stated length. The Editors will accept plates for publication only (a) when they make a significant important scientific or clinical contribution to the paper, and (b) when the photographs supplied are of a quality that justifies publication in this form. Illustrations are usually reproduced in black and white. Authors wishing to submit colour illustrations will be asked to contribute towards the costs.

Footnotes. These should be avoided as far as possible. When they must be used, as in Tables, reference should be made by the symbols *, **, ***, †, ††, †††, in that order.

Acknowledgements. These must be as short as possible.

Animals and Their Diets. The full binomial Latin names should be included for all experimental animals other than common laboratory animals. The strain, and the source of laboratory animals should be stated. The diet on which the animals are maintained should also be stated together with the address of the source from which it has been obtained.

Ethics of Animal Experimentation. Animal experiments should be performed in accordance with the legal requirements of the local or national authority. Procedures should be such that animals do not suffer unnecessarily. For example, a study in which procedures lead to deaths of more than 10% of the animals will not be considered. Similarly, a paper using a procedure performed without anesthetic in which the animals can be assumed to have suffered will not be considered. In short, the Editors will not accept papers where the ethical aspects are, in their opinion, open to doubt and which used procedures that would not be acceptable in the countries of the majority of readers of this journal.

Ethics of Human Experimentation. The Editors agree with the principles laid down in the Declaration of Helsinki (1964) [*British Medical Journal* (1964) **ii**, 177-178; see also the Report of the Medical Research Council for 1962-63, pp. 21-15] Authors should ensure that their work complies with these declarations. Papers describing experimental work with humans should include a statement that the Ethics Committee of the Institution in which the work was performed has approved it and should state that the subjects have given informed consent to the work. If necessary, the Editors may require to see a copy of the ethical approval.

Wider Ethical Guidelines. *Alcohol and Alcoholism* subscribes to the Farmington Consensus statement [see *Alcohol and Alcoholism* 33, 6-7 (1998)] and the Ethical Practice Guidelines of the International Society for Addiction Journal Editors (ISAJE), which can be accessed on the ISAJE website (**http://isaje.com**)

The ISAJE guidelines have been developed after consultation with recommendations and other documents produced by a variety of bodies, including those of the Committee on Publication Ethics (COPE), modification of the latter by *Drug and Alcohol Dependence*, the US National Institutes of Health (NIH), Office of Research Integrity, and the "Integrity in Science" project of the Center for Science in the Public Interest (CSPI).

Conflict of Interest. This journal takes a serious view on various ethical issues related to publishing in this field. As well as familiarizing themselves with guidelines relating to these issues at the ISAJE website and elsewhere, authors should also pay special attention to issues related to "conflict of interest" before submission of their work to this journal.

Authors should each declare to the Chief Editors any interests which could constitute a real, potential or apparent conflict of interest with respect to his/her involvement in the publication, between: (1) commercial entities and the participant personally; (2) commercial entities and the administrative unit with which the participant has an employment relationship. "Commercial entity" refers to any company, business, industry, association (e.g. trade association), organization, or other unit with commercial interest.

Authors must declare to the Chief Editors any significant financial or other relations (e.g. directorship, consultancy or speaker fee) of him(her)self with companies, trade associations, unions or groups (including civic associations and public interest groups) that may gain or lose financially from the results or conclusions in the study, review, commentary, editorial or Letter to the Editors.

All sources of funding for the study, should be declared in the Funding sources should be described in a way that allows the average reader to recognize any potential conflicts of interest.

Experimental Hazards. Authors should draw attention to any particular chemical or biological hazard that may be involved in carrying out the experiments described. Where appropriate, the safety precautions that were taken should be stated. Alternatively, a statement may be included to indicate that an acceptable code of practice has been followed, with references to the relevant standards.

SI Units. *Alcohol and Alcoholism* uses the recommended SI symbols for units [see *Pure and Applied Chemistry* (1970) **21**, 1-44; IUPAC *Manual of Symbols and Terminology for Physico-chemical Quantities and Units* (1979) Pergamon Press, Oxford].

Other Technical Information. Details of technical data, e.g. chromatography, enzymes, isotope experiments, and other physical aspects and constants, mathematics and abbreviations of biochemicals are as published in the *Biochemical Journal* (1993) **289**, 1-15.

Statistics. The Editors emphasize the importance of correct statistical design, analysis and presentation. Authors are advised to consider all statistical aspects t the stage of planning the project, as badly designed studies may not be salvageable later. Statistical methods should be accompanied by indices of precision (e.g. means accompanied by confidence intervals). Authors are advised to consult the following: Altman, D. G., Gore, S. M., Gardner, M. J. and Pocock, S. J. (1983) Statistical guidelines for contributors to medical journals. *British Medical Journal* **286**, 1489-1493.

References. This is a modified Harvard style system. In the text, references for papers by three or more authors are given as the first author et al., and the year. When more than one reference is mentioned at a time in the text, the references should be listed chronologically. In the list of references, the references should be typed double-spaced in alphabetical order and entries should be as follows:

Journal references: (1) Authors' names; (2) year of publication; (3) title of paper; (4) journal name in full; (5) volume number; (6) first and last page numbers.

Example:
Badawy, A. A.-B., Punjani, N. F. and Evans, M. (1981a) The role of liver tryptophan pyrrolase in the opposite effects of chronic administration and subsequent withdrawal of drugs of dependence, on rat brain tryptophan metabolism. *Biochemical Journal* **196**, 171-180.

Book references: (1) Authors, names; (2) year of publication; (3) title of article; (4) title of book and volume number, if any; (5) editor(s); (6) first and last page numbers of article; (7) publisher's name; (8) city of publication.

Example:
Alkana, R. L. and Noble, E. P. (1979) Amethystic agents - reversal of acute ethanol intoxication in humans. In *Biochemistry and Pharmacology of Ethanol*, Vol. 2, Majchrowiez, E. and Noble, E. P.eds, pp. 349-374. Plenum Press, New York.

Only papers published or accepted for publication (and therefore in press) can be included in the list of references. Personal communications, unpublished work or work submitted for publication can be quoted only in the text.

Drug and Dosage Selection. Authors must make every effort to ensure the accuracy of information, particularly with regard to drug selection and dose. However, appropriate information sources should be consulted, especially for new or unfamiliar drugs or procedures. It is the responsibility of every practitioner to evaluate the appropriateness of a particular opinion in the context of actual clinical situations and with due consideration to new developments.

Correction to Proofs. Proofs will be sent to the first-named author unless otherwise indicated. Authors are fully responsible for corrections of any typographical errors, Additional alterations may be subject to an extra charge.

Copyright. It is a condition of publication in the Journal that authors assign copyright to the Medical Council on Alcohol. This ensures that requests from third parties to reproduce articles are handled efficiently and consistently and will also allow the article to be as widely disseminated as possible. In assigning copyright, Authors may use their own material in other publications provided that the Journal is acknowledged as the original place of publication, and Oxford University Press is notified in writing and in advance.

Alcoholism Treatment Quarterly

ADDRESS FOR SUBMISSION:

Thomas F. McGovern, Editor
Alcoholism Treatment Quarterly
Texas Tech University
Department of Neuropsychiatry
Health Sciences Center
3601 4th Street
Lubbock, TX 79430-0001
USA
Phone: 806-743-2820 ext. 248
Fax: 806-743-4250
E-Mail: thomas.mcgovern@ttmc.ttuusc.edu
Web: www.haworthpress.com
Address May Change:

PUBLICATION GUIDELINES:

Manuscript Length: 21-25
Copies Required: Four
Computer Submission: No
Format: N/A
Fees to Review: 0.00 US$

Manuscript Style:
    Chicago Manual of Style

CIRCULATION DATA:

Reader: Practitioners
Frequency of Issue: Quarterly
Copies per Issue: Less than 1,000
Sponsor/Publisher: Haworth Press, Inc.
Subscribe Price: 75.00 US$ Individual
    200.00 US$ Institution
    450.00 US$ Library

REVIEW INFORMATION:

Type of Review: Blind Review
No. of External Reviewers: 2
No. of In House Reviewers: 0
Acceptance Rate: 60%
Time to Review: 4 - 6 Months
Reviewers Comments: Yes
Invited Articles: 0-5%
Fees to Publish: 0.00 US$

MANUSCRIPT TOPICS:
Alcoholism & Drug Addiction; Counseling Process; Family Counseling & Therapy; Learning & Conditioning; Neuropsychology; Psychiatry

MANUSCRIPT GUIDELINES/COMMENTS:

About the Journal
Alcoholism Treatment Quarterly is an exciting professional journal for clinicians working with persons who are alcoholic and their families. Designed to bridge the gap between research journals and information for the general public, it addresses the specific concerns of professional alcoholism counselors, social workers, psychologists, physicians, clergy, nurses, employee assistance professionals, and others who provide direct services to persons who are alcoholic.

The journal features articles specifically related to the treatment of alcoholism, highlighting new and innovative approaches to care, describing clinical problems and solutions, and detailing practical, unique approaches to intervention and therapy. Original research and articles about theory development and policy issues in alcoholism are included. *Alcoholism Treatment Quarterly* particularly welcomes material giving the personal and humanistic aspects of professional alcoholism counseling and therapy from both the counselor/therapist's view as well as that of the client.

The journal
- details the "how to" approaches of intervention and therapy
- presents case studies and commentaries by counselors and therapists
- publishes original research and articles related to theory development
- serves as a vehicle to integrate diverse approaches and perspectives in the field
- emphasizes the art as well as the science inherent in the treatment of alcoholism
- advocates the recognition of special treatment needs of alcoholic clients and their families
- enhances professionalism in the field of counseling and therapy
- promotes the quality of treatment provided to the alcoholic and his/her family in all domains of the recovery process

Instructions for Authors

1. **Original Articles Only**. Submission of a manuscript to this Journal represents a certification on the part of the author(s) that it is an original work, and that neither this manuscript nor a version of it has been published elsewhere nor is being considered for publication elsewhere.

2. **Manuscript Length**. Your manuscript may be approximately 15-25 typed pages. Sentences should be double-spaced (including references and abstract). Lengthier manuscripts may be considered, but only at the discretion of the Editor. Sometimes, lengthier manuscripts may be considered if they can be divided up into sections for publications in successive Journal issues.

3. **Manuscript Style**. References, citations, and general style of manuscripts for this journal should follow the Chicago style (as outlined in the latest edition of the *Manual of Style* of the University of Chicago Press.) References should be double-spaced and placed in alphabetical order. The use of footnotes within the text is discouraged. Words should be underlined only when it is intended that they be typeset in italics.

If an author wishes to submit a paper that has been already prepared in another style, he or she may do so. However, if the paper is accepted (with or without reviewer's alterations), the author is fully responsible for retyping the manuscript in the correct style as indicated above. Neither the Editor nor the Publisher is responsible for re-preparing manuscript copy to adhere to the Journal's style.

4. **Manuscript Preparation**
Margins. Leave at least a one-inch margin on all four sides.
Paper. Use clean, white 8 ½" x 11" bond paper.
Number of copies. 4 (the original plus three photocopies).
Cover page. Important—staple a cover page to the manuscript, indicating only the article title (this is used for anonymous refereeing).

Second "title page". Enclose a regular title page but do not staple it to the manuscript. Include the title again, plus:

- full authorship
- an ABSTRACT of about 100 words. (Below the abstract provide 3–10 key words for index purposes).
- a header or footer on each page with abbreviated title and pg number of total (e.g., pg 2 of 7)
- an introductory footnote with authors' academic degrees, professional titles, affiliations, mailing and e-mail addresses, and any desired acknowledgment of research support or other credit.

5. **Return Envelopes.** When you submit your four manuscript copies, also include:

- a 9" x 12" envelope, self-addressed and stamped (with sufficient postage to ensure return of your manuscript);
- a regular envelope, stamped and self-addressed. This is for the Editor to send you an "acknowledgement of receipt" letter.

6. **Spelling, Grammar, and Punctuation.** You are responsible for preparing manuscript copy which is clearly written in acceptable, scholarly English and which contains no errors of spelling, grammar, or punctuation. Neither the Editor nor the Publisher is responsible for correcting errors of spelling and grammar. The manuscript, after acceptance by the Editor, must be immediately ready for typesetting as it is finally submitted by the author(s). Check your paper for the following common errors:

- dangling modifiers
- misplaced modifiers
- unclear antecedents
- incorrect or inconsistent abbreviations

Also, check the accuracy of all arithmetic calculations, statistics, numerical data, text citations, and references.

7. **Inconsistencies Must Be Avoided.** Be sure you are consistent in your use of abbreviations, terminology, and in citing references, from one part of your paper to another.

8. **Preparation of Tables, Figures, and Illustrations.** Any material that is not textual is considered artwork. This includes tables, figures, diagrams, charts, graphs, illustrations, appendices, screen captures, and photos. Tables and figures (including legend, notes, and sources) should be no larger than 4 ½ X 6 ½ inches. Type styles should be Helvetica (or Helvetica narrow if necessary) and no smaller than 8 point. We request that computer-generated figures be in black and white and/or shades of gray (preferably no color, for it does not reproduce well). Camera-ready art must contain no grammatical, typographical, or format errors and must reproduce sharply and clearly in the dimensions of the final printed page (4 ½ x 6 ½ inches). Photos and screen captures must be on disk as a TIF file, or other graphic file format such as JPEG or BMP. For rapid publication we must receive black-and-white glossy or matte positives (white background with black images and/or wording) in addition to files on disk. Tables should be created in the text document file using the software's Table feature.

9. **Submitting Art**. Both a printed hard copy and a disk copy of the art must be provided. We request that each piece of art be sent in its own file, on a disk separate from the disk containing the manuscript text file(s), and be clearly labeled. We reserve the right to (if necessary) request new art, alter art, or if all else has failed in achieving art that is presentable, delete art. If submitted art cannot be used, the Publisher reserves the right to redo the art and to change the author for a fee of $35.00 per hour for this service. The Haworth Press, Inc. is not responsible for errors incurred in the preparation of new artwork. Camera-ready artwork must be prepared on separate sheets of paper. Always use black ink and professional drawing instruments. On the back of these items, write your article title and the journal title lightly in soft-lead pencil (please do not write on the face of art). In the text file, skip extra lines and indicate where these figures are placed. Photos are considered part of the acceptable manuscript and remain with the Publisher for use in additional printings.

10. **Electronic Media**. Haworth's in-house typesetting unit is able to utilize your final manuscript material as prepared on most personal computers and word processors. This will minimize typographical errors and decrease overall production time. Please send the first draft and final draft copies of your manuscript to the journal Editor in print format for his/her final review and approval. After approval of your final manuscript, please submit the final approved version both on printed format ("hard copy") and floppy diskette. On the outside of the diskette package write:
1. the brand name of your computer or word processor
2. the word processing program and version that you used
3. the title of your article, and
4. the file name.

Note: Disk and hard copy must agree. In case of discrepancies, it is The Haworth Press' policy to follow hard copy. Authors are advised that no revisions of the manuscript can be made after acceptance by the Editor for publication. The benefits of this procedure are many with speed and accuracy being the most obvious. We look forward to working with your electronic submission which will allow us to serve you more efficiently.

11. **Alterations Required by Referees and Reviewers**. Many times a paper is accepted by the Editor contingent upon changes that are mandated by anonymous specialist referees and members of the Editorial Board. If the Editor returns your manuscript for revisions, you are responsible for retyping any sections of the paper to incorporate these revisions (if applicable, revisions should also be put on disk).

12. **Typesetting**. You will not be receiving galley proofs of your article. Editorial revisions, if any, must therefore be made while your article is still in manuscript. The final version of the manuscript will be the version you see published. Typesetter's errors will be corrected by the production staff of The Haworth Press. Authors are expected to submit manuscripts, disks, and art that are free from error.

13. **Reprints**. The senior author will receive two copies of the journal issue and 25 complimentary reprints of his or her article. The junior author will receive two copies of the journal issue. These are sent several weeks after the journal issue is published and in

46

circulation. An order form for the purchase of additional reprints will also be sent to all authors at this time. (Approximately 4-6 weeks is necessary for the preparation of reprints.) Please do not query the Journal's Editor about reprints. All such questions should be sent directly to The Haworth Press, Inc., Production Department, 37 West Broad Street, West Hazleton, PA 18202. To order additional reprints (minimum: 50 copies), please contact The Haworth Document Delivery Center, 10 Alice Street, Binghamton, NY 13904-1580; 1-800-342-9678 or Fax (607) 722-6362.

14. **Copyright**. Copyright ownership of your manuscript must be transferred officially to The Haworth Press, Inc. before we can begin the peer-review process. The Editor's letter acknowledging receipt of the manuscript will be accompanied by a form fully explaining this. All authors must sign the form and return the original to the Editor as soon as possible. Failure to return the copyright form in a timely fashion will result in a delay in review and subsequent publication.

American Indian and Alaska Native Mental Health Research

ADDRESS FOR SUBMISSION:

Journal Manager
American Indian and Alaska Native Mental
   Health Research
NCAIANMHR, Psychiatry, UCHSC
Nighthorse Campbell Native
   Mental Health Building
PO Box 6508, Mail Stop F800
Aurora, CO 80045-0508
USA
Phone: 303-724-1414
Fax: 303-724-1474
E-Mail: billie.greene@uchsc.edu
Web: See Guidelines
Address May Change:

PUBLICATION GUIDELINES:

Manuscript Length: 11-15
Copies Required: Four
Computer Submission: No
Format: N/A
Fees to Review: 0.00 US$

Manuscript Style:
   American Psychological Association,
   (Fifth Edition)

CIRCULATION DATA:

Reader: Academics
Frequency of Issue: 2 Times/Year
Copies per Issue: N/A, Online
Sponsor/Publisher: University of Colorado
   Health Sciences Center, American Indian
   & Alaska Native Programs
Subscribe Price:

REVIEW INFORMATION:

Type of Review: Editorial Review
No. of External Reviewers: 3
No. of In House Reviewers: 2
Acceptance Rate: 75%
Time to Review: 2 - 3 Months
Reviewers Comments: Yes
Invited Articles: 31-50%
Fees to Publish: 0.00 US$

MANUSCRIPT TOPICS:
Abnormal Psychology; Adolescent Psychology; Alcoholism & Drug Addiction; Behavior Modification; Child Psychology; Counseling Process; Developmental Psychology; Educational Psychology; Experimental Psychology; Family Counseling & Therapy; Gerontology; Research Methods & Statistics; Social Psychology

MANUSCRIPT GUIDELINES/COMMENTS:

Call for Papers
The *Journal* cordially invites authors to submit articles to be considered for publication. We are a professionally refereed scientific journal and will entertain submissions containing empirical research, program evaluations, case studies, unpublished dissertations, and other articles in the behavioral, social, and health sciences which clearly relate to the mental health status of American Indians and Alaska Natives.

48

In publication since 1987, this journal remains the only one of its kind to publish exclusively on American Indian and Alaska Native health. The *Journal* is viewed by thousands of users each month (i.e., an average of 10,000 hits per month recorded for Online Issues from the UCHSC Web Statistics page in 2003). It is indexed in the PubMed, E-Psyche, and UMI databases.

Authors may submit manuscripts for consideration by a letter of intent to the Journal Manager, National Center for American Indian and Alaska Native Mental Health Research, University of Colorado Health Sciences Center, Department of Psychiatry, Nighthorse Campbell Native Health Building, P.O. Box 6508, Mail Stop F800, Aurora, CO 80045-0508.

Submit manuscripts in triplicate, typewritten, and double-spaced. All copies should be clear and readable. Dittoed or mimeographed copies are not acceptable. Please retain the original as we cannot assume responsibility for returning your manuscripts. Articles should average 3,000 words; however, concisely written articles of any length will be considered. An abstract of 75 words or less that highlights at least six key words used in the body of the work should precede the manuscript, and be typed on a separate page.

Prepare your manuscripts in accordance with the *Publication Manual of the American Psychological Association* (APA) (5th ed.). Manuscripts submitted which do not follow APA standards in content and organization will not be considered. Instructions for typing, preparing tables, figures, references, and abstracts can be found in the *Manual*. All manuscripts are subject to editing for sexist language. Authors should stress new data, comparisons with previous data, and their relevance to American Indian and Alaska Native mental health. The emphasis here is on development of positive mental and social functioning of American Indians and Alaska Natives through understanding the relevant processes and conditions.

APA policy prohibits an author from submitting the same manuscript for concurrent consideration by two or more journals. Authors submitting a manuscript previously considered for publication in another APA journal should make note of that in their submission letter. APA policy also prohibits duplicate publication, that is, publication of a manuscript that has already been published in whole or substantial part in another journal.

The term, "American Indian/Alaska Native" will refer to descendants of tribes of pre-Columbian natives of the Western Hemisphere. Emphasis will be placed on those now living in the United States, but will not necessarily exclude residents of Canada, the Pacific Islands, Central or South America. In the absence of tribal affiliation, "American Indian and/or Alaska Native," not Native American, is the preferred designation.

Consistent with current trends in the publishing world, articles, if accepted, will be published via the Internet in electronic form. The established web-site for published articles is a component of the National Center for American Indian and Alaska Native Mental Health Research. Articles published after 01/01/99 may be accessed by the general public at the following web-site: **http://www.uchsc.edu/ai/ncaianmhr/journal/issues.htm**

All U.S. and international copyright laws remain in effect.

American Journal of Community Psychology

ADDRESS FOR SUBMISSION:

William S. Davidson II, Editor
American Journal of Community
  Psychology
Michigan State University
Department of Psychology
135 Synder Hall
East Lansing, MI 48824-1117
USA
Phone: 517-355-1814
Fax: 517-432-2945
E-Mail: davidso7@msu.edu
Web: www.wkap.nl/journals
Address May Change: 12/31/2007

PUBLICATION GUIDELINES:

Manuscript Length: 26-30
Copies Required: Four
Computer Submission: No
Format:
Fees to Review: 0.00 US$

Manuscript Style:
  American Psychological Association

CIRCULATION DATA:

Reader: Academics
Frequency of Issue: Bi-Monthly
Copies per Issue: 2,001 - 3,000
Sponsor/Publisher: American Psychological
  Association, Society for Community
  Research and Action
Subscribe Price: 134.00 US$ Individual
  655.00 US$ Institution
  134.00 Euro Indv., $653 Euro Inst.

REVIEW INFORMATION:

Type of Review: Blind Review
No. of External Reviewers: 3
No. of In House Reviewers: 1
Acceptance Rate: 11-20%
Time to Review: 2 - 3 Months
Reviewers Comments: Yes
Invited Articles: 0-5%
Fees to Publish: 0.00 US$

MANUSCRIPT TOPICS:

Community Psychology; Decision Making Theory; Gender Roles; Group Dynamics; Human Relations; Psychology of Women

MANUSCRIPT GUIDELINES/COMMENTS:

The *American Journal of Community Psychology* publishes empirical research, reports of community interventions, theoretical papers, and literature reviews in the area of community psychology. Topics of interest include, but are not limited to: individual and community mental and physical health; educational, legal, and work environment processes, policies, and opportunities; family, institutional, and community processes; social welfare and social justice; studies of social problems; and evaluations of interventions. Papers are welcome that concern prevention of problems in living, promotion of emotional and physical health, well being and competence, empowerment of historically disenfranchised groups, collective social action, social networks, institutional and organizational change, self and mutual help and community-based interventions such as collaborative research, advocacy, consultation, training, and planning. Both quantitative and qualitative research methods are appropriate, as are investigations which address a variety of levels of analysis, including neighborhood, organizational, group, social, and individual. The *American Journal of Community Psychology* actively encourages the submission of manuscripts concerned with underrepresented populations and issues of human diversity in community psychology.

1. Manuscripts, in quadruplicate and in English, should be sent to the Editor:

Monographs not exceeding 200 double-spaced manuscript pages (including figures and tables) are also appropriate for submission. Prior consultation with the Editor is recommended to help determine the scope of a planned monograph.

2. Submission is a representation that the manuscript has not been published previously and is not currently under consideration for publication elsewhere. A statement transferring copyright from the authors (or their employers, if they hold the copyright) to Plenum Publishing Corporation will be required before the manuscript can be accepted for publication. The Editor will supply the necessary forms for this transfer. Such a written transfer of copyright, which previously was assumed to be implicit in the act of submitting a manuscript, is necessary under the U.S. Copyright Law in order for the publisher to carry through the dissemination of research results and reviews as widely and effectively as possible.

3. The style of the 1994 (fourth) edition of the *Publication Manual of the American Psychological Association* should guide the preparation of manuscripts, particularly with respect to such matters as the citation of references and the use of abbreviations, numbers, and symbols. Academic affiliations of all authors and the full mailing address of the one author who will receive all correspondence should be included. In order to allow blind review, authors should avoid identifying information in the body of a manuscript. Full identifying information, including address for correspondence, should be placed on a cover page. Include a stamped, self-addressed postcard for confirmation of receipt of manuscript.

4. Authors are required to state in their initial submission letter or to provide a signed statement that they have complied with APA ethical standards in their treatment of individuals participating in the research or intervention described in the manuscript. They should note that the research has been approved by their organizational unit responsible for the protection of human subjects. (Copies of both the APA *Publication Manual* and APA *Code of Ethics* may be obtained from the American Psychological Association, Order Department, 750 1st St., S.E., Washington, D.C. 20002.)

5. It is the policy of the journal to avoid the use of the term "subjects." Research participants, respondents, or a more specific appropriate designation should be used. The journal further urges contributors to clarify how informed consent was gathered and to describe the nature and impact of feedback to settings involved in the research or intervention. In addition, it encourages the inclusion of descriptive material relevant to understanding the nature of the settings or communities where the work was carried out as well as the nature of the relationship between professionals and the participants or respondents. It is most important that the text describe, as appropriate, the background characteristics of participants in detail. Ordinarily, this includes information on gender, age, racial and ethnic background, sexual orientation, disability status, and socioeconomic status.

6. Type *all* material **double-spaced** and submit **four** copies that are dark, sharp, and clear (including copies of all illustrations and tables).

7. A 150-word abstract is to be provided. A list of 4-6 key words is to be provided directly below the abstract. Key words should express the precise content of the manuscript, as they are used for indexing purposes.

8. Tables should be numbered in one consecutive series of Roman numerals and referred to by number in the text. Each table should be typed on a separate sheet of paper and should have a descriptive title centered above the table.

9. Illustrations (photographs, drawings, diagrams, and charts) are to be numbered in one consecutive series of Arabic numerals and referred to by number in the text. Photographs should be large, glossy prints, showing high contrast. Either the original drawings or high-quality photographic prints are acceptable. Identify figures on the back with author's name and number of the illustration. Each figure should have an accompanying caption. The list of captions for illustrations should be typed (double-spaced) on a separate sheet of paper. Electronic artwork submitted on disk should be in the TIFF or EPS format (1200 dpi for line and 300 dpi for half-tones and gray-scale art). Color art should be in the CYMK color space. Artwork should be on a separate disk from the text, and hard copy *must* accompany the disk.

10. After a manuscript has been accepted for publication and after all revisions have been incorporated, manuscripts should be submitted to the Editor's Office as hard copy accompanied by electronic files on disk. Label the disk with identifying information – software, journal name, and first author's last name. **The disk *must* be the one from which the accompanying manuscript (finalized version) was printed out**. The Editor's Office cannot accept a disk without its accompanying, matching hard-copy manuscript.

11. **The journal makes no page charges**. Reprints are available to authors, and order forms with the current price schedule are sent with proofs.

American Journal of Evaluation

ADDRESS FOR SUBMISSION:

Robin Lin Miller, Editor
American Journal of Evaluation
Michigan State University
Department of Psychology
316 Psychology Building
East Lansing, MS 48824-1116
USA
Phone: 517-432-5640
Fax: 517-353-4873
E-Mail: aje@eval.org
Web: www.sagepub.com
Address May Change: 12/31/2004

PUBLICATION GUIDELINES:

Manuscript Length: 26-40
Copies Required: Six (4 w/out ID, 2 w/ID)
Computer Submission: No
Format: N/A
Fees to Review: 0.00 US$

Manuscript Style:
    American Psychological Association

CIRCULATION DATA:

Reader: Academics, Practitioners
Frequency of Issue: Quarterly
Copies per Issue: 3,001 - 4,000
Sponsor/Publisher: American Evaluation
    Association (AEA) / Sage Publications
Subscribe Price: 130.00 US$ Individual
    393.00 US$ Institution

REVIEW INFORMATION:

Type of Review: Blind Review
No. of External Reviewers: 3+
No. of In House Reviewers: 1
Acceptance Rate: 21-30%
Time to Review: 3 Months
Reviewers Comments: Yes
Invited Articles: 20%
Fees to Publish: 0.00 US$

MANUSCRIPT TOPICS:
Program and Policy Evaluation; Research Methods & Statistics

MANUSCRIPT GUIDELINES/COMMENTS:

The *American Journal of Evaluation (AJE)* publishes original papers about the methods, theory, practice, and findings of evaluation. The general goal of *AJE* is to present the best work in and about evaluation, in order to improve the knowledge base and practice of its readers. Because the field of evaluation is diverse, with different intellectual traditions, approaches to practice, and domains of application, the papers published in *AJE* will reflect this diversity. Nevertheless, preference is given to papers that are likely to be of interest to a wide range of evaluators and that are written to be accessible to most readers.

Individuals interested in contributing to the Ethical Challenges, Exemplars, Teaching Evaluation, and Book Reviews sections should contact the relevant section editor (see Contribution Categories). All other manuscripts should be addressed to: Dr. Robin Lin Miller, Editor, AJE, Michigan State University, Department of Psychology, 316 Psychology Building, East Lansing, MI 48824-1116. Submission letters should specify that the manuscript is not currently under consideration elsewhere and has not been published elsewhere in the same or a substantially similar form.

A total of six double-spaced typewritten copies should be submitted. On two copies, each author's name, title, full mailing address, telephone number(s), and e-mail address should be listed. Author information should be omitted on four copies (for blind review).

Manuscripts should be prepared following the style of the *Publication Manual of the American Psychological Association*, 4th Edition. References, citations in text, tables, and figures should all conform to the *APA* style. Any figures should be camera-ready.

Authors whose works have been accepted for publication will be asked to submit the final manuscript on a disk prepared with an IBM-compatible word processor. WordPerfect or Word formats are preferred, but others can be used. (Please contact Robin Miller for specific guidelines.)

If prospective contributors have questions or are uncertain about the appropriateness of possible submissions, they are welcome to contact Robin Miller via email at **aje@eval.org** or by phone at (517) 353-5010.

American Journal of Orthopsychiatry

ADDRESS FOR SUBMISSION:

Nancy Felipe Russo, Editor
American Journal of Orthopsychiatry
Arizona State University
Department of Psychology
Box 1104
Tempe, AZ 85287-1104
USA
Phone:
Fax:
E-Mail: nancy.russo@asu.edu
Web: www.amerortho.org
Address May Change:

PUBLICATION GUIDELINES:

Manuscript Length: 11-30
Copies Required: Four
Computer Submission: No
Format: N/A
Fees to Review: 0.00 US$

Manuscript Style:
    American Psychological Association

CIRCULATION DATA:

Reader: No Reply
Frequency of Issue: Quarterly
Copies per Issue: 5,001 - 10,000
Sponsor/Publisher: American
   Orthopsychiatric Association
Subscribe Price: 70.00 US$ Individual
   90.00 US$ Institution

REVIEW INFORMATION:

Type of Review: Blind Review
No. of External Reviewers: 2
No. of In House Reviewers: 0
Acceptance Rate: 25%
Time to Review: 4 - 6 Months
Reviewers Comments: Yes
Invited Articles: 5%
Fees to Publish: 0.00 US$

MANUSCRIPT TOPICS:
Adolescent Psychology; Child Psychology; Family Counseling & Therapy; Human Rights; Justice, Social Justice; Mental Health; Psychiatry; Social Psychology; Thinking & Cognition

MANUSCRIPT GUIDELINES/COMMENTS:

Topics Include. Mental Health Services and Policies; Human Rights and Mental Health; Minority and Mental Health; Refugees and Mental Health; Family and Social Systems

The *Journal* is dedicated to informing public policy, professional practice, and knowledge production relating to mental health and social responsibility, from a multidisciplinary and interprofessional perspective. Clinical, theoretical, research, or expository papers that are essentially synergistic and directed at concept or theory development, reconceptualization of major issues, explanation, and interpretation are especially welcomed for Editorial Board consideration. Selection of articles for publication is based on their originality, adequacy of method, significance of findings, contribution to theory, relevance to service delivery and public policy, and clarity and brevity of presentation.

Submission should be in quadruplicate (four clean copies), typed on one side of firm paper, double spaced, with generous margins. Manuscripts should be in final form, with consistent headings and subheadings, in roman typeface (i.e., no boldface, italics, etc.), and should include a cover letter with mailing address, day-time telephone number, and fax number if available. Manuscripts should be prepared for blind review, and each should be accompanied by an abstract of approximately 50 words.

Original typescripts should be retained by authors. Only photocopies or computer-generated duplicates should be submitted, since rejected manuscripts are disposed of following review. In special circumstances that require return of a manuscript, return envelope and postage should accompany submission; however, the Journal assumes no responsibility for each return.

The entire manuscript must be double-spaced, including quotations, footnotes, references, and tables.

Footnotes should be worked back into the text or deleted where possible, where essential, they should appear at the bottom of the manuscript page on which they are cited and be indicated by the asterisk system.

References should be prepared in conformance with the style set forth in the *Publication Manual of the American Psychological Association*, Fourth Edition.

The American Orthopsychiatric Association assumes no responsibility for any statements of fact or opinion in the papers printed, nor does acceptance of advertising in the Journal imply endorsement of the Association of any of the products or services advertised.

The Editorial Board reserves the right to reject any manuscript, to suggest modifications prior to publication, and to edit accepted manuscripts in conformance with Journal style and standards.

American Journal of Psychoanalysis (The)

ADDRESS FOR SUBMISSION:

Giselle Galdi, Editor
American Journal of Psychoanalysis (The)
329 East 62 Street
New York, NY 10021
USA
Phone:
Fax:
E-Mail:
Web: See Guidelines
Address May Change:

PUBLICATION GUIDELINES:

Manuscript Length: 1-30
Copies Required: Five
Computer Submission: No
Format: N/A
Fees to Review: 0.00 US$

Manuscript Style:
American Psychological Association

CIRCULATION DATA:

Reader: Academics, Professors,
    Researchers, Clinicians in private practice
Frequency of Issue: Quarterly
Copies per Issue: No Reply
Sponsor/Publisher: Association for the
    Advancement of Psychoanalysis
Subscribe Price: 65.00 US$ Individual
    418.00 US$ Institution

REVIEW INFORMATION:

Type of Review: Blind Review
No. of External Reviewers: 2
No. of In House Reviewers: 1
Acceptance Rate: 50%
Time to Review: 2 - 3 Months
Reviewers Comments: Yes
Invited Articles:
Fees to Publish: 0.00 US$

MANUSCRIPT TOPICS:
Counseling Process; Psychoanalysis

MANUSCRIPT GUIDELINES/COMMENTS:

Website. http://www.wkap.nl/journalhome.htm/0002-9548

The American Journal of Psychoanalysis invites contributions from scholars and practitioners in the psychoanalysis and related fields. Original articles must be offered for exclusive publication. The Editors reserve the right to reject any manuscript submitted, whether on invitation or on the initiative of the writer, and to make whatever suggestions for change as deemed necessary for publication.

According to the 1978 U.S. Copyright Law, the transfer of copyright from author to publisher must be explicit. Authors of articles accepted for publication will receive the necessary form for signature. Authors are fully responsible for statements made in their articles. Published articles do not necessarily reflect the views of the Association for the Advancement of Psychoanalysis.

Preparation and Submission of Manuscripts. Original papers (of no more than 30 pages, including references) will be considered for publication and should be submitted to the Editor (see below). All manuscripts will be blind peer-reviewed to maintain the highest quality and to verify relevance, accuracy, and clarity of presentation. Manuscripts must be typed double-spaced on 8 ½ × 11 in. bond paper with 1½ in. margins on all sides of the page. **The original and four copies** must be submitted; one copy must be retained by the author, as the journal cannot be responsible for manuscripts.

The title page should include full names of authors, degrees, academic and professional affiliations, the complete mailing address, telephone number, fax number, and e-mail address of the author to whom page proofs are to be sent.

The second page should contain the title of the paper and an *abstract* of no more than 100 words as well as 3 to 5 *key words* listed below the abstract.

The 2001 *Publication Manual of the American Psychological Association* (Fifth Edition) should be used as a guide in preparation of manuscripts: Manuscript pages must be numbered consecutively. Footnotes are to be avoided if possible. When their use is absolutely necessary, footnotes should be numbered consecutively using Arabic numbers and should be typed at the end of the article, preceding the References section. *References* are cited by name and year in the text. They must be typed double-spaced on a separate sheet, and arranged in alphabetical order by first author; do not number. Several references by the same author should be listed in chronological order (if the same year, use a, b, c, etc., after the year). Name(s) of author(s) must be followed by the year of the original publication (in parentheses), the title, the name of the publication, volume number, and beginning and end pages. Publisher's name and city of publication are required for books. The year of publication of the edition used must be included when different from the original publication year.

Examples:
Book
Horney, K. (1991). *Neurosis and human growth.* New York: W.W. Norton & Company. (Original work published in 1950).

Edited book
Ferenczi, S. (1976). The problem of the termination of the analysis. In M. S. Bergmann & F. R. Hartman (Eds.), *The evolution of psychoanalytic technique* (pp. 207-215). New York: Columbia University Press. (Original work published 1928).

Journal article
Martin, A. (1945). The body's participation in dilemma and anxiety phenomena. *The American Journal of Psychoanalysis, 5,* 28-48.

After a manuscript has been accepted for publication and after all revisions have been incorporated, manuscripts should be submitted to the Editor's Office as hard copy accompanied by electronic files on disk. Label the disk with identifying information — software, journal name, and first author's last name. **The disk *must* be the one from which the accompanying manuscript (finalized version) was printed out.** The Editor's Office cannot accept a disk without its accompanying, matching hard-copy manuscript. Electronic artwork submitted on disk should be in the TIFF or EPS format (1200 dpi for line and 300 dpi for half-tones and gray-scale art). Color art should be in the CYMK color space. Artwork should be on a separate disk from the text, and hard copy *must* accompany the disk.

Correspondence and Book Reviews. *The American Journal of Psychoanalysis* welcomes relevant responses to papers published in the journal, as well as concise reviews (up to 700 words) of current psychoanalytic books.

Address Manuscripts, Correspondence, Books for review, and Book Reviews to: Giselle Galdi, Ph.D., Editor, The American Journal of Psychoanalysis, 329 East 62nd Street, New York, NY 10021, USA.

Springer Open Choice. In addition to the normal publication process (whereby an article is submitted to the journal and access to that article is granted to customers who have purchased a subscription), Springer now provides an alternative publishing option: Springer Open Choice. A Springer Open Choice article receives all the benefits of a regular subscription-based article, but in addition is made available publicly through Springer's online platform SpringerLink. To publish via Springer Open Choice, upon acceptance please visit **www.springeronline.com/openchoice** to complete the relevant order form and provide the required payment information. Payment must be received in full before publication or articles will publish as regular subscription-model articles. We regret that Springer Open Choice cannot be ordered for published articles.

American Journal of Psychology

ADDRESS FOR SUBMISSION:

Donelson E. Dulany, Editor
American Journal of Psychology
University of Illinois-Urbana-Champaign
Department of Psychology
603 E Daniel Street
Champaign, IL 61820-6975
USA
Phone: 217-333-2971
Fax: 217-244-5876
E-Mail: ddulany@psych.uiuc.edu
Web: www.press.uillinois.edu/journals
Address May Change:

PUBLICATION GUIDELINES:

Manuscript Length: 16-30 varies
Copies Required: Four
Computer Submission: No
Format: Disk for Final Version
Fees to Review: 0.00 US$

Manuscript Style:
  American Psychological Association

CIRCULATION DATA:

Reader: Academics
Frequency of Issue: Quarterly
Copies per Issue: 2,001 - 3,000
Sponsor/Publisher: University of Illinois
  Press
Subscribe Price: 65.00 US$ Individual
  140.00 US$ Institution
  10.00 US$ Add for Foreign

REVIEW INFORMATION:

Type of Review: Editorial Review
No. of External Reviewers: 2-3
No. of In House Reviewers: 1
Acceptance Rate: 21-30%
Time to Review: 2 - 3 Months
Reviewers Comments: Yes
Invited Articles: 6-10%
Fees to Publish: 0.00 US$

MANUSCRIPT TOPICS:
Attention; Experimental Psychology; History of Psychology; Learning & Conditioning; Memory; Neuropsychology; Sensation & Perception; Thinking & Cognition

MANUSCRIPT GUIDELINES/COMMENTS:

AJP explores the basic science of the mind, publishing reports of original research in experimental psychology, theoretical presentations, combined theoretical and experimental analyses, historical commentaries, obituaries of prominent psychologists, and in-depth reviews of significant books. Issued quarterly.

Editorial Statement
This is a very special journal, deeply involved in the history of psychology, the organ of publication of some of its most distinguished and influential contributors. Founded in 1887 by G. Stanley Hall and edited in its early years by Titchener, Boring, and Dallenbach, the *American Journal of Psychology* has published some of the most innovative and formative papers in psychology.

60

The domain of the *Journal* is the basic science of mind, those aspects of mind we call cognitive, but also those aspects we call affective and cognitive. It is the theoretical and experimental enterprise at the heart of the discipline of psychology and fundamental to that intersection of disciplines now known as cognitive science.

The range is stunningly broad, but I would like some unifying focus on a fundamental set of philosophically and historically significant topics that have arisen throughout the discipline: the roles of consciousness and non-conscious processes; automaticity and the attentional, volitional, and deliberative; the forms and personal significance of memory; conceptual abstraction and induction; causality as perceived, inferred, and characterized; the senses and limits of rationality; relations of language to thought; the processes that constitute intelligence; the roles and limits of symbolic representation; mental activity as revealed by brain imaging or neuropathology; the uses and limits of introspection; and a cluster of puzzles having to do with apprehension of reality, from certain classical perceptual phenomena to commonplaces and disturbances in experience of self.

Submission Information
Manuscripts of articles and notes should be submitted to:
Donelson E.Dulany, American Journal of Psychology
University of Illinois at Urbana-Champaign
603 E. Daniel St., Champaign, IL 61820

Articles on the history of psychology, as well as correspondence concerning obituaries, should be addressed to:
Rand B. Evans
Harvard Collection of Historical Scientific Instruments
One Oxford Street, Science Center, Harvard University
Cambridge, MA 02138

Books intended for review and invited reviews should be sent to:
Dominic W. Massaro
Department of Psychology. University of California, Santa Cruz
1156 High Street, Santa Cruz, CA 95064

Notes for Contributors
Contributors are asked to follow the style described in the *Publication Manual of the American Psychological Association,* 4th ed. (1994), and to consult "Appendix B. Checklist for Manuscript Submission," in the *Manual* as a guide. In submitting a manuscript, be especially sure to remember the following instructions.:

- Submit four photocopies of your manuscript printed on both sides of each page. Include complete sets of photocopied tables and figures. Please do not send glossy prints. None will be returned unless explicitly requested.
- Everything should be double-spaced – abstract, text, references, notes, captions – everything.
- An address and telephone number (and an e-mail address and fax number, if possible) should be included for future correspondence.
- The abstract should not exceed 960 characters and spaces (approximately 120 words).

- Special mathematical symbols and abbreviations should be identified.
- All elements in a figure should be large enough to be readable when the drawing is reduced to fit the maximum width of 11 cm.
- All titles in the reference list should be spelled out rather than abbreviated.
- References cited in the text should agree with those in the reference list.
- A copy of the letter of permission for the use of previously published material (e.g., long extracts and reproductions of figures) should be included.
- The submitted manuscript should not be under concurrent review elsewhere.

If you elect to omit from your manuscript any information that is critical to the evaluation of your data (analyses of variance summary tables, means, variances, correlation and factor matrices), provide four copies of that material for use by the editors and consultants in reviewing the paper.

Authors of articles may order offprints at the time they return page proofs or may request tear sheets. Book reviewers are sent tear sheets of their reviews.

Book Reviews
(Book Review Editor - Dominic W. Massaro)
The *American Journal of Psychology* reviews books in various areas of cognitive/ experimental psychology, philosophy of mind and science, neuroscience, and cognitive science more generally. Given our page limitations, we must be selective about what books we review. Rather than duplicate to some extent book review journals such as Contemporary Psychology, we are seeking a somewhat more ambitious type of book review. We aim to review books that present a latest statement in some area of interest. The goal of the book review would be to include within the context of the review the reviewer's opinion on the state of the art, important questions, productive and not-so-productive approaches to the questions, and prospects for future inquiry. Although the review is open-ended, the target length might be somewhere between 1500 and 3000 words. This charge should be much more challenging and enjoyable than a prototypical book review. In addition to soliciting authors or reviews for specific books of our choosing, we will also consider proposals from reviewers. Scholars interested in reviewing books for the journal should inform the book review editor. Scholars are also encouraged to submit a proposal for a book they would like to review for the journal.

American Journal of Psychotherapy

ADDRESS FOR SUBMISSION:

T. Byram Karasu, Editor-in-Chief
American Journal of Psychotherapy
Belfer Education Center
Room 405
1300 Morris Park Avenue
Bronx, NY 10461
USA
Phone: 718-430-3503
Fax: 718-430-8907
E-Mail: info@ajp.org
Web: www.ajp.org
Address May Change:

PUBLICATION GUIDELINES:

Manuscript Length: 16-20
Copies Required: Three
Computer Submission: Yes Email
Format:
Fees to Review: 0.00 US$

Manuscript Style:
    See Manuscript Guidelines

CIRCULATION DATA:

Reader: Academics, Practitioners
Frequency of Issue: Quarterly
Copies per Issue: 1,001 - 2,000
Sponsor/Publisher: Association for the
    Advancement of Psychotherapy
Subscribe Price:

REVIEW INFORMATION:

Type of Review: Blind Review
No. of External Reviewers: 1-2
No. of In House Reviewers: 1-2
Acceptance Rate: 50%
Time to Review: N/A
Reviewers Comments: Yes
Invited Articles: 6-10%
Fees to Publish: 0.00 US$

MANUSCRIPT TOPICS:
Counseling Process

MANUSCRIPT GUIDELINES/COMMENTS:

Founded in 1939, the *American Journal of Psychotherapy* (*AJP*) has long been a leader in the publication of eclectic articles for all psychotherapists. Transtheoretic in reach (offering information for psychotherapists across all theoretical foundations), the goal of *AJP* is to present an overview of the psychotherapies, subsuming a host of schools, techniques, and psychological modalities within the larger domain of clinical practice under broad themes including dynamic, behavioral, spiritual, and experiential.

The *Journal* offers varying viewpoints on the "who, when, why, and how" of psychotherapy. The *Journal* also serves as a conceptual bridge using the developmental process to reconcile major psychotherapeutic paradigms of the past and present.

It is the intent of the Editor-in-Chief to have the *Journal's* audience extend to the entire therapeutic community of practitioners and their patients.

Author Guidelines

Submission of Papers. Authors are requested to submit their original manuscript and figures with two copies to: Editorial Office, Belfer Educational Center, Room 405, 1300 Morris Park Avenue, Bronx, NY 10469. We will also accept files submitted as an e-mail attachment (**info@ajp.org**) and will make every attempt to open the file. If this is not possible we will request a hardcopy from the author.

Paper submission implies it has not been published previously, is not being considered for publication elsewhere. If the manuscript is accepted, the author agrees it will not be republished elsewhere without consent of the publisher.

Review process. All manuscripts undergo blinded peer review. Authors should ensure the body of the manuscript contains no clues to their identity.

Manuscript Preparation. Manuscripts must be typewritten, double-spaced with wide margins (including reference page) on one side of white paper. A font size no smaller than 10 point is required. Except for original research papers, manuscript should not exceed 20 typed pages.

All manuscripts must contain:
- Cover sheet with title and subtitle of the papers
- List of all authors/contributors with institutional affiliations. Indicate corresponding author, including telephone and Fax numbers, e-mail and full postal address
- Abstract page. Each manuscript must include an abstract of no more than 150 words
- Include up to five keywords for indexing purposes

The Editors reserve the right to adjust style to standards of Journal uniformity. Authors should retain a copy of their manuscript for their files. Original manuscripts may be discarded after publication.

Tables, figures and illustrations should be kept to a minimum. Provide all illustrations in camera-ready form, suitable for reproduction (which may include reduction). Lettering should be large enough to be legible after reduction to the 4 ½" x 7" type area of the *Journal*. When possible, incorporate tabular material into the text. Mark all illustrations on the back with the figure number and the author's name. All figures are to have a caption. Line drawings should be of a good quality printout on white paper in black ink. Photocopies are not suitable for reproduction. If submitting photograph, supply them as they are to be reproduced (e.g. black and white or color). If necessary, mark a scale on the photograph. Note that authors will be charged for color reproduction.

Electronic submission. A disc containing a copy of the paper should accompany the final version. Please include both an ASCII file and a text file, with the type and release of the word processing software used. Please ensure that the hardcopy and electronic manuscript match exactly.

Proofs. Proofs will be sent to the corresponding author and should be returned within 48 hours of receipt. Any queries should be answered in full. Corrections should be restricted to typesetting errors; any others may be charged to the author.

Reprints. Copies of the article can be ordered at using the order form sent to the corresponding author after the manuscript has been accepted. Orders for reprints produced after publication will incur a surcharge. (Available at **www-ajp.org**.)

Copyright. All authors must sign the author agreement before the article can be published. (Available at www-ajp.org.)

Citations in text. Follow the American Psychological Association guidelines. The following typify common rules:
- Drake (1984) discovered that . . .
- In a recent article (Drake, 1984) it was discovered . . .
- Drake, Adams, and Smith (1992) found . . .
- It was found later (Drake et al., 1992) . . . that [this illustrates a subsequent citation for Drake, Adams, & Smith]
- Judd and Ryner (1981) demonstrated . . .
- B.H. Diamond (1983) and G.C. Diamond, (1983); G.C. Diamond (1981); Smith & Thomas, (1985b).

Reference style. All references must be placed at the end of the paper, in alphabetical order, following the American Psychological Association guidelines. (examples taken from the *Publication Manual of the American Psychological Association* , Fifth edition, 2001.

Periodical. Smith, A.A., Jones, B.B. & Barnes, C.C. (1994). *Title of article Title of Periodical*, xx, xxx-xxx.

Book. Smith, A.A,, (1994). *Title of book*. Location: Publisher.

Book chapter. Smith, A.A., & Jones B.B. (1994). Title of chapter. In A. Editor, B. Editor, & C. Editor (Eds.), Title of book (pp. xx-xxx). Location: Publisher.
Online periodical: Smith, A.A., Jones, B.B. & Barnes, C.C (2002). Title of article. Title of Periodical, xx, xxx-xxx. Retrieved month day, year, from sources.

Online document. Smith, A.A.,(2000). *Title of work*. Retrieved month day, year, from source.

The American Journal of Psychotherapy (ISSN 0002-9564) is published four (4) times per year by the:
    Association for the Advancement of Psychotherapy, Belfer Education Center
    Room 405, 1300 Morris Park Avenue, Bronx, New York 10461
    Phone: (718)430-3503; Fax: (718)430-8907; Email: **info@ajp.org**

American Journal on Addictions

ADDRESS FOR SUBMISSION:

Sheldon I. Miller, Editor
American Journal on Addictions
PO Box 27327
Shawnee Mission, KS 66225-7327
USA
Phone: 913-469-0709
Fax: 913-469-0913
E-Mail: aja@aaap.org
Web: http://www.tandf.co.uk/journals
Address May Change:

PUBLICATION GUIDELINES:

Manuscript Length: 8-10
Copies Required: Three
Computer Submission: Yes Disk or Email
Format: WordPerfect
Fees to Review: 0.00 US$

Manuscript Style:
 , American Medical Association

CIRCULATION DATA:

Reader: Academics, Practitioners
Frequency of Issue: 5 Times/Year
Copies per Issue:
Sponsor/Publisher: Taylor & Francis
Subscribe Price: 136.00 US$ Individual
 282.00 US$ Institution

REVIEW INFORMATION:

Type of Review: Editorial Review
No. of External Reviewers: 2
No. of In House Reviewers: 1
Acceptance Rate: 95%
Time to Review: 2 - 3 Months
Reviewers Comments: Yes
Invited Articles: 0-5%
Fees to Publish: 0.00 US$

MANUSCRIPT TOPICS:
Alcoholism & Drug Addiction

MANUSCRIPT GUIDELINES/COMMENTS:

Aims and Scope
The *American Journal on Addictions* is the official journal of the American Academy of Addiction Psychiatry. The Academy encourages research on the etiology, prevention, identification, and treatment of substance abuse; thus, the journal provides a forum for the dissemination of information in the extensive field of addiction.

Each issue of this quarterly publication covers a wide variety of topics ranging from codependence to genetics, epidemiology to dual diagnostics, etiology to neuroscience, and much more. Features of the journal, all written by experts in the field, include special overview articles, clinical or basic research papers, clinical updates, and book reviews within the area of addictions.

Instructions For Authors
Note to Authors. Please make sure your contact address information is clearly visible on the outside of all packages you are sending to Editors.

Manuscript. *The American Journal on Addictions* publishes special overview articles, original clinical or basic research papers, clinical updates, book reviews, and letters within the area of addictions. Submission of material to this journal is understood to imply that it or substantial parts of it have not been published, accepted for publication, or submitted for consideration elsewhere. Upon acceptance of an article, author(s) will be required to assign copyright ownership in writing to the *American Academy of Addiction Psychiatry*.

Submission Procedure. Submit original and three copies along with a computer diskette version using MS Word or WordPerfect to Sheldon I. Miller. M.D., Editor, *The American Journal on Addictions*, PO Box 27327, Shawnee Mission, KS 66225-7327. A cover letter must be included indicating that the material is intended for publication and specifying for which section of the journal it is to be considered (Special or Regular Articles, Book Reviews, Clinical Update Series, or Letters to the Editor). Books to be considered for review should be sent to Roger D. Weiss, M.D., Book Review Editor, *The American Journal on Addictions*, PO Box 27327, Shawnee Mission, KS 66225-7327. Anyone wishing to review books for the journal should apply to Dr. Weiss at the same address. All accepted manuscripts, artwork, and photographs become the property of the American Academy of Addiction Psychiatry. Upon acceptance, contributors are required to supply the final version of the material both in hardcopy and on computer diskette. A PC-based format using MS Word or WordPerfect is preferred. Questions about submitting material electronically can be directed to the Publisher.

A Microsoft Word author template file, which also includes more detailed instructions in its **"Read Me"** file, can be downloaded from the "Instructions for Author's" web page.

Peer Review. All manuscripts, including those written at the invitation of the editor, are subject to peer review by at least two experts. Upon completion of the review (usually an eight-week process), the Author(s) will be advised of the decision on the manuscript. If revisions are deemed necessary, this feedback will be based on detailed from the reviewers. Revised material is due in a timely fashion to avoid the necessity of returning to the peer review stage. At the discretion of the Editor, reviewer comments will be included with the return of rejected manuscripts. Please note that all reviews remain anonymous.

Manuscripts, including tables, figures, and references, should be prepared in accordance with the *American Medical Association Manual of Style*, Eighth Edition. All manuscripts must be typed, double-spaced, on 8.5 x 11 inch paper with a 1-inch margin all around. Dot matrix printouts and others not conforming to these requirements will be returned un-reviewed.

Title Page. Should contain the article title, names and institutional affiliations of all authors and complete mailing address, phone, fax, and e-mail address of the author to whom all correspondence should be sent.

Abstract. Should be typed on a separate page and should not exceed 100 words.

Illustrations. Crisp, clear, black and white (camera-ready) artwork should be submitted. Four-color illustrations will be considered; however, the author will be required to bear the full cost involved in their printing and publication. The charge for the first figure is $1,200. Subsequent figures, totaling no more than four text pages, are $500 each. Good quality color prints should be provided in their final size.

References. Should be listed on separate pages following the text and should be typed double-spaced. References are numbered and listed in the order of appearance in the text; the appropriate reference number in parentheses follows the text citation. Do not arrange the reference list alphabetically. Be sure *all* references have been cited in text. List only the first three authors in the reference list and designate one or more authors after the third as "et al." Journal names should be abbreviated as they appear in *Index Medicus*; journals not currently indexed there should not be abbreviated.

Proofs. One set of page proofs is sent to the designated author. Proofs should be checked and returned within 48 hours.

Offprints and Complimentary Copies. The corresponding author of each article will receive 25 free reprints of the article. Additional reprints of the article may be ordered from Brunner/Mazel by using the order form included with the page proofs.

Permissions. Authors are responsible for obtaining permission to reproduce copyrighted material from other sources.

American Journal on Mental Retardation

ADDRESS FOR SUBMISSION:

William E. MacLean Jr., Editor
American Journal on Mental Retardation
University of Wyoming
Department of Psychology
Dept. 3415
1000 E. University Avenue
Laramie, WY 82071
USA
Phone: 307-766-5433
Fax: 307-766-5432
E-Mail: maclean@uwyo.edu
Web: aamr.allenpress.com
Address May Change:

PUBLICATION GUIDELINES:

Manuscript Length: 20
Copies Required: Electronic
Computer Submission: Yes Internet
Format: N/A
Fees to Review: 0.00 US$

Manuscript Style:
    American Psychological Association

CIRCULATION DATA:

Reader: Academics
Frequency of Issue: 6 Times/Year
Copies per Issue: 2,001 - 3,000
Sponsor/Publisher: American Assn. on
    Mental Retardation / Allen Press
Subscribe Price: 140.00 US$,$165 Print
    126.00 US$, $149 Online Only
    151.00 US$, $198 Print + Online

REVIEW INFORMATION:

Type of Review: Blind Review
No. of External Reviewers: 3
No. of In House Reviewers: 1
Acceptance Rate: 25%
Time to Review: 2 - 3 Months
Reviewers Comments: Yes
Invited Articles: 0-5%
Fees to Publish: 0.00 US$

MANUSCRIPT TOPICS:
Exceptional Child; Mental Retardation

MANUSCRIPT GUIDELINES/COMMENTS:

Editorial Policy
The American Journal on Mental Retardation (ISSN 0895-8017) is published by the American Association on Mental Retardation. It is a scientific, scholarly, and archival multidisciplinary journal for reporting original contributions of the highest quality to knowledge of mental retardation, its causes, treatment, and prevention. Such contributions include (a) reports of empirical research on characteristics of people with mental retardation, individual differences in and correlates of such characteristics, and factors that alter those characteristics or correlates; (b) systematic reviews and tightly conceived theoretical interpretations of relevant research literatures; and (c) reports of evaluative research on new treatment procedures or programs. In general, the preferred approach is scientific, evidence-based, and theory-guided. Annotated bibliographies, anecdotal case reports, descriptions of

treatment procedures or programs, personal accounts, and descriptive reports on new tests and their standardization are not published.

Each submitted paper is reviewed by experts in the area of the paper's content. To be published, a paper must conform to the highest standards of professional development of the disciplines identified with its content. Research papers are judged on the importance of the questions asked, soundness of conceptualization and rationale, relevance of research operations to the questions, reliability of results, logic of conclusions, and clarity and economy of presentations. Reports of studies using educational and psychological tests designed for practical use are accepted only if the tests meet the criteria described in the *Standards for Educational and Psychological Testing* (American Psychological Association, 1985). Literature reviews, theoretical reinterpretations, and scholarly reassessments are judged on relevance of focus, incisiveness with which issues are defined, completeness of coverage of relevant literature, consistency in the application of evaluative criteria, soundness of inferences and conclusions, and novelty and probable fruitfulness of interpretation. Such papers must include new insights in order to be acceptable for publication.

Data-Sharing
After research results are published, authors do not withhold the data on which their conclusions are based from other competent professionals who seek to verify the substantive claims through reanalysis and who intend to use such data only for that purpose, provided that the confidentiality of the participants can be protected and unless legal rights concerning proprietary data preclude their release.

INFORMATION FOR AUTHORS
Manuscript Submission
In order for your manuscript to enter our review process, please submit your manuscript electronically by going to the following web address: **http://ajmr.allentrack.net**

At that page there is a place for registered members to enter their login name and password. If you do not have an account, or if you don't know if you have an account, you can click on the link that says, "New authors should register for an account." If you click on the link, you will be taken to a page to verify whether the system already has any information about you. Your information may have already been entered if you served as a reviewer for *AJMR* previously. Please enter the requested information and the verification will proceed.

After completing the form on the proximate web page, including entering a login name and password, you will have established an account and will need to log into the system. Once logged in, there will be a link with instructions on how to submit a new manuscript. Please follow those instructions to upload your manuscript.

Before submitting a manuscript, please gather the following information: All Authors information, Title and Running Title (you may copy and paste these from your manuscript), Abstract (you may copy and paste this from your manuscript), Key words, Manuscript files in Word (doc), WordPerfect (wpd), or Rich Text Format (rtf), Figures/Images in Tagged Image Format (tif), Postscript (ps), Encapsulated Postscript (eps), Portable Document Format (pdf), JPEG (jpg), Excel (xls), GIF (gif), or Adobe Photoshop (psd) formats.

Please remove any personally identifying information from the manuscript files to aid us in maintaining an anonymous review policy.

Manuscripts should be prepared in accordance with the 2001 *Publication Manual of the American Psychological Association* (APA, 5th ed.). The instructions given there for preparing tables, figures, references, metrics, and abstracts should be followed. Regular articles are to include an abstract containing a maximum of 120 words. The editor in charge is responsible for obtaining reviews and deciding on the disposition of all manuscripts (acceptance, rejection, or requests for revision). Once a manuscript is accepted for publication, the remainder of the production process is coordinated by the Senior Editor, Yvette Taylor, 10886 Ravel Ct., Boca Raton, FL 33498; e-mail, **ytaamr@aol.com**; phone, 561-482-0341. You may contact Yvette Taylor for any technical questions about manuscript preparations.

Books, tests, etc. being offered for review and reviews of such materials should be sent to Connie Kasari, Graduate School of Education and Information Studies, UCLA, Box 951521, Moore Hall, 405 Hilgard Ave., Los Angeles, CA 90095.

Ethical Standards
All investigations using human participants must have been approved by the human subjects review committee of the author's institution. Submission of a manuscript to *AJMR* while that paper is under review by another journal is unacceptable. Presentation of a manuscript in electronic form on the Internet is considered to constitute publication and may be grounds for rejection of the paper by this journal.

Form
All sections of the manuscript (including quotations, references, tables, and footnotes) should be double-spaced on 8 by 11-inch paper with at least a 1-inch margin on all sides. Authors should retain the original. Copies will not usually be returned. The preferred length of manuscripts is 20 typed pages or less, but somewhat greater length may be accepted depending on the complexity and importance of the research reported. Brief reports are generally 5-10 manuscript pages and contain a limited number of findings in comparison to research articles.

Abbreviations and Terminology
Abbreviations should be held to a minimum. The names of groups or experimental conditions should usually not be abbreviated. The full names of tests should be given when they are first mentioned, with the common shortened form in parentheses. When context makes it clear whether an author is referring to people with mental retardation or when it is otherwise unnecessary to refer to intellectual level or diagnostic category, authors should use the most descriptive generic terms, such as children, students, or persons, without using qualifiers such as "with mental retardation," "with handicaps," or "with developmental disabilities." Under no circumstances should *retarded* be used as a noun. Prepositional constructions such as "students with mental retardation," or "individuals who have mental retardation" are preferred over adjectival constructions such as "mentally retarded people" except when clear communication dictates occasional use of adjectival designations. Because *normal* has multiple meanings and may inappropriately imply *abnormal* where it is not applied, this word

should not be used. Instead, more operationally descriptive terms such as "intellectually average pupils" should be used.

Numerical and Illustrative Presentations and References

The metric system should be used for all expressions of linear measures, weight, and volume. Tables and figures should be kept to a minimum. Information should be presented only once - whether in the text or in a table or figure. For this reason, short tables may be deleted or combined into larger ones during the copy-editing process. Lines should not be typed or inked within tables, and all columns should be provided with headings. AllenTrack accepts figures in JPEG, TIFF, GIF, EPS, PDF, or Postscript formats. Figure captions should be typed on a separate sheet, but other types of lettering may appear on the figures themselves. All such lettering must be of professional quality (not typewritten) and large enough to withstand a reduction of approximately 50% in size. Release forms (signed, dated, witnessed, and notarized) must accompany photographs of human subjects. Care should be taken to conceal the identity of persons in such photographs. Authors must also secure permission to use any copyrighted tables or figures. References should conform to the American Psychological Association style.

Footnotes

Content footnotes are not used. Footnotes should be kept to a minimum, for example those (a) acknowledging grant support or help in carrying out the research or in preparation of the manuscript, (b) noting change in affiliation of an author, or (c) stating the availability of supplementary information.

Copyright Assignment

In view of the U.S. Copyright Revision Act of 1976, if a manuscript is accepted for publication, authors are asked to sign a Copyright Assignment and Agreement form conveying all copyright ownership, including electronic rights, to AAMR.

American Psychologist

ADDRESS FOR SUBMISSION:

Norman B. Anderson, Editor-in-Chief
American Psychologist
750 First Street N.E.
Washington, DC 20002-4242
USA
Phone: 202-336-5500
Fax:
E-Mail: Apeditor@apa.org
Web: www.apa.org
Address May Change:

PUBLICATION GUIDELINES:

Manuscript Length: 21-25 Max, double-
spaced
Copies Required:
Computer Submission: Yes See Guidelines
Format:
Fees to Review: 0.00 US$

Manuscript Style:
American Psychological Association

CIRCULATION DATA:

Reader: Academics
Frequency of Issue: Monthly
Copies per Issue: Over 113,000
Sponsor/Publisher: American Psychological
Association
Subscribe Price: 198.00 US$ Individual
449.00 US$ Institution

REVIEW INFORMATION:

Type of Review: Blind Review
No. of External Reviewers: 3
No. of In House Reviewers: 0
Acceptance Rate: 12%
Time to Review: 6 Months
Reviewers Comments: Yes
Invited Articles: 31-50%
Fees to Publish: 0.00 US$

MANUSCRIPT TOPICS:

Abnormal Psychology; Adolescent Psychology; Child Psychology; Counseling Process;
Developmental Psychology; Experimental Psychology; Learning & Conditioning; Personality;
Physiological Psychology; Psychobiology; Psychological Testing; Psychopathology; Research
Methods & Statistics; Sensation & Perception; Thinking & Cognition

MANUSCRIPT GUIDELINES/COMMENTS:

Topics Include. Current issues, empirical, theoretical, and practical articles on broad aspects
of psychology.

Manuscript Preparation. Authors should prepare manuscripts according to the *Publication
Manual of the American Psychological Association* (5th ed.). Manuscripts should be no more
than 25 double-spaced pages, including references. All manuscripts must include an abstract
containing a maximum of 120 words. Formatting instructions, including instructions on
preparing tables, figures, references, metrics, and abstracts, appear in the *Manual*. All
manuscripts are copyedited for bias-free language. Comments should be submitted no later
than two months from the date of the issue containing the article to which they respond.
(Comments on comments are rarely considered.) Comments on matters of APA policy are
also considered. Comments must be limited to 1,000 words (about five pages) and should

contain no more than nine references. As in all manuscripts, authors should include page numbers and references for quotes. *APA* can now place supplementary materials online, which will be available via the journal's Web page as noted above. To submit such materials, please see **www.apa.org/journals/supplementalmaterial.html** for details.

Publication Policy. APA policy prohibits an author from submitting the same manuscript for concurrent consideration by two or more publications. APA policy prohibits as well publication of any manuscript that has already been published in whole or substantial part elsewhere. Authors have an obligation to consult journal editors if there is any question concerning prior publication of part or all of their submitted manuscripts. Authors are required to obtain and provide to APA prior to production all necessary permissions to reproduce in print and electronic form any copyrighted work, including, for example, test materials (or portions thereof) and photographs of people. Also, authors of research reports submitted to APA journals are expected to have their data available throughout the editorial review process and for at least five years after the date of publication. Of course, APA expects authors submitting to this journal to adhere to the APA ethical standards regarding previous publication of data (Standard 8.13) and making research data available (Standard 8.14). Authors of research reports will be required to state in writing that they have complied with APA ethical standards in the treatment of their sample, human or animal, or to describe the details of treatment. A copy of the APA Ethical Principles may be obtained at www.apa.org/ethics/ or by writing the APA Ethics Office, 750 First Street, NE, Washington, DC 20002-4242. APA requires authors to reveal any possible conflict of interest in the conduct and reporting of research (e.g., financial interests in a test or procedure, funding by pharmaceutical companies for drug research).

Review Policy. The first step in the AP editorial review process is performed by the *AP* Editor-in-Chief/APA, CEO. Approximately 70% of author-submitted manuscripts are returned without review within 30 days for a host of reasons: Empirical manuscripts are more appropriate for one of the APA primary journals; topic of the manuscript or style of the writing is too specialized for the broad *AP* readership; the same topic was recently covered in the journal; inappropriate content or style; or other, more typical reasons such as the paper does not offer a major contribution to the field or is simply not written well enough. As a matter of policy, the identities of authors and reviewers are masked. Manuscripts that are peer reviewed are circulated without their title pages to mask the identity of the authors. Each copy of a manuscript should include a separate title page with authors' names and affiliations, and these should not appear anywhere else on the manuscript. Footnotes that identify the authors should be typed on a separate page. Authors should make every effort to see that the manuscript itself contains no clue to their identity.

Manuscript Submission. Submit manuscripts electronically via the Manuscript Submission Portal at **www.apa.org/journals/amp**. In addition to addresses and phone numbers, authors should supply electronic mail addresses and fax numbers, if available. Authors should keep a copy of the manuscript to guard against loss. General correspondence may be directed to Norman B. Anderson, Editor-in-Chief, American Psychologist, 750 First Street, NE, Washington, DC 20002-4242. **E-Mail Address**. To contact the editorial office of the *American Psychologist* via electronic mail (Internet), contact **APeditor@apa.org**.

Animal Behaviour

ADDRESS FOR SUBMISSION:

Animal Behaviour
  ELECTRONIC SUBMISSION AT:
https://www.editorialmanager.com/anbeh/
Phone:
Fax:
E-Mail: See Guidelines
Web: www.animalbehavior.org
Address May Change: 6/30/2006

PUBLICATION GUIDELINES:

Manuscript Length: 26-30
Copies Required: Electronic
Computer Submission: Yes
Format: See Guidelines
Fees to Review: 0.00 US$

Manuscript Style:
  See Manuscript Guidelines

CIRCULATION DATA:

Reader: Academics
Frequency of Issue: Monthly
Copies per Issue: 5,001 - 10,000
Sponsor/Publisher: Animal Behavior
  Society (ABS), Association for the Study
  of Animal Behaviour (ASAB)
Subscribe Price: 900.00 US$ Institution
  1013.00 US$ Euro Institution
  See Website - More Details

REVIEW INFORMATION:

Type of Review: Editorial Review
No. of External Reviewers: 2
No. of In House Reviewers: 0-1
Acceptance Rate: 40%
Time to Review: 3 Months
Reviewers Comments: Yes
Invited Articles: 0-5%
Fees to Publish: 0.00 US$

MANUSCRIPT TOPICS:

Animal Cognition; Learning & Conditioning; Neurology; Neuropsychology; Physiological Psychology; Psychobiology; Sensation & Perception; Social Psychology; Thinking & Cognition

MANUSCRIPT GUIDELINES/COMMENTS:

North American Office Address:
  Animal Behaviour Editorial Office
  Indiana University
  2611 East 10th Street - #170
  Bloomington, IN 47408-2603
  USA
  Phone: 812-856-5541; Fax: 812-856-5542; E-mail: **aboffice@indiana.edu**

UK Office Address:
  Dr A.K. Turner, Managing Editor
  School of Life & Environmental Sciences
  University of Nottingham
  University Park
  Nottingham NG7 2RD, U.K.
  Fax: (115) 9 513 249; E-mail: **angela.turner@nottingham.ac.uk**

First published in 1953, *Animal Behaviour* is a leading international publication and has wide appeal, containing critical reviews, original papers, and research articles on all aspects of animal behaviour. Book Reviews and Books Received sections are also included.

Growing interest in behavioural biology and the international reputation of *Animal Behaviour* prompted an expansion to monthly publication in 1989. *Animal Behaviour* continues to be the journal of choice for biologists, ethologists, psychologists, physiologists, and veterinarians with an interest in the subject.

Research Areas Include: behavioural ecology, evolution of behaviour, sociobiology, ethology, behavioural psychology, behavioural physiology, population biology, sensory behaviour, navigation and migration.

Notice To Contributors
1. *Animal Behaviour* publishes original papers relating to all aspects of the behaviour of animals, including humans. Papers may be field, laboratory or theoretical studies or critical reviews. Preference is given to studies that test explicit hypotheses rather than being purely descriptive and that are likely to be of interest to the broad readership of the journal. Requirements for reviews are given below (see Reviews).

2. Submissions should be made electronically via Editorial Manager. **https://www.editorialmanager.com/anbeh/** Correspondence about book reviews should be sent to Dr P. Loesche, Department of Psychology, Box 351525, University of Washington, Seattle, WA 98195, U.S.A. (fax: 206 616 4794; email: **loes@u.washington.edu**). Hard copies are not required in addition to copies submitted electronically.

3. Authors submitting a manuscript do so on the understanding that if it is accepted for publication, copyright in the article, including the right to reproduce the article in all forms and media, shall be assigned exclusively to the Journal. Transfer of copyright does not take effect until the manuscript is accepted for publication.

4. Papers accepted for publication become the copyright of the Journal, and permission for republication elsewhere must be obtained from the Publishers. See **http://www.elsevier.com/**

5. Papers are accepted on the understanding that they are subject to editorial revision and that they are contributed only to this journal.

6. The author will receive two sets of proofs plus the original manuscript, and should correct the marked proof and return it to the appropriate editorial office within 24 hours. The author will receive 50 offprints free of charge and may purchase additional offprints; orders for these should be sent to the Publishers with the return of the marked proofs.

7. Elsevier assigns a unique digital object identifier (DOI) to every article it publishes. The DOI appears on the title page of the article. It is assigned after the article has been accepted for publication and persists throughout the lifetime of the article. Owing to its persistence, it can be used to query Academic Press for information on the article during the production

process, to find the article on the Internet through various Web sites, including SCIENCE DIRECT, and to cite the article in academic references.

Instructions For Authors

Detailed submission guidelines are posted at **https://www.editorialmanager.com/anbeh/**

Prospective authors should consult these instructions carefully before preparing manuscripts for submission. The Editorial Offices may decline to review manuscripts that do not comply with the requirements for content and format and papers that are accepted but incorrectly prepared may be subject to delays in the press. The Editorial Offices will edit papers in accordance with the house style and will help authors to communicate effectively, particularly where the author's first language is not English. Authors may find recent articles in *Animal Behaviour* to be useful models.

Animal Cognition

ADDRESS FOR SUBMISSION:

Tatiana Czeschlik, Chief Editor
Animal Cognition
 ONLINE SUBMISSIONS
Editorial Office
Muehltalstrasse 9
D-69121 Heidelberg,
Germany
Phone: +49 6221 418314
Fax: +49 6221 418315
E-Mail: animal.cognition@t-online.de
Web: www.springeronline.com
Address May Change:

PUBLICATION GUIDELINES:

Manuscript Length: 16-25
Copies Required: Four
Computer Submission: Yes via Website
Format:
Fees to Review: 0.00 US$

Manuscript Style:
 , Springer-Verlag

CIRCULATION DATA:

Reader: Academics
Frequency of Issue: Quarterly
Copies per Issue: No Reply
Sponsor/Publisher: Springer-Verlag
Subscribe Price: 361.00 US$

REVIEW INFORMATION:

Type of Review: Editorial Review
No. of External Reviewers: 3
No. of In House Reviewers: 1
Acceptance Rate: 50%
Time to Review: 2 - 3 Months
Reviewers Comments: Yes
Invited Articles: 0-5%
Fees to Publish: 0.00 US$

MANUSCRIPT TOPICS:
Comparative Psychology; Decision Making Theory; Evolutiionary Psychology

MANUSCRIPT GUIDELINES/COMMENTS:

Aims and Scope. *Animal Cognition* is an interdisciplinary journal publishing current research from various backgrounds and disciplines (ethology, behavioral ecology, animal behavior and learning, cognitive sciences, comparative psychology and evolutionary psychology) on all aspects of animal (and human) cognition in an evolutionary framework.

The aim of the journal is to establish the course of the evolution of "intelligence", of the mechanisms, functions and adaptive value of basic and complex cognitive abilities from invertebrates to humans.

Animal Cognition publishes original empirical and theoretical work, reviews, short communications and correspondence on the mechanisms and evolution of biologically rooted cognitive-intellectual structures.

Experiments and field studies with animals and humans and the comparative method will be given preference, but simulation models and theoretical analyses will be also considered.

Papers on the following topics are particularly welcome:
- How do animals categorize and recognize individuals (potential mates, offspring), food, spatial patterns?
- How do animals form concepts?
- Which rules of logic and decision are used and how do these work?
- What satisficing heuristics do animals use?
- How do animals reason about their social world?
- How do animals learn by observation, imitation and instruction?
- Animal time perception and use; causality detection
- Innate reaction patterns and innate bases of learning
- Numerical competence and frequency expectancies
- Symbol use; communication
- Problem solving, animal thinking and use of tools
- Modularity of the mind
- How do these topics relate to the natural ecology of the species concerned?

Manuscript Submission. Authors should submit their articles to *Animal Cognition* online via the website **http://ancog.manuscriptcentral.com/** to facilitate even quicker and more efficient processing. Electronic submission substantially reduces the editorial processing and reviewing time and shortens overall publication time.

Editorial office. Tatiana Czeschlik, Chief Editor, Editorial Office Animal Cognition, Muehltalstrasse 9, D-69121 Heidelberg, Germany, Email: **animal.cognition@t-online.de**; Fax: +49-6221-418315

Legal requirements. Submission of a manuscript implies: that the work described has not been published before (except in the form of an abstract or as part of a published lecture, or thesis); that it is not under consideration for publication anywhere else; that its publication has been approved by all co-authors, if any, as well as by the responsible authorities - tacitly or explicitly - at the institute where the work has been carried out. The publisher will not be held legally responsible should there be any claims for compensation.

The "Copyright Transfer Statement" has to be signed and faxed to the publisher together with the corrected proofs (see below) with which it will be provided by the publisher shortly after the manuscript has been accepted for publication.

Manuscript Preparation
- All manuscripts are subject to peer review and copy editing.
- All manuscripts should be in English and typewritten (12 pt) with double spacing and wide margins. Use a normal, plain font (e.g., Times New Roman) for text.
- Reviews should cover a topic of current interest and present novel insights or conclusions. Reviews should include at least the following sections: Abstract, Introduction, Discussion / Conclusions, References (see below for more details).

- Original papers must present scientific results that are essentially new and that have not been published or are not being considered for publication elsewhere.
- Short Communications should also report novel results. Their length is limited to 15 000 characters including spaces and 2 figures or tables.
- Use the automatic page numbering function to number the pages.
- Lines should be numbered consecutively throughout the text.
- For indents use tab stops or other commands, not the space bar.
- Use the equation editor of your word processing program or MathType for equations.
- Abbreviations should be defined at first mention in the abstract and again in the main body of the text and used consistently thereafter.
- Essential footnotes to the text should be numbered consecutively and placed at the bottom of the page to which they refer.
- Genus and species names should be in italics. The common names of animals should not be capitalized.

Please arrange your manuscript as follows:
- Title page. including name(s) of author(s), a concise and informative title, affiliation(s) of the author(s), e-mail address, telephone and fax numbers of the corresponding author. The title of a manuscript dealing with a particular species should include both the genus/species name and the common name.
- Abstract (no more than 250 words)
- Key words: 3-5
- Introduction
- Methods
- Results
- Discussion
- Acknowledgements (if applicable). Please include, at the end of the acknowledgements, a declaration that the experiments comply with the current laws of the country in which they were performed. The Chief Editor reserves the right to reject manuscripts that do not comply with the above-mentioned requirement. The author will be held responsible for false statements or for failure to fulfill the above-mentioned requirements.
- References. Literature citations in the text should indicate the author's surname with the year of publication in parentheses, e.g. Carlin (1992); Brooks and Carlin (1992). If there are more than two authors, only the first should be named, followed by "et al."

References at the end of the paper should be listed in alphabetical order by the first author's name. If there is more than one work by the same author or team of authors in the same year, a, b, etc. is added to the year both in the text and in the list of references.

Journal papers: name(s) and initial(s) of all authors; year; full title; journal title abbreviated in accordance with international practice; volume number; first and last page numbers

Example: Miklósi Á, Polgárdi R, Topál J, Csányi V (2000) Intentional behaviour in dog-human communication:an experimental analysis of 'showing' behaviour in the dog. Anim Cogn 3:159-166

If available, the Digital Object Identifier (DOI) of the cited literature should be added at the end of the reference in question.

Example: Semmann D, Krambeck H-J, Milinski M (2004) Strategic investment in reputation. Behav Ecol Sociobiol DOI 10.1007/s00265-004-0782-9

Single contributions in a book: name(s) and initial(s) of all authors; year; title of article; editor(s); title of book; edition; volume number; publisher; place of publication; page numbers

Example: Noirot C (1992) Sexual castes and reproductive strategies in termites. In: Engels W (ed) Social insects. Springer, Berlin Heidelberg New York, pp 5-35

Book: name and initial(s) of all authors; year; title; publisher; place of publication

Example: Barth FG (2002) A Spider's World- Senses and Behavior. Springer, Berlin Heidelberg New York

Tables and figures

Tables must be numbered consecutively with arabic numerals and should have a title explaining any abbreviation used in that table. Footnotes to tables should be indicated by superscript lower-case letters. Each table should be on a separate page together with the title.

Illustrations must be restricted to the minimum needed to clarify the text. All figures (photographs, graphs or diagrams) should be cited in the text, and numbered consecutively throughout. Figure parts should be identified by lower-case roman letters (a, b, etc.). If illustrations are supplied with uppercase labeling, lower-case letters will still be used in the figure legends and citations.

Figure legends must be brief, self-sufficient explanations of the illustrations. The legends should be placed at the end of the text.
- Line drawings. Inscriptions should be legible, with initial capital letters and appropriately scaled to the size of the drawing. Scanned line drawings should be digitized with a resolution of 800 dpi relative to the final figure size.
- Halftone illustrations (black and white and color). Magnification should be indicated by scale bars. For scanned halftone illustrations, a resolution of 300 dpi is usually sufficient, TIFF is the preferred file format.
- Color illustrations. The authors will be expected to make a contribution (485 € per paper, plus 16% VAT) towards the extra costs of color reproduction and printing. Save color illustrations as RGB (8 bits per channel) in TIFF format.
- Plates. Several figures or figure parts should be grouped in a plate on one page.
- Vector graphics. Fonts used in the vector graphics must be included. Please do not draw with hairlines. The minimum line width is 0.2 mm (i.e., 0.567 pt) relative to the final size. EPS is the preferred file format. EPS files must always contain a preview in TIFF of the figure.

- Size of figures. The figures, including legends, should either match the column width (86 mm) or the print area of 176 x 236 mm. The publisher reserves the right to reduce or enlarge illustrations.

Electronic Supplementary Material

Electronic Supplementary Material (ESM) for a paper will be published in the electronic edition of this journal provided the material is:
- submitted in electronic form together with the manuscript
- accepted after peer review

ESM may consist of:
- information that cannot be printed: animations, video clips, sound recordings (use QuickTime, .avi, .mpeg, animated GIFs, or any other common file format)
- information that is more convenient in electronic form: sequences, spectral data, etc.
- large quantities of original data that relate to the paper, e.g. additional tables, large numbers of illustrations (color and black & white), etc.

Legends must be brief, self-sufficient explanations of the ESM. The file size should not exceed 2 MB. ESM is to be numbered and referred to as S1, S2, etc. After acceptance for publication, ESM will be published as received from the author in the online version only. Reference will be given in the printed version.

Proofreading. Authors are informed by e-mail that a temporary URL has been created from which they can obtain their proofs. Proofreading is the responsibility of the author. Authors should make their proof corrections (formal corrections only) on a printout of the pdf file supplied, checking that the text is complete and that all figures and tables are included. Substantial changes in content, e.g. new results, corrected values, title and authorship are not allowed without the approval of the responsible editor. In such a case please contact the Editorial Office before returning the proofs to the publisher. After online publication, corrections can only be made in exceptional cases and in the form of an Erratum, which will be hyperlinked to the article.

Online First. Papers will be published online about one week after receipt of the corrected proofs. Papers published online can already be cited by their DOI. After release of the printed version, the paper can also be cited by issue and page numbers

Offprints. Twenty-five offprints of each contribution are supplied free of charge. If you wish to order additional offprints you must return the order form which is provided with the proofs and return it together with the corrected proofs. When ordering additional offprints, an author is entitled to receive, upon request, a pdf file of the article for own personal use.

Aphasiology

ADDRESS FOR SUBMISSION:

Chris Code, Editor
Aphasiology
Exeter University
Washington Singer Laboratories
Department of Psychology
Perry Road
Exeter, EX4 4QG
UK
Phone: +44 (0) 1392 264626
Fax: +44 (0) 1392 264623
E-Mail: c.f.s.code@exeter.ac.uk
Web: http://www.tandf.co.uk/journals
Address May Change:

PUBLICATION GUIDELINES:

Manuscript Length: N/A
Copies Required: Four
Computer Submission: Yes
Format: RTF or Word
Fees to Review: 0.00 US$

Manuscript Style:
        American Psychological Association

CIRCULATION DATA:

Reader: Academics, Practitioners
Frequency of Issue: Monthly
Copies per Issue:
Sponsor/Publisher: Psychology Press Ltd.
    (Taylor & Francis Ltd.)
Subscribe Price: 695.00 US$ Individual
    1649.00 US$ Institution

REVIEW INFORMATION:

Type of Review: Editorial Review
No. of External Reviewers: 2
No. of In House Reviewers: 0
Acceptance Rate:
Time to Review: 2 - 3 Months
Reviewers Comments: Yes
Invited Articles:
Fees to Publish: 0.00 US$

MANUSCRIPT TOPICS:
Aphasia/Aphasiology; Neuropsychology

MANUSCRIPT GUIDELINES/COMMENTS:

Website. http://www.tandf.co.uk/journals/titles/02687038.asp

Instructions for Authors
Note to Authors. Please make sure your contact address information is clearly visible on the outside of all packages you are sending to Editors.

General Guidelines
Aphasiology is concerned with all aspects of language impairment and related disorders resulting from brain damage. The journal encourages papers which address theoretical, empirical, and clinical topics from any disciplinary perspective; cross disciplinary work is welcome. *Aphasiology* publishes peer reviewed clinical and experimental research papers, review essays, theoretical notes, comments, and critiques. Research reports can take the form

of group studies, single case studies, or surveys, on psychological, linguistic, medical, and social aspects of aphasia. Ideas for Clinical Fora are welcome.

Aphasiology publishes several kinds of contribution:
- review articles - peer-refereed, reflective theoretically based papers exploring existing thinking, methodologies, and presenting new perspectives.
- research reports - accounts of qualitative and quantitative enquiries, including implications for future practice and directions for future research.
- clinical forums - discussion and exchanges of views on key clinical issues.
- research notes - short reports on work of a preliminary nature.
- book reviews - concise and critical insights into newly published books.

Contacting the Editors
Professor Chris Code, School of Psychology, Washington Singer Laboratories, Exeter University, Perry Road, Exeter, EX4 4QG, UK. Email: **C.F.S.Code@exeter.ac.uk** Tel: +44 01392 264642. Fax: +44 01392 264623

North and South American Submissions
Professor Robert Marshall, Rehabilitation Sciences and Division of Communication Disorders, University of Kentucky, UK Wetherington Building, Room 124-F, 900 S. Limestone, Lexington, KY, 40536-0200, USA.

Book Reviews
Books for review, or offers to review a book, should be sent to:
Professor Roelien Bastiaanse, Book Review Editor, Faculteit der Letteren, Rijksuniversiteit Groningen, PO Box 716, 9700 Groningen, The Netherlands.

Submitting a paper to *Aphasiology*
Please read these Guidelines with care and attention: failure to follow them may result in your paper being delayed. Note especially the referencing conventions used by *Aphasiology* and the requirement to avoid gender-, race-, and creed-specific language, and for adherence to the Ethics of Experimentation.

Aphasiology considers all manuscripts at the Editor's discretion; and the Editor's decision is final.

Copyright. It is a condition of publication that authors vest or license copyright in their articles, including abstracts, in Psychology Press Ltd. This enables us to ensure full copyright protection and to disseminate the article, and the journal, to the widest possible readership in print and electronic formats as appropriate. Authors may, of course, use the material elsewhere after publication providing that prior permission is obtained from Taylor & Francis Ltd. Authors are themselves responsible for obtaining permission to reproduce copyright material from other sources. To view the 'Copyright Transfer Frequently Asked Questions please visit **www.tandf.co.uk/journals/copyright.asp**.

Aphasiology considers all manuscripts on the strict condition that they have been submitted only to *Aphasiology*, that they have not been published already, nor are they under consideration for publication, nor in press elsewhere. Authors who fail to adhere to this condition will be charged all costs which *Aphasiology* incurs, and their papers will not be published.

- Submissions should be sent to one of the Editors above.
- Please write clearly and concisely, stating your objectives clearly and defining your terms. Your arguments should be substantiated with well reasoned supporting evidence.
- In writing your paper, you are encouraged to review articles in the area you are addressing which have been previously published in the journal, and where you feel appropriate, to reference them. This will enhance context, coherence, and continuity for our readers.
- For all manuscripts, gender-, race-, and creed-inclusive language is mandatory.
- Ethics of Experimentation. Contributors are required to follow the procedures in force in their countries which govern the ethics of work done with human subjects. The Code of Ethics of the World Medical Association (Declaration of Helsinki) represents a minimal requirement.
- Abstracts are required for all papers submitted, they should be between 150 and 400 words and should precede the text of a paper; see 'Abstracts'.
- Manuscripts should be printed on **one single side** of A4 or 8 x 11 inch white good quality paper, **double-spaced** throughout, including the reference section.
- **Four copies** of the manuscript must be submitted.
- Authors should include telephone and fax numbers as well as e-mail addresses on the cover page of manuscripts.
- Bionotes should be contained on a separate sheet and be located at the beginning of a paper.
- **Accepted** manuscripts in their **final, revised versions**, should be submitted as Microsoft Word files in PC format on disk, as well as hard copy.

Journal Production Editor: **isobel.muir@psypress.co.uk**

Copyright Permission
Contributors are required to secure permission for the reproduction of any figure, table, or extensive (more than six manuscript lines) extract from the text, from a source which is copyrighted - or owned - by a party other than Psychology Press Ltd or the contributor.

This applies both to direct reproduction or 'derivative reproduction' - when the contributor has created a new figure or table which derives substantially from a copyrighted source.

The following form of words can be used in seeking permission:

Dear [COPYRIGHT HOLDER]

I/we are preparing for publication an article entitled
[STATE TITLE]
to be published by Psychology Press Ltd in *Aphasiology*.

I/we should be grateful if you would grant us permission to include the following materials:
[STATE FIGURE NUMBER AND ORIGINAL SOURCE]
We are requesting non-exclusive rights in this edition and in all forms. It is understood, of course, that full acknowledgement will be given to the source.

Please note that Psychology Press Ltd are signatories of and respect the spirit of the STM Agreement regarding the free sharing and dissemination of scholarly information.

Your prompt consideration of this request would be greatly appreciated.

Yours faithfully

Abstracts
Structured Abstracts. Authors submitting papers should note that from Volume 16 Issue 1 (2002), the journal is introducing Structured Abstracts. There is good evidence that Structured Abstracts are clearer for readers and facilitate better appropriate indexing and citation of papers.

The essential features of the Structured Abstract are given below. Note in particular that any clinical implications should be clearly stated.

Abstract (Between 150-400 words)
- *Background.* Describe the background to the study;
- *Aims.* State the aims and objectives of the study including any clear research questions or hypotheses.
- *Methods & Procedures.* To include outline of the methodology and design of experiments; materials employed and subject/participant numbers with basic relevant demographic information; the nature of the analyses performed.
- *Outcomes & Results.* Outline the important and relevant results of the analyses.
- *Conclusions.* State the basic conclusions and implications of the study. State, clearly and usefully, if there are implications for management, treatment or service delivery.

Review Abstract
- *Background.* Outline the background to the review.
- *Aims.* State the primary objective of the paper; the reasons behind your critical review and analyses of the literature; your approach and methods if relevant.
- *Main Contribution.* The main outcomes of the paper and results of analyses; and any implications for future research and for management, treatment or service delivery.
- *Conclusions.* State your main conclusions.

Code of Experimental Ethics and Practice
Contributors are required to follow the procedures in force in their countries which govern the ethics of work done with human or animal subjects. The Code of Ethics of the World Medical Association (Declaration of Helsinki) represents a minimal requirement.

When experimental animals are used, state the species, strain, number used, and other pertinent descriptive characteristics.

For human subjects or patients, describe their characteristics.

For human participants in a research survey, secure the consent for data and other material - verbatim quotations from interviews, etc. - to be used.

When describing surgical procedures on animals, identify the pre anaesthetic and anaesthetic agents used and state the amount of concentration and the route and frequency of administration for each. The use of paralytic agents, such as curare or succinylcholine, is not an acceptable substitute for anaesthetics. For other invasive procedures on animals, report the analgesic or tranquillising drugs used; if none were used, provide justification for such exclusion.

When reporting studies on unanaesthetized animals or on humans, indicate that the procedures followed were in accordance with institutional guidelines.

Specific permission for facial photographs of patients is required. A letter of consent must accompany the photographs of patients in which a possibility of identification exists. It is not sufficient to cover the eyes to mask identity.

Format
Papers should be prepared in the format prescribed by the American Psychological Association. For full details of this format, please see *the Publication Manual of the APA* (5th edition).

The publishers **strongly encourage** the submission of final, accepted manuscripts on disk (accompanied by hard copy). Click here for guidelines for presentation of final manuscripts on disk.

Typescripts. The style and format of the typescripts should conform to the specifications given in the *Publication Manual of the APA* (5th edition). Typescripts should be **double spaced** on **one side** only of A4 paper, with adequate margins, and numbered throughout. The title page of an article should contain only:
1.   the title of the paper (as concise as possible), the name(s) of the authors and full postal address(es) of their institution(s);
2.   a short title not exceeding 40 letters and spaces, which will be used for page headlines;
3.   name and address of the author to whom correspondence and proofs should be sent;
4.   your telephone, fax and e-mail numbers, as this helps speed of processing considerably.

Abstract. As above.

Headings. Indicate headings and subheadings for different sections of the paper clearly. Do not number headings.

Acknowledgements. These should be as brief as possible and typed on a separate sheet at the beginning of the text.

Permission to quote. Any direct quotation, regardless of length, must be accompanied by a reference citation that includes a page number. Any quote over six manuscript lines should have formal written permission to quote from the copyright owner. It is the author's responsibility to determine whether permission is required from the copyright owner and, if so, to obtain it.

Footnotes. These should be avoided unless absolutely necessary. Essential footnotes should be indicated by superscript figures in the text and collected on a separate sheet at the end of the manuscript.

Reference citations within the text. Use authors' last names, with the year of publication in parentheses after the last author's name, e.g., "Jones and Smith (1987)"; alternatively: "(Brown, 1982; Jones & Smith, 1987; White, Johnson, & Thomas, 1990)". On first citation of references with three or more authors, give all names in full, thereafter use first author "et al.". If more than one article by the same author(s) in the same year is cited, the letters a, b, c, etc., should follow the year.

Reference list. A full list of references quoted in the text should be given at the end of the paper in alphabetical order of authors' surnames (or chronologically for a group of references by the same authors), commencing as a new sheet, typed double spaced. Titles of journals and books should be given in full, e.g.,

Books
Baddeley, A. D. (1999). *Essentials of human memory*. Hove, UK: Psychology Press.

Chapter in edited book
Plomin, R., & Dale, P. S. (2000). Genetics and early language development: A UK study of twins. In D. V. M. Bishop & L. B. Leonard (Eds.), *Speech and language impairments in children: Causes, characteristics, intervention and outcome* (pp. 35-51). Hove, UK: Psychology Press.

Journal article
Schwartz, M. F., & Hodgson, C. (2002). A new multiword naming deficit: Evidence and interpretation. *Cognitive Neuropsychology*, 19, 263-288.

Tables. These should be kept to the minimum. Each table should be typed double spaced on a separate sheet, giving the heading, e.g., "Table 2", in Arabic numerals, followed by the legend, followed by the table. Make sure that appropriate units are given. Instructions for placing the table should be given in parentheses in the text, e.g., "(Table 2 about here)".

Figures should only be used when essential. Where possible, related diagrams should be grouped together to form a single figure. Figures should be drawn to professional standards and it is recommended that the linear dimensions of figures be approximately twice those intended for the final printed version. (Maximum printed figure size 181 mm x 114 mm, including caption.) Make sure that axes of graphs are properly labelled, and that appropriate units are given. Each of these should be on a separate page, not integrated with the text. Figures will be reproduced directly from originals supplied by the author(s). These must be of good quality, clearly and completely lettered. Make sure that axes of graphs are properly labelled, and that appropriate units are given. Photocopies will reproduce poorly, as will pale or broken originals. Dense tones should be avoided, and never combined with lettering. Avoid pale tints, especially in bar graphs. Half-tone figures should be clear, highly-contrasted black and white glossy prints.

The figure captions should be typed in a separate section, headed, e.g., "Figure 2", in Arabic numerals. Instructions for placing the figure should be given in parentheses in the text, e.g., "(Figure 2 about here)". More detailed Guidelines for the Preparation of Figure Artwork are available from the publisher: Psychology Press Ltd, 27 Church Road, Hove, East Sussex BN3 2FA, UK (Email: **isobel.muir@psypress.co.uk**).

Statistics. Results of statistical tests should be given in the following form:

"... results showed an effect of group, $F(2, 21) = 13.74$, $MSE = 451.98$, $p < .001$, but there was no effect of repeated trials, $F(5, 105) = 1.44$, $MSE = 17.70$, and no interaction, $F(10, 105) = 1.34$, $MSE = 17.70$."

Other tests should be reported in a similar manner to the above example of an F -ratio. For a fuller explanation of statistical presentation, see pages 136-147 of the *APA Publication Manual* (5th ed.). For guidelines on presenting statistical significance, see pages 24-25.

Abbreviations. Abbreviations should be avoided except in the most standard of cases. Experimental conditions should be named in full, except in tables and figures.

After Acceptance of Publication in the Journal
Early electronic offprints (e-prints). Specified corresponding authors will receive their article by email as a complete PDF. This allows the author to print up to 50 copies, free of charge, and disseminate them to colleagues. In many cases, this facility will be available up to two weeks prior to print publication of the article. One copy of the journal issue in which their paper appears will be sent by post to all specified corresponding authors free after print publication. Paper offprints can still be purchased by authors if they complete the enclosed offprint order form and return with payment together with their corrected proofs.

Proofs. Page proofs will be emailed to the corresponding author as a PDF attachment to check for typesetting accuracy. No changes to the original typescript will be permitted at this stage. A list of queries raised by the copy editor will also be emailed. Proofs should be returned promptly with the original copy-edited manuscript and query sheet.

Volume contents and author index. The list of contents and the author index for the whole of the year's issues are published in the last issue of the year of each journal. For *Aphasiology*, this is issue 12 (December).

Processing your article electronically
We strongly encourage you to send us the final, revised version of your article in both hard (paper) and electronic (disk) forms. This Guide sets out the procedures which will allow us to process your article efficiently. It is divided into two sections:
1. a guide for authors using standard word-processing software packages
2. a guide for authors using graphics software packages

There are some general rules which apply to both options.
- these guides do not apply to authors who are submitting an article for consideration and peer review; they apply only to authors whose articles have been reviewed, revised, and accepted for publication
- print out your hard (paper) copy from the disk you are sending; it is *essential* that the hard-copy printout is identical to the material on the disk; where versions differ, the hard copy will take precedence. We advise that you maintain back-ups of your files
- save and send your files on a standard 3.5 inch high density disk (Mac or PC); please do not attempt to send the article via file transfer protocol or email
- when saving your article onto a disk, please make sure that the files do not exceed a manageable size
- ensure that the files are not saved as read only
- virus-check your disk before sending it to the Editor
- label your disk
- package disks in such a way as to avoid damage in the post
- disks are not returnable after publication

If you are not sure about the usability of your disk, contact:
Journals Production, Psychology Press, 27 Church Road, Hove, East Sussex, BN3 2FA, UK. Telephone: +44 1273 207411; Fax: +44 1273 205612; Email: **info@psypress.co.uk**

1. A guide for authors using standard word-processing software packages
For the main text of your article, most standard PC or Mac word-processing software packages are acceptable, although we prefer Microsoft Word in a PC format.

Word-processed files should be prepared according to the journal style. For a style guide contact the production department at Psychology Press - address and other contact details above, or see the web page: **www.psypress.co.uk**

Avoid the use of embedded footnotes. For numbered tables, use the table function provided with the word-processing package.

All text should be saved in one file with the complete text (including the title page, abstract, all sections of the body of the paper, references), followed by numbered tables and the figure captions.

You should send the following to the Editor:
- a 3.5-inch disk containing the final, accepted version of the paper

- include an ASCII/text only version on the disk as well as the word processed version if possible
- two hard copy printouts, double spaced, single-sided

Disks should be clearly labeled with the following information:
1. Journal title
2. Name of author
3. File names contained on disk
4. Hardware used (PC or Mac)
5. Software used (name and version)

Sample disk label: text
Journal title
A.N. Author
article.doc
IBM PC
MS Word for Windows 7.0

2. A guide for authors using graphics software packages

We welcome figures on disk, but care and attention to these guidelines is essential, as importing graphics packages can often be problematic.
1. Figures must be saved on a separate disk from the text.
2. High quality reproducible hard copy for all black and white line figures (printed out from your electronic files at a minimum of 600 dpi) must be supplied in case the disks are unusable.
3. Avoid the use of color and tints. Line figures will be reproduced in black and white unless color printing is agreed in advance with the Editor. Subtle variations in gray tones which are distinguishable on screen may not be distinct when printed, and should be avoided. Strong contrasts such as black/white and cross-hatched patterns give a better printed result.
4. Figures should be produced as near to the finished size as possible. If the figure is to be reduced to fit the final printed page, allow for this reduction when selecting lettering size and line weight.
5. Half-tones, scans, photographs and transparencies should be supplied as original hard copy, but if you are also supplying them on disk, please ensure that they are saved at a minimum of 1200 dpi. Photocopies cannot be accepted.
6. Half-tones, scans, photographs and transparencies will not normally be reproduced in color unless first agreed by the journal editor. In some cases it may be possible to present figures in black and white in the printed journal, but in color in the online journal, if the originals are suitable.
7. All figures must be numbered in the order in which they occur (e.g. Figure 1, Figure 2 etc.). In multi-part figures, each part should be labeled (e.g. Figure 1 (a), Figure 1 (b) etc.).The figure captions must be saved as a separate file with the text and numbered correspondingly.
8. The filename for the graphic should be descriptive of the graphic e.g. Figure1, Figure2a.

Applied Cognitive Psychology

RESS FOR SUBMISSION:

m Davies, Editor
d Cognitive Psychology
rsity of Leicester
ology Department
rsity of Leicester
ter, LE1 7RH

+44 1162 522157
+44 1162 522067
: gmd@le.ac.uk
vww.wileyeurope.com/product
s May Change:

PUBLICATION GUIDELINES:

Manuscript Length: 11-25
Copies Required: Three
Computer Submission: No
Format: N/A
Fees to Review: 0.00 US$

Manuscript Style:
    American Psychological Association

ULATION DATA:

: Academics, Practitioners
ncy of Issue: 8 Times/Year
per Issue: Less than 1,000
r/Publisher: Society for Applied
arch in Memory and Cognition
be Price: 280.00 US$ Individual
.00 US$ Institution
00 US$ SARMAC Member

REVIEW INFORMATION:

Type of Review: Choice
No. of External Reviewers: 2
No. of In House Reviewers: 1
Acceptance Rate: 21-30%
Time to Review: 2 - 3 Months
Reviewers Comments: Yes
Invited Articles: 0-5%
Fees to Publish: 0.00 US$

SCRIPT TOPICS:
ve Psychology; Experimental Psychology; Social Psychology; Thinking & Cognition

SCRIPT GUIDELINES/COMMENTS:

d Scope
Cognitive Psychology seeks to publish the best papers dealing with psychological
of memory, learning, thinking, problem solving, language, and consciousness as they
the real world. *Applied Cognitive Psychology* will publish papers on a wide variety of
nd from diverse theoretical perspectives. The journal focuses on studies of human
ance and basic cognitive skills in everyday environments including, but not restricted
es of eyewitness memory, autobiographical memory, spatial cognition, skill training,
and skilled behavior. Articles will normally combine realistic investigations of real
vents with appropriate theoretical analyses and proper appraisal of practical
ons. While empirical research remains the primary focus of the journal, *Applied*
Psychology also publishes theoretical articles, reviews and surveys.

9. Files should be saved as TIFF (tagged image file format), Po: (encapsulated PostScript), containing all the necessary font informatio file of the application (e.g., CorelDraw/Mac, CorelDraw/PC).

Disks should be clearly labeled with the following information:
1. Journal title
2. Name of author
3. Figures contained on disk
4. Hardware used (PC or Mac)
5. Software used (name and version)

Sample disk label: figures
Journal title
A.N. Author
Figures 1-10
Macintosh
Adobe Illustrator 5.5

ADD

Grah;
Appl;
Univ
Psyct
Univ
Leice
UK
Phone
Fax:
E-Ma
Web:
Addre

CIRC

Reade
Frequ
Copie;
Spons
Res
Subsc
92:
40.

MAN(
Cognit

MAN(

Aims a
Applied
analyse
occur ir
issues ;
perform
to, stud;
expertis
world
implica
Cogniti

Applied Cognitive Psychology is the official journal of the Society for Applied Research in Memory and Cognition (SARMAC). The aim of the Society is to promote the communication of applied research in memory and cognition within and between the applied and basic research communities. Don Read is the Editor representing SARMAC, elected by the Governing Board of the Society. All manuscripts originating in North America should be sent to Don Read. Manuscripts originating in Australasia should be sent to the Australasian Editor, Martine Powell. Manuscripts from the rest of the world should be sent to the Founding Editor, Graham Davies.

INSTRUCTIONS TO AUTHORS
Initial Manuscript Submission. Submit three copies of the manuscript (including copies of tables and illustrations) as follows:

Manuscripts originating in North America should be sent to: Professor Don Read, Department of Psychology, University of Victoria, P.O. Box 3050, Victoria, BC, Canada V8W 3P5.

Manuscripts originating in Australasia should be sent to: Professor Martine Powell, School of Psychology, Deakin University, 221 Burwood Hwy, Burwood, VIC 3125, Australia.

Manuscripts from the rest of the world should be sent to: Professor Graham Davies, Department of Psychology, The University of Leicester, University Road, Leicester LE1 7RH, U.K.

Authors **must** also supply:
- an electronic copy of the final version (see section below),
- a Copyright Transfer Agreement with original signature(s) - without this we are unable to accept the submission, and
- permission grants - if the manuscript contains extracts, including illustrations, from other copyright works (including material from on-line or intranet sources) it is the author's responsibility to obtain written permission from the owners of the publishing rights to reproduce such extracts using the Wiley Permission Request Form. Permission grants should be submitted with the manuscript.

Submitted manuscripts should not have been previously published and should not be submitted for publication elsewhere while they are under consideration by Wiley. Submitted material will not be returned to the author unless specifically requested.

Electronic submission. The electronic copy of the final, revised manuscript must be sent to the Editor **together with** the paper copy. Disks should be PC or Mac formatted; write on the disk the software package used, the name of the author and the name of the journal. We are able to use most word processing packages, but prefer Word or WordPerfect.

Illustrations must be submitted in electronic format where possible. Save each figure as a separate file, in **TIFF** or **EPS** format preferably, and include the source file. Write on the disk the software package used to create them; we favor dedicated illustration packages over tools such as Excel or PowerPoint.

Manuscript style. The language of the journal is English. All submissions including book reviews must have a title, be printed on one side of the paper, be double-line spaced and have a margin of 3cm all round. Illustrations and tables must be printed on separate sheets, and not be incorporated into the text.

- The **title page** must list the full title, the short title, and names and affiliations of all authors. Give the full address, including email, telephone and fax, of the author who is to check the proofs.
- Include the name(s) of any **sponsor(s)** of the research contained in the paper, along with **grant number(s)**.
- Supply a **summary** of up to 150 words for all articles. This should be a concise summary of the whole paper, not just the conclusions, and is understandable without reference to the rest of the paper. It should contain no citation to other published work.

Reference style. References should be quoted in the text as name and year within brackets and listed at the end of the paper alphabetically. Where reference is made to more than one work by the same author published in the same year, identify each citation in the text as follows: (Collins, 1998a), (Collins, 1998b). Where three or more authors are listed in the reference list, please cite in the text as (Collins *et al.*, 1998).

All references must be complete and accurate. Online citations should include date of access. If necessary, cite unpublished or personal work in the text but do not include it in the reference list.

References should be listed in the following style:
Herrmann DJ.1982. Know thy memory: the use of questionnaires to assess and study memory. *Psychological Bulletin* **92**: 434-452.

Commons ML, Nevin JA, Davison MC. 1991. *Signal detection: mechanisms, models and applications,* Lawrence Erlbaum: New Jersey.

Morris PE. 1979. Strategies for learning and recall. In *Applied Problems in Memory,* Gruneberg MM and Morris PE (eds.) Academic Press: London; 25-57.

The Geriatric Website. 1999. http://www.wiley.com/oap/ [1 April 1999]

Illustrations. Supply each illustration on a separate sheet, with the lead author's name and the figure number, with the top of the figure indicated, on the reverse. Supply original **photographs**; photocopies or previously printed material will not be used. Line artwork must be high-quality laser output (not photocopies). Tints are not acceptable; lettering must be of a reasonable size that would still be clearly legible upon reduction, and consistent within each figure and set of figures. Supply artwork at the intended size for printing.

The cost of printing **color** illustrations in the journal will be charged to the author. If color illustrations are supplied electronically in either TIFF or EPS format, they **may** be used in the PDF of the article at no cost to the author, even if this illustration was printed in black and white in the journal. The PDF will appear on the *Wiley InterScience* site.

Copyright. To enable the publisher to disseminate the author's work to the fullest extent, the author must sign a Copyright Transfer Agreement, transferring copyright in the article from the author to the publisher, and submit the original signed agreement with the article presented for publication. A copy of the agreement to be used (which may be photocopied) can be found in the first issue of each volume of *Applied Cognitive Psychology*. Copies may also be obtained from the journal editor or publisher, or may be printed from this website.

Further information. Proofs will be sent to the author for checking. This stage is to be used only to correct errors that may have been introduced during the production process. Prompt return of the corrected proofs, preferably within two days of receipt, will minimize the risk of the paper being held over to a later issue. 25 complimentary offprints will be provided to the author who checked the proofs, unless otherwise indicated. Further offprints and copies of the journal may be ordered. There is no page charge to authors.

Applied Developmental Science

ADDRESS FOR SUBMISSION:

Richard M. Lerner, Editor
Applied Developmental Science
Tufts University
Bergstrom Chair in Applied Dev. Science
Eliot-Pearson Dept of Child Development
105 College Avenue
Medford, MA 02155
USA
Phone: 617-627-5558
Fax: 617-627-5596
E-Mail: richard.lerner@tufts.edu
Web: http://ase.tufts.edu/adsi
Address May Change:

PUBLICATION GUIDELINES:

Manuscript Length: 26-30+
Copies Required: Two + 1 disk
Computer Submission: Yes Disk
Format: MS Word
Fees to Review: 0.00 US$

Manuscript Style:
    American Psychological Association

CIRCULATION DATA:

Reader: Academics
Frequency of Issue: Quarterly
Copies per Issue: Less than 1,000
Sponsor/Publisher: Lawrence Erlbaum
    Associates, Inc.
Subscribe Price:

REVIEW INFORMATION:

Type of Review: Blind Review
No. of External Reviewers: 3
No. of In House Reviewers: No Reply
Acceptance Rate: 21-30%
Time to Review: 2 - 3 Months
Reviewers Comments: Yes
Invited Articles: 6-10%
Fees to Publish: 0.00 US$

MANUSCRIPT TOPICS:
Adolescent Psychology; Adulthood; Applied Developmental Science; Child Psychology;
Developmental Psychology

MANUSCRIPT GUIDELINES/COMMENTS:

The focus of *Applied Developmental Science* (*ADS*) is the synthesis of research and
application to promote positive development across the life span. Applied developmental
scientists use descriptive and explanatory knowledge about human development to provide
preventive and/or enhancing interventions. The conceptual base of *ADS* reflects the view that
individual and family functioning is a combined and interactive product of biology and the
physical and social environments that continuously evolve and change over time. *ADS*
emphasizes the nature of reciprocal person-environment interactions among people and across
settings. Within a multidisciplinary approach, *ADS* stresses the variation of individual
development across the life span-including both individual differences and within-person
change-and the wide range of familial, cultural, physical, ecological, and historical settings of
human development.

The audience for *ADS* includes developmental, clinical, school, counseling, aging, educational, and community psychologists; life course, family, and demographic sociologists; health professionals; family and consumer scientists; human evolution and ecological biologists; and practitioners in child and youth governmental and nongovernmental organizations.

Instructions to Contributors

Submit two manuscript copies (including two sets of illustrations, one of which is the original) and one disk copy (formatted in Microsoft Word) to:

Dr. Richard M. Lerner , Editor
Bergstrom Chair in Applied Developmental Science
Eliot-Pearson Department of Child Development
Tufts University
105 College Avenue
Medford, MA 02155

All copies should be clear, readable, and on paper of good quality. A dot matrix or unusual typeface is acceptable only if it is clear and legible. Prepare manuscripts according to the *Publication Manual of the American Psychological Association* (5th ed.). Any manuscript not in this style will automatically be returned to the author. Type all components of the manuscript double-spaced, including title page, abstract, text, quotes, acknowledgments, references, appendices, tables, figure captions, and footnotes. The abstract should be 100-150 words, typed on a separate sheet of paper. Authors must use nonsexist language in their articles. For information on this requirement, read "Guidelines for Nonsexist Language in APA Journals," which appeared in the June 1977 issue of the *American Psychologist*, or consult the *Manual*.

All manuscripts submitted will be acknowledged promptly. Authors should keep copies of their manuscripts to guard against loss. All manuscripts are reviewed by consultants with special competence in the area represented by the manuscript. Articles and reviews must be judged to be of substantial importance to the broad, multidisciplinary readership of *Applied Developmental Science* as well as meet a high level of scientific acceptability. Manuscripts should include descriptions of participant populations, ethical procedures, research methods, and intervention strategies adequate for critique and replication. If not already described in the manuscript, a document describing the content and psychometric properties of any instruments used in the research which are not well-established in the literature is to be included with the manuscript at the time of submission.

Authors are responsible for all statements made in their work and for obtaining permission from copyright owners to reprint or adapt a table or figure or to reprint a quotation of 500 words or more. Authors should write to the original author(s) and publisher to request nonexclusive world rights in all languages to use the material in the article and in future editions. Provide copies of all permissions and credit lines obtained.

Only original manuscripts, written in English, are considered. In a cover letter, authors should state that the findings reported in the manuscript have not been published previously and that the manuscript is not being simultaneously submitted elsewhere. Authors should also state that they have complied with the ethical standards most relevant to their research discipline, e.g., guidelines from the American Psychological Association, the American Sociological Association, or the American Academy of Child Psychiatry. Upon acceptance, the authors are required to sign a publication agreement transferring the copyright from the author to the publisher. Accepted manuscripts become the permanent property of the journal.

Applied Measurement in Education

ADDRESS FOR SUBMISSION:

Barbara Plake, James Impara, Co-Editors
Applied Measurement in Education
University of Nebraska, Lincoln
Buros Center for Testing
21 Teachers College Hall
Lincoln, NE 68588-0352
USA
Phone: 402-472-6203
Fax: 402-472-6207
E-Mail: bplakel@unl.edu; jimpara@unl.edu
Web:
Address May Change:

PUBLICATION GUIDELINES:

Manuscript Length: 20-40 pages
Copies Required: Four
Computer Submission: Yes International
   only
Format: DOS, MAC or Other
Fees to Review: 0.00 US$

Manuscript Style:
       American Psychological Association

CIRCULATION DATA:

Reader: Academics
Frequency of Issue: Quarterly
Copies per Issue: Less than 1,000
Sponsor/Publisher: Lawrence Erlbaum
   Associates, Inc.
Subscribe Price: 50.00 US$ Individual
      405.00 US$ Institution
      75.00 US$ Add Outside US/Canada

REVIEW INFORMATION:

Type of Review: Blind Review
No. of External Reviewers: 3
No. of In House Reviewers: 1
Acceptance Rate: 21-30%
Time to Review: 2 - 3 Months
Reviewers Comments: Yes
Invited Articles: 11-20%
Fees to Publish: 0.00 US$

MANUSCRIPT TOPICS:
Educational Psychology; Psychological Testing; Research Methods & Statistics

MANUSCRIPT GUIDELINES/COMMENTS:

Applied Measurement In Education, sponsored by the Buros Center for Testing, is a scholarly journal dedicated to the application of educational and psychological measurement research to the educational process. Its intended audience consists of researchers and practitioners who are interested in research likely to have an impact on educational measurement practice. A major aim of the journal is to provide both a greater understanding of educational measurement issues and an improved use of measurement techniques in education.

Types of manuscripts that will be considered for publication in *Applied Measurement In Education* include (a) reports of original applied research focusing on measurement issues in educational contexts, (b) presentations of innovative strategies for solving existing educational measurement problems, and (c) integrative reviews of research pertaining to contemporary measurement issues. An additional section of the journal will be dedicated to providing comparative reviews of tests and methods currently used in addressing specific educational measurement needs. The editors also welcome proposals for special issues dealing with a focused treatment of a particular area of applied educational measurement. Manuscripts dealing exclusively with the validation of specific measures are not considered.

Manuscript Submission
Submit four manuscript copies to Applied Measurement In Education, 21 Teachers College Hall, University of Nebraska-Lincoln, Lincoln, NE 68588-0352. Only original manuscripts submitted to *Applied Measurement In Education* will be considered for publication. The cover letter should include a statement that the manuscript is not being simultaneously submitted elsewhere. Manuscripts will not be returned.

Format and Organization
Manuscripts should be prepared according to the guidelines in the *Publication Manual of the American Psychological Association* (5th ed.). Double-space all text. On the first page, indicate the title of the manuscript, the names and affiliations of authors, and the name and address of the person to whom reprint requests are to be sent; suggest a shortened version of the title of the manuscript for use as a running head (40 characters or fewer, including spaces). On the second page, provide a 100 to 175-word abstract. On the third page (the first text page), type the title of the manuscript.

Permissions
Authors are responsible for all statements made in their work and for obtaining permission from copyright owners to use a lengthy quotation (100 words or more) or to reprint or adapt a table or figure published elsewhere. Authors should write to both author(s) and publisher of such material to request nonexclusive world rights in all languages for use in the article and in future editions of it.

Content
Do not use new technical words, psychological jargon or slang, or terminology not consistent with the style guidelines in the *Publication Manual of the APA*. Define any abbreviations or acronyms the first time they are used.

Figures and Tables
All figures and tables should be numbered separately using Arabic numerals and should be grouped at the end of the manuscript. Clearly visible notes within the text should indicate approximate placement of figures and tables. Figures must be professionally prepared and must be camera-ready. Type figure captions on a separate sheet. Write the article title and figure number lightly in pencil on the back of each piece of artwork. Refer to the *Publication Manual of the APA* for format of tables. Double-space.

References
Double-space. Compile references alphabetically (see the *Publication Manual of the APA* for multiple-author citations and references). Spell out names of journals. Provide page numbers of chapters in edited books. Text citations must correspond accurately to the references in the reference list.

Page Proofs

Authors are sent page proofs of their manuscripts and are asked to proofread them for printers errors and other defects. Correction of typographical errors will be made without charge; other alterations will be charged to the author.

Reprints

Authors may order article reprints of their articles when they receive page proofs. Printing considerations do not permit the ordering of reprints after authors have returned proofs.

Dear Journal Contributor

Now that your manuscript has been accepted for publication, we at Lawrence Erlbaum Associates, Inc. (LEA) would like to open the communication lines-offer our preproduction assistance, inform you of your responsibilities, and introduce you to our journal production process. We believe this early dialogue will get our collaboration off on the right foot.

This letter is divided into five sections: Keeping in Touch; Understanding the Publication Process; Preparing a Manuscript; Preparing the Word-Processed, Electronic File and Disk; and Taking Action.

Keeping in Touch

The Editor of the journal is your primary source of information and advice. However, if you have a question the Editor is unable to answer, feel free to contact the LEA Production Editor or Electronic Publishing Manager. (The Editor can put you in touch with these individuals.)

The journal is on a tight production schedule, so . . .

1. If you move or are away for an extended period during the time your manuscript is in production, please let the Editor and Production Editor know where you can be reached (address and phone number). You can imagine the delays that occur when the Production Editor (a) mails typeset page proofs to an old address or (b) phones a contributor with an important question, only to learn that the contributor is on overseas sabbatical and did not leave a forwarding number.

2. Call the Production Editor if you are unable to return page proofs within two days of receipt.

Understanding the Publication Process

1. You return a finalized, complete, correctly formatted manuscript – printout and disk – to the Editor.

2. The Editor compiles an issue of manuscripts and disks from several contributors and forwards the issue to the Production Editor.

3. The Production Editor reviews the manuscripts and disks. If your manuscript is not prepared correctly – see Preparing a Manuscript – the Production Editor returns it to the Editor so you can revise it. (Production on the issue is suspended until all manuscripts are ready.)

4. When all manuscripts are ready, the Production Editor copyedits and typesets the issue and sends each contributor (a) two sets of page proofs of the respective article, (b) a list of queries concerning the article, and (c) a reprint request form.

5. You proofread your typeset pages, indicate corrections on both sets, keep one set for your records, and return to the Production Editor (a) the other set, (b) answers to the queries and (c) the reprint request form (with payment if ordering reprints).

6. The Production Editor finalizes the issue and sends it to the printer.

Preparing the Manuscript
Take a few moments now to make certain that your manuscript is complete and that it complies with the editorial guidelines appearing in the *Publication Manual of the American Psychological Association* (5th ed.). (The manual is available from the APA Order Department, P.O. Box 92984, Washington, DC 20090-2984; phone: 800-374-2721; fax: 202-336-5502; e-mail: order@apa.org; online: www.apa.org/books/) You may find it helpful to consult "Appendix A: Checklist for Manuscript Submission" and "Appendix B: Checklist for Transmitting Accepted Manuscripts for Electronic Production" appearing on pages 379 through 386 of the *APA Manual*, the contributor information appearing in the journal, and/or the following summary of requirements for acceptable manuscripts. If you have any questions whatsoever, please ask for clarification.

Typing. Use 8 ½ - x 11-in. nonsmear paper. Set all margins at 1 in. Type all components double-spaced, including title page, abstract, text, acknowledgments, references, appendices, tables, figure captions, and footnotes. Indent all paragraphs and make sure the entire manuscript is neat and readable. Use superscript numbers to cite footnotes; type all footnotes on a separate page (not at the bottom of the pages on which they are cited). Indicate in the manuscript approximately where each figure or table is to be positioned; type all figure captions on a separate page.

Abstract. If an abstract is required, consult the Editor or the journal for the limit on length. Provide key words or phrases if required.

References. Provide complete, APA-formatted references and text citations and make sure the two correspond exactly. Pages 207 through 281 of the *APA Manual* provide (a) detailed guidelines on preparing references and citations and (b) many excellent sample references and citations. When typing a reference for a chapter in an edited book, be sure to add the inclusive page numbers of the chapter.

Tests, Scales, Subscales, Factors, Variables, Effects. See *APA Manual* regarding capitalization. *Statistics.* See *APA Manual* regarding presentation. *Acronyms.* Define on first mention.

Figures. Submit (a) high-quality laser prints, professionally prepared black-and-white originals or camera-ready glossy reproductions and (b) photocopies of all figures. (c) as many computer files for these figures as you have (see Preparing the Word-Processed, Electronic File and Disk). Please note that figures appearing in the journal will look only as good as what you provide. Make sure lettering and details are crisp, clear, and large enough so that they will be legible upon reduction. (Figures are reduced in size in order to conserve space on the printed page.)

All hard copies for which we do not have computer files will be scanned electronically, so please avoid using gray shading or dot screens in graphs. Use solid black or white or diagonal lines to distinguish columns instead (for further examples and guidelines, see *APA Manual*, pp. 176-201).

Make sure each figure is identified. Assess whether textual information appearing on a piece of artwork might be best presented as part of the caption; alter artwork and caption accordingly.

Permissions. You are responsible for all statements made in your work and for obtaining permission from the copyright owner(s) to reprint or adapt a table or figure or to reprint quotes from one source totaling 500 words or more. Write to original author(s) and publisher to request nonexclusive world rights in all languages for use of the material in the article and in future print and nonprint editions. Please note that you must obtain permission for any lines of poetry or song lyrics you quote as well as for prose, and that you will be liable for any licensing fees required for such use. Provide copies of all permissions and credit lines obtained. Attached to this letter are (a) a sample permission request form you can copy/adapt and use in order to secure permissions and (b) sample credit lines from the *APA Manual.*

Concordance of Elements. Make sure your manuscript is complete and internally consistent. Each reference must be cited in text at least once; each citation must have a corresponding reference. Likewise, each figure, table, and footnote must be cited; if a figure, table, or footnote is cited in text, the corresponding element must be included with the manuscript.

Preparing the Word-Processed, Electronic File and Disk
Now is the time to submit the word-processed, electronic file (as well as an ASCII version) and a disk for copyediting and typesetting. Working with an electronic manuscript allows us to capture your keystrokes-thereby maintaining the accuracy of your article and reducing the time between research and publication.

Shortening the production schedule involves combining the stages of author review of copyedited articles and subsequent review of typeset page proofs into a single review of proofs made from copyedited disk files via desktop publishing. With timely publication the concern of all involved, we assume you will (a) accept minor editorial changes that do not alter intended meanings and (b) alter page proofs only to correct errors, update publication information, and respond to editors, queries. As substantial alterations will not be made after manuscripts have been typeset, please take the time now to make sure that your manuscript and its file are complete and identical and that they represent your 'final say."

Our first choice for format is WordPerfect or Word on an IBM-formatted disk. Other formats are acceptable.

IBM-Compatible Users. Submit a PC disk containing two files: (a) the file produced with your word processor and (b) the same file saved as ASCII DOS text or MS-DOS text. If we are unable to read the native file produced by your word processor, we can try the ASCII or MS-DOS file.

Macintosh Users. Submit a high-density Mac disk containing two files: (a) the file produced with your word processor and (b) the same file saved as ASCII DOS text or MS-DOS text. If we are unable to read the native file produced by your word processor, we can try the ASCII or MS-DOS file.

Other Computer Users. Please try to convert and transfer your file to an IBM-compatible or Mac disk; then follow directions for IBM-compatible or Mac users. If unable to do so, please contact the Electronic Publishing Manager.

However you submit your electronic manuscript, please (a) let us know computer type (IBM-compatible, Macintosh), word processor (including version number), and file name; and (b) make sure the content of the files exactly matches that of the printed, accepted, finalized manuscript.

In addition, if your figures were prepared using a computer and you can obtain files from which the hard copies were printed, please include these on your disk (or on additional disks if they are too large).

If you have any questions regarding disk preparation, please contact the LEA Electronic Journal Publishing Manager.

Taking Action
In a nutshell, now is the time for you to (a) make sure your manuscript is formatted correctly, (b) check on permissions, and (c) send the finalized manuscript--printout and disk--to the Editor.

We hope this letter has been informative, and we look forward to working with you. If you think of any way we can improve the production process, by all means let us know. We're here to help.

Sincerely,

Journal Production Office
Lawrence Erlbaum Associates, Inc.
10 Industrial Avenue
Mahwah, New Jersey 07430-3362
Voice: (201) 236-9500
FAX: (201) 236-0072
Production Fax: (201) 236-6396

Sample Permission Request Form

I am writing an article tentatively entitled:

_____

to be Published in the journal:

_____

by Lawrence Erlbaum Associates, Inc., and would like your permission to obtain nonexclusive world rights in all languages to reprint/adapt the following material in the article and the future editions of the article:

_____

_____

_____

Should I use the American Psychological Association format for credit lines? If not, type your credit line here:

_____

_____

A copy of this letter is enclosed. Please sign and return both copies to me at this address:

_____

_____

Thank you for granting this request.

Name:_____Signature:_____Date:_____

Copyright holder hereby grants permission to use the material in the manner described above.

Name:_____Signature:_____Date:_____

Sample Credit Lines from _APA Manual_

3.73 Tables from Another Source

Authors must obtain permission to reproduce or adapt all or part of a table (or figure) from a copyrighted source. It is not necessary to obtain permission from APA to reproduce one table (or figure) from an APA article provided you obtain the author's permission and give full credit to APA as copyright holder and to the author through a complete and accurate citation. When you wish to reproduce material from sources not copyrighted by APA, contact the copyright holders to determine their requirements for both print and electronic reuse. If you have any doubt about the policy of the copyright holder, you should request permission. Always enclose the letter of permission when transmitting the final version of the accepted manuscript for production.

Any reproduced table (or figure) must be accompanied by a note at the bottom of the reprinted table (or in the figure caption) giving credit to the original author and to the copyright holder. If the table (or figure) contains test items, see the cautionary note in section 3.93. Use the following form for tables or figures. (For copyright permission footnotes in text [see section 3.41 for permission to quote], use the following form, but substitute the indented superscript footnote number for the word Note.)

Material reprinted from a journal article
Note. From [or The data in column 1 are from] "Title of Article," by A. N. Author and C. O. Author, 2000, <u>Title of Journal, 50,</u> p. 22. Copyright 2000 by the Name of Copyright Holder. Reprinted [or Adapted] with permission.

Material reprinted from a book
Note. From [or The data in column 1 are from] <u>Title of Book</u> (p. 103), by A. N. Author and C. O. Author, 1999, Place of Publication: Publisher. Copyright 1999 by the Name of Copyright Holder. Reprinted [**or** Adapted] with permission.

Note. Guidelines are from *Publication Manual of the American Psychological Association* (5th ed., pp. 174-175), 2001, Washington, DC: American Psychological Association. Copyright 2001 by the American Psychological Association. Reprinted with permission.

Applied Multivariate Research

ADDRESS FOR SUBMISSION:

John E. Cornell, Review Editor
Applied Multivariate Research
GRECC/ALMMVH (182)
7400 Merton Minter Blvd.
San Antonio, TX 78284
USA
Phone: 519-253-3000 ext. 2229
Fax: 519-973-7021
E-Mail:
Web: www.samr.net
Address May Change:

PUBLICATION GUIDELINES:

Manuscript Length: 26-30
Copies Required: Three
Computer Submission: No
Format: N/A
Fees to Review: 0.00 US$

Manuscript Style:
    American Psychological Association

CIRCULATION DATA:

Reader: Academics, Professors,
    Researchers
Frequency of Issue: 3 Times/Year
Copies per Issue: Less than 1,000
Sponsor/Publisher: Society for Applied
    Multivariate Research
Subscribe Price: 29.00 US$
    35.00 US$ Outside US

REVIEW INFORMATION:

Type of Review: Blind Review
No. of External Reviewers: 2
No. of In House Reviewers: 1
Acceptance Rate:
Time to Review: 2 - 3 Months
Reviewers Comments: Yes
Invited Articles: 0-5%
Fees to Publish: 0.00 US$

MANUSCRIPT TOPICS:

Other Content, Including Multidisciplinary; Psychological Testing; Research Methods &
Statistics

MANUSCRIPT GUIDELINES/COMMENTS:

The journal *Applied Multivariate Research* is sponsored by the Society for Applied
Multivariate Research and specializes in publishing methodological and content papers that
deal with the application of both classical and more modern multivariate statistical techniques,
as well as measurement issues, in applied settings. This may include examples of well
conducted applied research where the data are analyzed using multivariate statistical
techniques; methodologically oriented papers dealing with any of a variety of issues that come
up in applied research (e.g., extreme sample sizes, distributional characteristics, missing data,
poorly conditioned data, etc.); or, applied measurement content or method papers. In terms of
methodological papers, the journal will entertain papers dealing with theoretical and
mathematical issues in multivariate statistical analysis, but will give preference to papers
focusing on pragmatic solutions to common applied problems.

The journal also publishes papers in two specialized sections. The first is Consultant's Corner, which may include strategies for dealing with issues in analysis of data from applied settings, or summaries of work in progress along with invited commentary. The second section will contain book and software reviews.

Submission Instructions
Submit three copies of your manuscript, prepared in accordance with the most recent edition of the *Publication Manual of the American Psychological Association* along with a cover letter. Please prepare your manuscripts so that the author(s) names or other identifying information do not appear on two of the three manuscript copies. Manuscripts will be sent for blind review by a reviewer deemed to be qualified to assess the work. Please make submissions to

John E. Cornell, Ph. D.
Review Editor
GRECC/ALMMVH (182)
7400 Merton Minter Blvd
San Antonio, TX 78284, U.S.A.

General Inquiries, Including Subscriptions
Please send general inquiries to Dennis L. Jackson, Editor, *Applied Multivariate Research*.
Email: **djackson@uwindsor.ca**

Dennis L. Jackson
Assistant Professor, Psychology
University of Windsor
401 Sunset Avenue
Windsor, Ontario N9B 3P4
Phone: (519) 253-3000 Ext. 2229
Fax: (519) 973-7021

Applied Neuropsychology

ADDRESS FOR SUBMISSION:

Cecil R. Reynolds, Editor-in-Chief
Applied Neuropsychology
Texas A&M University
Department of Educational Psychology
MS 4225
College Station, TX 77843-4225
USA
Phone: 512-656-5075
Fax: 512-321-4785
E-Mail: See Guidelines
Web: www.erlbaum.com
Address May Change:

PUBLICATION GUIDELINES:

Manuscript Length: 23-32
Copies Required: Four
Computer Submission: Yes Email preferred
Format: MS Word attachment
Fees to Review: 0.00 US$

Manuscript Style:
American Psychological Association

CIRCULATION DATA:

Reader: Academics, Practitioners
Frequency of Issue: Quarterly
Copies per Issue: 1,001 - 2,000
Sponsor/Publisher: Lawrence Erlbaum
Associates, Inc.
Subscribe Price: 90.00 US$ Individual
340.00 US$ Institution US/Canada
120.00 US$ Indv., $370 Non-US/Can

REVIEW INFORMATION:

Type of Review: Blind Review
No. of External Reviewers: 2-3
No. of In House Reviewers: 1
Acceptance Rate: 39-45%
Time to Review: 1 - 2 Months
Reviewers Comments: Yes
Invited Articles: 21-30%
Fees to Publish: 0.00 US$

MANUSCRIPT TOPICS:
Neuropsychology

MANUSCRIPT GUIDELINES/COMMENTS:

Electronic Journal Only: $81 Individual $306 Institution

Editorial Scope
Neuropsychologists around the world often find themselves working as isolated specialists in private practice or on multidisciplinary clinical teams. *Applied Neuropsychology* offers them a community forum in which to discuss the implications of the latest neuropsychological research and theory for day-to-day practice. This engaging journal publishes full-length articles, brief communications, case studies, and reviews of the nature, course, or treatment of clinical neuropsychological dysfunctions in the context of the scientific literature. The coverage ranges across a full spectrum from assessment to brain functioning and neuroimaging as well as neuropsychological intervention and rehabilitation.

Audience

Clinical and cognitive neuropsychologists, neuroscientists, speech pathologists, occupational therapists, physicians, and other interested professionals.

INSTRUCTIONS TO CONTRIBUTORS

Manuscript Preparation

Use a word processor to prepare manuscript. Using 8½- × 11-in. nonsmear paper, type all components (a) double-spaced, (b) 1,800 to 2,000 characters per page (70 to 75 characters per line [including spaces] × 25 to 27 lines per page), (c) on one side of the paper, (d) with each component beginning on a new page, and (e) in the following order—title page (p. 1), abstract (p. 2), text (including quotations), references, appendices, footnotes, tables, and figure captions. Consecutively number all pages (including photocopies of figures). Indent all paragraphs.

Title Page and Abstract. On page 1, type (a) article title, (b) author name(s) and affiliation(s), (c) running head (abbreviated title, no more than 45 characters and spaces), (d) acknowledgments, and (e) name and address of the person to whom requests for reprints should be addressed. On page 2, type an abstract (£ 150 words) and key words (£ 8).

Editorial Style and References. Prepare manuscripts according to the *Publication Manual of the American Psychological Association* (5th ed.; APA Order Department, P.O. Box 2710, Hyattsville, MD 20784 USA). Follow "Guidelines to Reduce Bias in Language."

Double-space references. Compile references alphabetically (see *APA Manual* for multiple-author citations and references). Spell out names of journals. Provide page numbers of chapters in edited books. Text citations must correspond accurately to the references in the reference list.

Tables. Refer to *APA Manual* for format. Double-space. Provide each table with explanatory title; make title intelligible without reference to text. Provide appropriate heading for each column in table. Indicate clearly any units of measurement used in table. If table is reprinted or adapted from another source, include credit line. Consecutively number all tables.

Figures and Figure Captions. Figures should be (a) high-resolution illustrations or (b) glossy, high-contrast black-and-white photographs.

Do not clip, staple, or write on back of figures; instead, write article title, figure number, and *TOP* (of figure) on label and apply label to back of each figure. Consecutively number figures. Attach photocopies of all figures to manuscript.

Consecutively number captions with Arabic numerals corresponding to the figure numbers; make captions intelligible without reference to text; if figure is reprinted or adapted from another source, include credit line.

Cover Letter, Permissions, Credit Lines

In cover letter, include contact author's postal and e-mail addresses and phone and fax numbers. Only original manuscripts will be considered for publication in *Applied*

Neuropsychology. The cover letter should include a statement that the findings reported in the manuscript have not been previously published and that the manuscript is not being simultaneously submitted elsewhere.

Authors are responsible for all statements made in their work and for obtaining permission to reprint or adapt a copyrighted table or figure or to quote at length from a copyrighted work. Authors should write to original author(s) and original publisher to request nonexclusive world rights in all languages to use the material in the article and in future editions. Include copies of all permissions and credit lines with the manuscript. (See p. 140 of *APA Manual* for sample credit lines.)

Manuscript Submission
Submit manuscripts to the Editor via email as an attachment if at all possible:
Cecil R. Reynolds
Department of Educational Psychology
MS 4225
Texas A&M University
College Station, TX 77843-4225
Email: **appliedneuropsychology@earthlink.net**

Manuscript Review and Acceptance
All manuscripts are peer reviewed. Authors of accepted manuscripts submit (a) disk containing two files (word-processor and ASCII versions of final version of manuscript), (b) printout of final version of manuscript, (c) camera-ready figures, (d) copies of all permissions obtained to reprint or adapt material from other sources, and (e) copyright-transfer agreement signed by all co-authors. Use a newly formatted disk and clearly label it with journal title, author name(s), article title, file names (and descriptions of content), names of originating machine (e.g., IBM, Mac), and word processor used.

It is the responsibility of the contact author to ascertain that all co-authors approve the accepted manuscript and concur with its publication in the journal.

Content of files must exactly match that of manuscript printout, or there will be a delay in publication. Manuscripts and disk are not returned.

Production Notes
Authors' files are copyedited and typeset into page proofs. Authors read proofs to correct errors and answer editors' queries.

Applied Psycholinguistics

ADDRESS FOR SUBMISSION:

Usha Goswami, Editor
Applied Psycholinguistics
University of Cambridge
Faculty of Education
Shaftesbury Road
Cambridge, CB2 2BX
United Kingdom
Phone: +44 (0) 1223 369631
Fax: +44 (0) 1223 324421
E-Mail: See Guidelines
Web:
Address May Change:

PUBLICATION GUIDELINES:

Manuscript Length: 20
Copies Required: Four
Computer Submission: Yes
Format: N/A
Fees to Review: 0.00 US$

Manuscript Style:
American Psychological Association

CIRCULATION DATA:

Reader: Academics
Frequency of Issue: Quarterly
Copies per Issue: No Reply
Sponsor/Publisher: University; Cambridge
University Press
Subscribe Price: 90.00 US$ Individual
195.00 US$ Inst Print Only
190.00 US$ Inst Electronic /218 +Print

REVIEW INFORMATION:

Type of Review: Editorial Review
No. of External Reviewers: 2
No. of In House Reviewers: 1
Acceptance Rate: 21-30%
Time to Review: 3 Months
Reviewers Comments: Yes
Invited Articles: 0-5%
Fees to Publish: 0.00 US$

MANUSCRIPT TOPICS:
Language Acquisition; Neurolinguistics; Neuropsychology; Psycholinguistics; Reading - Normal & Deviant

MANUSCRIPT GUIDELINES/COMMENTS:

Applied Psycholinguistics publishes original articles on the psychological processes involved in language. The articles address the development, use, and impairment of language in all its modalities, including spoken, signed, and written, with a particular emphasis on crosslinguistic studies. Studies appearing in *Applied Psycholinguistics* need to have a clear applied relevance to professionals in a variety of fields, including linguistics, psychology, speech and hearing, reading, language teaching, special education, and neurology. Contributors should explicitly consider the relevance of their work to the larger community, as well as its theoretical and psychological significance. Specific topics featured in the journal include: language development (the development of speech perception and production, the acquisition and use of sign language, studies of discourse development, second language learning); language disorders in children and adults (including those associated with brain damage, retardation and autism, specific learning disabilities, hearing impairment); literacy development (early literacy skills, dyslexia and other reading disorders, writing development and disorders, spelling development and disorders); and psycholinguistic processing (lexical access, time course of language processing, semantics, and syntax).

In addition to research reports, theoretical reviews will be considered for publication, as will keynote articles and commentaries (the latter normally invited by the Editors) journal will occasionally publish issues devoted to special topics within its purview.

Manuscript Submission

Authors should send their manuscripts either electronically as an E-mail attachment or as four paper copies and an electronic file. (Authors who submit via E-mail should also send a paper copy.) Articles pertaining to language development (speech perception and production), literacy development, and psycholinguistic processing (lexical access and the time course of language processing) should be sent to Usha Goswami. Articles related to language development (sign language, bilingualism, and second language learning), language disorders, and psycholinguistic processing (semantics and syntax) should be sent to Martha Crago.

Usha Goswami, Faculty of Education, University of Cambridge, Shaftesbury Road, Cambridge, CB2 2BX, United Kingdom, Fax +44 (0) 1223 324421
Email: **educ-applied-psycholinguistics@lists.cam.ac.uk**

Martha Crago, Beatty Hall, McGill University, 1266 Pine Avenue West, Montreal, Quebec H3G 1A8, Canada, Fax +1 514 398 3878
E-mail: **applied.psycholinguistics@mcgill.ca**

Submissions may be full-length articles (original research or theoretical reviews), critical responses to articles previously published in *Applied Psycholinguistics*, or (usually) invited keynote articles with accompanying commentaries.

Spelling, Capitalization, and Punctuation should be consistent within each article and should follow the style recommended in the Fifth Edition of the *Publication Manual of the American Psychological Association.*

A Title should be given for each article. An **Auxiliary Short Title** should be given for any article whose title exceeds 50 characters. The author's name should be given in the form preferred for publication; the affiliation should include the author's full mailing address, telephone number, an email address or fax number.

An Abstract should be prepared for each article (limited to 120 words).

Author's personal note(s) should appear in the **Acknowledgement** section.

Notes should be numbered consecutively throughout the text and appear as a unit following the acknowledgment section.

Tables and Figures should be numbered consecutively throughout the article and appear as a unit following the reference section.

Bibliographic Citations in the text must include the author's last name and the date of publication and may include page references. Complete bibliographic information for each citation should be included in the list of references. Examples of correct styling for bibliographic citations are: Brown (1973), Ingram (1976, 54-55), Smith and Miller (1966), (Smith & Miller, 1966), (Peterson, Danner & Flavell, 1972) and subsequently (Peterson et al., 1972). If more than one, citations should be listed in alphabetical order.

References should be cited in the text and should be typed in alphabetical order using the following style:

Brown, R. (1973). Schizophrenia, language and reality. *American Psychologist*, 28, 395-403.
Ingram D. (1976). *Phonological disability in children*. New York: Elsevier,
Krashen, S.D. (1978). Individual variation in the use of the Monitor. In W.C. Ritchie (Ed.) *Second language acquisition research*. New York: Academic Press.
Smith, F. & Miller, G.A. (Eds.). (1966). *The genesis of language*. Cambridge, Mass: M.I.T. Press.

Titles of journals should not be abbreviated. Unpublished citations should be listed in the references.

Preparation of the Manuscript
The entire manuscript, including footnotes and references, must be typed double-spaced on 8 ½ x 11 inch or A4 paper, with 1 inch margins Manuscript pages should be numbered consecutively. Each element of the article should begin on a new page and should be arranged as follows: title page (title, short title, author's full name, affiliation, and mailing address), abstract, text, appendices, acknowledgments, notes, references, tables and figures.

Each table and figure should be submitted on a separate page and should be titled. Figures should be ready for photographic reproduction; they cannot be redrawn by the publisher. Charts, graphs, or other artwork should be professionally rendered or computer generated. Photographs should be glossy black-and-white prints; 8 by 10 inch enlargements are preferred. All labels and details on figures should be clearly printed and large enough to remain legible after a 50% reduction.

Copyediting and Proofreading
The publisher reserves the right to copyedit and proofread all articles accepted for publication. The lead author will review the copyedited manuscript only if changes have been substantial. Page proof of an article will be sent to the lead author for correction of typographical errors only; authors must notify the editorial office of any changes within 48 hours or approval will be assumed.

The Fifth Edition of the *Publication Manual of the American Psychological Association* should be consulted for instructions on aspects of manuscript preparation and style not covered in these instructions. The Editors may find it necessary to return manuscripts for reworking and retyping that do not conform to requirements.

The lead author will receive 25 offprints of his or her article or note without charge; additional copies may be purchased if ordered at proof stage.

Submission of an article or note implies that it has not been published elsewhere. Authors are responsible for obtaining written permission to publish material (quotations, illustrations, etc.) for which they do not own the copyright. Contributors of accepted articles will be asked to assign their copyrights on certain conditions to Cambridge University Press.

Applied Psychological Measurement

ADDRESS FOR SUBMISSION:

Mark Reckase, Editor
Applied Psychological Measurement
Michigan State University
461 Erickson Hall
East Lansing, MI 48824
USA
Phone: 517-355-8537
Fax: 517-353-6393
E-Mail: reckase@msu.edu or
    apm@msu.edu
Web: www.sagepub.com
Address May Change:

PUBLICATION GUIDELINES:

Manuscript Length: 21-25
Copies Required: Four
Computer Submission: No
Format: N/A
Fees to Review: 0.00 US$

Manuscript Style:
    American Psychological Association

CIRCULATION DATA:

Reader: Academics, Practitioners
Frequency of Issue: Quarterly
Copies per Issue: 1,001 - 2,000
Sponsor/Publisher: Sage Publications
Subscribe Price: 79.00 US$ Individual
    416.00 US$ Institution
    55.00 Pounds Indv., 291 Pounds Inst.

REVIEW INFORMATION:

Type of Review: Blind Review
No. of External Reviewers: 3
No. of In House Reviewers: 1
Acceptance Rate: 11-20%
Time to Review: 2 - 3 Months
Reviewers Comments: Yes
Invited Articles: 6-10%
Fees to Publish: 0.00 US$

MANUSCRIPT TOPICS:
Psychological Testing; Research Methods & Statistics

MANUSCRIPT GUIDELINES/COMMENTS:

Applied Psychological Measurement (*APM*) publishes empirical research on the application of techniques of psychological measurement to substantive problems in all areas of psychology and related disciplines.

The general classes of studies published include (1) reports on the development and application of innovative measuring techniques, (2) reports of methodological developments in the solution of measurement problems, (3) studies comparing applications of different measurement techniques, (4) studies investigating the limits of applicability of measurement methodologies, (5) empirical studies in the methodology of validation and reliability, and (6) critical reviews of measurement methodology. Reports of the development of new measurement instruments and studies of the validity and reliability of psychological measuring instruments are published only if they have a methodological focus.

Methodologically oriented studies in the measurement of ability, aptitude, personality, interests, and social and perceptual variables will be considered, as will studies in test development and unidimensional and multidimensional scaling. This journal does not publish papers that are purely statistical in nature, unless they are demonstrably related to applied measurement problems (e.g., problems in the estimation of parameters in measurement models, or problems in the determination of validity or reliability of measurement techniques).

Brief Reports will also be considered for publication. These papers report on exploratory, small-sample, and replication studies, as well as brief technical notes. Brief Reports are limited to two published pages, or about 1,000 manuscript words, including tables, figures, and references (about four typed double-spaced manuscript pages). Brief Reports do not require an abstract, and summaries at the end of the paper should be avoided. Similarly, the literature review should be kept to a minimum.

The **Computer Program Exchange** publishes abstracts of computer programs and subroutines useful in the solution of applied measurement problems or in the instruction of measurement concepts. Only abstracts designed for the exchange of software that would be otherwise unavailable will be published; information about programs developed for commercial distribution should be made available by advertisement. Abstracts should be limited to two typed double-spaced manuscript pages. They should include the following information: name of program or subroutine; a brief description of its purpose and function; description of the programming language; computer(s) on which it is operational and any unusual computer requirements in terms of size of memory, disks, and so forth; nature of documentation available; form in which program is available (e-mail, disk); cost of acquisition; name and mailing address of the program's author; and the author's e-mail address. Acceptable abstracts will be published on a space-available basis. Abstracts that are unacceptable in content or form will be returned to the author. Send abstracts for the Computer Program Exchange to the Computer Program Exchange Editor, Niels G. Waller, Department of Psychology and Human Development, Box 512 Peabody, Vanderbilt University, Nashville, TN 37203, USA, e-mail: **niels.waller@vanderbilt.edu**. Two printed copies of the abstract should be accompanied by the text of the abstract as an ASCII file on a DOS-compatible disk. Submissions should also include one copy of the executable software, the program source code, software documentation, and sample input and output files.

Software Notes are brief reports of a researcher's experience with commercially available software programs. They report on unexpected experiences or observations based on use of a program that will help others recognize or avoid potential problems with the program. As an example, see the Software Note on page 89 of the Volume 21, Number 1, March 1997 issue. Software Notes are published on a space-available basis with minimal editing. They should be submitted to the Editor as an ASCII file on a DOS-compatible disk along with two printed copies.

Computer Software Reviews are published for new or upgraded, commercially available computer packages for personal computers. DOS, Windows, or Macintosh software for item and test analysis, item response theory calibration and applications, item banking and test construction, computerized adaptive testing, and other statistical analyses related to measurement are reviewed by invitation. Readers or software authors/publishers may request reviews of software packages by corresponding with the Computer Software Review Editor or by sending software packages for review. Readers interested in being considered as software reviewers should write to Richard M. Luecht, Computer Software Review Editor, Educational Research Methodology, School of Education, University of North Carolina, Curry 209, PO. Box 26171, Greensboro, NC 27402-6171, USA.

Book Reviews of important new books are published. Although book reviews are published by invitation, readers may suggest books to be considered for review. Similarly, readers who wish to be considered as reviewers should write to the Book Review Editor, Steve Reise, Department of Psychology, Franz Hall, University of California, Los Angeles, CA 90095, USA, e-mail: **reise@psych.ucla.edu.**

For the Record provides an opportunity for authors of books reviewed in this journal, or authors whose work is cited in our articles, to publish comments on those reviews or citations. For the Record offers authors a mechanism for responding to what they may consider to be misinterpretations, errors, or misrepresentations of their work. Authors' comments should he brief and restricted to correcting (1) errors of fact or (2) errors of interpretation. Comments on Book Reviews should be submitted to the Book Review Editor, Steve Reise, Department of Psychology, Franz Hall, University of California, Los Angeles, CA 90095, USA, e-mail: **reise@psych.ucla.edu**; comments on Software Reviews should be sent to the Software Review Editor, Richard M. Luecht, Educational Research Methodology, University of North Carolina, Curry 209, P .O. Box 26171, Greensboro, NC 27402-6171; comments on articles should be submitted to the Editor. All submissions should be typed, double-spaced, and submitted in duplicate.

Announcements of general interest to readers will be published. Highest priority will be given to announcements of meetings, symposia, workshops, and the like. Other announcements that will be considered include the availability of technical reports or other publications with limited circulation, notices of new publications, or brief items of general interest to applied measurement specialists. Send two printed copies of the announcement and the text of the announcement as an ASCII file on a DOS-compatible disk to the Editor at the address below.

Submission of manuscripts. Three copies of each manuscript should be submitted to the Editor, David J. Weiss, 461 Erickson Hall, Michigan State University, East Lansing, MI 48864, USA, phone 517-355-8537, fax 517-353-6393. Manuscripts that are prepared on word processors can be printed single-spaced. Manuscripts will be acknowledged when they are received. Authors may also communicate with the Editor by e-mail at **reckase@msu.edu.** Authors should retain a copy of their manuscript because none of the three copies submitted will be returned. Manuscripts will be reviewed "blind" if the author removes all identifying material from two titled copies of the manuscript. It is understood that papers submitted for publication have not been previously published and will not be simultaneously submitted for publication consideration elsewhere, and if accepted for publication, such papers will not be published elsewhere, in any language, without the written consent of the publisher.

Publication cost and reprints. *APM* does not require authors to pay costs of publication. Authors will receive 10 reprints in tearsheet form and 2 complimentary copies of the issue in which their article appears (if there is more than one author, reprints and issues will be divided among them). Authors of book reviews and guest editors will receive 2 complimentary copies of the issue. Authors may purchase additional reprints of their article.

Preparation of Manuscripts

Authors should carefully prepare their manuscripts in accordance with the following instructions.

Manuscripts should be as concise as possible, yet sufficiently detailed to permit adequate communication and critical review. Authors should follow the style of the *Publication Manual of the American Psychological Association* (fourth edition, 1994).

When possible, authors should prepare their manuscripts (including tables) on word-processing equipment that is capable of outputting files on disks or transmitting files by the Internet, because manuscripts are typeset from disks or files provided by authors. *APM* can process ASCII files received on DOS-compatible disks, Apple Macintosh disks, or ASCII or word processor files transmitted over the Internet. Most non-ASCII files produced by major word processors can be processed for typesetting. Authors will receive information for submitting the final copy of their manuscript by electronic means upon final acceptance of their paper.

The first page of the paper should contain the article title, the names and affiliations of all authors, and the name and complete mailing address of the person to whom all correspondence should be sent. The second page should contain an abstract of no more than 250 words, and five to seven index terms or phrases that will be published following the abstract and will appear in the volume and cumulative indexes. The title of the paper should be repeated on page 2.

The following sections should be prepared as indicated:

References. Text citations and references should follow the style of the *Publication Manual of the American Psychological Association* (fourth edition, 1994).

Tables. Tables should be numbered consecutively with Arabic numerals. Each table should be fully titled and typed on a separate page. Footnotes to tables should be identified by superscript lowercase letters and placed at the bottom of the table. All tables should be referred to in the text. Tables should be typed single-spaced.

Figures. Copies of figures should be sent on first submission of a manuscript; original figures will be requested when a manuscript is accepted for publication. All figure titles should be on a separate page. All figures should be referred to in the text.

Equations. Equations should be typed on separate lines in the text. All equations should be referred to in the text, or be a natural part of the text, including appropriate punctuation. All equations should be numbered consecutively in parentheses on the right-hand side. References to equations in the text should be to "Equation 1" not "(1)."

120

Acknowledgments. All acknowledgments (e.g., financial support, review by others) will appear at the end of the manuscript, following the references.

Address. The complete mailing address of the author should follow the acknowledgments. In the case of multiple authors, the address of the author(s) who should be contacted for further information and/or reprint requests should be supplied. The author's e-mail address also should be provided.

Applied Psychophysiology and Biofeedback

ADDRESS FOR SUBMISSION:

Frank Andrasik, Editor-in-Chief
Applied Psychophysiology and Biofeedback
University of West Florida
Institute for Human & Machine Cognition
40 South Alcaniz Street
Pensacola, FL 32501
USA
Phone: 850-202-4460
Fax: 850-202-4440
E-Mail: fandrasi@ai.uwf.edu
Web: www.wkap.nl/journalhome.htm/
Address May Change:

PUBLICATION GUIDELINES:

Manuscript Length: 21-25
Copies Required: Five
Computer Submission: Yes Disk & Email
Format: Prefer MS Word
Fees to Review: 0.00 US$

Manuscript Style:
    American Psychological Association

CIRCULATION DATA:

Reader: Academics, Practitioners
Frequency of Issue: Quarterly
Copies per Issue: Confidential
Sponsor/Publisher: Association for Applied
    Psychophysiology and Biofeedback /
    Kluwer Academic Plenum Publishers
Subscribe Price: 88.00 US$ Individual
    523.00 US$ Instititution

REVIEW INFORMATION:

Type of Review: Editorial Review
No. of External Reviewers: 3
No. of In House Reviewers: 1
Acceptance Rate: 50%
Time to Review: 2 - 3 Months
Reviewers Comments: Yes
Invited Articles: 11-20%
Fees to Publish: 0.00 US$

MANUSCRIPT TOPICS:
Abnormal Psychology; Alcoholism & Drug Addiction; Applied Psychophysiology;
Biofeedback; Learning & Conditioning; Physiological Psychology; Psychobiology;
Psychopathology; Research Methods & Statistics

MANUSCRIPT GUIDELINES/COMMENTS:

Journal Scope
Applied Psychophysiology and Biofeedback is an international, interdisciplinary journal
devoted to study of the interrelationship of physiological systems, cognition, social and
environmental parameters, and health. Priority is given to original research, basic and applied,
with contributes to the theory, practice, and evaluation of applied psychophysiology and
biofeedback. Submissions are also welcomed for consideration in several additional sections
that appear in the journal. They consist of conceptual and theoretical articles; evaluative
reviews; the Clinical Forum, which includes separate categories for innovative case studies,
clinical replication series, extended treatment protocols, and clinical notes and observations;
the Discussion Forum, which includes a series of papers centered around a topic of importance
to the field; Innovations in Instrumentation; Letters to the Editor, commenting on issues raised

in articles previously published in the journal; and select book reviews. *Applied Psychophysiology and Biofeedback* is the official publication of the Association for Applied Psychophysiology and Biofeedback.

Instructions to Contributors

1. Manuscripts should be submitted to the Editor:

Frank Andrasik, Ph.D, Editor-in-Chief
Applied Psychophysiology and Biofeedback
Institute for Human and Machine Cognition
University of West Florida
40 South Alcaniz Street
Pensacola, FL 32502
e-mail: **fandrasik@ihmc.us**

The Journal uses nonblind review, but authors may elect blind review. The author must state this intent clearly in a covering letter and remove all identifying information from the manuscript prior to submission.

2. Submission is a representation that the manuscript has not been published previously and is not currently under consideration for publication elsewhere. A statement transferring copyright from the authors (or their employers, if they hold the copyright) to Kluwer Academic/Plenum Publishers will be required before the manuscript can be accepted for publication. The Editor will supply the necessary forms for this transfer. Such a written transfer of copyright, which previously was assumed to be implicit in the act of submitting a manuscript, is necessary under the U.S. Copyright Law in order for the publisher to carry through the dissemination of research results and reviews as widely and effectively as possible.

3. Manuscripts are to be typed double-spaced. Academic or professional affiliations of all authors and the full mailing address, phone number, and e-mail address of the one author who will review the proofs should be included. A brief running title should appear at the top of each page. Electronic submission is preferred. If submitted by surface mail, an original and four high-quality copies (including copies of all illustrations and tables) are required.

4. An abstract of 200 words or less is to be provided.

5. A list of up to 5 descriptive key words (or phrases) is to be provided directly below the abstract. Key words should express the precise content of the manuscript, as they are used for indexing purposes, both internal and external.

6. Tables should be numbered and referred to by number in the text. Each table should be typed on a separate sheet of paper and should have a descriptive title.

7. Illustrations (photographs, drawings, diagrams, and charts) are to be numbered in one consecutive series of Arabic numerals, and referred to by number in the text. Photographs should be large, glossy prints, showing high contrast. Drawings should be prepared with India ink. Either the original drawings or high-quality photographic prints are acceptable. Identify

figures on the back with author's name and number of the illustration. Each figure should have an accompanying caption. The list of captions for illustrations should be typed on a separate sheet of paper. Electronic artwork submitted on disk should be in TIFF or EPS format (1200 dpi for line and 300 dpi for half-tones and gray-scale art). Color art should be in the CMYK color space. Artwork should be on a separate disk from the text, and hard copy *must* accompany the disk.

8. The 2001 (fifth) edition of the *Publication Manual of the American Psychological Association* should be used as the style guide for the preparation of manuscripts, particularly with respect to such matters as the citing of references and the use of abbreviations, numbers, and symbols.

9. The description of the procedures should be sufficiently detailed to allow replication of the experiment, or clinical procedure, by a reader trained in applied psychophysiology.

10. After a manuscript has been accepted for publication and after all revisions have been incorporated, manuscripts are to be submitted to the Editor's Office as hard copy accompanied by electronic files on disk. Label the disk with identifying information—software, journal name, and the first author's last name. The disk **must** be the one from which the accompanying manuscript (finalized version) was printed out. The Editor's Office cannot accept a disk without its accompanying, matching hard-copy manuscript.

11. The journal makes no page charges. Reprints are available to authors, and order forms with the current price schedule are sent with proofs.

Archives of Clinical Neuropsychology

ADDRESS FOR SUBMISSION:

Wm. Drew Gouvier, Editor
Archives of Clinical Neuropsychology
Louisiana State University
ACN Editorial Office
LSU Department of Psychology
Baton Rouge, LA 70803-5501
USA
Phone: 225-578-1494
Fax: 225-578-4661
E-Mail: acn@lsu.edu
Web: www.elsevier.com
Address May Change: 1/1/2008

PUBLICATION GUIDELINES:

Manuscript Length: 16-20
Copies Required: Five
Computer Submission: No
Format: N/A
Fees to Review: 0.00 US$

Manuscript Style:
American Psychological Association

CIRCULATION DATA:

Reader: Academics, Practitioners
Frequency of Issue: 8 Times/Year
Copies per Issue: 5,001 - 10,000
Sponsor/Publisher: National Academy of
Neuropsychology / Elsevier Science
Publishing Co.
Subscribe Price: 515.00 US$ Institution
210.00 US$ Associated Personnal

REVIEW INFORMATION:

Type of Review: Blind Review
No. of External Reviewers: 3+
No. of In House Reviewers: 0
Acceptance Rate: 40%
Time to Review: 2 - 3 Months
Reviewers Comments: Yes
Invited Articles: 6-10%
Fees to Publish: 0.00 US$

MANUSCRIPT TOPICS:
Gerontology; Neuropsychology; Psychological Testing

MANUSCRIPT GUIDELINES/COMMENTS:

Aims And Scope
Archives of Clinical Neuropsychology is a bimonthly journal sponsored by the National Academy of Neuropsychology. The journal publishes original contributions dealing with psychological aspects of the etiology, diagnosis, and treatment of disorders arising out of dysfunction of the central nervous system. *Archives of Clinical Neuropsychology* will also consider manuscripts involving the established principles of the profession of neuropsychology: (a) delivery and evaluation of services, (b) ethical and legal issues, and (c) approaches to education and training. Preference will be given to empirical reports and key reviews. Brief research reports and commentaries on published articles (not exceeding two printed pages) will also be considered. At the discretion of the editor, rebuttals to commentaries may be in invited. Occasional papers of a theoretical nature will be considered.

Audience. Neuropsychologists, Psychologists, Psychiatrists, Neurologists, Neuroscientists

Submission Requirements

Manuscripts and all correspondence should be submitted to the Editor-elect, Wm. Drew Gouvier, Ph.D, Director, Psychological Services Center, Associate Professor, Louisiana State University, Department of Psychology, 236 Audubon Hall, Baton Rouge, LA. 70803. **acn@lsu.edu**. Manuscripts dealing with children or youth for the Grand Rounds section of the journal should be submitted to Nancy Nussbaum, Austin Neurological Clinic, 711-F West 38th St., Austin, TX 78705-4129; and manuscripts dealing with adults for the Grand Rounds section should be submitted to Tim Bennett, Brain Injury Recovery Program, 1049 Robertson, Ft. Collins, CO 80524. Book and Test Reviews are by solicitation are handled by A. MacNeill Horton, Jr. Submit 4 copies of your completed manuscript, in English. Clean, readable, high-quality white bond copies should be submitted; the original manuscript is not required. Allow ample margins on all sides and type double-spaced throughout. A letter to the Editor must be enclosed, requesting review and possible publication; the letter must also state that the manuscript has not been previously published and has not been submitted elsewhere. The corresponding author's address, telephone and FAX numbers, and E-mail address if available (as well as any upcoming address change) should be included; this individual will receive all editorial correspondence.

Manuscripts submitted will receive a blind review by at least two editorial consultants. Therefore, the cover page alone should contain any information relevant to the authorship of the manuscript. Authors should ensure that the paper itself contains no footnotes or statements which allow the reviewer to identify the author. Upon acceptance for publication, the author(s) must complete a Transfer of Copyright Agreement form.

Brief reports will receive the same blind review as other manuscripts, however, due to the fact that they represent a replication or a specialized topic, the paper will not be accepted as a regular article. Authors must be willing to make an extended report of the manuscript available to readers upon request.

Computer Disks

Authors are encouraged to submit a computer disk (5.25" or 3.5") HD/DD disk) containing the *final* version of the papers along with the *final* manuscript to the editorial office. Please observe the following criteria: (1) Send only hard copy when first submitting your paper. (2) When your paper has been refereed, revised if necessary and accepted, send a disk containing the final version with the final hard copy. Make sure that the disk and the hard copy match exactly. (3) Specify what software was used, including which release, e.g., WordPerfect 6.0. (4) Specify what computer was used (either IBM compatible PC or Apple Macintosh). (5) Include the text file and separate table and illustration files, if available. (6) The file should follow the general instructions on style/arrangement and, in particular, the reference style of this journal as given in the Instructions to Contributors. (7) The file should be single-spaced and should use the wrap-around end-of-line feature, i.e., no returns at the end of each line. All textual elements should begin flush left; no paragraph indents. Place two returns after every element such as title, headings, paragraphs, figure and table call-outs. (8) Keep a back-up disk for reference and safety.

126

Title Page
The title page should list: (1) the article; (2) the authors' names and affiliations at the time the work was conducted; (3) corresponding author's address, telephone and fax numbers and E-mail address if available; (4) a concise running title; and (5) an unnumbered footnote giving address for reprint requests and any acknowledgements.

Abstract
An abstract should be submitted that does not exceed 150 words in length. This should be typed on a separate page following the title page.

Keywords
Authors should include up to six keywords with their article. Keywords should be selected from the APA list of index descriptors, unless otherwise agreed with the Editor.

Style and References
Manuscripts should be carefully prepared using the *Publication Manual of the American Psychological Association*, 3rd ed., 1983 for style. The reference section must be double-space and all works cited must be listed. Avoid abbreviations of journal titles and incomplete information.

Sample Journal Reference: Raymond, M.J. (1964). The treatment of addiction by aversion conditioning with apomorphine. *Behaviour Research and Therapy*, **3**, 287-290.
Sample Book Reference: Barlow, D.H. Hayes, S.C. & Nelson, R.O. (1984)

Tables and Figures
Do not send glossy prints, photographs or original artwork until acceptance. Copies of all tables and figures should be included with each copy of the manuscript. Upon acceptance of a manuscript for publication, original, camera-ready figures and any photographs must be submitted, un-mounted and on glossy paper. Photocopies, blue ink or pencil are not acceptable. Use black India ink, and type figure legends on a separate sheet. Write the article title and figure number lightly in pencil on the back of each.

Page Proofs and Reprints
Page proofs of the article will be sent to the corresponding author. These should be carefully proofread. Except for typographical errors, corrections should be minimal, and rewriting the text is not permitted. Corrected page proofs must be returned within 48 hours of receipt. Along with the page proofs, the corresponding author will receive a form for ordering reprints and full copies of the issue in which the article appears. Twenty-five (25) free reprints are provided; orders for additional reprints must be received before printing in order to qualify for lower prepublication rates. All coauthor reprint requirements should be included on the reprint order form.

Copyright
Publications are copyrighted for the protection of the authors and the publisher. A *Transfer of Copyright Agreement* will be sent to the author whose manuscript is accepted. The form must be completed and returned to the publisher before the article can be published.

Archives of Sexual Behavior

ADDRESS FOR SUBMISSION:

Kenneth J. Zucker, Editor
Archives of Sexual Behavior
Child &Adolescent Gender Identity Clinic
Child Psychiatry Program
Ctr-Addiction & Mental Health,Clarke Div
250 College Street
Toronto, Ontario, M5T 1R8
Canada
Phone: 416-535-8501 x 4040
Fax: 416-979-4668
E-Mail: ken_zucker@camh.net
Web: www.wkap.nl
Address May Change: 1/1/2006

PUBLICATION GUIDELINES:

Manuscript Length: 16-30+
Copies Required: Four
Computer Submission: No
Format: N/A
Fees to Review: 0.00 US$

Manuscript Style:
American Psychological Association

CIRCULATION DATA:

Reader: Academics, Practitioners
Frequency of Issue: 6 Times/Year
Copies per Issue: Less than 1,000
Sponsor/Publisher: International Academy
of Sex Research / Kluwer Academic
Publisher
Subscribe Price: 129.00 US$ Individual
815.00 US$ Library
128.00 Euro Indv., 814 Euro Library

REVIEW INFORMATION:

Type of Review: Blind Review
No. of External Reviewers: 2-3
No. of In House Reviewers: 0
Acceptance Rate: 40-50%
Time to Review: 2 - 3 Months
Reviewers Comments: Yes
Invited Articles: 6-10%
Fees to Publish: 0.00 US$

MANUSCRIPT TOPICS:

Child Sexual Abuse; Comparative Approaches; Epidemiology of Sexual Behavior; Gender
Roles; Human Sexuality; Impact of HIV/AIDS; Intergroup Relations; Paraphilias; Sex
Therapy; Sexual Function and Dysfunction; Sexual Orientation; Sexual Psychopharmacology

MANUSCRIPT GUIDELINES/COMMENTS:

Aims & Scope. *Archives of Sexual Behavior*, the official publication of the International
Academy of Sex Research, is dedicated to the dissemination of information in the field of
sexual science, broadly defined. Research on both animals and humans is welcomed.
Contributions from various biological and social science disciplines are encouraged. The
journal publishes empirical papers, on a variety of topics germane to sexual science, including
gender identity, sexual orientation, sexual function and dysfunction, paraphilias, sexual
psychopharmacology, sex therapy, and impact of HIV/AIDS and other STDs. The journal also
publishes theoretical papers and integrative review articles, including meta-analysis, and
welcomes both quantitative and qualitative approaches. In addition to empirical research
articles and theoretical reviews, the Journal also has a Letters to the Editor section and a newly

launched Clinical Case Report Series, which publishes clinical reports of heuristic value. The journal also has a Book Review section (by invitation only). Proposals for special issues can be discussed with the Editor.

1. Manuscripts should be sent to the Editor:
   Kenneth J. Zucker, Ph.D.
   Child and Adolescent Gender Identity Clinic
   Child Psychiatry Program
   Center for Addiction and Mental Health - Clarke Division
   250 College Street, Toronto, Ontario M5T 1R8, Canada
   Web: **www.catchword.com/titles/00040002.htm**

For book reviews, two copies of the book should be sent to the address above.

2. Submission is a representation that the manuscript has not been published previously and is not currently under consideration for publication elsewhere. A statement transferring copyright from the authors (or their employers, if they hold the copyright) to Kluwer Academic/Plenum Publishers will be required before the manuscript can be accepted for publication. The Editor will supply the necessary forms for this transfer. Such a written transfer of copyright, which previously was assumed to be implicit in the act of submitting a manuscript, is necessary under the U.S. Copyright Law in order for the publisher to carry through the dissemination of research results and reviews as widely and effectively as possible.

3. Type double-spaced on one side of U.S. (8 ½ x 11 inch) or A4 white paper, using 1-inch margins on all sides, and submit the original and two copies (including copies of all illustrations and tables). In order to facilitate masked review, leave all identifying information off the manuscript.

4. A title page is to be provided and should include the title of the article, author's name (including highest degree received), author's affiliation, and suggested running head (no more than 80 characters, including spaces). Academic affiliations of all authors should be included. The affiliation should include the department, institution, city, and state (or nation) and should be typed as a footnote to the author's name. For office purposes, the title page should include the complete mailing addresses, telephone number, fax number, and e-mail address of the corresponding author designated to review proofs.

5. An abstract, preferably no longer than 250 words, is to be provided as the second page.

6. A list of 4-5 key words is to be provided directly below the abstract. Key words should express the precise content of the manuscript, as they are used for indexing purposes.

7. Illustrations (photographs, drawings, diagrams, and charts) are to be numbered in one consecutive series of Arabic numerals. Photographs should be large, glossy prints, showing high contrast. Drawings may be prepared with India ink or may be computer generated if dark, sharp and clear (no dot matrix). Either the original drawings or good-quality photographic prints are acceptable. Identify figures on the back with author's name and number of the

illustration. Each figure should have an accompanying caption. The list of captions for illustrations should be typed on a separate sheet of paper. Electronic artwork submitted on disk should be in TIFF or EPS format (1200 dpi for line and 300 dpi for half-tones and gray-scale art). Color art should be in the CMYK color space. Artwork should be on a separate disk from the text, and hard copy *must* accompany the disk.

8. Tables should be numbered and referred to by number in the text. Each table should be typed on a separate sheet of paper and should have a descriptive title. Center the title above the table, and type explanatory footnotes (indicated by superscript lowercase letters) below the table.

9. List references alphabetically at the end of the paper and refer to them in the text by name and year in parentheses. References should include (in this order): last names and initials of *all* authors, year published, title of article, name of publication, volume number, and inclusive pages. The style and punctuation of the references should conform to strict APA style - illustrated by the following examples:

Journal Article. Meston, C. M., & Frohlich, P. F. (2000). The neurobiology of sexual function. *Archives of General Psychiatry, 57,* 1012-1030.

Book. Dixson, A. F. (1998). *Primate sexuality: Comparative studies of the prosimians, monkeys, apes, and human beings.* New York: Oxford University Press.

Chapter in a Book. Bem, D. (2000). The exotic-becomes-erotic theory of sexual orientation. In J. Bancroft (Ed.), *The role of theory in sex research* (pp. 67-81). Bloomington, IN: Indiana University Press.

10. Footnotes should be avoided. When their use is absolutely necessary, footnotes should be numbered consecutively using Arabic numerals and should be typed at the bottom of the page to which they refer. Place a line above the footnote, so that it is set off from the text. Use the appropriate superscript numeral for citation in the text.

11. The 2001 *Publication Manual of the American Psychological Association* (Fifth Edition) should be used as the style guide for the preparation of manuscripts, particularly with respect to such matters as the citing of references and the use of abbreviation, numbers, and symbols. Manuscripts departing significantly from the Fifth Edition style will not be reviewed until a corrected manuscript has been received.

12. After a manuscript has been accepted for publication and after all revisions have been incorporated, manuscripts should be submitted to the Editor's Office as hard copy accompanied by electronic files on disk. Label the disk with identifying information - software, journal name, and first author's last name. The disk *must* be the one from which the accompanying manuscript (finalized version) was printed out. The Editor's Office cannot accept a disk without its accompanying, matching hard-copy manuscript.

13. The journal makes no page charges. Reprints are available to authors, and order forms with the current price schedule are sent with proofs.

Archives of Suicide Research

ADDRESS FOR SUBMISSION:

Antoon A. Leenaars, Editor
Archives of Suicide Research
880 Ouellette Avenue, Suite 7806
Windsor, Ontario, N9A 1C7
Canada
Phone: 1-519-253-9377
Fax: 1-519-253-8486
E-Mail: draalse@wincom.net
Web: http://www.tandf.co.uk/journals
Address May Change:

PUBLICATION GUIDELINES:

Manuscript Length: 16-20
Copies Required: Three
Computer Submission: No
Format: N/A
Fees to Review: 0.00 US$

Manuscript Style:
    American Psychological Association

CIRCULATION DATA:

Reader: Academics, Practitioners
Frequency of Issue: Quarterly
Copies per Issue:
Sponsor/Publisher: Routledge Journals (
    Taylor & Francis)
Subscribe Price: 116.00 US$ Individual
    249.00 US$ Institution
    71.00 Pounds Indv., 151 Pounds Inst.

REVIEW INFORMATION:

Type of Review: Blind Review
No. of External Reviewers: 2
No. of In House Reviewers: 2
Acceptance Rate: Varies
Time to Review: 2 - 3 Months
Reviewers Comments: Yes
Invited Articles: 0-5%
Fees to Publish: 0.00 US$

MANUSCRIPT TOPICS:
Adolescent Psychology; Family Counseling & Therapy; Group Dynamics; Physiological Psychology; Psychiatry; Psychobiology; Suicidology

MANUSCRIPT GUIDELINES/COMMENTS:

Aims and Scope
Archives of Suicide Research, the official journal of the International Academy of Suicide Research (IASR), is the international journal in the field of suicidology. The journal features original, refereed contributions on the study of suicide, suicidal behavior, its causes and effects, and techniques for prevention. The journal incorporates research-based and theoretical articles contributed by a diverse range of authors interested in investigating the biological, pharmacological, psychiatric, psychological, and sociological aspects of suicide.

The editors of *ASR* are mindful of the dichotomy between general (quantitative/nomothetic) methods of research and practice and approaches that utilize specific case studies (qualitative/idiographic). While eagerly accepting work from suicidologists situated on both sides of this division, the editors ultimately wish to cultivate a forum that attempts to reconcile and merge these oppositional modes. It is their belief that, by amalgamating the general and the specific, the field of suicidology will become a more scientific discipline - a discipline that encourages the open exchange of knowledge and techniques. And it is the mission of *ASR* to be the primary conduit through which the results of such exchanges will be enthusiastically disseminated.

Features of the journal include:
- Book Reviews
- Research Reviews
- News and notes in the field of Suicidology
- Case Studies

Readership
Suicidologists, psychologists, psychiatrists, clinicians, researchers, mental health, social workers, graduate/undergraduate students.

Instructions for Authors
Note to Authors. Please make sure your contact address information is clearly visible on the outside of all packages you are sending to Editors.

Submission of Manuscripts. Submit original and three copies in English, along with a computer diskette version using MS Word or WordPerfect, to Dr. A.A. Leenaars, 880 Ouellette Avenue, Suite 7806, Windsor, Ontario, Canada N9A 1C7. Telephone: 519-253-9377; Fax: 519-253-8486. A cover letter must be included indicating that the material is intended for publication. All accepted manuscripts, artwork, and photographs become the property of the International Academy for Suicide Research. Upon acceptance, contributors are required to supply the final version of the material both in hardcopy and on computer diskette. A PC-based format using MS Word or WordPerfect is preferred. Manuscripts, including tables, figures, and references, should be prepared in accordance with the *American Psychological Association* 5th Edition. All manuscripts must be typed, double-spaced, on 8.5 x 11 inch paper with a 1-inch margin all around.

Authors should also supply a shortened version of the title suitable for the running head, not exceeding 50 character spaces. Each article should be summarized in an abstract of no more that 100 words and have 3-5 keywords. Avoid abbreviations, diagrams, and reference to the text.

Illustrations. Illustrations submitted (line drawings, halftones, photos, photomicrographs, etc.) should be clean originals or digital files. Digital files are recommended for highest quality reproduction and should follow these guidelines:
- 300 dpi or higher
- sized to fit on journal page
- EPS, TIFF, or PSD format only
- submitted as separate files, not embedded in text files

Color illustrations will be considered for publication; however, the author will be required to bear the full cost involved in their printing and publication. The charge for the first figure is $1,200.00. Subsequent figures, totaling no more than 4 text pages, are $500.00 each. Good quality color prints should be provided in their final size. Figures needing reduction or enlargement will be charged an additional 25 percent. The publisher has the right to refuse publication of any artwork deemed unacceptable.

Tables and Figures. Tables and figures should not be embedded in the text, but should be included as separate sheets or files. A short descriptive title should appear above each table with a clear legend and any footnotes suitably identified below. All units must be included. Figures should be completely labeled, taking into account necessary size reduction. Captions should be typed, double-spaced, on a separate sheet. All original figures should be clearly marked in pencil on the reverse side with the number, author's name, and top edge indicated.

References. Should be listed on separate pages following the text and should be typed double-spaced. References should be listed alphabetically. Be sure all references have been cited in the text.

Proofs. One set of page proofs is sent to the designated author. Proofs should be checked and returned within 48 hours.

Offprints and Complimentary Copies. The corresponding author of each article will receive up to 3 complimentary issues. Offprints of the article and additional issues may be ordered from Taylor & Francis by using the order form included with the page proofs.

Permissions. Authors are responsible for obtaining permission to reproduce copyrighted material from other sources.

Arts in Psychotherapy (The)

ADDRESS FOR SUBMISSION:

Robyn Flaum Cruz, Editor-in-Chief
Arts in Psychotherapy (The)
Western Psychiatric Institute and Clinic
3811 O'Hara Street, Rm. 886-A
Pittsburgh, PA 15213
USA
Phone: 412-246-5493
Fax: 412-586-9025
E-Mail: cruzrf@upmc.edu
Web: www.elsevier.com
Address May Change:

PUBLICATION GUIDELINES:

Manuscript Length: 21-25
Copies Required: Three
Computer Submission: Yes Online
Format: N/A
Fees to Review: 0.00 US$

Manuscript Style:
American Psychological Association

CIRCULATION DATA:

Reader: Academics, Practitioners
Frequency of Issue: 5 Times/Year
Copies per Issue: 1,001 - 2,000
Sponsor/Publisher: Elsevier Science Press
Subscribe Price: 119.00 US$ Individual
613.00 US$ Institution
41.00 US$ Students

REVIEW INFORMATION:

Type of Review: Blind Review
No. of External Reviewers: 2
No. of In House Reviewers: 1
Acceptance Rate: 11-20%
Time to Review: 2 - 3 Months
Reviewers Comments: No
Invited Articles: 0-5%
Fees to Publish: 0.00 US$

MANUSCRIPT TOPICS:
Counseling Process; Creative Arts Therapies; Educational Psychology; Relationship Between Arts Therapies & Psychology

MANUSCRIPT GUIDELINES/COMMENTS:

Aims and Scopes
The Arts in Psychotherapy published 5 issues per annum, is an international journal for professionals in the fields of mental health and education. The journal publishes articles (including illustrations) by art, dance/movement, drama, music, and poetry psychotherapists, as well as psychiatrists and psychologists, which reflect the theory and practice of these disciplines. There are no restrictions on philosophical orientation or application.

The Arts in Psychotherapy reports news and comments on national and international conferences and current education information relevant to the creative arts in therapy. The journal also includes book reviews, invites letters to the Editors, and welcomes dialogue between contributors.

Audience. Creative arts therapists, psychiatrists, psychotherapists, psychologists, professionals in mental health.

Guide for Authors

The International Journal of The Arts in Psychotherapy is an interdisciplinary journal, and each article should address the interrelationship between an aesthetic process and a psychotherapeutic one. Authors should grapple with such general questions as:

- How is the creative process a healing one?
- When and under what set of circumstances is the creative process a healing one?
- Where does the meeting between art forms and psychotherapy occur?
- Why is the creative process a healing one?

These and related general inquiries should be framed into more specific researchable questions situated within the given discipline(s) of the author.

Authors should consider working within a sound methodological framework leading to the following kinds of studies:

1. Clinical case studies and group research designs;
2. Theoretical studies, attempting to critique or expand on existing theory, or attempting to create new theoretical concepts and models;
3. Aesthetic studies, examining a creative process for its healing functions;
4. Ethnographic studies, utilizing a participant-observer approach;
5. Quantitative studies, applying appropriate statistical instruments and measures of reliability and validity;
6. Critical studies of social. cultural or political phenomena that impact on the arts psychotherapy field;
7. Studies in literary or arts criticism from a therapeutic point of view;
8. Psycho-biography of a prominent arts figure (e.g., Virginia Woolf, Frida Kahlo, Martha Graham, Eugene O'Neill, Bela Bartok);
9. State of the art studies, reviewing research within a given arts therapy discipline and speculating as to future directions.

Descriptive studies may also be submitted for consideration in the section called "Brief Reports." Thus, they should be concise and relatively brief.

Authors from diverse fields are invited to submit articles: from all arts psychotherapy disciplines, from the social sciences and medical professions, from philosophy and literature, and, of course, from the creative arts fields. The Journal encourages those who wish to develop a series of related articles or theoretical speculations to submit appropriate work over time.

Illustrations of artwork are limited to 10 examples. Articles should be submitted in triplicate, typed double-spaced and with pages numbered. Please see "Information for Contributors" on the inside back cover for more detailed information on submission requirements, including disk submission.

Information for Contributors

The Arts in Psychotherapy is published 5 issues per annum. Neither the Editors nor the Publisher accept responsibility for the views or statements expressed by authors. This Journal should be cited in lists of references as *The Arts in Psychotherapy*.

Manuscripts. Send manuscripts to Editor-in-Chief, Robyn Flaum Cruz, The Arts in Psychotherapy, Western Psychiatric Institute and Clinic, 3811 O'Hara Street, Rm. 886-A, Pittsburgh, PA 15213. Enclose self-addressed, stamped envelope with manuscript.

Manuscripts must be submitted in triplicate. They should be typewritten on one side of the paper, double-spaced (including references) with pages numbered, and they must be carefully checked. Corrections to proofs should be restricted to printer's errors only. Other than these, very substantial alterations will be charged to the author. Authors should retain one copy of manuscript in case of loss. Neither Editors nor Publisher are responsible for such loss.

The articles submitted must contain original material and must not have been published previously. Papers accepted by the Journal may not be published elsewhere in any language without the consent of The Editors and Publisher. All rights and permission must be obtained by the contributor. Patients'/Clients' productions may not be used without written permission from patients/clients or their guardians. These permissions should be sent upon acceptance of manuscripts for publication.

The title of the paper, the author's name, telephone and fax numbers, e-mail address (if available) and full postal address to which proofs should be sent and the name and address of the institution, hospital, etc. where the work was carried out should be typed on a separate page, as manuscripts are sent out for blind review.

References should be placed at the end of the paper on a separate sheet, in alphabetical order and arranged to follow American Psychological Association guidelines as set forth in their *Publication Manual* (4th ed.).

Computer Disks. Authors are encouraged to submit a 3.5" HD/DD computer disk to the editorial office; 5.25" HD/DD disks are acceptable if 3.5" disks are unavailable. Please observe the following criteria:

1. Send only hard copy when first submitting your paper.
2. When your paper has been refereed, revised if necessary, and accepted, send a disk containing the final version with the final hard copy. Make sure that the disk and the hard copy match exactly (otherwise the diskette version will prevail).
3. Specify what software was used, including which release, e.g., WordPerfect 6.0a.
4. Specify what computer was used (IBM compatible PC, Apple Macintosh, etc.).
5. The article file should include all textual material (text, references, tables, figure captions, etc.) and separate illustration files, if available.
6. The file should follow the general instructions on style/arrangement and, in particular, the reference style of this journal as given in the Instructions to Contributors.

7. The file should be single-spaced and should use the wrap-around end-of-line feature, i.e., *returns at the end of paragraphs only*. Place two returns after every element such as title, headings, paragraphs, figure and table call-outs.
8. Keep a back-up disk for reference and safety.

Illustrations and diagrams should be kept to a minimum. They should have the author's name and the figure number written in light pencil on the reverse side. Captions accompanying illustrations should be type written on separate sheets. Diagrams and graphs must be drawn with India ink on stout paper or tracing linen. The lettering should be large enough to be legible after the diagram has been reduced in size for printing.

Photographs and photomicrographs must be submitted un-mounted and on white glossy paper. All diagrams must be submitted in a form suitable for direct reproduction.

Tables and figures should be constructed so as to be intelligible without reference to the text, each table and column being provided with a heading. The same information should be reproduced in both tables and figures.

Business communication. All communications concerning reprints, advertising, subscriptions, changes in address, etc., should be addressed to the publisher, Elsevier Science Inc., 655 Avenue of the Americas, New York, NY 10010.

Reprints. The corresponding contributor will receive a form for ordering reprints and copies of the journal issue in which the article appears. The page proofs for proofreading will be sent with this form. Late orders cannot be filled since reprints are run at the time the journal is printed. Twenty-five (25) reprints will be provided gratis.

Copyright. Publications are copyrighted for the protection of the authors and the publisher. A Transfer of Copyright Agreement will be sent to the author whose manuscript is accepted. The form must be completed and returned to the Publisher before the article can be published.

Asian Journal of Social Psychology

ADDRESS FOR SUBMISSION:

Kwok Leung, Editor
Asian Journal of Social Psychology
City University of Hong Kong
Department of Marketing
83 Tat Chee Avenue
Kowloon Tong,
Hong Kong
Phone: 852-27889592
Fax: 852-27889085
E-Mail: mkkleung@cityu.edu.hk
Web: www.sites.psych.unimelb.edu.au/aa
Address May Change:

PUBLICATION GUIDELINES:

Manuscript Length: 26-30
Copies Required: Three
Computer Submission: Yes
Format: MS Word or WordPerfect
Fees to Review: 0.00 US$

Manuscript Style:
    American Psychological Association

CIRCULATION DATA:

Reader: Academics
Frequency of Issue: 3 Times/Year
Copies per Issue: Less than 1,000
Sponsor/Publisher: Asian Assn. of Social
    Psychology, Japanese Group Dynamics
    Assn./Blackwell Publishers
Subscribe Price: 64.00 US$ Personal
    23.00 US$ Student
    274.00 US$ Institution

REVIEW INFORMATION:

Type of Review: Editorial Review
No. of External Reviewers: 2
No. of In House Reviewers: 0
Acceptance Rate: 21-30%
Time to Review: 2 - 3 Months
Reviewers Comments: Yes
Invited Articles: 11-20%
Fees to Publish: 0.00 US$

MANUSCRIPT TOPICS:
Personality; Social Psychology

MANUSCRIPT GUIDELINES/COMMENTS:

Aims and Scope
The *Asian Journal of Social Psychology* stimulates research and encourages academic exchanges for the advancement of social psychology in Asia. It publishes theoretical and empirical papers, as well as book reviews by Asian scholars and those interested in Asian cultures and societies.

Coverage includes all aspects of social processes such as development, cognition, personality, health, counseling, organization and education. The journal encourages interdisciplinary integration with social sciences and humanities.

How to Submit Your Article
Authors should submit 3 copies of their manuscript together with a computer disk containing the manuscript file (IBM-compatible or Mackintosh). Electronic submission to the Editor is

138

also acceptable. Only original articles that have not been published before in any languages will be considered. Submissions must contain an abstract of approximately 100 words, and double-spacing should be used throughout. Authors need to follow the format described in the *Publication Manual of the American Psychological Association (4th ed)*. If a blind review is preferred, please inform the Editor in the cover letter and make sure that the authors' identity is masked in the manuscript. Authors can submit their manuscript in English, Chinese, Japanese or Korean.

Please send all manuscripts to the Editor.

For further information on *Asian Journal of Social Psychology*, including contents, article abstracts and notes for contributors, visit the Blackwell publishers website:
   http://www.blackwellpublishers.co.uk

Assessment

ADDRESS FOR SUBMISSION:

Yosef S. Ben-Porath, Editor
Assessment
Kent State University
Department of Psychology
Kent, OH 44242-0001
USA
Phone: 330-672-3580
Fax: 330-672-4826
E-Mail: assessment@kent.edu
Web: See Guidelines
Address May Change:

PUBLICATION GUIDELINES:

Manuscript Length: 20-30
Copies Required: N/A
Computer Submission: Yes Required
Format: MS Word, WordPerfect
Fees to Review: 0.00 US$

Manuscript Style:
American Psychological Association

CIRCULATION DATA:

Reader: Academics, Practitioners
Frequency of Issue: Quarterly
Copies per Issue: 500
Sponsor/Publisher: Sage Publications
Subscribe Price: 79.00 US$ Individual
   375.00 US$ Institution
   79.00 US$ Indv., $375 Inst. Non U.S.

REVIEW INFORMATION:

Type of Review: Peer Review
No. of External Reviewers: 3
No. of In House Reviewers: No Reply
Acceptance Rate: 21-30%
Time to Review: 2 - 3 Months
Reviewers Comments: Yes
Invited Articles: 0-5%
Fees to Publish: 0.00 US$

MANUSCRIPT TOPICS:
Psychological Testing

MANUSCRIPT GUIDELINES/COMMENTS:

Description
Assessment publishes important articles derived from psychometric research, clinical comparisons, theoretical formulations and literature reviews that fall within the broad domain of clinical and applied psychological assessment. The journal presents information of direct relevance to the use of assessment measures, including the practical applications of measurement methods, test development and interpretation practices, and advances in the description and prediction of human behavior.

The scope of the journal extends from the evaluation of individuals and groups in clinical, counseling, health, forensic, organizational, industrial, and educational settings; to the assessment of treatment efficacy, program evaluation, job performance and the study of behavior outcomes.

140

Journal Submission Guidelines

The editor invites manuscripts covering a broad range of topics and techniques in the area of assessment. These may include empirical studies of assessment of personality, psychopathology, cognitive functions or behavior, articles dealing with general methodological or psychometric topics relevant to assessment, or comprehensive literature reviews in any of these areas. Research participants may represent both clinical and nonclinical populations. Submission of articles addressing forensic assessment issues is encouraged. The editor also seeks manuscripts addressing multicultural, cross-cultural, and international aspects of assessment.

Manuscript Submission. Manuscripts must be submitted in electronic form in Microsoft Word, Corel Wordperfect, or Rich Text Format (rtf). Figures may be submitted using any of the formats listed below. A masked blind review process may be requested, in which case the authors should add a masked title page following the title page. To expedite processing, manuscripts may be submitted as electronic attachments along with a cover letter to **assessment@kent.edu**. Alternatively, authors may submit their manuscript on an IBM compatible floppy disk to ASSESSMENT, Department of Psychology, Kent State University, Kent, OH 44242. Questions should be directed to the same e-mail address or to the ASSESSMENT editorial office at 330-672-3580.

Brief reports may be submitted for publication and should be limited to 1,000 words, including an abstract of 75 words or less. The brief report format should be used for carefully designed and executed investigations of research topics of specialized interest that make a significant contribution to the literature but do not require a full-length manuscript. In addition, comments may be submitted as brief manuscripts responding to articles published in the journal. Comments should be no longer than 1,000 words and will be selected for publication based on an editorial review process. Comments based on topics other than articles published in the journal will not be accepted.

Authors submitting manuscripts to the journal should not simultaneously submit them to another journal, nor should manuscripts have been published elsewhere, including the World Wide Web, in substantially similar form or with substantially similar content.

Preparation of Manuscripts. Authors should carefully prepare their manuscripts in accordance with the following instructions.

Authors should use the *Publication Manual of the American Psychological Association* (5th edition, 2001) as a guide for preparing manuscripts for submission. All manuscript pages, including reference lists and tables, must be typed double-spaced.

The first page of the paper should contain the article title, the names and affiliations of all authors, authors' notes or acknowledgments, and the names and complete mailing addresses of the corresponding author. The second page should contain an abstract of no more than 150 words and five to seven keywords that will be published following the abstract.

The following sections should be prepared as indicated:

Tables. Each table should be fully titled, single-spaced on a separate page, and placed at the end of the paper. Tables should be numbered consecutively with Arabic numerals. Footnotes to tables should be identified with superscript lowercase letters and placed at the bottom of the table. All tables should be referred to in the text.

Figures. Electronic copies of figures can be submitted in one of the following formats: Microsoft PowerPoint or Word, Tagged Image File Format (.TIF), Joint Photographic Experts Group (.JPG), or Adobe Acrobat Portable Document Format (.PDF). All figures should be referred to in text. Each figure should appear on a separate page at the end of the paper, and all titles should appear on a single, separate page.

Endnotes. Notes should appear on a separate page before the References section. Notes should be numbered consecutively and each endnote should be referred to in text with a corresponding superscript number.

References. Text citations and references should follow the style of the *Publication Manual of the American Psychological Association* (5th edition, 2001).

Australian Journal of Clinical Hypnotherapy and Hypnosis

ADDRESS FOR SUBMISSION:

Lindsay Duncan, Editor
Australian Journal of Clinical Hypnotherapy
    and Hypnosis
1103/242 Elizabeth Street
Surry Hills, NSW 2010
Australia
Phone: +61 2 9264 2292
Fax: +61 2 9280 2102
E-Mail: lduncan@ihug.com.au
Web: .australianacademicpress.com.au
Address May Change:

PUBLICATION GUIDELINES:

Manuscript Length: 11-15
Copies Required: Three
Computer Submission: Yes Disk or Email
Format: MS Word Compatible
Fees to Review: 0.00 US$

Manuscript Style:
    American Psychological Association

CIRCULATION DATA:

Reader: Academics, Practitioners
Frequency of Issue: 2 Times/Year
Copies per Issue: Less than 1,000
Sponsor/Publisher: Australian Society of
    Clinical Hypnotherapy
Subscribe Price: 28.50 AUS$ Individual
    36.50 AUS$ Library/Institution
    41.50 AUS$ Foreign

REVIEW INFORMATION:

Type of Review: Editorial Review
No. of External Reviewers: 1
No. of In House Reviewers: 2
Acceptance Rate: 60%
Time to Review: 1 - 2 Months
Reviewers Comments: Yes
Invited Articles: 0-5%
Fees to Publish: 0.00 US$

MANUSCRIPT TOPICS:
Counseling Process; Hypnosis; Hypnotherapy

MANUSCRIPT GUIDELINES/COMMENTS:

Information for Contributors
The *Journal* has a semi-annual publication schedule with issues presented in March and September. The *Journal* will publish original clinical, research, review, theoretical, historical and related reports dealing with the professional application of hypnosis and hypnotherapy. A state-of-the-art, selected bibliography focusing on specific areas of interest will also be published. All manuscripts, books for review, other editorial matters and journal enquiries should be addressed to the Editor (address above).

Preparation of Manuscripts
All of the materials submitted to the *Journal* are reviewed by members of the Editorial Board and selected reviewers. The materials are evaluated on the basis of merit, contribution and interest. The name of the author is not considered.

Manuscripts are required to be submitted in triplicate. They are to be typewritten on one side of quarto (A4 - 22cm x 28cm) bond paper. The submissions are double-spaced and do not usually exceed 4,500 words.

A brief biography of no more than 30 words should be included for each author outlining their area of work in hypnosis and where they work.

Upon acceptance of their article for publication, authors who have prepared manuscripts on and IBM-compatible PC or Apple Macintosh computer should submit a copy of their work on disk in addition to the final printed copies. All copies of the manuscript are to be set in the same manner described above for typed manuscripts. Acceptable word processing program formats are: Word Perfect, Microsoft Word, WordStar, Office Writer, Microsoft Works, and Mac Write. Disks may be supplied in either 3.5 inch or 5.24 inch formats. The word processing program used and version number are to be specified in writing on the title page of the manuscript. Computer disks should be packed in Australia Post postpak (DM size) and placed with the manuscript copies in a large sturdy envelope. Indicate on the outside on the envelope that a computer disk is contained inside.

The editorial board of the *Australian Journal of Clinical Hypnotherapy and Hypnosis* has adopted the *Publication Manual of the American Psychological Association*, Fourth Edition (1994) as the guideline for reference citations. The manual is available from APA Publications Sales, 1200 Seventeenth St., N.W., Washington D.C. 20036, U.S.A.

1. *References*. References are referred to in the text by the author's surname and the date of publication in parenthesis. For example, (Jones, 1981), or "Jones (1981) discussed the issues of ..." Reference lists are presented at the end of the article. The lists combine journals, books and other materials.

The citations are listed by the author's names in inverted order, and are alphabetized letter by letter. When more than one author's works are listed, they are arranged by the year of publication with the earliest year listed first.

References are not numbered.

Journal Entry
Author. year of publication. Title. Name of Journal, volume number (issue number), inclusive pages.
For example:
Parder, A. (1981) Fears and therapeutic manipulations. The Australian Journal of Clinical Hypnotherapy, 2(2), 101-110.

Book entry
Author. Publication date. Title. City of Publication: publisher's name.
For example:
Kroger, W.S. & Fezler, W.D. (1976) Hypnosis and behaviour modification: Imagery conditioning. Philadelphia: J.B. Lippincott

144

The *Publication Manual* is consulted for more complicated reference problems, writing styles, headings, quotations, punctuation, capitalization and italics questions.

The use of footnotes is strongly discouraged.

All references must be verified as part of the submission process. Therefore, photostatic copies of all of the articles cited, including full reference information i.e., journal issue cover and table of contents, must be forwarded. In addition, copies of the full reference information, i.e. title and copyright pages and quoted passages for all books cited must also be submitted.

2. *Abstract.* An abstract of not more than 150 words, typed on a separate page accompanies each manuscript. The abstracts and articles should contain a presentation of the problem, theoretical bias, central thesis, method, results and conclusions.

3. *Cover page.* A separate cover page is required showing title, author's name(s) and affiliation and the address of the person to whom proof and reprint requests may be sent.

The materials presented in the *Journal* are copyrighted. Apart from any fair dealing for the purposes of private study, research, criticism or review, as permitted under the Copyright Act, no part may be reproduced by any process without written permission. The copyright is held by the *Australian Journal of Clinical Hypnotherapy and Hypnosis.* Copyright releases are available through the Journal Editor.

The *Journal* has been adopted as the official Journal of the Australian Society of Clinical Hypnotherapists.

Behavior Research Methods, Instruments, & Computers

ADDRESS FOR SUBMISSION:

John H. Krantz, Editor
Behavior Research Methods, Instruments, &
    Computers
Hanover College
P.O. Box 890
Hanover, IN 47243
USA
Phone: 812-866-7316
Fax: 812-866-7114
E-Mail: krantzj@hanover.edu
Web: www.psychonomic.org/brm
Address May Change:

PUBLICATION GUIDELINES:

Manuscript Length: No Limit
Copies Required: Four
Computer Submission: Yes Email
Format:
Fees to Review: 0.00 US$

Manuscript Style:
    American Psychological Association

CIRCULATION DATA:

Reader: Academics
Frequency of Issue: Quarterly
Copies per Issue: 2,001 - 3,000
Sponsor/Publisher: Psychonomic Society
Subscribe Price: 79.00 US$ Individual
        194.00 US$ Institution

REVIEW INFORMATION:

Type of Review: Editorial Review
No. of External Reviewers: 2
No. of In House Reviewers: 1
Acceptance Rate: 46%
Time to Review: 2 - 3 Months
Reviewers Comments: Yes
Invited Articles: 21-30%
Fees to Publish: 0.00 US$

MANUSCRIPT TOPICS:
Experimental Psychology; Psychological Testing; Research Methods & Statistics

MANUSCRIPT GUIDELINES/COMMENTS:

Research Topics
Computers and Data Processing, Operations Research/Statistics, Research Methods, Instrumentation Techniques, Computer Program Abstracts, Instructional Technology, Human-computer Interaction.

Behavioral & Cognitive Neuroscience Reviews

ADDRESS FOR SUBMISSION:

Joseph E. Steinmetz, Editor
Behavioral & Cognitive Neuroscience
   Reviews
Indiana University
Department of Psychology
1101 E 10th Street
Bloomington, IN 47405-7007
USA
Phone: 812-855-3991
Fax:
E-Mail: steinmet@indiana.edu
Web: http://bcnr.sagepub.com
Address May Change:

PUBLICATION GUIDELINES:

Manuscript Length: 30+
Copies Required: Three
Computer Submission: Yes Disk, Email
Format: MS Word
Fees to Review: 0.00 US$

Manuscript Style:
   American Psychological Association

CIRCULATION DATA:

Reader: Academics
Frequency of Issue: Quarterly
Copies per Issue: Less than 1,000
Sponsor/Publisher:
Subscribe Price: 97.00 US$ Indv. Print
   1019.00 US$ Inst. Print + Online

REVIEW INFORMATION:

Type of Review: Editorial Review
No. of External Reviewers: 2
No. of In House Reviewers: 0
Acceptance Rate: 80%
Time to Review: 1 - 2 Months
Reviewers Comments: Yes
Invited Articles: 50% +
Fees to Publish: 0.00 US$

MANUSCRIPT TOPICS:

Alcoholism & Drug Addiction; Experimental Psychology; Learning & Conditioning;
Neuropsychology; Neuroscience; Physiological Psychology; Psychiatry; Psychobiology;
Sensation & Perception; Thinking & Cognition

MANUSCRIPT GUIDELINES/COMMENTS:

Manuscripts, including references and figure captions, must be double-spaced throughout and should be submitted in triplicate for review. The manuscript should adhere to the format of the *Publication Manual of the American Psychological Association* (Fourth Edition) and include an abstract of not more than 150 words. All pages should be numbered and a running head typed in the upper left-hand corner of each page. Clean, camera-ready tables and figures should each appear on a separate page and be placed at the end of manuscript. In a cover letter that accompanies the manuscript, the author should provide a brief summary of the purpose and focus of the paper along with the names of 3-4 reviewers who could serve as expert reviewers for the manuscript. Upon acceptance, authors will be required to provide a copy of the final revised manuscript saved on computer disk along with two hard copies. Submission to *BCNR* implies that the manuscript has not been published elsewhere and is not under consideration by any other journal. Manuscripts should be submitted to: Joseph E. Steinmetz, Ph.D., Editor-in-Chief, Behavioral and Cognitive Neuroscience Reviews, Department of Psychology, Indiana University, 1101 E 10th Street Bloomington, IN 47405-7007 USA

Behavioral and Brain Sciences

ADDRESS FOR SUBMISSION:

Paul Bloom & Barbara Finlay, Co-Editors
Behavioral and Brain Sciences
Phone: 203-432-4619; 607-255-6394
Fax: 203-432-7172; 607-255-8433
E-Mail: bbs@bbsonline.org
Web: See Guidelines
Address May Change: 12/31/2006

PUBLICATION GUIDELINES:

Manuscript Length: 30+
Copies Required:
Computer Submission: Yes Email
Format: MS Word, RTF, HTML, PDF
Fees to Review: 0.00 US$

Manuscript Style:
    See Manuscript Guidelines

CIRCULATION DATA:

Reader: Academics, Professors,
    Researchers
Frequency of Issue: Bi-Monthly
Copies per Issue: 2,001 - 3,000
Sponsor/Publisher:
Subscribe Price: 598.00 US$
    533.00 US$
    498.00 US$

REVIEW INFORMATION:

Type of Review: Editorial Review
No. of External Reviewers: 3+
No. of In House Reviewers: 0
Acceptance Rate: 0-5%
Time to Review: 1 - 2 Months
Reviewers Comments: Yes
Invited Articles: 50% +
Fees to Publish: 0.00 US$

MANUSCRIPT TOPICS:
Neuropsychology; Psychobiology; Sensation & Perception; Thinking & Cognition

MANUSCRIPT GUIDELINES/COMMENTS:

Behavioral and Brain Sciences (*BBS*) is a unique scientific communication medium, providing the service of Open Peer Commentary for reports of significant current work in psychology, neuroscience, behavioral biology or cognitive science. If a manuscript is judged by *BBS* referees and editors to be appropriate for Commentary (see Criteria below), it is circulated electronically to a large number of commentators selected (with the aid of systematic bibliographic searches and e-mail Calls for Commentators) from the *BBS* Associateship and the worldwide biobehavioral science community, including individuals recommended by the author. If you are not a *BBS* Associate and wish to enquire about joining, please see the instructions for associate membership at:
    http://www.*BBS*online.org/Instructions/associnst.html.

Once the Commentary stage of the process has begun, the author can no longer alter the article, but can respond formally to all commentaries accepted for publication. The target article, commentaries, and authors' responses then co-appear in *BBS*. (Note: Continuing Commentary submissions are no longer being accepted.)

Criteria for acceptance. To be eligible for publication, a paper should not only meet the standards of a journal such as *Psychological Review* or the *International Review of Neurobiology* in terms of conceptual rigor, empirical grounding, and clarity of style, but the author should also offer an explicit 500 word rationale for soliciting Commentary, and a list of suggested commentators (complete with e-mail addresses).

A *BBS* target article an be: (i) the report and discussion of empirical research that the author judges to have broader scope and implications than might be more appropriately reported in a specialty journal; (ii) an unusually significant theoretical article that formally models or systematizes a body of research; or (iii) a novel interpretation, synthesis, or critique of existing experimental or theoretical work. Occasionally, articles dealing with social or philosophical aspects of the behavioral and brain sciences will be considered.

The service of Open Peer Commentary will be primarily devoted to original unpublished manuscripts written specifically for *BBS* treatment. However, a recently published book whose contents meet the standards outlined above spontaneously and multiply nominated by the *BBS* Associateship may also be eligible for Commentary. In such a *BBS* Multiple Book Review, a comprehensive, article-length precis by the author is published together with the commentaries and the author's response. In special cases, Commentary will also be extended to a position paper or an already published article that deals with particularly influential or controversial research or that has itself proven to be especially important or controversial. In normal cases however, *BBS* submissions may not be already published (either in part or whole) or be under consideration for publication elsewhere and submission of an article is considered expressly to imply this. Multiple book reviews and previously published articles appear by invitation only. Self-nominations cannot be considered, neither can non-spontaneous (i.e. author elicited) nominations. However, the *BBS* Associateship and professional readership of *BBS* are encouraged to nominate current topics, books and authors for Commentary; e-mail **bbs@bbsonline.org**

In all the categories described, the decisive consideration for eligibility will be the desirability of Commentary for the submitted material. Controversiality simpliciter is not a sufficient criterion for soliciting Commentary: a paper may be controversial simply because it is wrong or weak. Nor is the mere presence of interdisciplinary aspects sufficient: general cybernetic and "organismic" disquisitions are not appropriate for *BBS*. Some appropriate rationales for seeking Open Peer Commentary would be that: (1) the material bears in a significant way on some current controversial issues in behavioral and brain sciences; (2) its findings substantively contradict some well-established aspects of current research and theory; (3) it criticizes the findings, practices, or principles of an accepted or influential line of work; (4) it unifies a substantial amount of disparate research; (5) it has important cross-disciplinary ramifications; (6) it introduces an innovative methodology or formalism for broader consideration; (7) it meaningfully integrates a body of brain and behavioral data; (8) it places a hitherto dissociated area of research into an evolutionary or ecological perspective; etc. In order to assure communication with potential commentators (and readers) from other *BBS* specialty areas, all technical terminology must be clearly defined or simplified, and specialized concepts must be fully described. In case of doubt of appropriateness for *BBS* commentary, authors should e-mail **bbs@bbsonline.org** detailing their proposal for the submission before submitting the entire electronic paper.

A note on commentaries. The purpose of the Open Peer Commentary service is to provide a concentrated constructive interaction between author and commentators on a topic judged to be of broad significance to the biobehavioral science community. Commentators should provide substantive criticism, interpretation, and elaboration as well as any pertinent complementary or supplementary material, such as illustrations; all original data will be refereed in order to assure the archival validity of *BBS* commentaries. Commentaries and articles should be free of hyperbole and remarks ad hominem. Please refer to and follow exactly the *BBS* Instructions for Commentators before submitting your invited commentary: **http://www.*BBS*online.org/Instructions/cominst.html**

Style and format for target articles. Target Articles must not exceed 14,000 words (and should ordinarily be considerably shorter); commentaries should not exceed 1,000 words, excluding references. Spelling, capitalization, and punctuation should be consistent within each article and commentary and should follow the style recommended in the latest edition of *A Manual of Style*, The University of Chicago Press. It is advisable to examine a recent issue of *BBS* as a model.

Target articles should be submitted in MSWord format as an email attachment to **bbs@bbsonline.org** (RTF, PDF or HTML formats are also acceptable). Figures should appear in the body of the text, not at the end of the paper, and must be supplied as separate TIFF, EPS, JPEG. or GIF files. However, if your article is accepted, TIFF or EPS format will be requested for publication since printing requires resolutions of at least 1100dpi. (Please note that costs for color figure reproduction will be passed along to the author. Color printing is expensive, and authors are encouraged to find alternative methods for presentation of their argument.) *BBS* temporarily archives the manuscript submitted for refereeing to a (nonpublic) Web Site accessible to the selected referees only. This is to accelerate and facilitate the refereeing process; after refereeing is completed, your manuscript will be removed, once accepted, the pre-copyedited final draft will then be archived publicly for potential commentators. The copyedited final draft will be posted for the invited commentators.

Please make sure your target article file has ALL of the following in this order: Four Separate Word Counts (for the abstract, main text, references, and entire text - total + addresses etc.), an Indexable Title, Full Name(s), Institutional Address(es), E-mail Address(es) and Homepage URL(s) for all authors (where available), Short Abstract (100 words), Long Abstract (250 words), 5-l0 Keywords (in alphabetical order), approx. 12,000 word Main Text (with paragraphs separated by full blank lines, not tab indents), and Alphabetical Reference List. Target article authors must also provide numbered headings and subheadings to facilitate cross-reference by commentators. Tables and figures (i.e., photographs, graphs, charts, or other artwork) should be numbered consecutively, and should appear in its appropriate location. Every table should have a title; every figure, a caption.

Endnotes and appendices should be grouped together at the end of the paper and should ideally be locally linked to in the text to facilitate the reader (and of course the referee's task). Acknowledgements should be placed at the end of the paper.

The short abstract will appear by way of an advertisement, one issue in advance of the publication issue. The long abstract will be circulated to referees and then potential commentators should the paper be accepted, and will appear with the printed article. *BBS*'s rigorous timetable constraints (requiring the coordination of target articles, commentaries and author's responses within the publishing queue) make it extremely difficult for us to process follow-up drafts of your submission. Please make sure that the paper you submit is the carefully checked final draft to which you wish the referees to address.

Please also ensure that your submission has been proof-read by a native English speaker before submission. This, of course, greatly improves its chances at the refereeing stage.

References. Bibliographic citations in the text must include the author's last name and the date of publication and may include page references. Complete bibliographic information for each citation should be included in the list of references. Please also include and link to the WWW URL for any paper for which it exists. Examples of correct styles are: Brown (1973); (Brown 1973); Brown 1973; 1978); (Brown 1973; Jones 1976); (Brown & Jones 1978); (Brown et al. 1978). References should be in alphabetical order in the style of the following examples. Do not abbreviate journal titles:

Freeman, W. J. (1958) Distribution in time and space of prepyriform electrical activity. *Journal of Neurophysiology* 2:644-66. http:l;/cogprints.soton.ac.uk/abs/neuro/199806009

Dennet, D. C. (1991) Two contrasts: Folk craft versus folk science and belief versus opinion. In. *The future of folk psychology, Intentionality and cognitive science*, ed. J D. Greenwood, pp. 26-7. Cambridge University Press, http://cogprints.soton.ac.uk/abs,phil/l99804005

Bateson, P.P.G. & Hinde, R.A., eds. (1978) *Growing points in ethology*. Cambridge University Press.

Editing. The publishers reserve the right to edit and proof all articles and commentaries accepted for publication. Authors of target articles will be given the opportunity to review the copy-edited manuscript and page proofs. Commentators will be asked to review copy-editing only when changes have been substantial; commentators will not see proofs. Both authors and commentators should notify the editorial office of all corrections within 48 hours or approval will be assumed.

Author response to commentaries. All invited commentaries received before the deadline are posted as they are received to a hidden URL only accessible to the Authors and Editors. Authors are notified of this hidden URL once the commentary invitations have been sent. Please note that no commentary is officially accepted until the Editor in charge has formally reviewed it and notified both the authors and the Editorial Coordinator. Please refer to and follow exactly the *BBS* Commentary Response Instructions at http://www.*BBS*onlilie.org/Instructions/conu-espinst.html before submitting your response. Authors of target articles receive 50 offprints of the entire treatment, and can purchase additional copies. Commentators will also be given an opportunity to purchase offprints of the entire treatment.

1. What is the rejection rate for *BBS*?

(Please note that these answers are rough estimates.)
The rejection rate of all articles submitted: 95%
The rejection rate of refereed articles: 85%

2. How long is the time period from submission of a manuscript to acceptance?

This all depends on how many rounds of refereeing are required before acceptance. One round will take approximately eight weeks from submission to the first disposition letter from the Editor. Depending then on how long the author takes to revise and resubmit, the next round will take approximately the same amount of time before a decision is rendered on the revision. I could give you an average based on those from the past: 8-14 months.

3. From acceptance to publication?

This is also dependent upon two things - one: the time it takes from acceptance to sending the article out for copyediting (could take up to three weeks), the weeks it takes to copyedit the final accepted draft, and the time it takes for the author to return the copyedited draft for commentary authors to use for their commentaries. The time it takes for the author to submit a response to the commentators, and the time it takes to have the response copyedited etc. I could give you an average based on those from the past: 6-8 months.

4. What is the approximate circulation of the journal?
2100

5. What is the current impact factor?
8.730 (ISI 2002)

6. Does *BBS* accept case studies?

I hope this answers your question. A *BBS* target article can be:
i. the report and discussion of empirical research that the author judges to have broader scope and implications than might be more appropriately reported in a specialty journal.

ii. an unusually significant theoretical article that formally models or systematizes a body of research.

iii. a novel interpretation, synthesis, or critique of existing experimental or theoretical work.

Occasionally, articles dealing with social or philosophical aspects of the behavioral and brain sciences will be considered.

The service of open Peer commentary will be primarily devoted to original unpublished manuscripts written specifically for *BBS* treatment. However, a recently published book whose contents meet the standards outlined above spontaneously and multiply nominated by the *BBS* Associateship may also be eligible for commentary. in such a *BBS* Multiple Book Review, a comprehensive, article length precis by the author is published together with the commentaries and the author's response. In special cases, Commentary will also be extended to a position paper or an already published article that deals with particularly influential or controversial research or that has itself proven to be especially important or controversial.

In normal cases however, *BBS* submissions may not be already published (either in part or whole) or be under consideration for publication elsewhere and submission of an article is considered expressly to imply this.

Multiple book reviews and previously published articles appear by invitation only. self nominations cannot be considered, neither can non-spontaneous (i.e. author-elicited) nominations. However, the *BBS* Associateship and professional readership of *BBS* are encouraged to nominate current topics, books and authors for Commentary.

In all the categories described, the decisive consideration for eligibility will be the desirability of commentary for the submitted material.

Controversiality simpliciter is not a sufficient criterion for soliciting Commentary: a paper may be controversial simply because it is wrong or weak. Nor is the mere presence of interdisciplinary aspects sufficient general cybernetic and "organismic" disquisitions are not appropriate for *BSS*.

Behavioral Ecology and Sociobiology

ADDRESS FOR SUBMISSION:

Tatiana Czeschlik, Chief Editor
Behavioral Ecology and Sociobiology
 ONLINE SUBMISSIONS
Editorial Office
Muehltalstrasse 9
D-69121 Heidelberg,
Germany
Phone: +49 6221 418314
Fax: +49 6221 418315
E-Mail: behav.ecol.sociobiol@t-online.de
Web: link.springer.de/journals/bes/
Address May Change:

PUBLICATION GUIDELINES:

Manuscript Length: 16-25
Copies Required: Five
Computer Submission: Yes via Website
Format:
Fees to Review: 0.00 US$

Manuscript Style:
 , Springer-Verlag Style

CIRCULATION DATA:

Reader: Academics
Frequency of Issue: Monthly
Copies per Issue: No Reply
Sponsor/Publisher: Springer-Verlag
Subscribe Price: 2252.00 US$

REVIEW INFORMATION:

Type of Review: Editorial Review
No. of External Reviewers: 2-3
No. of In House Reviewers: 1
Acceptance Rate: 21-30%
Time to Review: 2 - 3 Months
Reviewers Comments: Yes
Invited Articles: 0-5%
Fees to Publish: 0.00 US$

MANUSCRIPT TOPICS:
Evolutiionary Psychology; Experimental Psychology; Sociobiology

MANUSCRIPT GUIDELINES/COMMENTS:

Aims and Scope
The journal publishes reviews, original contributions and commentaries dealing with quantitative empirical and theoretical studies in the field of the analysis of animal behavior on the level of the individual, population and community. Special emphasis is placed on the proximate mechanisms, ultimate functions and evolution of ecological adaptations of behavior.

Aspects of particular interest:
• Intraspecific behavioral interactions, with special emphasis on social behavior Interspecific behavioral mechanisms, e.g., of competition and resource partitioning, mutualism, predator-prey interactions, parasitism
• Behavioral ecophysiology

- Orientation in space and time
- Relevant evolutionary and functional theory

Purely descriptive material is not acceptable for publication unless it is concerned with the analysis of behavioral mechanisms or with new theory.

Manuscript submission
Authors should submit their articles to *Behavioral Ecology and Sociobiology* online via the website **http://bes.manuscriptcentral.com/** to facilitate even quicker and more efficient processing. Electronic submission substantially reduces the editorial processing and reviewing time and shortens overall publication time.

Editorial Office
Behavioral Ecology and Sociobiology has one central editorial office which deals with all submissions. After submission, manuscripts are allocated to one of the Associate Editors. Contact details:

Tatiana Czeschlik, Editorial Office
Behavioral Ecology and Sociobiology
Muehltalstrasse 9
69121 Heidelberg, Germany
E-mail: **Behav.Ecol.Sociobiol@t-online.de**; Fax: +49-6221-418315

Legal requirements
Submission of a manuscript implies: that the work described has not been published before (except in the form of an abstract or as part of a published lecture, or thesis); that it is not under consideration for publication anywhere else; that its publication has been approved by all co-authors, if any, as well as by the responsible authorities - tacitly or explicitly - at the institute where the work has been carried out. The publisher will not be held legally responsible should there be any claims for compensation.

The "Copyright Transfer Statement" has to be signed and faxed to the publisher together with the corrected proofs (see below) with which it will be provided by the publisher shortly after the manuscript has been accepted for publication

Manuscript preparation
- All manuscripts are subject to peer review and copy editing.
- Behavioral Ecology and Sociobiology accepts Reviews, Original papers and Commentaries:
  - Reviews should cover a topic of current interest. There is no limit to the length of a review.
  - Original articles must present scientific results that are essentially new and should be structured according to the guidelines given below. The length of original articles should not exceed 11 printed pages (one printed page corresponds to approximately: 850 words text, or 3 illustrations with their legends, or 55 references). There will be a charge of 150 €, plus 16% VAT, for each page exceeding this limit.

- Commentaries are comments exclusively on papers previously published in this journal. They should not exceed 6 manuscript pages, including title page and references, and are published in the FORUM section.
- Manuscripts must be written in English and should be typed in double-line spacing throughout with at least 2.5 cm (1 inch) margins.
- Use a normal, plain font (e.g., Times New Roman) for text.
- Use the automatic page numbering function to number the pages.
- Lines in the text should be numbered.
- For indents use tab stops or other commands, not the space bar.
- Use the equation editor of your word processing program or MathType for equations.
- Abbreviations should be defined at first mention in the abstract and again in the main body of the text and used consistently thereafter.
- Essential footnotes to the text should be numbered consecutively and placed at the bottom of the page to which they refer.
- Genus and species names should be in italics. The common names of animals should not be capitalized.

Please arrange your manuscript as follows:
- Title page. Including name(s) of author(s), a concise and informative title, affiliation(s) of the author(s), e-mail address, telephone and fax numbers of the corresponding author. The title of a manuscript dealing with a particular species should include both the genus/species name and the common name.
- Abstract. Each manuscript must be preceded by an abstract presenting the most important results and conclusions in no more than 250 words.
- 3-5 key words indicating the scope of the manuscript should be supplied.
- Introduction
- Methods
- Results
- Discussion
- Acknowledgements. Please include, at the end of the acknowledgements, a declaration that the experiments comply with the current laws of the country in which they were performed. The Chief Editor reserves the right to reject manuscripts that do not comply with this. The author will be held responsible for false statements or for failure to fulfill the above-mentioned requirements.
- References. Literature citations in the text should indicate the author's surname with the year of publication in parentheses, e.g. Carlin (1992); Brooks and Carlin (1992). If there are more than two authors, only the first should be named, followed by "et al."

References at the end of the paper should be listed in alphabetical order by the first author's name. If there is more than one work by the same author or team of authors in the same year, a, b, etc. is added to the year both in the text and in the list of references.

Journal papers: name(s) and initial(s) of all authors; year; full title; journal title abbreviated in accordance with international practice; volume number; first and last page numbers

Example: Pirez N, Farina WM (2004) Nectar-receiver behavior in relation to the reward rate experienced by foraging honey bees. Behav Ecol Sociobiol 55:574-582

If available, the Digital Object Identifier (DOI) of the cited literature should be added at the end of the reference in question.

Example: Semmann D, Krambeck H-J, Milinski M (2004) Strategic investment in reputation. Behav Ecol Sociobiol DOI 10.1007/s00265-004-0782-9

Single contributions in a book: name(s) and initial(s) of all authors; year; title of article; editor(s); title of book; edition; volume number; publisher; place of publication; page numbers

Example: Noirot C (1992) Sexual castes and reproductive strategies in termites. In: Engels W (ed) Social insects. Springer, Berlin Heidelberg New York, pp 5-35

Book: name and initial(s) of all authors; year; title; publisher; place of publication

Example: Hölldobler B, Wilson EO (1990) The ants. Springer, Berlin Heidelberg New York

Tables and figures

Tables must be numbered consecutively with arabic numerals and should have a title explaining any abbreviation used in that table. Footnotes to tables should be indicated by superscript lower-case letters.

Illustrations must be restricted to the minimum needed to clarify the text. All figures (photographs, graphs or diagrams) should be cited in the text, and numbered consecutively throughout. Figure parts should be identified by lower-case roman letters (a, b, etc.). If illustrations are supplied with uppercase labeling, lower-case letters will still be used in the figure legends and citations.

Figure legends must be brief, self-sufficient explanations of the illustrations. The legends should be placed at the end of the text.

- Line drawings. Inscriptions should be legible, with initial capital letters and appropriately scaled to the size of the drawing. Scanned line drawings should be digitized with a resolution of 800 dpi relative to the final figure size.
- Halftone illustrations (black and white and color). Magnification should be indicated by scale bars. For scanned halftone illustrations, a resolution of 300 dpi is usually sufficient, TIFF is the preferred file format.
- Color illustrations. The authors will be expected to make a contribution (485 € per paper, plus 16% VAT) towards the extra costs of color reproduction and printing. Save color illustrations as RGB (8 bits per channel) in TIFF format.
- Plates. Several figures or figure parts should be grouped in a plate on one page.
- Vector graphics. Fonts used in the vector graphics must be included. Please do not draw with hairlines. The minimum line width is 0.2 mm (i.e., 0.567 pt) relative to the final size. EPS is the preferred file format. EPS files must always contain a preview in TIFF of the figure.

Electronic Supplementary Material

Electronic Supplementary Material (ESM) for a paper will be published in the electronic edition of this journal provided the material is:
- submitted in electronic form together with the manuscript
- accepted after peer review

ESM may consist of:
- information that cannot be printed: animations, video clips, sound recordings (use QuickTime, .avi, .mpeg, animated GIFs, or any other common file format)
- information that is more convenient in electronic form: sequences, spectral data, etc.
- large quantities of original data that relate to the paper, e.g. additional tables, large numbers of illustrations (color and black & white), etc.

Legends must be brief, self-sufficient explanations of the ESM. The file size should not exceed 2 MB. ESM is to be numbered and referred to as S1, S2, etc. After acceptance for publication, ESM will be published as received from the author in the online version only. Reference will be given in the printed version

Proofreading

Authors are informed by e-mail that a temporary URL has been created from which they can obtain their proofs. Proofreading is the responsibility of the author. Authors should make their proof corrections (formal corrections only) on a printout of the pdf file supplied, checking that the text is complete and that all figures and tables are included. Substantial changes in content, e.g. new results, corrected values, title and authorship are not allowed without the approval of the responsible editor. In such a case please contact the Editorial Office before returning the proofs to the publisher. After online publication, corrections can only be made in exceptional cases and in the form of an Erratum, which will be hyperlinked to the article.

Online First

Papers will be published online about one week after receipt of the corrected proofs. Papers published online can already be cited by their DOI. After release of the printed version, the paper can also be cited by issue and page numbers.

Offprints

Two complimentary copies of the issue in which a paper has appeared are sent to the corresponding author. If you wish to order offprints you must return the order form which is provided with the proofs and return it together with the corrected proofs. When ordering offprints, an author is entitled to receive, upon request, a pdf file of the article for own personal use.

Behavioral Medicine

ADDRESS FOR SUBMISSION:

Julia Kilmer, Editor
Behavioral Medicine
Heldref Publications
1319 Eighteenth Street, NW
Washington, DC 20036-1802
USA
Phone: 202-296-6267
Fax: 202-331-0358
E-Mail: bmed@heldref.org
Web: www.heldref.org
Address May Change:

PUBLICATION GUIDELINES:

Manuscript Length: 16-20
Copies Required: Four
Computer Submission: Yes
Format: MS Word
Fees to Review: 0.00 US$

Manuscript Style:
, JAMA Style Manual

CIRCULATION DATA:

Reader: Academics, Practitioners
Frequency of Issue: Quarterly
Copies per Issue: Less than 1,000
Sponsor/Publisher: Heldref Publications,
   Inc.
Subscribe Price: 73.00 US$ Individual
   144.00 US$ Institution

REVIEW INFORMATION:

Type of Review: Blind Review
No. of External Reviewers: 3
No. of In House Reviewers: 0
Acceptance Rate: 21-30%
Time to Review: 6-8 Months
Reviewers Comments: Yes
Invited Articles: 0-5%
Fees to Publish: 0.00 US$

MANUSCRIPT TOPICS:
Adulthood; Behavior Medicine; Behavior Modification; Family Counseling & Therapy;
Mind-Body Medicine (Psychosomatic Medicine); Research Methods & Statistics

MANUSCRIPT GUIDELINES/COMMENTS:

Scope
Behavioral Medicine is an interdisciplinary journal of research and practice that deals with
psychosocial influences on health and behavior and the implications and applications of
research findings in this field. It publishes original controlled research studies, both
experimental and clinical; evaluation studies; occasional review articles; case reports; and
book reviews.

In addition to the studies described above, the journal seeks three-part, coordinated
submissions on a theme topic that deal in depth with (a) a review of the literature on a health
problem that can be treated through the use of sound psychological or behavioral
interventions; (b) the evidence from clinical field trials and applied research for the usefulness
of the behavioral intervention; (c) an analysis of the policy implications of the therapy and

means of introducing it into mainstream health practice. Wherever possible, the economic impact of new or evolving therapies should be included in the discussion.

Those who are interested in submitting such a three-article series should work directly with the executive editors of *Behavioral Medicine*, providing a detailed outline of their proposal; the names and qualifications of participating authors; and an estimate of the time frame for completion. Proposals should be submitted to the managing editor, Behavioral Medicine, Heldref Publications, 1319 Eighteenth Street, NW, Washington, DC 20036-1802 (202-296-6267, X-214; fax: 202-296-5149).

Submission Requirements

1. Send four copies of the manuscript to Managing Editor, Behavioral Medicine, Heldref Publications, 1319 18th St NW, Washington, DC 20036-1802.

2. Include an abstract of no more than 150 words and 3 to 5 index terms. The article title should be short, specific, and clear; text in research submissions should be divided into sections headed Method, Results, and Comment.

3. List authors' names, academic degrees, affiliations, current positions, telephone, fax, electronic mail numbers, and addresses on a separate page; indicate who is to serve as corresponding author.

4. Include a separate letter stating that the manuscript has not been submitted simultaneously to any other publication.

5. Double space manuscripts in all parts, including references, tables, figures, and notes. Use 1-inch margins, leave right margin unjustified, and number the pages. Please do not use elaborate typographic effects.

6. Type tables on a separate sheet of paper; use them sparingly as a non-redundant enhancement of the text. Send figures in camera-ready form.

7. Follow the *American Medical Association Manual of Style*, 9th edition, Baltimore: Williams & Wilkins; 1998, in matters of medical and scientific usage and reference format.

8. Include written permission from publishers and authors to reproduce or adapt previously published tables or figures.

9. Await acceptance before sending disks; details about appropriate word-processing programs for Heldref Publications will be sent at that time.

10. Indicate approval by the institutional review board for all studies involving human subjects; describe how subjects gave informed consent.

Editorial Process

Authors are responsible for the accuracy of all material submitted. Before submitting a manuscript, authors should proofread carefully, double-checking all statistics, numbers and symbols, references, and tables.

Manuscripts are blind reviewed, usually by at least two consulting editors and an executive editor. When reviews have been completed (after about 4 months), the managing editor will notify the corresponding author of the editors' decision to accept, reject, or ask for revisions and resubmission of the manuscript. Review comments will be forwarded to the author; rejected manuscripts will not normally be reconsidered.

Accepted manuscripts are generally published within 1 year of acceptance. Each author receives two complimentary copies of the journal issue in which the article appears. Additional copies or reprints (minimum order 50) are available to authors at a reduced price.

References

Limit references to those cited in the text. They should be numbered with superscripts in order of appearance. *Behavioral Medicine* does not use the author-date system of references. Abbreviations of journal names should conform to those used in *Index Medicus*. Common forms are as follows:

Journal Article

1. Beecher HK. Ethics and clinical research. *N Engl J Med.* 1966;274:1354--1360.

Book

2. Pearson K. *The Grammar of Science.* 2nd ed. London,: Adam and Charles Black; 1900.

Article in Book

3. Lambrinos J, Papadakos PJ. The analysis of risks, costs, and benefits in critical care. In: Fein LA, Strosberg MD, eds. *Managing the Critical Care Unit.* Rockville, MD: Aspen Systems; 1987: 358-370.

Other

4. References to material submitted for publication but not yet accepted should be noted parenthetically in the text as unpublished data; personal communications cited should include full name and date of communication. Quoted material must include a notation of the pages on which it appeared in the referenced source [eg.,..."[7(pp43-45)]].

Behavioural and Cognitive Psychotherapy

ADDRESS FOR SUBMISSION:

Paul Salkovskis, Editor
Behavioural and Cognitive Psychotherapy
University of Oxford
Department of Psychiatry
Institute of Psychiatry
De Crepigny Park
Denmark Hill, London, SE5 8AF
UK
Phone: 020 7848 5039
Fax: 020 7848 5037
E-Mail: journal.editor@babcp.com
Web: www.babcp.org
Address May Change:

PUBLICATION GUIDELINES:

Manuscript Length: 1-25
Copies Required: Four
Computer Submission: Yes
Format: MS Word
Fees to Review: 0.00 US$

Manuscript Style:
     American Psychological Association,
     BPS

CIRCULATION DATA:

Reader: Academics, Practitioners
Frequency of Issue: Quarterly
Copies per Issue: 4,001 - 5,000
Sponsor/Publisher: British ASSN for
     Behavioural & Cognitive Psychotherapy
Subscribe Price:

REVIEW INFORMATION:

Type of Review: Editorial Review
No. of External Reviewers: 3
No. of In House Reviewers: 1
Acceptance Rate: 21-30%
Time to Review: 1 - 2 Months
Reviewers Comments: Yes
Invited Articles: 0-5%
Fees to Publish: 0.00 US$

MANUSCRIPT TOPICS:
Abnormal Psychology; Adolescent Psychology; Behavior Modification; Child Psychology;
Learning & Conditioning; Psychopathology; Thinking & Cognition

MANUSCRIPT GUIDELINES/COMMENTS:

Aims and Scope
Behavioural and Cognitive Psychotherapy is an international multidisciplinary journal aimed
primarily at members of the helping and teaching professions. Published quarterly, the journal
features original research papers, covering both experimental and clinical work, that
contribute to the theory, practice and evolution of behaviour therapy. Under the guidance of
an international Editorial team, *Behavioural and Cognitive Psychotherapy* aims to reflect and
influence the continuing changes in the concepts, methodology and techniques of behavioural
and cognitive psychotherapy. A particular feature of the journal is its broad ranging scope -
both in terms of topics and types of study covered. *Behavioural and Cognitive Psychotherapy*
encompasses most areas of human behaviour and experience, and represents many different

research methods, from randomized controlled trials to detailed case studies. It also includes reviews of recently published literature in this field.

INSTRUCTIONS TO AUTHORS
Submission
Articles written in English and not submitted for publications elsewhere should be sent to:

Paul M. Salkovskis, Editor
Behavioural and Cognitive Psychotherapy
Department of Psychiatry, Institute of Psychiatry
De Crespigny Park, Denmark Hill, London SE5 8AF, UK
Tel 020 7848 5039; Email: **journal.editor@babcp.com**

Manuscript Preparation
Four copies of the manuscript must be submitted. Original figures should be supplied at the time of submission. Articles must be typed double-spaced throughout on standard sized paper (preferably A4) allowing wide margins all round. Where unpublished material e.g. behaviour rating scales, therapy manuals etc., is referred to in an article, copies should be submitted to facilitate review.

Manuscripts will be sent out for review exactly as submitted. Authors who want a blind review should mark three copies of their article 'review copy', omitting from these copies details of authorship and other identifying information. Submission for blind review is encouraged.

Abbreviations where used must be standard. The Systeme International (SI) should be used for all units: where metric units are used the SI equivalent must also be given. Probability values and power statistics should be given with statistical values and degrees of freedom (e.g. $F(1,34)$ - 123.07. $p<.001$), but such information may be included in tables rather than in the main text.

Spelling must be consistent within an article, either using British usage (*The Shorter Oxford English Dictionary*), or American usage (*Webster's new collegiate dictionary*). However, spelling the list of references must be literal to each publication.

Details of style not specified here may be determined by reference to the *Publication Manual of the American Psychological Association* or the style manual of the British Psychological Society.

Articles should conform to the following scheme:
a. *Title page.* The title should phrase concisely the major issues. Author(s) to be given with departmental affiliations and addresses, grouped appropriately. A running head of no more than 40 characters should be indicated.
b. *Abstract.* The abstract should include up to six keywords which could be used to describe the article. This should summarize the article in no more than 200 words.
c. *Text.* This should begin with an introduction, succinctly introducing the point of the paper to those interested in the general area of the journal. *Attention should be paid to the*

Editorial Statement which appears in the January and July issues at the back of the Journal. References within the text should be given in the form Jones and Smith (1973) or (Jones & Smith, 1973). When there are three or up to and including five authors the first citation should include all authors; subsequent citations should be given as Williams *et al.* (1973). Authors with the same surname should be distinguished by their initials. The approximate positions of table and figures should be indicated in the text. Footnotes should be avoided where possible.

d. *Reference notes(s).* A list of all cited unpublished or limited circulation material, numbered in order of appearance in the text, giving as much information as possible about extant manuscripts.

e. *References.* All citations in the text should be listed in strict alphabetical order according to surnames. Multiple references to the same author (s) should be listed chronologically, using a, b, etc., for entries within the same year. Formats for journal articles, books and chapters should follow these examples:

BECKER. M. R., & GREEN, L. W. (1975). A family approach to compliance with medical treatment: A selective review of the literature. *International Journal of Health Education, 18,* 173-182.

THARP, R. G., & WETZEL, R. J. (1969). *Behaviour modification in the natural environment.* New York: Academic Press.

ROSKIES, E., & LAZARUS, R. S. (1980). Coping theory and the teaching of coping skills. In P.O. Davidson & S. M. Davidson (Eds), *Behavioural medicine: Changing health lifestyles.* New York: Brunner/Mazel.

f. *Footnotes.* The first, and preferably only, footnote will appear at the foot of the first page of each article, and subsequently may acknowledge previous unpublished presentation (e.g. dissertation, meeting paper) financial support, scholarly or technical assistance, or a change in affiliation. A concluding (or only) paragraph must be the name and full mailing address of the author to whom reprint requests or other inquiries should be sent.

g. *Tables.* Tables should be numbered and given explanatory titles.

h. *Figure captions.* Numbered captions should be typed on a separate page.

i. *Figures* Original drawings or prints must be submitted for each line or half-tone illustration. Figures should be clearly labeled and be camera -ready wherever possible.

Proofs, Reprints and Copyright
On acceptance a 3.5 soft copy will be requested. Proofs of accepted articles will be sent to authors for the correction of printers' errors; authors' alterations may be charged. Authors submitting a manuscript do so on the understanding that if it is accepted for publication exclusive copyright of the paper shall be assigned to the Association. In consideration of the assignment of copyright, 25 copies of each paper will be supplied. Further reprints may be ordered at extra cost; the reprint order form will be sent with the proofs. The publishers will not put any limitation on the personal freedom of the author to use material contained in the paper in other works.

Brain and Cognition

ADDRESS FOR SUBMISSION:

Sidney J. Segalowitz, Editor
Brain and Cognition
Phone: 905-688-5550 ext. 3465
Fax: 905-688-6922
E-Mail: b-c@elsevier.com
Web: www.ees.elsevier.com/brcg/
Address May Change:

CIRCULATION DATA:

Reader: Academics
Frequency of Issue: 9 Times/Year
Copies per Issue: Mostly Online
Sponsor/Publisher: Elsevier-Academic
 Press
Subscribe Price: 443.00 US$ Personal
 364.00 US$ SFN
 265.00 US$ INS, APS, APA

PUBLICATION GUIDELINES:

Manuscript Length: 11-25
Copies Required: Four
Computer Submission: Yes Email or Web
Format: MS Word, WordPerfect, PDF
Fees to Review: 0.00 US$

Manuscript Style:
 American Psychological Association

REVIEW INFORMATION:

Type of Review: Editorial Review
No. of External Reviewers: 2-3
No. of In House Reviewers: 1
Acceptance Rate: 11-20%
Time to Review: 1-3 Months
Reviewers Comments: Yes
Invited Articles: No Reply
Fees to Publish: 0.00 US$

MANUSCRIPT TOPICS:
Neuropsychology; Physiological Psychology; Thinking & Cognition

MANUSCRIPT GUIDELINES/COMMENTS:

Brain and Cognition publishes original research articles, case histories, theoretical articles, critical reviews, historical articles, and scholarly notes; each contribution will be relevant to any aspect of human neuropsychology or cognitive neuroscience other than those specific to purely linguistic issues. Appropriate topics include but are not limited to memory, cognition, emotion, perception, movement, or praxis in relationship to brain structure or function. Each will have theoretical import, either formulating new hypotheses or supporting or refuting new or previously established hypotheses. The interdisciplinary focus of *Brain and Cognition* includes but is not limited to the fields of psychology, neurology, psychiatry, speech pathology, neuroanatomy, neurophysiology, philosophy, and computer science. Manuscripts of several different types are solicited: research articles, theoretical integrations, single or multiple case history studies, critical reviews of books of interest to the journal's readership, and short (limited to 10 typed manuscript pages, maximum 3000 words) scholarly notes and discussion. Short research reports that are especially timely and groundbreaking are eligible for rapid review and publication (and should indicated as such).

Submission of Manuscripts

Manuscripts must be written in English and should be in APA format. All manuscripts should be submitted to **http://ees.elsevier.com/brcg**. Authors are requested to submit the text, tables, and artwork in electronic form to this address. Each manuscript should be accompanied by a letter outlining the basic findings of the paper and their significance. Authors should also state that the manuscript, or parts of it, have not been and will not be submitted elsewhere for publication.

Please note that an editable file is needed for production purposes after acceptance. We ask that you submit source files in the case that your manuscript is accepted. Authors are requested to include a cover letter, manuscript, tables, and figures as well as any ancillary materials. If you are not able to submit an electronic version, please contact the *BRCG* Editorial Office at:

Brain and Cognition, Editorial Office, 525 B Street, Suite 1900, San Diego, CA 92101-4495, USA, Telephone: (619) 699-6316; Fax: (619) 699-6700; E-mail: **b-c@elsevier.com**

There are no submission fees or pages charges.

Language data may be given in English when clearly identifiable; otherwise, they should be transcribed into the phonetic alphabet of the International Phonetic Association (IPA).

The preferred format for papers submitted electronically is MS Word or WordPerfect, but .pdf or .dvi files are acceptable. Submission of the final version, once accepted for publication, must be in an editable format, such as a recent version of MS Word or WordPerfect, and the figures should be in some common graphics format such as .jpg, .tif, or equivalent. The manuscript will be edited according to the style of the journal, and authors must read the proofs carefully.

Only original papers will be considered. Manuscripts are accepted for review with the understanding that the same work has not been published, that it is not under consideration for publication elsewhere, and that its submission for publication has been approved by all of the listed authors and by the institutions where the work was carried out. If human or animal subjects were involved in the research, authors must note in their letter of submittal that the research was conducted using appropriate ethical guidelines. Any person cited as a source of personal communication must have given her or his approval of such citation. Written authorization may be required at the Editor's discretion.

Articles and any other material published in *Brain and Cognition* represent the opinions of the author(s) and should not be construed to reflect opinions of the Editor(s) and the Publisher. Manuscripts that do not meet the general criteria or standards for publication in *Brain and Cognition* will be immediately returned to the authors, without detailed review.

Upon acceptance of an article, authors will be asked to transfer copyright (for more information on copyright, see http://authors.elsevier.com). This transfer will ensure the widest possible dissemination of information. A letter will be sent to the corresponding author confirming receipt of the manuscript. A form facilitating transfer of copyright will be provided after acceptance.

If material from other copyrighted works is included, the author(s) must obtain written permission from the copyright owners and credit the source(s) in the article. Elsevier has preprinted forms for use by authors in these cases: contact Elsevier's Rights Department, Oxford, UK: phone (+44) 1865 843830, fax (+44) 1865 853333, e-mail **permissions@elsevier.com**. Requests may also be completed on-line via the Elsevier home page (http://www.elsevier.com/locate/permissions).

Preparation of Manuscripts
Manuscripts should be double-spaced throughout. Pages should be numbered consecutively even if transmitted electronically and organized as follows:

The *title page* (p.1) should contain the article title, author(s) name(s) and affiliation(s), and the complete mailing address of the author to whom all correspondence should be sent (including e-mail address and telephone and fax numbers).

The *abstract* (p.2) must be a single paragraph that summarizes the main findings of the paper in approximately 100 words. After the abstract a list of up to 10 keywords that will be useful for indexing or searching should be included.

The *Introduction* should be as concise as possible.

Materials and methods should be sufficiently detailed to enable the experiments to be reproduced.

Results and *Discussion* may be combined and may be organized into subheadings.

References should be cited in the text by surname of the author and the publication date in parentheses, e.g., Gall (1825) or (Gall & Spurzheim, 1810). If more than one article was published by the same author in a given year, the correct style is Bouillaud (1825a) or (Bouillaud, 1852a, 1825b). All references must be listed alphabetically at the end of the article, beginning on a separate sheet, and typed double-spaced. Journal titles should be written out in full, not abbreviated. Only articles that have been published or are in press should be included in the references. Unpublished results or personal communications should be cited as such in text. The following examples show style of capitalization and punctuation for journal articles, books, and chapters in edited books. Please use the following style:

Bryden, M. P. (1982). *Laterality: Functional asymmetry in the intact brain*. New York: Academic Press.

Sergent, J. (1986). Prolegomena to the use of the tachistoscope in neuropsychological research. *Brain and Cognition*, 5, 127-130.

168

Whitaker, H. A. (1998). Neurolinguistics from the Middle Ages to the Pre-modern Era: Historical vignettes. In B. Stemmer & H. A. Whitaker(Eds.), *Handbook of neurolinguistics* (pp. 27-54). San Diego: Academic Press.

Tables. Tables should be numbered in order of appearance with Arabic numerals. Type each table double-spaced on a separate page with a short descriptive title typed above and with essential footnotes below. Keep in mind the dimensions of the journal when planning the number of columns in a table.

Figures. Number figures consecutively with Arabic numerals. Please visit our Web site at http://authors.elsevier.com/artwork for detailed instructions on preparing electronic artwork.

Color Figures. One free page of color is available to authors if the editors deem the color to be scientifically significant. However, if together with the accepted article, authors submit usable color figures, then Elsevier will ensure, at *no additional charge*, that these figures will appear in color on the Web (e.g., ScienceDirect and other sites) regardless of whether these illustrations are reproduced in color in the printed version. For color reproduction in print, authors will receive information regarding the costs from Elsevier after receipt of your accepted article. [Please note: Because of technical complications that can arise in converting color figures to "gray scale" (for the printed version should you not opt for color in print), please submit in addition usable black-and-white files corresponding to all the color illustrations.]

Preparation of Supplementary Material

Elsevier now accepts electronic supplementary material to support and enhance your scientific research. Supplementary files offer additional possibilities for publishing supporting applications, movies, animation sequences, high-resolution images, background datasets, sound clips, and more. Supplementary files supplied will be published online alongside the electronic version of your article in Elsevier Web products, including ScienceDirect (http://www.sciencedirect.com). To ensure that your submitted material is directly usable, please provide the data in one of our recommended file formats. Authors should submit the material in electronic format together with the article and supply a concise and descriptive caption for each file. Please note, however, that supplementary material will not appear in the printed journal. Files can be stored on 3.5-inch diskette, ZIP disk, or CD (either MS-DOS or Macintosh). For more detailed instructions, please visit our Author Gateway at http://authors.elsevier.com, click on "Artwork instructions," and then click on "Multimedia files."

Proofs. PDF proofs will be sent by e-mail to the corresponding author. To avoid delay in publication, only necessary changes should be made, and corrections should be returned promptly. Authors will be charged for alterations in excess of 10% of the cost of composition.

Reprints. Twenty-five (25) reprints will be provided free of charge. Additional reprints may be ordered.

British Journal of Clinical Psychology

ADDRESS FOR SUBMISSION:

Gillian Hardy & Michael Barkham, Editors
British Journal of Clinical Psychology
ONLINE SUBMISSIONS ONLY
Phone: +44 116 254 9568
Fax: +44 116 247 0787
E-Mail: bjcp@bpsjournals.co.uk
Web: http://bjcp.edmgr.com
Address May Change: 1/1/2010

PUBLICATION GUIDELINES:

Manuscript Length: 16-20
Copies Required: Electronic
Computer Submission: Yes Required
Format:
Fees to Review: 0.00 US$

Manuscript Style:
American Psychological Association

CIRCULATION DATA:

Reader: Academics, Professors,
Researchers
Frequency of Issue: Quarterly
Copies per Issue: 3,001 - 4,000
Sponsor/Publisher: The British
Psychological Society
Subscribe Price: 85.00 US$ Individual
322.00 US$ Institution

REVIEW INFORMATION:

Type of Review: Blind Review
No. of External Reviewers: 3
No. of In House Reviewers: 0
Acceptance Rate: 21-30%
Time to Review: 2 - 3 Months
Reviewers Comments: Yes
Invited Articles: 0-5%
Fees to Publish: 0.00 US$

MANUSCRIPT TOPICS:
Abnormal Psychology; Behavior Modification

MANUSCRIPT GUIDELINES/COMMENTS:

The *British Journal of Clinical Psychology* publishes original contributions to scientific knowledge in clinical psychology. This includes descriptive comparisons, as well as studies of the assessment, aetiology and treatment of people with a wide range of psychological problems in all age groups and settings. The level of analysis of studies ranges from biological influences on individual behaviour through to studies of psychological interventions and treatments on individuals, dyads, families and groups, to investigations of the relationships between explicitly social and psychological levels of analysis.

The following types of paper are invited:
- Papers reporting original empirical investigations;
- Theoretical papers, provided that these are sufficiently related to the empirical data;
- Review articles which need not be exhaustive but which should give an interpretation of the state of the research in a given field and, where appropriate, identify its clinical implications;
- Brief reports and comments.

1. Circulation
The circulation of the *Journal* is worldwide. Papers are invited and encouraged from authors throughout the world.

2. Length
Papers should normally be no more than 5,000 words, although the Editor retains discretion to publish papers beyond this length in cases where the clear and concise expression of the scientific content requires greater length.

3. Reviewing
The journal operates a policy of anonymous peer review. Papers will normally be scrutinised and commented on by at least two independent expert referees (in addition to the Editor) although the Editor may process a paper at his or her discretion. The referees will not be aware of the identity of the author. All information about authorship including personal acknowledgements and institutional affiliations should be confined to the title page (and the text should be free of such clues as identifiable self-citations e.g. 'In our earlier work...').

4. Online submission process
1) All manuscripts must be submitted online at **http://bjcp.edmgr.com**.

First-time users: click the REGISTER button from the menu and enter in your details as instructed. On successful registration, an email will be sent informing you of your user name and password. Please keep this email for future reference and proceed to LOGIN. (You do not need to re-register if your status changes e.g. author, reviewer or editor).
Registered users: click the LOGIN button from the menu and enter your user name and password for immediate access. Click 'Author Login'.

2) Follow the step-by-step instructions to submit your manuscript.

3) The submission must include the following as separate files:
- Title page consisting of manuscript title, authors' full names and affiliations, name and address for corresponding author.
- Abstract
- Full manuscript omitting authors' names and affiliations. Figures and tables can be attached separately if necessary.

4) If you require further help in submitting your manuscript, please consult 'Tutorial for Authors' (PDF, 130Kb).

Authors can log on at any time to check the status of the manuscript.

5. Manuscript requirements
Contributions must be typed in double spacing with wide margins. All sheets must be numbered.
- Tables should be typed in double spacing, each on a separate page with a self-explanatory title. Tables should be comprehensible without reference to the text. They

should be placed at the end of the manuscript with their approximate locations indicated in the text.

- Figures can be included at the end of the document or attached as separate files, carefully labelled in initial capital/lower case lettering with symbols in a form consistent with text use. Unnecessary background patterns, lines and shading should be avoided. Captions should be listed on a separate page. The resolution of digital images must be at least 300 dpi.
- For articles containing original scientific research, a structured abstract of up to 250 words should be included with the headings: Objectives, Design, Methods, results, Conclusions. Review articles should use these headings: Purpose, Methods, Results, Conclusions.
- For reference citations, please use APA style. Particular care should be taken to ensure that references are accurate and complete. Give all journal titles in full.
- SI units must be used for all measurements, rounded off to practical values if appropriate, with the Imperial equivalent in parentheses.
- In normal circumstances, effect size should be incorporated.
- Authors are requested to avoid the use of sexist language.
- Authors are responsible for acquiring written permission to publish lengthy quotations, illustrations etc for which they do not own copyright.

For Guidelines on editorial style, please consult the *APA Publication Manual* published by the American Psychological Association, Washington DC, USA (http://www.apastyle.org).

6. Brief reports and comments

These allow publication of research studies and theoretical, critical or review comments with an essential contribution to make. They should be limited to 2000 words, including references. The abstract should not exceed 120 words and should be structured under these headings: Objective, Method, Results, Conclusions. There should be no more than one table or figure, which should only be included if it conveys information more efficiently than the text. Title, author and name and address are not included in the word limit.

7. Supplementary data

Supplementary data too extensive for publication may be deposited with the British Library Document Supply Centre. Such material includes numerical data, computer programs, fuller details of case studies and experimental techniques. The material should be submitted to the Editor together with the article, for simultaneous refereeing.

8. Post acceptance

PDF page proofs are sent to authors via email for correction of print but not for rewriting or the introduction of new material. Authors will be provided with a PDF file of their article prior to publication for easy and cost-effective dissemination to colleagues.

9. Copyright

To protect authors and journals against unauthorised reproduction of articles, The British Psychological Society requires copyright to be assigned to itself as publisher, on the express condition that authors may use their own material at any time without permission. On acceptance of a paper submitted to a journal, authors will be requested to sign an appropriate assignment of copyright form.

10. Checklist of requirements

- Abstract (100-200 words)
- Title page (include title, authors' names, affiliations, full contact details)
- Full article text (double-spaced with numbered pages and anonymised)
- References (APA style). Authors are responsible for bibliographic accuracy and must check every reference in the manuscript and proofread again in the page proofs.
- Tables, figures, captions placed at the end of the article or attached as separate files.

British Journal of Educational Psychology

ADDRESS FOR SUBMISSION:

Julie Dockrell, Editor
British Journal of Educational Psychology
ONLINE SUBMISSIONS ONLY AT
http://bjep.edmgr.com
Phone: +44 116 254 9568
Fax: +44 116 247 0787
E-Mail: bjep@bpsjournals.co.uk
Web: http://www.bpsjournals.co.uk
Address May Change: 1/1/2007

PUBLICATION GUIDELINES:

Manuscript Length: 26-30
Copies Required: Electronic
Computer Submission: Yes Required
Format:
Fees to Review: 0.00 US$

Manuscript Style:
    American Psychological Association

CIRCULATION DATA:

Reader: Academics
Frequency of Issue: Quarterly
Copies per Issue: 2,001 - 3,000
Sponsor/Publisher: The British
    Psychological Society
Subscribe Price: 74.00 US$ Individual
    215.00 US$ Institution

REVIEW INFORMATION:

Type of Review: Blind Review
No. of External Reviewers: 2
No. of In House Reviewers: 0
Acceptance Rate: 21-30%
Time to Review: 2 - 3 Months
Reviewers Comments: Yes
Invited Articles: 0-5%
Fees to Publish: 0.00 US$

MANUSCRIPT TOPICS:
Educational Psychology

MANUSCRIPT GUIDELINES/COMMENTS:

The *British Journal of Educational Psychology* seeks to publish psychological research that makes a significant contribution to the understanding and practice of education. The aims are to give access to research to a broad, international readership including researchers, practitioners and students in education. Empirical, theoretical and methodological papers are welcomed, including action research, case studies, critical reviews of the literature, experimental studies and surveys. Important criteria in the selection process are quality of argument and execution, clarity in presentation and educational significance.

1. Circulation
The circulation of the *Journal* is worldwide. Papers are invited and encouraged from authors throughout the world.

2. Length
Papers should normally be no more than 5,000 words, although the Editor retains discretion to publish papers beyond this length in cases where the clear and concise expression of the scientific content requires greater length.

3. Reviewing

The journal operates a policy of anonymous peer review. Papers will normally be scrutinised and commented on by at least two independent expert referees (in addition to the Editor) although the Editor may process a paper at his or her discretion. The referees will not be aware of the identity of the author. All information about authorship including personal acknowledgements and institutional affiliations should be confined to the title page (and the text should be free of such clues as identifiable self-citations e.g. 'In our earlier work...').

4. Online submission process

1) All manuscripts must be submitted online at **http://bjep.edmgr.com**.

First-time users: click the REGISTER button from the menu and enter in your details as instructed. On successful registration, an email will be sent informing you of your user name and password. Please keep this email for future reference and proceed to LOGIN. (You do not need to re-register if your status changes e.g. author, reviewer or editor).

Registered users: click the LOGIN button from the menu and enter your user name and password for immediate access. Click 'Author Login'.

2) Follow the step-by-step instructions to submit your manuscript.

3) The submission must include the following as separate files:
- Title page consisting of manuscript title, authors' full names and affiliations, name and address for corresponding author.
- Abstract
- Full manuscript omitting authors' names and affiliations. Figures and tables can be attached separately if necessary.

4) If you require further help in submitting your manuscript, please consult 'Tutorial for Authors' (PDF, 130Kb).

Authors can log on at any time to check the status of the manuscript.

5. Manuscript requirements
- Contributions must be typed in double spacing with wide margins. All sheets must be numbered.
- Tables should be typed in double spacing, each on a separate page with a self-explanatory title. Tables should be comprehensible without reference to the text. They should be placed at the end of the manuscript with their approximate locations indicated in the text.
- Figures can be included at the end of the document or attached as separate files, carefully labelled in initial capital/lower case lettering with symbols in a form consistent with text use. Unnecessary background patterns, lines and shading should be avoided. Captions should be listed on a separate page. The resolution of digital images must be at least 300 dpi.

- All articles should be preceded by a Structured Abstract of not more than 250 words using six required headings: Background, Aims, Sample(s), Methods, Results and Conclusions, with Comment as optional. These headings may need some adaptation in the case of theoretical papers and reviews.
- For reference citations, please use APA style. Particular care should be taken to ensure that references are accurate and complete. Give all journal titles in full.
- SI units must be used for all measurements, rounded off to practical values if appropriate, with the Imperial equivalent in parentheses.
- In normal circumstances, effect size should be incorporated.
- Authors are requested to avoid the use of sexist language.
- Authors are responsible for acquiring written permission to publish lengthy quotations, illustrations etc for which they do not own copyright.

For Guidelines on editorial style, please consult the *APA Publication Manual* published by the American Psychological Association, Washington DC, USA (http://www.apastyle.org).

6. Supplementary data
Supplementary data too extensive for publication may be deposited with the British Library Document Supply Centre. Such material includes numerical data, computer programs, fuller details of case studies and experimental techniques. The material should be submitted to the Editor together with the article, for simultaneous refereeing.

7. Post acceptance
PDF page proofs are sent to authors via email for correction of print but not for rewriting or the introduction of new material. Authors will be provided with a PDF file of their article prior to publication for easy and cost-effective dissemination to colleagues.

8. Copyright
To protect authors and journals against unauthorised reproduction of articles, The British Psychological Society requires copyright to be assigned to itself as publisher, on the express condition that authors may use their own material at any time without permission. On acceptance of a paper submitted to a journal, authors will be requested to sign an appropriate assignment of copyright form.

9. Checklist of requirements
- Abstract (100-200 words)
- Title page (include title, authors' names, affiliations, full contact details)
- Full article text (double-spaced with numbered pages and anonymised)
- References (APA style). Authors are responsible for bibliographic accuracy and must check every reference in the manuscript and proofread again in the page proofs.
- Tables, figures, captions placed at the end of the article or attached as separate files.

British Journal of Guidance and Counselling

ADDRESS FOR SUBMISSION:

Jennifer M. Kidd & Paul Wilkins, Co-Eds
British Journal of Guidance and Counselling
University of London
Birkbeck College
Department of Organizational Psychology
Malet Street
London, WCIE 7HX
UK
Phone: +44 (0) 2076 316759
Fax: +44 (0) 2076 316750
E-Mail: j.kidd@bbk.ac.uk
Web: http://www.tandf.co.uk/journals
Address May Change:

PUBLICATION GUIDELINES:

Manuscript Length: 26-30
Copies Required: Four
Computer Submission: No
Format: N/A
Fees to Review: 0.00 US$

Manuscript Style:
     American Psychological Association

CIRCULATION DATA:

Reader: Academics, Practitioners, Trainers,
     Counsellors
Frequency of Issue: Quarterly
Copies per Issue:
Sponsor/Publisher: Careers Research and
     Advisory Center (CRAC)/ Routledge
     Journals (Taylor & Francis)
Subscribe Price: 120.00 Pounds $216 US
     Ind
       288.00 Pounds $514 US Institution

REVIEW INFORMATION:

Type of Review: Blind Review
No. of External Reviewers: 3
No. of In House Reviewers: No Reply
Acceptance Rate: 40%
Time to Review: 2 - 3 Months
Reviewers Comments: Yes
Invited Articles: 6-10%
Fees to Publish: 0.00 US$

MANUSCRIPT TOPICS:
Career Counselling & Guidance; Counseling Process; Family Counseling & Therapy

MANUSCRIPT GUIDELINES/COMMENTS:

Aims and Scope
British Journal of Guidance & Counselling is the leading forum for debate between academics, trainers and practitioners in the field, publishing high-quality, international contributions in the following areas:
* the theory and practice of guidance and counseling
* the provision of guidance and counseling services
* training and professional issues

Theoretical and empirical studies relating to the practice of guidance and counseling are reported, drawing on a variety of disciplines, encompassing both quantitative and qualitative methodologies, and ranging in scope from large-scale surveys to individual case-studies. The journal also explores the links between various areas of guidance and counseling and their relationship to such cognate fields as education, psychotherapy and social work.

In addition to regular papers, the journal features special articles under the headings 'A Personal View', 'Interview', 'In Practice' and 'Debate', along with book reviews and frequent Symposia focusing on areas of particular interest.

British Journal of Guidance & Counselling is published on behalf of the Careers Research and Advisory Center.

Instructions for Authors
Note to Authors. Please make sure your contact address information is clearly visible on the outside of all packages you are sending to Editors.

Articles should be original: if any material overlaps with material which the author has published or is submitting elsewhere, this should be made clear when the article is submitted. Manuscripts relating to guidance should be sent to Dr Jenny Kidd, Department of Organizational Psychology, Birkbeck College, University of London, Malet Street, London, WC1 7HX, UK. Manuscripts relating to counseling should be sent to Dr Paul Wilkins, Centre for Human Communication, Manchester Metropolitan University, 799 Wilmslow Road, Didsbury, M20 2RR, UK (papers covering both fields or related fields can be sent to either). Main articles should normally be about 3,000-6,000 words in length; short research reports and notes on practice should be 1,500-2,500 words in length. All articles should be written in a clear and straight-forward style, and implications for guidance and counseling practice should be discussed. Sexist language should be avoided: guidelines on non-sexist use of language are available from the Editor. Detailed statistical evidence should in general be summarized in the text though a limited number of tables may be included if they are clear and comprehensible to lay readers. An abstract of 60-120 words should be provided at the beginning of the article.

Electronic Submission. Authors should send the final, revised version of their articles in both hard copy paper and electronic disk forms. It is essential that the hard copy (paper) version *exactly* matches the material on disk. Please print out the hard copy from the disk you are sending. Submit three printed copies of the final version with the disk to the journal's editorial office. Save all files on a standard 3.5 inch high-density disk. We prefer to receive disks in Microsoft Word in a PC format, but can translate from most other common word processing programs as well as Macs. Please specify which program you have used. Do not save your files as "text only" or "read only".

A Personal View. Articles in the 'A Personal View' section should represent a personal statement about a topical issue which the author feels needs airing in relation to the development of guidance and counseling. They should be opinionated but informed, and brief (1,500-3,000 words); they may also be controversial and speculative.

Interview. Articles in the 'Interview' section should represent interviews with individuals whose experience and views are likely to be of wide interest to those involved in theory, policy and practice in the guidance and counseling field. They should preferably be 3,000-5,000 words in length. Suggestions for people to be interviewed, and offers to conduct interviews, should be passed to the Editor.

In Practice. Articles for the 'In Practice' section should provide descriptions and comments on new or experimental services or practices. Alternatively, they should be case-studies which are interesting in their own right and raise issues of a more general nature for the practice of guidance and counseling. They should preferably be 1,500-3,000 words in length.

Debate. Articles for the 'Debate' section should comprise responses to articles which have appeared in previous issues of the journal. They should preferably be 750-1,500 words in length.

The manuscripts should be typed on one side of A4 paper with double-spacing and with a margin to the left. They should conform to the style set out below. Four clear copies should be submitted, and a copy should be retained by the author. Manuscripts are normally sent to three independent referees. Manuscripts should be submitted in the style of the American Psychological Association (*Publication Manual*, 4th edition, 1994). To enable the refereeing procedure to be anonymous and impartial, the name(s) and institution(s) of the author(s) should not be included at the head of the article, but should be typed on a separate sheet and submitted with it.

References should follow a modified version of the style of the American Psychological Association. All publications cited in the text should be listed following the text; similarly, all references listed must be mentioned in the text. Within the text, references should be indicated by the author's name and year of publication in parentheses, e.g. (Folkman, 1992) or (Sartory & Stern, 1979), or if there are more than two authors (Gallico et al., 1985). Where several references are quoted consecutively, or within a single year, within the text the order should be alphabetical, e.g. (Mawson, 1992; Parry & Watts, 1989) and (Grey, 1992; Kelly, 1992; Smith, 1992). If more than one paper from the same author(s) and year are listed, the date should be followed by (a), (b), etc., e.g. (Cobb, 1992a).

The references should be listed alphabetically by author on a separate sheet(s) (double-spaced) in the following standard form, capitalization and punctuation:
a. *for periodical articles* (titles of journals should not be abbreviated): BALK, D. (1979). How teenagers cope with sibling death. School Counselor, 31, 150-158.
b. *for books*: LOWENFELD, M. (1979). The World Technique. Chicago: Phoenix Books.
c. *for chapters within multi-authored books*: BEDNAR, R.L. & KAUL, T.J. (1978). Experimental group research: current perspectives. In S.L. GARFIELD & A.E. BERGIN (Eds), Handbook of Psychotherapy and Behaviour Change (pp. 75-89). Chichester: Wiley.

Journal titles should not be abbreviated and unnecessary references should be avoided.

Tables and figures should be supplied on separate sheets and should be numbered consecutively in the text in Arabic numerals (e.g. Table 3 or Fig. 3). Their approximate position in the text should be indicated. Units should appear in parentheses in the column heading but not in the body of the table. Words or numerals should be repeated on successive lines; 'ditto' or 'do' should not be used.

Copyright: It is a condition of publication that authors vest copyright in their articles, including abstracts, in Careers Research and Advisory Center. This enables us to ensure full copyright protection and to disseminate the article, and the journal, to the widest possible readership in print and electronic formats as appropriate. Authors may, of course, use the article elsewhere after publication without prior permission from Careers Research and Advisory Center, provided that acknowledgement is given to the Journal as the original source of publication, and that Taylor & Francis is notified so that our records show that its use is properly authorized.

Client material. Care must be taken to disguise the identity of clients. Where case-study material is presented on a particular client which may enable the client's identity to be recognized by him/herself or by others, written consent must be requested from the client concerned; assurance that such consent has been obtained should be provided to the editor, and should also where appropriate be mentioned within the article as part of the description of the methodology used. Any liability to clients on the grounds of infringing confidentiality belongs to the author(s).

Proofs will be sent to the author if there is sufficient time to do so. Proofs, including proofs of illustrations, are supplied for checking and for essential corrections only, not for general revision or alteration. Proofs should be corrected and returned to the Editor within 3 days of receipt.

Offprints. Fifty offprints of each paper are supplied free. Additional copies may be purchased and should be ordered when the proofs are returned. Offprints, together with a complete copy of the relevant journal issue, are sent about three weeks after publication.

British Journal of Mathematical and Statistical Psychology

ADDRESS FOR SUBMISSION:

David Clark-Carter, Editor
British Journal of Mathematical and
    Statistical Psychology
British Psychological Society
    ONLINE SUBMISSIONS ONLY
St. Andrews House
48 Princess Road East
Leicester, LE1 7 DR
UK
Phone: 01782 294515
Fax: 01782 745506
E-Mail: d.clark-carter@statts.ac.uk
Web: www.bps.org.uk/publications/jms_5
Address May Change: 12/31/2006

PUBLICATION GUIDELINES:

Manuscript Length: 5,000 words max
Copies Required: Four
Computer Submission: Yes
Format: MS Word
Fees to Review: 0.00 US$

Manuscript Style:
    American Psychological Association

CIRCULATION DATA:

Reader: Academics
Frequency of Issue: 2 Times/Year
Copies per Issue: Less than 1,000
Sponsor/Publisher: British Psychological
    Society
Subscribe Price: 70.00 US$ Individual
    250.00 US$ Institution
    35.00 Pounds Indiv. & 134 Pounds Inst.

REVIEW INFORMATION:

Type of Review: Blind Review
No. of External Reviewers: 2
No. of In House Reviewers: 0
Acceptance Rate: 21-30%
Time to Review: 2 - 3 Months
Reviewers Comments: Yes
Invited Articles: 0-5%
Fees to Publish: 0.00 US$

MANUSCRIPT TOPICS:
Research Methods & Statistics

MANUSCRIPT GUIDELINES/COMMENTS:

Journal Scope
The Journal is recognized internationally as publishing high quality articles in quantitative psychology. Contributions are invited on any aspect of mathematics or statistics of relevance to psychology; these include statistical theory and methods, decision making, mathematical psychology, psychometrics, psychophysics and computing. Reviews, expository articles, short notes, as well as papers of an historical or philosophical nature, in any of these areas are also most welcome. Book and statistical software reviews are a regular feature in the journal.

Notes for Contributors
The *British Journal of Mathematical and Statistical Psychology* publishes articles relating to any areas of psychology which have a greater mathematical or statistical or other formal

aspect of their argument than is usually acceptable to other journals. Articles which have a clear reference to substantive psychological issues are preferred. New models for psychological processes, new approaches to existing data, critiques of existing models and improved algorithms for estimating the parameters of a model, are examples of articles which may be favored. The following series of questions are used in relation to those papers submitted for review:

- Is a psychological or substantive context identified?
- Is relevant previous work referred to?
- Is the problem well identified?
- Are alternative solutions considered?
- Are the mathematical or statistical arguments competent and correct?
- Is an example necessary? If given, is the example trivial?
- Is the abstract adequate?

1. Circulation
The circulation of the Journal is worldwide. Papers are invited and encouraged from authors throughout the world.

2. Length
Papers should normally be no more than 5,000 words, although the Editor retains discretion to publish papers beyond this length in cases where the clear and concise expression of the scientific content requires greater length.

3. Refereeing
The journal operates a policy of anonymous peer review. Papers will normally be scrutinised and commented on by at least two independent expert referees (in addition to the Editor) although the Editor may process a paper at his or her discretion. The referees will not be made aware of the identity of the author. All information about authorship including personal acknowledgements and institutional affiliations should be confined to the title page (and the text should be free of such clues as identifiable self-citations e.g. 'In our earlier work...').

4. Online submission process
1) All manuscripts must be submitted online at **http://bjmsp.edmgr.com**.

First-time users: click the REGISTER button from the menu and enter in your details as instructed. On successful registration, an email will be sent informing you of your user name and password. Please keep this email for future reference and proceed to LOGIN.

(You do not need to re-register if your status changes e.g. author, reviewer or editor).

Registered users: click the LOGIN button from the menu and enter your user name and password for immediate access. Click 'Author Login'.

2) Follow the step-by-step instructions to submit your manuscript.

182

3) The submission must include the following as separate files:

- Title page consisting of manuscript title, authors' full names and affiliations, name and address for corresponding author.
- Abstract
- Full manuscript omitting authors' names and affiliations. Figures and tables can be attached separately if necessary.

4) If you require further help in submitting your manuscript, please consult Tutorial for Authors.

Authors can log on at any time to check the status of the manuscript.

5. Manuscript requirements

- Contributions must be typed in double spacing with wide margins. All sheets must be numbered.
- Tables should be typed in double spacing, each on a separate page with a self-explanatory title. Tables should be comprehensible without reference to the text. They should be placed at the end of the manuscript with their approximate locations indicated in the text.
- Figures can be included at the end of the document or attached as separate files, carefully labelled in initial capital/lower case lettering with symbols in a form consistent with text use. Unnecessary background patterns, lines and shading should be avoided. Captions should be listed on a separate page. The resolution of digital images must be at least 300 dpi.
- All articles should be preceded by an Abstract of between 100 and 200 words, giving a concise statement of the intention and results or conclusions of the article.
- For reference citations, please use APA style. Particular care should be taken to ensure that references are accurate and complete. Give all journal titles in full.
- SI units must be used for all measurements, rounded off to practical values if appropriate, with the Imperial equivalent in parentheses.
- In normal circumstances, effect size should be incorporated.
- Authors are requested to avoid the use of sexist language.
- Authors are responsible for acquiring written permission to publish lengthy quotations, illustrations etc for which they do not own copyright.

For Guidelines on editorial style, please consult the *APA Publication Manual* published by the American Psychological Association, Washington DC, USA (http://www.apastyle.org)

6. Publication ethics
See website for details on Code of Conduct and Principles of Publishing
http://bps.org.uk/publications/jMS_6.cfm

7. Supplementary data
Supplementary data too extensive for publication may be deposited with the British Library Document Supply Centre. Such material includes numerical data, computer programs, fuller

details of case studies and experimental techniques. The material should be submitted to the Editor together with the article, for simultaneous refereeing.

8. Post acceptance
PDF page proofs are sent to authors via email for correction of print but not for rewriting or the introduction of new material. Authors will be provided with a PDF file of their article prior to publication for easy and cost-effective dissemination to colleagues.

9. Copyright
To protect authors and journals against unauthorised reproduction of articles, The British Psychological Society requires copyright to be assigned to itself as publisher, on the express condition that authors may use their own material at any time without permission. On acceptance of a paper submitted to a journal, authors will be requested to sign an appropriate assignment of copyright form.

10. Checklist of requirements
- Abstract (100-200 words)
- Title page (include title, authors' names, affiliations, full contact details)
- Full article text (double-spaced with numbered pages and anonymised)
- References (APA style). Authors are responsible for bibliographic accuracy and must check every reference in the manuscript and proofread again in the page proofs.
- Tables, figures, captions placed at the end of the article or attached as a separate file.

British Journal of Sociology

ADDRESS FOR SUBMISSION:

Bridget Hutter, Editor
British Journal of Sociology
London School of Economics and
   Political Science
Houghton Street
London,, WC2A 2AE
UK
Phone: 011 020 7955 7283
Fax: 011 020 7955 6311
E-Mail: bjs@lse.ac.uk
Web: www.blackwellpublishing.com/bjos
Address May Change:

PUBLICATION GUIDELINES:

Manuscript Length: 8000 words
Copies Required: Five
Computer Submission: Yes
Format: Word Documents
Fees to Review: 0.00 US$

Manuscript Style:
   See Manuscript Guidelines,
   www.blackwellpublishing.com/bjos

CIRCULATION DATA:

Reader: Academics
Frequency of Issue: Quarterly
Copies per Issue: No Reply
Sponsor/Publisher: Blackwell Publishing
Subscribe Price: 352.00 US$ Instution
   50.00 US$ Individual/Personnal

REVIEW INFORMATION:

Type of Review: Blind Review
No. of External Reviewers: 3
No. of In House Reviewers: 1
Acceptance Rate: No Reply
Time to Review: No Reply
Reviewers Comments: Yes
Invited Articles: Yes
Fees to Publish: 0.00 US$

MANUSCRIPT TOPICS:
Decision Making Theory; General Sociology; Group Dynamics; Human Relations; Industry & Organization

MANUSCRIPT GUIDELINES/COMMENTS:

Aims and Scope
Well established, widely read and highly respected, *The British Journal of Sociology* is essential reading for all sociologists wishing to keep abreast of current developments across the whole discipline.

Special features include:
• articles covering the entire span of sociological thought and research
• international contributors
• current coverage of developments in research and analysis
• review section giving wide-ranging coverage of contemporary scholarship
• special issues covering major problems of empirical and theoretical importance

From its beginnings in 1950, under the founding editorship of Morris Ginsberg, D.V.Glass and T.H. Marshall, *The British Journal of Sociology* has had as its editors many of the leading figures in British sociology.

The *BJS* has long been established as one of the world's leading journals in sociology. The journal deservedly has an influence which stretches well beyond the immediate field of sociology itself. Under its present able editorship, the *BJS* has consolidated and expanded its already formidable reputation.
Anthony Giddens, Professor of Sociology, Cambridge University.

The London School of Economics and Political Science (LSE) is unique in the United Kingdom in its concentration on teaching and research across the full range of the social, political and economic sciences. Founded in 1895 by Beatrice and Sidney Webb, the LSE is one of the largest colleges within the University of London and has an outstanding reputation for academic excellence nationally and internationally.

Email:**bjs@lse.ac.uk**

Canadian Journal of Behavioural Science

ADDRESS FOR SUBMISSION:

Lorne M. Sulsky, Editor
Canadian Journal of Behavioural Science
Wilfred Laurier University
School of Business and Economics
75 University Avenue West
Waterloo, Ontario, N2L 3C5
Canada
Phone: 519-884-0710 ext. 2662
Fax: 519-884-0201
E-Mail: lsulsky@wlu.ca
Web:
Address May Change:

PUBLICATION GUIDELINES:

Manuscript Length: 26-30
Copies Required: Four
Computer Submission: Yes Disk
Format: MS Word
Fees to Review: 0.00 US$

Manuscript Style:
   American Psychological Association

CIRCULATION DATA:

Reader: Academics
Frequency of Issue: Quarterly
Copies per Issue: 4,001 - 5,000
Sponsor/Publisher: Canadian Psychological
   Association
Subscribe Price: 55.00 US$ Individual
   95.00 US$ Institution
   58.85 CAN$ Indv., 101.65 CAN$ Inst.

REVIEW INFORMATION:

Type of Review: Blind Review
No. of External Reviewers: 2
No. of In House Reviewers: 0
Acceptance Rate: 21-30%
Time to Review: 4 - 6 Months
Reviewers Comments: Yes
Invited Articles: 0-5%
Fees to Publish: 0.00 US$

MANUSCRIPT TOPICS:
Abnormal Psychology; Adolescent Psychology; Adulthood; Alcoholism & Drug Addiction;
Behavior Modification; Child Psychology; Counseling Process; Developmental Psychology;
Educational Psychology; Exceptional Child; Family Counseling & Therapy; Industrial-
Organizational Psychology; Psychopathology; Research Methods & Statistics; Social
Psychology

MANUSCRIPT GUIDELINES/COMMENTS:

Mandate
The *Canadian Journal of Behavioural Science* normally publishes original, empirical
contributions in the following areas of psychology: abnormal, behavioural, community,
counseling, educational, environmental, developmental, health, industrial-organizational,
clinical neuropsychological, personality, psychometrics, and social. A limited amount of space
is also available in the journal for brief reports with theoretical and practical implications. In
addition to presenting important case studies, the Brief Reports section can also be used for
psychometric reports, to disseminate Canadian norms or forms for standardized tests, and for
summarizing program evaluation studies.

Formats
All manuscripts should be prepared for a diverse audience, should be written in French or English using non-sexist language, and should follow the style described in the *Publication Manual of the American Psychological Association*, 5th edition, 2001 (double-spaced throughout, 2.54cm margins on all sides, 12-point font). Brief Reports will be no longer than five journal pages, so a Brief Report manuscript would not normally exceed 2500 words in text and would have no more than one table or figure. Authors of a Brief Report must state that a fuller report will be provided upon request. A digital copy of the manuscript should accompany paper copies submitted to the editor.

Conditions
Each manuscript submission should be accompanied by a cover letter to the editor from the corresponding author stating: a) that the manuscript is not and will not be under concurrent consideration by another publication; b) that all co-authors have read and approved of the submission; and c) that the treatment of participants has been in compliance with relevant ethical standards.

Addresses
In addition to postal addresses and phone numbers, the corresponding author should supply an e-mail address for editorial correspondence. All English manuscripts should be sent in quadruplicate (along with the digital copy), with three copies bearing no author identification to facilitate blind review, to:

Dr. Lorne M. Sulsky
Canadian Journal of Behavioural Science
School of Business and Economics
Wilfred Laurier University
75 University Avenue West
Waterloo, Ontario N2L 3C5
Email: **lsulsky@wlu.ca**

Canadian Journal of Experimental Psychology

ADDRESS FOR SUBMISSION:

Peter Dixon, Editor
Canadian Journal of Experimental
  Psychology
University of Alberta
Department of Psychology
Edmonton, AB T6G 2E9
Canada
Phone: 780-492-2318
Fax: 780-492-1768
E-Mail: cjep@ualberta.ca
Web: www.cpa.ca/psynopsis/cont.htm
Address May Change: 12/31/2005

PUBLICATION GUIDELINES:

Manuscript Length: 26-30
Copies Required: Four
Computer Submission: Yes Email
Format: Prefer .pdf; See Guidelines
Fees to Review: 0.00 US$

Manuscript Style:
  American Psychological Association

CIRCULATION DATA:

Reader: Academics
Frequency of Issue: Quarterly
Copies per Issue: 1,001 - 2,000
Sponsor/Publisher: Canadian Psychological
  Association
Subscribe Price: 55.00 US$ Individual
  95.00 US$ Institution
  58.85 CAN$ Indv./ 101.65 CAN$ Inst.

REVIEW INFORMATION:

Type of Review: Blind Review
No. of External Reviewers: 2
No. of In House Reviewers: 0
Acceptance Rate: 21-30%
Time to Review: 1 - 2 Months
Reviewers Comments: Yes
Invited Articles: 21-30%
Fees to Publish: 0.00 US$

MANUSCRIPT TOPICS:
Experimental Psychology; Learning & Conditioning; Sensation & Perception; Thinking & Cognition

MANUSCRIPT GUIDELINES/COMMENTS:

The Journal publishes original research papers that advance understanding of the field of experimental psychology, broadly considered. This includes, but is not restricted to, cognition, perception, motor performance, attention, memory, learning, language, decision making, development, comparative psychology, and neuroscience. The Journal will publish: (a) papers reporting empirical results that advance knowledge in a particular research area, (b) papers describing theoretical, methodological, or conceptual advances that are relevant to the interpretation of empirical evidence in the field, and (c) brief reports (less than 2500 words) that describe new results or analyses with clear theoretical or methodological import. It is the policy of the Journal to minimize publication lag and editorial decision time on brief reports. Occasionally, the Journal will publish book reviews judged to be of broad interest to the experimental psychology research community.

Manuscripts may be submitted in French or in English and should conform to the format described in the *Publication Manual of the American Psychological Association*. Please consult the Manual particularly concerning manuscript page order and the form of headings, references, tables, and figures. Please avoid almost all abbreviations and the use of footnotes for substantive information. Papers must be composed in 12-point type size. The entire text should be double-spaced (at least 24 point spacing) with 1-inch margins all around. Figures and illustrations must be of professional presentation quality. Papers should include an abstract of 125 words.

Authors are encouraged to submit manuscripts electronically. The preferred format is an Adobe PDF file included as an email attachment, although other formats are possible. Paper submissions should be in quadruplicate. If authors wish their papers to be reviewed blind, three of the four paper copies (or an additional electronic version) should have information identifying the authors and their affiliations removed. For paper submissions, an email message should be sent listing the title of the manuscript, the authors, and the abstract. Each submission should be accompanied by a cover letter stating: a) that the manuscript is not and will not be under concurrent consideration by another publication; b) that all co-authors have read and approved of the submission; and c) that the treatment of participants complies with relevant ethical standards.

Submissions will be acknowledge by email upon receipt. Original manuscripts and all correspondence should be directed to:

Peter Dixon, Editor
Canadian Journal of Experimental Psychology
Department of Psychology
University of Alberta
Edmonton, Alberta
T6G 2E9
Phone: (780) 492-2318; Fax: (780) 492-1768; E-mail: **cjep@ualberta.ca**

Canadian Journal of Psychiatry

ADDRESS FOR SUBMISSION:

Joel Paris, Editor-in-Chief
Canadian Journal of Psychiatry
701-141 Laurier Avenue West
Ottawa, Ontario, K1P 5J3
Canada
Phone: 613-234-2815 ext. 226
Fax: 613-234-9857
E-Mail: cjp@cpa-apc.org
Web: www.cpa-apc.org
Address May Change:

CIRCULATION DATA:

Reader: Academics, Practioners
Frequency of Issue: 14 Times/Year
Copies per Issue: 5,001-7,000
Sponsor/Publisher:
Subscribe Price:
    160.00 CAN$ Indv & Inst in Canada
    160.00 US$ US & Overseas

PUBLICATION GUIDELINES:

Manuscript Length: 16-20
Copies Required: Three
Computer Submission: Yes Disk or Email
Format: MS Word, WordPerfect
Fees to Review: 0.00 US$

Manuscript Style:
    Chicago Manual of Style, Uniform
    Requirements for Ms. to Biomedical
    Journals

REVIEW INFORMATION:

Type of Review: Editorial Review
No. of External Reviewers: 2
No. of In House Reviewers: 1
Acceptance Rate: 30%
Time to Review: 4 - 6 Months
Reviewers Comments: Yes
Invited Articles: 21-30%
Fees to Publish: 0.00 US$

MANUSCRIPT TOPICS:
Psychiatry

MANUSCRIPT GUIDELINES/COMMENTS:

General Policies
The requirements stated below, available4 from 3 sources, are in accordance with *Uniform Requirements for manuscripts Submitted to Biomedical Journals.*

Prior Publication
The Canadian Journal of Psychiatry accepts manuscripts for consideration with the understanding that they represent original material, have not been published previously except in abstract form, are not being considered for publication elsewhere, and have been approved by each author. This information must be stated in the cover letter that accompanies the manuscript.

Copyright Transfer. The Journal requires transfer of copyright to the Canadian Psychiatric Association so that the author(s) and the Association are protected from misuse of copyrighted material. A copyright transfer form will be forwarded to the corresponding author along with the letter accepting the manuscript for publication.

Submission of Manuscripts

The original manuscript and e copies should be submitted, either in French or in English, the editorial office. All correspondence will be sent to the first-named author unless other wise specified. Papers should be accompanied by a cover letter indicating that the paper is intended for publication and that the manuscript has been read by all authors. A statement that informed consent has been obtained must appear in the manuscripts that report results on human subjects.

Authors will be notified of the receipt of their paper and of the number assigned to it. This number must be included in all further correspondence or telephone inquiries. The corresponding author of submitted papers must notify the Journal of changes of address. Original papers will not be returned to authors.

Once a paper has been accepted for publication, the corresponding author will be invited to provide a copy of the manuscript on diskette formatted in Word Perfect 5.1 or later versions. Please include a return address for reprint requests, a telephone number, and a fax number with your correspondence.

Types of Articles

Research Papers and Review Articles

General papers and review articles should not exceed 4000 words, including structured abstract. The word count must appear on the title page. The word count will be enforced so the *Journal* can publish as many papers each issue as possible.

Brief Communications

Preliminary reports and spin-off studies will be published as Brief Communications. These will be no more than 1500 words including structured abstract.

Book Reviews

Books of interest to *Journal* readers include general psychiatry, specific areas of psychiatry and the subspecialties, and popular fiction and nonfiction dealing with mental health issues. Please limit your reviews to 750 words and indicate in the review whether you have any personal ties to the authors or editors.

At the top of the review, include your name, the title of the book, authors or editors of the book, city of publication, publisher, year of publication, number of pages, and price in CAN or US dollars. Include your rating of the book (excellent, good, fair, or not recommended).

Wherever possible, answer the following questions in the review:
- What is the purpose of the book, including major points or new ideas?
- How well does the book fulfill the purpose for which it was written?
- How competent is the author or editor on the subject?
- Is the book well written?
- Is the book free from production errors?
- Is the price reasonable?

Letters to the Editor
Limit Letters to the Editor to 500 words. Do not include tables and figures. Case reports that make a valuable contribution to the literature will be published as Letters to the Editor. For case reports, include a section at the end of the letter, Funding and Support, where authors disclose all financial and personal connections to drug companies and all sources of funding and support for the research.

Preparing the Submission
The *Journal* uses the style book, *Scientific Style and Format: The CBE Manual for Authors, Editors and Publishers*. 6th ed. The style book is prepared by the style manual committee of the Council of Biology Editors (now the Council of Science Editors). Manuscript requirements are also based on Uniform Requirements for Manuscripts Submitted to Biomedical Journals prepared by the International Committee of Medical Journal Editors.

Please avoid unnecessary formatting, as we strip all formatting from manuscripts. For example, we strip heading styles, paragraph styles, tabs, endnote and footnote functions. Please do not use endnote and footnote functions as entire endnotes and reference lists may disappear when we strip the coding.

Double-space all parts of the submission, including case reports, quotations, references, and tables. Type manuscripts in upper and lower case on one side only of 8 ½ x 11 inch non-erasable bond paper. All 4 margins must be 1 ½ inches. Arrange the parts of the manuscript in the following order, with each item beginning a new page: 1) title page, 2) structured abstract, key words, and clinical implications and limitations, 3) text, 4) references, and 5) tables and figures. Number all pages.

A. Cover Letter
Authors must indicate that the manuscript represents original material, has not been published previously except in abstract form, is not being considered for publication elsewhere, and has been approved by each author.

Authors must affirm in writing that they have not entered into an agreement with a funding organization that limited their ability to complete the research as planned and to publish the results. Authors must also state that they have had full control of all primary data.

B. Title Page
- Make the title as brief and informative as possible.
- Limit authors listed in the by-line to principal researchers or writers; acknowledge collaborators in a footnote. Authors' first names are preferred to 2 initials.
- Provide professional, academic, and financial affiliations of each author. Include all financial relationships with funding and sponsoring organizations (for example, employment, consultancies, stock ownership, honoraria, and expert testimony).
- If the paper has been presented at a meeting, please give the name of the meeting, the place, and the date.
- Include the full address, telephone numbers, Fax number, and e-mail address of the corresponding author.

- Include a word count for the text and abstract; do not include the tables, figures, or references in this count.

C. Abstract, Key Words, and Clinical Implications and Limitations

Limit abstracts to 250 words. As much as possible, structure abstracts using the following headings: Objective (the primary purpose of the study), Method (basic procedures), Results (key findings), and Conclusions (principal conclusions). The *Journal* takes care of translating the abstract into the alternate language (French or English).

Include also 3 to 10 key words or short phrases, as well as 3 clinical implications and 3 limitations of the study.

D. Tables and Figures

Tables and figures should supplement text, not duplicate it, and should be understandable without reference to the text. Include a descriptive title and specify units of measurement for each table and figure. Keep the length and number of tables to a minimum. Full pages of tables and figures will not be published; authors should communicate this information in the text. Submit electronic copies of both tables and figures, along with print copies.

Include tables only when they present relevant numerical data; short tables can frequently be incorporated more concisely in the text. Tables will be edited to conform to the *Journal* style.

Some authors use asterisks to indicate footnotes in tables that contain probability levels. A single asterisk is used for the lowest level of probability, 2 for the next higher, and so on, with the specific levels given in the notes to the table (for examples, $*P < 0.05$ $**P < 0.01$ $***P < 0.001$).
Note: CJP style replaces asterisks with superscript letters to designate footnotes ($^aP < 0.05$ $^bP < 0.01$ $^cP < 0.001$).

Figures and charts should be professionally prepared as glossies or camera-ready prints. The *Journal* encourages the submissions of figures on disk in the program that they were created in, for example, Microsoft Excel, Microsoft Powerpoint, Microsoft Work (objects created with the draw tools), Corel Draw PC version, Corel Photopaint, Adobe Photoshop PC version. Other acceptable formats are eps, tif (300 dpi photographs without text), jpg (300 dpi), and gif (300 dpi).
Note: The *Journal* is produced in a PC environment and cannot support Mac software.

E. References

The *Journal* follows the citation sequence referencing style (see *CBE Manual*, Chapter 30). Number references and list them in order of appearance in the text. Follow the citation in text with the appropriate reference number in parenthesis. Do not arrange the list of references alphabetically.

Accuracy of citations is the author's responsibility. Use exact spelling, accents, and punctuation of the original reference. Ensure that all references listed have been cited in the text.

Do not include personal communications, unpublished manuscripts, or manuscripts submitted but not yet accepted, in the reference list. Note such citations in the text as (name, date, personal communication) or (unpublished observation). Manuscripts that are actually "in press" may be cited in the reference list as "forthcoming," with the journal or publisher and location included.

For more than 6 authors, the *Journal* lists the first 6 authors, followed by "and others." Abbreviate journal names using *Index Medicus* abbreviations: do not abbreviate journals not included in *Index Medicus*.

Type references in the style below, double-spaced throughout. References that do not conform to *Journal* style will be returned to the corresponding author for appropriate adjustment. Please note *CJP* conventions for punctuating, capitalizing, and use of en-dash for page ranges.
- Place book and article titles in "sentence case" (capitalize only the first word, acronyms, and proper nouns).
- Do not italicize titles.
- For more than 6 authors, list the first 6 authors, followed by "and others." Please note punctuation conventions with author names (for example, Doe J, not Doe, J).
- When citing journal articles, do not include a space after colons and semicolons.
- Abbreviate journal names using *Index Medicus* abbreviations. Do not abbreviate journals not included in *Index Medicus*.

Standard Journal Article
1. Author(s). Title. Journal title and year;volume:page range.

Sample
1. Silverstone PH, Lemay T, Elliot J, Hsu V, Starko R. The Prevalence of major depressive disorder and low self-esteem in medical inpatients. Can J Psychiatry 1996;41:67-74.

Book Chapter
2. Author(s). Chapter title. In: editor(s) name(s), editor. Book title. Place Published: Publisher; Year published. Page range.

Sample
2. Flach F. The resilience hypothesis and post traumatic disorder. In: Wolf ME, Mosnaim AD, editors. Post-traumatic stress disorder: etiology, phenomenology, and treatment. Washington (DC): American Psychiatric Press; 1990 p37-45.

Conference Presentation
3. Author(s). Title. Paper presented at (name of conference); inclusive conference dates; place of conference.

Sample
3. Labrie F. Androgen deficiency syndrome in women: role of androgen and their precursor DHEA in Women. Paper presented at the Female Sexual Function Forum; October, 2001; Boston (MA).

195

F. Funding and Support

Authors must disclose all sources of funding and support for the research described in the paper, in a section at the end of the paper. For grant support, please include the full name of the granting agency and grant number.

G. Acknowledgements

For individuals involved with specific content of the work, do not exceed 4 typed lines. The *Journal* does not allow acknowledgements of persons involved with the preparation or typing of manuscripts.

Submitting Research Papers, Review Papers, and Brief Communications

Submit the original manuscript and 3 copies should be submitted, either in French or in English, to the editorial office. Also include a diskette of the manuscript or send an electronic copy by e-mail, formatted in WordPerfect or Microsoft Word. All correspondence will be sent to the corresponding author unless otherwise specified. Papers should be accompanied by a cover letter indicating that the paper is intended for publication and that the manuscript has been read by all authors. A statement that informed consent has been obtained must appear in the manuscripts that report results on human subjects.

Authors will be notified of the receipt of their paper and of the number assigned to it. This number must be included in all further correspondence or telephone inquiries. The corresponding author of submitted papers must notify the *Journal* of changes of address. Original papers will not be returned to authors.

Review Process for Research Papers, Review Papers, and Brief Communications

All papers are reviewed to determine the originality, validity, and importance of content and conclusions. Authors will be sent reviewer comments that are judged to be useful to them. All reviewer comments remain anonymous. The authors will be informed of the final decision of the editor.

Accepted Manuscripts

Manuscripts are accepted with the understanding that the editor and the editorial staff have the right to make revisions aimed at greater conciseness, clarity, and conformity with *Journal* style. Accepted papers will be edited and the copyedited manuscript and page proofs sent to the corresponding author for corrections and answers to queries. Authors who will be away from their office for a long period or who change address after notification of acceptance should inform the *Journal* staff.

Copyright

The *Journal* requires transfer of copyright to the Canadian Psychiatric Association so that the author(s) and the Association are protected from misuse of copyrighted material. A copyright transfer form will be forwarded to the corresponding author along with the page proofs of the manuscript, prior to publication.

Media Release
The CPA has received increasing numbers of media inquiries. To quickly facilitate these requests, we ask that authors designate a spokesperson and permit the CPA to release the spokesperson's phone number and e-mail address to the media, upon request.

Permission to Reprint
Written permission to reprint material published in the *Journal* must be secured from *The Canadian Journal of Psychiatry*, Suite 260, 441 MacLaren Street, Ottawa, Ontario K2P 2H3, unless otherwise stated in the article.

Reprints
Reprints are provided for a fee. An order form for reprints will be sent to the corresponding author before publication of the paper. The reprints will be mailed about 2 weeks after the article has been published.

Questions
Contact the *Journal* editorial office for further information (Tel: 613-234-2815 ext 226; Fax: 613-234-9857 or email: **cjp@cpa-apc.org**).

Uniform Requirements for Manuscripts Submitted to Biomedical Journals
The requirements stated above are in accordance with *Uniform Requirements for Manuscripts Submitted to Biomedical Journals* (http://www.icmje.org). They are available from three other sources:
1. International Committee of Medical Journal Editors. Uniform requirements for manuscripts submitted to biomedical journals. New Engl J Med 1997;336:309-15.

2. International Committee of Medical Journal Editors. Uniform requirements for manuscripts submitted to biomedical journals. Br Med J 1991;302:338-41. 3. International Committee of Medical Journal Editors. Uniform requirements for manuscripts submitted to biomedical journals. Can Med Assoc J 1995;152:1459-65.

STYLE NOTES FOR CONTRIBUTORS
General
Abbreviations and Acronyms
- Do not use periods or spaces with abbreviations and acronyms.
- Do not use periods or spaces after the initials of a person's name or the initials of academic degrees. Do not separate groups of initials with spaces
- Do not introduce an abbreviation in the title of an article. Spell out the term in full unless it is sufficiently common and you do not need to define it. (See common abbreviations below.)
- Spell out abbreviations and acronyms on first occurrence in text followed by the abbreviation or acronym in parentheses. Do not spell out common abbreviations.

Common abbreviations. DSM, ICD, US, WHO, HIV, AIDS, ECG, SR (sustained release), SD (standard deviation), df (degrees of freedom), CI (confidence interval), ns (not significant), CT (computed tomography), MRI (magnetic resonance imaging), EEG (electroencephalogram).

Do not spell out units of measurement (for example, use mg, not milligram).

Age. Always specify the unit: years, months, or days. Use over and under, not more than and less than or older than and younger than (for example, "aged 75 years and over," "the group aged over 45 years," "between the ages of 45 and 65 years").

Among, between. Among is a preposition indicating a relation involving more than 2 units of the same kind. Between is a preposition indicating a relation involving 2 units of the same kind. Use between with more than 2 persons or things when they are being considered in pairs as well as in a group.

And/or. Try to avoid this legalistic term, and similar uses of the virgule (slash) in running text. The "/" should be reserved for formulas.

Average. In scientific usage, average should be reserved as a synonym for "statistical mean." "Typical" or "characteristic" can often replace non-statistical "average."

Disorders. Do not capitalize the names of disorders. Capitalize only those elements of a disorder's name that are proper nouns (for example, "senile dementia of the Alzheimer type"). DSM capitalizes disorders, but this is a style decision, not an element of the disorder's name.

Dosage and dose. Avoid expressions such as mg per day and mg/day. Use mg daily. Ensure that the frequency of administration is provided. Dosage refers to the amount and frequency of administration; it is not synonymous with a single dose. Dose refers to the amount of a drug administered at 1 time.

En dash. Use the word "to" to indicate a range of numbers rather than an en-dash except for tables and references. Similarly, do not use an en-dash if the phrasing is "between...and..." or "from...to..."

Gender and sex. "Gender" is the social, economic, and historical categories "man" and "woman," whereas "sex" refers to the biological categories "male" and "female." *CJP* style endeavors to respect this distinction and generally edits to "sex," unless it is clear that a socially defined role is being discussed (for example, gender identity disorder).

Passive voice. Favor the active rather than the passive voice to achieve a simpler and more vigorous style (for example, We undertook a literature review, not A literature review was undertaken).

Prefixes. *CJP* style follows the *CBE Manual* and generally does not hyphenate prefixes in scientific text. Do not hyphenate with most prefixes, even if this means that 2 vowels will occur together (meta-analysis, preexisting). Use a hyphen with the prefix quasi-. Hyphenate compounds starting with self (exception: self object transference). A hyphen is required when the word the prefix attaches to is capitalized (for example, non-European).

Quotation marks. Place periods and commas inside quotation marks. (*CJP* style deviates from the *CBE Manual.*)

Relation and relationship. In scientific writing, use relation for inanimate objects and relationship for 2 or more persons.

Smothered verbs. Avoid turning active verbs into non-active nouns (for example, We decided, not We made a decision).

Tables. Use an em dash to indicate that data are not available. Leave the table cell blank if data do not apply.

Titles of address. Use Dr X and Dr Y, not Drs X and Y. Do not use periods.

Sensitive Language

CJP style stresses that research subjects and those with mental disorders are individual human beings with an illness. Therefore, edit to ensure that the sense of the individual is retained, and that there is no stigma attached to a disorder. We avoid terms with a popular meaning that carries connotations we prefer to avoid. For example, "manic depressive" is replaced with "persons with major depressive disorder." Similarly, we change "controls" to "control subjects," and we avoid the term "schizophrenic." Instead of "a schizophrenic person," use "a person with schizophrenia." Instead of "schizophrenic treatment programs," use "treatment programs for schizophrenia" or "schizophrenia treatment programs," and so on, for various disorders.

Case and patient. Use case to mean instance, example, or episode and patient to mean person (for example, "We saw 12 patients," not "We saw 12 cases").

Race, Caucasian, Mongoloid and Negroid. The term "race" does not have a precise definition in biological terms. Whenever possible, draw on more sharply definable criteria such as country of birth or habitation or self-description.

"Caucasian" (or "Caucasoid"), "Mongoloid," and "Negroid" are terms based on an outmoded theory of racial distinction and are no longer used. Refer to CBE 25.3-25.5 p 487-9 for suggestions.

Male and female. Male and female are categories of biological sex and are terms normally applied to animals. Use men and women wherever possible. If a group of patients includes both adults and children, subjects can be called "male patients" and "female patients" (not "males" and "females").

Symbols, Formulas, and Equations

In general, use symbols in equations and formulas, but write terms in full in running text. For example, use the symbol ? 2 in a formula, but write "chi-square" when describing a statistical test in running text.

Asterisk. Some authors use asterisks to indicate footnotes in tables that contain probability levels. A single asterisk is used for the lowest level of probability, 2 for the next higher, and so on, with the specific levels given in the notes to the table (for examples, $*P < 0.05$ $**P < 0.01$ $***P < 0.001$).

Note: CJP style replaces asterisks with superscript letters to designate footnotes ($^aP < 0.05$ $^bP < 0.01$ $^cP < 0.001$).

Brackets, Parentheses, and Braces. CJP style follows the CBE guidelines (section 11.19) for enclosures such as parentheses and brackets, with the exception that the same order of use for these "fences" is followed both for nonmathematical prose and for equations. The order is ([{}]), for example, total scores ($t[161] = 5.61$, $P < 0.001$).

CI (confidence interval)
Do not spell out CI.

Note: numeric limits represented by a CI should be connected by "to" rather than en-dash. (*CBE* section 11.24). As well, *CJP* style does not use an equal sign (for example, 95%CI, __ to __ , not 95%CI = __ to __).

Decimal points. Use a zero before all decimals, including P values and correlation coefficients (for example, $P = 0.04$ $r = 0.45$).

Df (degrees of freedom). Often reported either as a subscript number or in parentheses after the related test. Should be reported with Student's t-test, analysis of variance (the F-test), and the chi-square. In general, edit to use subscript numbers. However, if this is not appropriate, replace parenthetical numbers with "df#__" (for example, $F_{2,154} = 29.94$, $P < 0.001$, or $x^2 = 12.14$, df 1, $P < 0001$).

En dash. Use as the minus symbol and to link numbers representing a range of values. *CJP* style uses the connective "to" when linking ranges to avoid possible ambiguity with the minus symbol (for example "with temperatures of -5 to 25°C", not -5-25°C).

Mean. Write as mean (if reported as $\underline{M}$ or X, edit to "mean").

Mean, Standard Deviation
Write as "mean#__, SD#__."

Numbers in text. *CJP* style follows the *CBE* manual. All numbers are expressed as numerals (not written out) except:
- when beginning a sentence
- when reporting consecutive numerical expressions in which 2 classes of numbers must be differentiated (for example, five, 72-kg men. Not 5, 72-kg men)
- when reporting large numbers in general expressions (e.g. a hundred, several thousand)
- when used in the text in a general, non-numerical way (for example, "one of the many reasons")

Ordinal numbers are treated in the same manner as cardinal numbers: they are expressed as numerals (for example, 2nd, not second, "Second, I'd like to thank the one and only...," "ranked 4th as a cause of death," "21st century." Do not superscript the suffix.

Operators. Operators are preceded and followed by a space. See the *CBE Manual* Table 11.12 (p 212) for common operators in arithmetic, algebra, and number theory.

P value. The symbol P should be presented upper case and in italic type. *CJP* style precedes the decimal with a zero for clarity (for example, $P = 0.01$).

Ranges of numbers. Use the term "to" rather than a hyphen or en-dash to report a range of numbers (for example, 2 to 5 kg , not 2-5 kg).

Ratios. Use a colon (:) only for exact ratios. Do not use a colon if the ratio is inexact (for example, The ratio of men to women was 3:4).

Spaces with units of measurement. Include a space between the numeral and its unit of measurement (for example, 136#mm#Hg).

Spaces within mathematical symbols. See *CBE* p 213 for style governing spacing within mathematical symbols. Note: operators are preceded and followed by a space (for example: n#=#246).

Standard Deviation. *CJP* style presents standard deviation as SD#__, not SD = __. This presentation but has been chosen for clarity and as a result of software limitations (for example, SD 4.6, not SD = 4.6).

Canadian Psychology/Psychologie Canadienne

ADDRESS FOR SUBMISSION:

Thomas Hadjistavropoulos, Editor
Canadian Psychology/Psychologie
   Canadienne
University of Regina
Department of Psychology
Regina, SK, S4S OA2
Canada
Phone: 306-585-4457
Fax: 306-337-2321
E-Mail: See Guidlelines
Web: See Guidelines
Address May Change: 12/31/2006

PUBLICATION GUIDELINES:

Manuscript Length: 26-30
Copies Required: Four
Computer Submission: Yes Email
Format:
Fees to Review: 0.00 US$

Manuscript Style:
   American Psychological Association

CIRCULATION DATA:

Reader: Academics
Frequency of Issue: Quarterly
Copies per Issue: 5,001 - 10,000
Sponsor/Publisher: Canadian Psychological
   Association
Subscribe Price: 65.00 US$
   105.00 US$

REVIEW INFORMATION:

Type of Review: Blind Review
No. of External Reviewers: 3
No. of In House Reviewers: 1
Acceptance Rate: 11-20%
Time to Review: 2 - 3 Months
Reviewers Comments: Yes
Invited Articles: 11-20%
Fees to Publish: 0.00 US$

MANUSCRIPT TOPICS:
Abnormal Psychology; Adolescent Psychology; Adulthood; Alcoholism & Drug Addiction; Behavior Modification; Child Psychology; Counseling Process; Developmental Psychology; Educational Psychology; Exceptional Child; Experimental Psychology; Family Counseling & Therapy; Gerontology; History of Psychology; Learning & Conditioning; Neuropsychology; Personality; Physiological Psychology; Psychiatry; Psychobiology; Psychological Testing; Psychopathology; Research Methods & Statistics; Sensation & Perception; Social Psychology; Thinking & Cognition

MANUSCRIPT GUIDELINES/COMMENTS:

Website: http://www.cpa.ca/Psynopsis/scholar.html

Authors are encouraged to submit their manuscripts in electronic format using e-mail (**Thomas.Hadjistavropoulos@uregina.ca**). Please submit two files; one with author identification and one without. Alternatively, manuscripts can be submitted in quadruplicate with three copies bearing no author identification to facilitate blind review. Authors are requested to follow the style described in the *Publication Manual of the American*

Psychological Association, 5th edition, 2001. For full length articles, an abstract of approximately 100 words is required, and we will be happy to publish a 600 word abstract in French. All manuscripts should be accompanied by a statement indicating that the work has not been previously published and that it is not simultaneously under consideration by another journal.

Following final acceptance of an article for publication, all authors will be required to submit a copy on diskette for production purposes. Complete diskette specifications will be sent out to authors with notice of acceptance. Please contact the Managing Editor for details.

Authors are advised that the editorial team will normally not consider empirical papers for publication in this journal. Exceptions to this will involve investigations that have broad implications for our field as a whole (e.g., a survey of psychologists' opinions about the future of our field).

Child & Family Behavior Therapy

ADDRESS FOR SUBMISSION:

Cyril M. Franks, Editor
Child & Family Behavior Therapy
c/o Charles Diament, Associate Editor
41 Reckless Place
Red Bank, NJ 07701
USA
Phone: 908-530-9331
Fax: 732-264-3309
E-Mail:
Web: www.haworthpressinc.com
Address May Change:

PUBLICATION GUIDELINES:

Manuscript Length: 21-25
Copies Required: Four
Computer Submission: No
Format: N/A
Fees to Review: 0.00 US$

Manuscript Style:
    American Psychological Association

CIRCULATION DATA:

Reader: Academics, Practitioners, Graduate
    Psychology Students
Frequency of Issue: Quarterly
Copies per Issue:
Sponsor/Publisher: Haworth Press, Inc.
Subscribe Price: 65.00 US$ Individual
    150.00 US$ Institution
    600.00 US$ Library

REVIEW INFORMATION:

Type of Review: Editorial Review
No. of External Reviewers: 2
No. of In House Reviewers: 1
Acceptance Rate: 21-30%
Time to Review: 2 - 3 Months
Reviewers Comments: Yes
Invited Articles: Yes
Fees to Publish: 0.00 US$

MANUSCRIPT TOPICS:

Abnormal Psychology; Academic Performance; Adolescent Psychology; Adulthood;
Alcoholism & Drug Addiction; Applied Behavior Analysis; Behavior Disorders; Behavior
Modification; Behavior Therapy; Developmental Disabilities; Developmental Psychology;
Experimental Psychology; Gerontology; History of Psychology; Learning & Conditioning;
Neuropsychology; Outcome Evaluation; Personality; Physiological Psychology; Psychiatry;
Psychological Testing; Psychopathology; Research Methods & Statistics; Thinking &
Cognition

MANUSCRIPT GUIDELINES/COMMENTS:

Editor: Cyril M. Franks, PhD
Distinguished Professor Emeritus
Rutgers University
315 Prospect Avenue
Princeton, NJ 08540-5330
Tel: (609) 924-2931
Fax: (609) 924-0117
E-mail: vfranks@aol.com

Associate Editor: Charles Diament, PhD
41 Reckless Place
Red Bank, NJ 07701
Tel: (908) 530-9330
Fax: (732) 264-3309
E-mail: DrCDiament@home.com

About the Journal
Behavior therapy is a powerful approach for treating a wide range of problems affecting children, adolescents, and families. *Child & Family Behavior Therapy* offers original research, case studies, and clinical applications to practitioners, parents, teachers, and counselors interested in the use of behavioral approaches. These empirically derived interventions – specifically designed to be practiced with children, adolescents, and their families – will facilitate the work of teachers, child psychologists, behavior therapists, behavior analysts, school counselors, family therapists, and researchers.

Topics addressed in *Child & Family Behavior Therapy* have included:
* interventions for parents as well as children
* social skill development
* behavioral intervention for children with ADHD, ASD, conduct disorders, and other impairments
* extensive book reviews
* homework for adolescents-self- and parental monitoring
* behavioral problems in preschoolers
* parental tolerance for child misbehavior
* the effectiveness of a standardized parenting skill program in reducing misbehavior
* the interaction of parenting styles and Attention Deficit Hyperactivity Disorder in Iranian parents
* interventions for infant and toddler sleep disturbance
* mothers' and fathers' discipline of hard-to-manage toddlers
* simplified habit reversal plus adjunct contingencies in the treatment of thumb sucking and hair pulling
* the effects of mothers' depression on the behavioral assessment of disruptive child behavior
* the behavioral treatment of a young adult with Post Traumatic Stress Disorder
* gender issues, cultural issues, ethnic issues, and family issues

Instructions for Authors
1. **Original Articles Only**. Submission of a manuscript to this Journal represents a certification on the part of the author(s) that it is an original work, and that neither this manuscript nor a version of it has been published elsewhere nor is being considered for publication elsewhere.

2. **Manuscript Length**. Your manuscript should be no longer than 25 typed pages including references and abstract. Tables and figures can be additional. Lengthier manuscripts may be considered, but only at the discretion of the Editor. Sometimes, lengthier manuscripts may be considered if they can be divided up into sections for publications in successive Journal issues.

3. **Manuscript Style**. References, citations, and general style of manuscripts for this Journal should follow the APA style (as outlined in the latest edition of the *Publication Manual of the American Psychological Association*). References should be double-spaced and placed in

alphabetical order. The use of footnotes within the text is discouraged. Words should be underlined only when it is intended that they be typeset in italics.

If an author wishes to submit a paper that has been already prepared in another style, he or she may do so. However, if the paper is accepted (with or without reviewer's alterations), the author is fully responsible for retyping the manuscript in the correct style as indicated above. Neither the Editor nor the Publisher is responsible for re-preparing manuscript copy to adhere to the Journal's style.

4. Manuscript Preparation

Margins. Leave at least a one-inch margin on all four sides.
Paper. Use clean, white 8 ½" x 11" bond paper.
Number of copies. 4 (the original plus three photocopies).
Cover page. Important — staple a cover page to the manuscript, indicating only the article title (this is used for anonymous refereeing).
Second "title page". Enclose a regular title page but do not staple it to the manuscript. Include the title again, plus:

- full authorship
- an ABSTRACT of about 100 words. (Below the abstract provide 3–10 key words for index purposes).
- a header or footer on each page with abbreviated title and pg number of total (e.g., pg 2 of 7)
- an introductory footnote with authors' academic degrees, professional titles, affiliations, mailing and e-mail addresses, and any desired acknowledgment of research support or other credit.

5. Return Envelopes. When you submit your four manuscript copies, also include:

- a 9" x 12" envelope, self-addressed and stamped (with sufficient postage to ensure return of your manuscript);
- a regular envelope, stamped and self-addressed. This is for the Editor to send you an "acknowledgement of receipt" letter.

6. Spelling, Grammar, and Punctuation. You are responsible for preparing manuscript copy which is clearly written in acceptable, scholarly English and which contains no errors of spelling, grammar, or punctuation. Neither the Editor nor the Publisher is responsible for correcting errors of spelling and grammar. The manuscript, after acceptance by the Editor, must be immediately ready for typesetting as it is finally submitted by the author(s). Check your paper for the following common errors:

- dangling modifiers
- misplaced modifiers
- unclear antecedents
- incorrect or inconsistent abbreviations

Also, check the accuracy of all arithmetic calculations, statistics, numerical data, text citations, and references.

7. **Inconsistencies Must Be Avoided**. Be sure you are consistent in your use of abbreviations, terminology, and in citing references, from one part of your paper to another.

8. **Preparation of Tables, Figures, and Illustrations**. Any material that is not textual is considered artwork. This includes tables, figures, diagrams, charts, graphs, illustrations, appendices, screen captures, and photos. Tables and figures (including legend, notes, and sources) should be no larger than 4 ½ X 6 ½ inches. Type styles should be Helvetica (or Helvetica narrow if necessary) and no smaller than 8 point. We request that computer-generated figures be in black and white and/or shades of gray (preferably no color, for it does not reproduce well). Camera-ready art must contain no grammatical, typographical, or format errors and must reproduce sharply and clearly in the dimensions of the final printed page (4 ½ x 6 ½ inches). Photos and screen captures must be on disk as a TIF file, or other graphic file format such as JPEG or BMP. For rapid publication we must receive black-and-white glossy or matte positives (white background with black images and/or wording) in addition to files on disk. Tables should be created in the text document file using the software's Table feature.

9. **Submitting Art**. Both a printed hard copy and a disk copy of the art must be provided. We request that each piece of art be sent in its own file, on a disk separate from the disk containing the manuscript text file(s), and be clearly labeled. We reserve the right to (if necessary) request new art, alter art, or if all else has failed in achieving art that is presentable, delete art. If submitted art cannot be used, the Publisher reserves the right to redo the art and to change the author for a fee of $35.00 per hour for this service. The Haworth Press, Inc. is not responsible for errors incurred in the preparation of new artwork. Camera-ready artwork must be prepared on separate sheets of paper. Always use black ink and professional drawing instruments. On the back of these items, write your article title and the journal title lightly in soft-lead pencil (please do not write on the face of art). In the text file, skip extra lines and indicate where these figures are placed. Photos are considered part of the acceptable manuscript and remain with the Publisher for use in additional printings.

10. **Electronic Media**. Haworth's in-house typesetting unit is able to utilize your final manuscript material as prepared on most personal computers and word processors. This will minimize typographical errors and decrease overall production time. Please send the first draft and final draft copies of your manuscript to the journal Editor in print format for his/her final review and approval. After approval of your final manuscript, please submit the final approved version both on printed format ("hard copy") and floppy diskette. On the outside of the diskette package write:
1) the brand name of your computer or word processor
2) the word processing program and version that you used
3) the title of your article, and
4) the file name.

Note: Disk and hard copy must agree. In case of discrepancies, it is The Haworth Press' policy to follow hard copy. Authors are advised that no revisions of the manuscript can be made after acceptance by the Editor for publication. The benefits of this procedure are many with speed and accuracy being the most obvious. We look forward to working with your electronic submission which will allow us to serve you more efficiently.

11. **Alterations Required by Referees and Reviewers**. Many times a paper is accepted by the Editor contingent upon changes that are mandated by anonymous specialist referees and members of the Editorial Board. If the Editor returns your manuscript for revisions, you are responsible for retyping any sections of the paper to incorporate these revisions (if applicable, revisions should also be put on disk).

12. **Typesetting**. You will not be receiving galley proofs of your article. Editorial revisions, if any, must therefore be made while your article is still in manuscript. The final version of the manuscript will be the version you see published. Typesetter's errors will be corrected by the production staff of The Haworth Press. Authors are expected to submit manuscripts, disks, and art that are free from error.

13. **Reprints**. The senior author will receive two copies of the journal issue and 25 complimentary reprints of his or her article. The junior author will receive two copies of the journal issue. These are sent several weeks after the journal issue is published and in circulation. An order form for the purchase of additional reprints will also be sent to all authors at this time. (Approximately 4-6 weeks is necessary for the preparation of reprints.) Please do not query the Journal's Editor about reprints. All such questions should be sent directly to The Haworth Press, Inc., Production Department, 37 West Broad Street, West Hazleton, PA 18202. To order additional reprints (minimum: 50 copies), please contact The Haworth Document Delivery Center, 10 Alice Street, Binghamton, NY 13904-1580; 1-800-342-9678 or Fax (607) 722-6362.

14. **Copyright**. Copyright ownership of your manuscript must be transferred officially to The Haworth Press, Inc. before we can begin the peer-review process. The Editor's letter acknowledging receipt of the manuscript will be accompanied by a form fully explaining this. All authors must sign the form and return the original to the Editor as soon as possible. Failure to return the copyright form in a timely fashion will result in a delay in review and subsequent publication.

Child & Youth Care Forum

ADDRESS FOR SUBMISSION:

Doug Magnuson & Sibylle Artz, Co-Eds.
Child & Youth Care Forum
University of Northern Iowa
School of HPELS
203 WRC
Cedar Falls, IA 50614-0241
USA
Phone: 319-273-5857; 250-721-6472
Fax: 319-273-5958; 250-721-7218
E-Mail: See Guidelines
Web: See Guidelines
Address May Change:

PUBLICATION GUIDELINES:

Manuscript Length: 21-25
Copies Required: Four
Computer Submission: Yes
Format: MS Word, rtf
Fees to Review: 0.00 US$

Manuscript Style:
American Psychological Association

CIRCULATION DATA:

Reader: Academics
Frequency of Issue: 6 Times/Year
Copies per Issue: 2,001 - 3,000
Sponsor/Publisher: Kluwer Academic
Subscribe Price: 84.00 US$ Individual
    576.00 US$ Library

REVIEW INFORMATION:

Type of Review: Blind Review
No. of External Reviewers: 2
No. of In House Reviewers: 1
Acceptance Rate: 21-50%
Time to Review: 2 - 3 Months
Reviewers Comments: Yes
Invited Articles: 0-5%
Fees to Publish: 0.00 US$

MANUSCRIPT TOPICS:
Adolescent Psychology; Child & Youth Care Work; Developmental Psychology; Family Counseling & Therapy; Youth Development; Youth Services

MANUSCRIPT GUIDELINES/COMMENTS:

Website. http/:www.kluweronline.com/issn/1053-1890

Child & Youth Care Forum (formerly *Child & Youth Care Quarterly*) is an independent, professional publication committed to the improvement of child and youth care practice in a variety of day and residential settings and to the advancement of this field. Designed to serve child and youth care practitioners, their supervisors, and other personnel in child and youth care settings as well as instructors in the field, the journal provides a channel of communication and debate including material on practice, selection and training, theory and research, and professional issues.

Manuscripts from day and residential child and youth care workers, supervisors, administrators, instructors, and others in the field are invited. Manuscript submissions require an abstract of about 100 words and a list of 3 to 5 key words should be included with each copy. In general, style should conform to that found in these pages and, where appropriate, to that of the *Publication Manual of the American Psychological Association*, 5th Edition, 1983. Except in unusual cases, manuscripts should not exceed about 15 to 20 pages, and shorter ones are often preferable. Artwork, tables, and/or figures should be included with the original manuscript and should be camera ready (photocopies unacceptable).

Electronic submission is preferred. Please send manuscript e-files to:
Dr. Sibylle Artz at **sartz@uvic.ca**.

If electronic transfer is not possible, please use the following instructions for sending hard copies to:
Doug Magnuson, Co-Editor, Child & Youth Care Forum, Assistant Professor, Youth/Human Service Administration, Director, Institute for Youth Leaders, School of HPELS, 203 WRC, University of Northern Iowa, Cedar Falls, IA 50614-0241

Paper manuscripts, including any quotations, references, or tables, should be double-spaced, typed on one side of 8½ × 11-in. paper. Margins should be ample. Four copies of each manuscript should be submitted; if return of a manuscript is desired should it not be accepted for publication, please enclose a self-addressed envelope with sufficient postage. After a manuscript has been accepted for publication and after all revisions have been incorporated, manuscripts should be submitted to the Editors Office as hard copy accompanied by electronic files on disk. Label the disk with identifying information — software, journal name, and first authors last name. **The disk *must* be the one from which the accompanying manuscript (finalized version) was printed out**. The Editors Office cannot accept a disk without its accompanying, matching hard-copy manuscript.

Springer Open Choice. In addition to the normal publication process (whereby an article is submitted to the journal and access to that article is granted to customers who have purchased a subscription), Springer now provides an alternative publishing option: Springer Open Choice. A Springer Open Choice article receives all the benefits of a regular subscription-based article, but in addition is made available publicly through Springer's online platform SpringerLink. To publish via Springer Open Choice, upon acceptance please visit www.springeronline.com/openchoice to complete the relevant order form and provide the required payment information. Payment must be received in full before publication or articles will publish as regular subscription-model articles. We regret that Springer Open Choice cannot be ordered for published articles.

Queries to the Co-Editor about proposed submissions are invited by mail, or by e-mail at:
Doug.Magnuson@uni.edu.

Child & Youth Services

ADDRESS FOR SUBMISSION:

Douglas Magnuson, Co-Editor
Child & Youth Services
University of Northern Iowa
School of HPELS
203 WRC
Cedar Falls, IA 50614-0241
USA
Phone: 319-273-5857
Fax: 319-273-5958
E-Mail: doug.magnuson@uni.edu
Web: See Guidelines
Address May Change:

PUBLICATION GUIDELINES:

Manuscript Length: 30+
Copies Required: Four
Computer Submission: Yes
Format: MS Word, rtf
Fees to Review: 0.00 US$

Manuscript Style:
   American Psychological Association

CIRCULATION DATA:

Reader: Academics, Practitioners
Frequency of Issue: 2 Times/Year
Copies per Issue: 1,001 - 2,000
Sponsor/Publisher: Haworth Press
Subscribe Price: 60.00 US$ Individual
   400.00 US$ Library

REVIEW INFORMATION:

Type of Review: No Reply
No. of External Reviewers: 2
No. of In House Reviewers: 1
Acceptance Rate: Other
Time to Review: 4 - 6 Months
Reviewers Comments: Yes
Invited Articles: 31-50%
Fees to Publish: 0.00 US$

MANUSCRIPT TOPICS:

Adolescent Psychology; Child & Youth Care Work; Child Psychology; Developmental Psychology; Family Counseling & Therapy; Human Services; Youth Development; Youth Services

MANUSCRIPT GUIDELINES/COMMENTS:

Website. http://www.haworthpressinc.com/store/product.asp?sku=J024

About the Journal
Helps you provide the support and assistance that younger people need!

Child & Youth Services is a unique journal devoted exclusively to the development and treatment of children and adolescents. The journal covers a variety of relevant topics, including current concerns, topics of long-range importance, and concepts that can generally enrich youth services. The valuable contributions you'll find in *Child & Youth Services* will further the academic literature on the subject and provide practical applications and interventions for day-to-day youth contact at home, in school, or in other environments.

Child & Youth Services provides a forum for both scholars and youth service providers. Each issue, with its own unique thematic approach, provides in-depth coverage of a particular area of interest in the field. As such, the journal provides text material for use in relevant courses where such a resource is not otherwise readily available. In practice, *Child & Youth Services* is widely used to update those already working in the areas covered, and to illuminate new perspectives for colleagues throughout the field.

Themes that have been covered by the journal include:
- Pain, Normality, and Struggle for Congruence: Reinterpreting Residential Care for Children and Youth
- Residential Child Care Staff Selection: Choose with Care
- Innovative Approaches in Working with Children and Youth: New Lessons from the Kibbutz
- We Are in the Streets Because They Are in the Streets: Street Social Education in Brazil
- Assaultive Youth: Responding to Physical Assaultiveness in Residential, Community, and Health Care Settings
- Transitioning Exceptional Children and Youth Into the Community: Research and Practice
- Family Perspectives in Child and Youth Services
- Helping the Youthful Offender: Individual and Group Therapies That Work
- Specialist Foster Family Care: A Normalizing Experience
- Perspectives in Professional Child and Youth Care
- The Watchers and the Waiters: America's Homeless Children
- Being in Child Care: A Journey Into Self

About the Editor
Doug Magnuson, PhD, is Assistant Professor, University of Northern Iowa, Youth & Human Services Department. He is also the Director of the Institute for Youth Leaders there. In addition to being Editor of Child & Youth Services, Dr. Magnuson is editor of the book Residential Education as an Option for At-Risk Youth. His research interests focus on residential education, ethics of youthwork practice, and moral development in informal education.

About the Editor Emeritus
Jerome Beker, EdD, is Professor of Youth Studies in the School of Social Work and Adjunct Professor of Educational Psychology at the University of Minnesota in St. Paul. He directed the University's Center for Youth Development and Research for over 10 years. In 1988-89, he was a Fulbright Scholar in Jerusalem, Israel, and he has published widely in the field. His previous work with social agencies, organizational and private camps, and public schools has focused on providing direct service to normal and disturbed youth both individually and in groups of various ages and socioeconomic groups. Dr. Beker's career has included supervisory, administrative, and research roles, as well as youth work training and staff and program development.

Dr. Beker received his EdD degree in Guidance and Student Personnel Administration from the Teachers College at Columbia University. As a Research Fellow with the National Institute of Mental Health, his postdoctoral studies at the New School for Social Research and Syracuse University included advanced courses in psychology, sociology, statistics, and the use of computers in behavioral science research.

Child Abuse & Neglect

ADDRESS FOR SUBMISSION:

John M. Leventhal, Editor-in-Chief
Child Abuse & Neglect
Editorial Office
205 Whitney Avenue, Suite 100
New Haven, CT 06511
USA
Phone: 203-764-9170
Fax: 203-764-9172
E-Mail: mary.roth@yale.edu
Web: www.elsevier.com
Address May Change:

PUBLICATION GUIDELINES:

Manuscript Length: 16-20 pp
  text+tables/figs.
Copies Required: Four
Computer Submission: Yes Email
Format: IBM Compatible
Fees to Review: 0.00 US$

Manuscript Style:
  American Psychological Association

CIRCULATION DATA:

Reader: , Multidiscplinary
Frequency of Issue: Monthly
Copies per Issue: More than 3500
Sponsor/Publisher: International Society for
  Prevention of Child Abuse & Neglect
  (ISPCAN) / Elsevier Science, Ltd.
Subscribe Price: 1500.00 US$ Institution
  115.00 US$ ISPCAN Member
  50.00 US$ ISPCAN Dev. Country
  Member

REVIEW INFORMATION:

Type of Review: Blind Review
No. of External Reviewers: 5+
No. of In House Reviewers: 2
Acceptance Rate: 21-30%
Time to Review: 4 - 6 Months
Reviewers Comments: Yes
Invited Articles: 0-5%
Fees to Publish: 0.00 US$

MANUSCRIPT TOPICS:
Abnormal Psychology; Adolescent Psychology; Behavior Modification; Child Psychology; Developmental Psychology; Educational Psychology; Experimental Psychology; Family Counseling & Therapy; Physiological Psychology; Psychiatry; Psychobiology; Psychological Testing; Psychopathology; Research Methods & Statistics; Social Psychology

MANUSCRIPT GUIDELINES/COMMENTS:

Topics Include. Abuse, emotional, physical, ritual, sexual, substance; Adolescents; Adult survivors, Advocacy; Bullying; Child abuse reporting; Child protection system; child welfare; Consequences of maltreatment; Cultural issues; Dating violence; Development, brain; Development, Child; Discipline/punishment; Domestic violence; Education/Teachers; Effects of war; Epidemiology/Methodology; Evaluation/Interviewing; Failure to thrive; Family violence; Fatalities & forensic medicine; Foster care/Out-of-home care; Home visitation; Homelessness/Street children; Indigenous populations; Issues in developing countries; Judicial/Legal/Law; Law enforcement; Medicine, pediatrics, nursing; Mental health; Munchausen Syndrome by Proxy; Neglect, child, general; Offender/Perpetrator (non-sexual, sexual - adolescent, sexual - adult); Policy; Prevention; Program evaluation; Psychiatry;

Psychology; Public health; Qualitative research; Risk assessment; Social work; Sociology; Statistics; Systems of care; Training

Aims and Scope

Child Abuse & Neglect The International Journal provides an international, multidisciplinary forum on all aspects of child abuse and neglect, with special emphasis on prevention and treatment; the scope extends further to all those aspects of life which either favor or hinder child development. While contributions will primarily be from the fields of psychology, psychiatry, social work, medicine, nursing, law enforcement, legislature, education, and anthropology, the Journal encourages the concerned lay individual and child-oriented advocate organizations to contribute.

Types of Contributions

1. Original, Theoretical, and Empirical Contributions: (16-20 pages of text): Include a clear introductory statement of purpose; historical review when desirable; description of method and scope of observations; full presentation of the results; brief comment/discussion on the significance of the findings and any correlation with others in the literature; section on speculation and relevance or implications; summary in brief which may include discussion. Abstracts and references are required.
2. Brief Communications: Shorter articles of 5-7 pages (abstracts and/or references optional).
3. Articles on Clinical Practice: Case studies (but not single cases), commentaries, process and program descriptions, clinical audit and outcome studies, original clinical practice ideas for debate and argument.
4. Invited Reviews: Plans for proposed reviews are invited in draft outline in the first instance. The editors will commission reviews on specific topics. Reviews submitted without invitation or prior approval will be returned.
5. Letters to the Editor: Letters and responses pertaining to articles published in *Child Abuse & Neglect* or on issues relevant to the field, brief and to the point, should be prepared in the same style as other manuscripts.
6. Announcements/Notices: Events of national or international multidisciplinary interests are subject to editorial approval and must be submitted at least 8 months before they are to appear.

Submission Requirements

Electronic submissions are invited and should be submitted directly to the editorial office (**mary.roth@yale.edu**). Alternatively, manuscripts may be submitted as hard copy (four [4] complete copies should be sent). Manuscripts may be submitted in English, French, or Spanish. The entire manuscript, including abstract, tables, and references, *must be double-spaced throughout using 12 pt. type. Pages must be numbered.* A letter to the editor-in-chief (John M. Leventhal) requesting review must be included, noting that the manuscript has not been previously published and is not under simultaneous review elsewhere; authors are welcome to suggest names (with complete contact information) of three (3) potential reviewers. Authors are responsible for obtaining written permission from the copyright owners to reprint any previously published material included in their article. The editors reserve the right to refuse any manuscript submitted, whether by invitation or otherwise, and to make suggestions and modifications before publication. Submitted papers must be in final form when submitted; manuscripts will be returned for reworking or retyping that do not conform to required style and format.

Where to Send Papers
The Editor, Child Abuse & Neglect The International Journal, 205 Whitney Avenue, Ste. 100, New Haven, CT 06511, USA. Please specify type of submission. Questions? E-mail **mary.roth@yale.edu** or call 203-764-9170.

Style and Manuscript Order
Manuscripts must be prepared following the general style guidelines set forth in the *Publication Manual of the American Psychological Association* (4th ed.). Submitted papers should be in final form ready for publication. Manuscripts will be returned for reworking or retyping that do not conform to requirements.

First Title Page
To facilitate blind reviews, all indication of authorship, including acknowledgements, must be limited to this page. Title page should include (1) full article title; (2) name, affiliation including city and state/country for each author at the time of the work; (3) name, mailing address, telephone, fax, and e-mail of corresponding author; (4) name and complete address for reprint requests; (5) 3-5 keywords for indexing purposes; and (6) all acknowledgements and support notes.

Second Title Page
Type only the title and remove other indications of author identity.

Practice Implications
Authors should provide a 100-word paragraph describing the practice implications of their manuscripts to help translate research into clinical practice. Please do not incorporate this page into the text of the paper itself.

Abstract
A structured abstract (Objective, Methods, Results, Conclusions) not to exceed 250 words in length covering the main factual points is required. Use complete sentences, and spell out acronyms at first mention.

Main Text
Should be clearly organized, with headings and subheadings as needed (3 weights of headings maximum). *If human subjects are involved, approval by an institutional review board and the informed consent of participants must be reported.* Avoid the use of first person (we, our, I). Footnotes must be incorporated into the text or deleted.

References
Style and formatting of bibliographic citations in the text and the reference section must adhere to the guidelines of the *Publication Manual of the American Psychological Association* (4th ed.). The *Journal* uses an alphabetical style rather than a numeric style both in the text and bibliography. No abbreviations of journal titles or use of et al. is permitted in the bibliography.

Tables/Figures
Cite each table/figure clearly in text. Tables should be arranged one to a page with a self-contained title that is understandable without reference to the text. Figures should be computer generated or professionally drawn, one per page, with legends on a separate sheet.

Copyright
Upon acceptance of the manuscript, authors must complete a Transfer of Copyright Agreement as well as provide additional materials and information requested by the editorial office.

Review, Editing, and Production
All initial submissions are acknowledged on receipt; all electronic resubmissions are acknowledged. Peer review is generally double-blind, although it is sometimes clear to one or the other who is involved. Scheduling and production processes currently take 6-8 months once manuscripts are accepted and all required information is in-house. The publisher and editor reserve the right to copyedit manuscripts to conform to Journal style. The corresponding author will receive page proofs for correction of typographical errors only. No rewriting of the original manuscript as accepted is allowed in the proof stage. Authors must return proofs within 48 hours of receipt; late corrections cannot be guaranteed. Twenty-five free reprints are provided; orders for additional reprints must be received before printing in order to qualify for lower pre-publication rates (co-author requirements must be included on this form).

Child Abuse Review

ADDRESS FOR SUBMISSION:

Nicky Stanley, Editor
Child Abuse Review
c/o Julia Walsh, Editorial Assistant
Guy's, King's & St Thomas' School of Med
Newcomen Centre, Guy's Hospital
St. Thomas Street
London, SE1 9RT
UK
Phone: +44 0 207 188 4532
Fax: +44 0 207 188 4629
E-Mail: julia.walsh@southwarkpct.nhs
Web: www.interscience.wiley.com
Address May Change:

PUBLICATION GUIDELINES:

Manuscript Length: See Guidelines
Copies Required: Five
Computer Submission: Yes Disk, Email
Format: PC or MAC, MS Word,
    WordPerfect
Fees to Review: 0.00 US$

Manuscript Style:
    See Manuscript Guidelines

CIRCULATION DATA:

Reader: Academics, Practitioners
Frequency of Issue: 6 Times/Year
Copies per Issue: 2,001 - 3,000
Sponsor/Publisher: John Wiley & Sons, Inc.
Subscribe Price: 130.00 US$ Indv Print
    315.00 US$ Inst Print
    See Website - More Details

REVIEW INFORMATION:

Type of Review: Blind Review
No. of External Reviewers: 100
No. of In House Reviewers: 8
Acceptance Rate: 40%
Time to Review: 2 - 3 Months
Reviewers Comments: Yes
Invited Articles: 6-10%
Fees to Publish: 0.00 US$

MANUSCRIPT TOPICS:
Child Protection; Child Psychology; Social Welfare

MANUSCRIPT GUIDELINES/COMMENTS:

Aims and Scope
Child Abuse Review provides a forum for all professionals working in the field of child protection, giving them access to the latest research findings, practice developments, training initiatives and policy issues. The Journal's remit includes all forms of maltreatment, whether they occur inside or outside the family environment. Papers are written in a style appropriate for a multidisciplinary audience international contributions are welcomed.

The Journal maintains a practice orientated focus and authors of research papers are encouraged to examine and discuss implications for practitioners. By always emphasizing research/practice links, it is the Editors' aim to promote practice relevant research and to facilitate the use of research findings, to enhance good practice and influence policy.

218

The Editorial Board, in all its activities, seeks to prevent discrimination on the grounds of age, gender, racial origin, culture, religious belief, language, disability, economic status or political views. The Journal has a policy of encouraging inclusive practice and for this reason authors are asked to consider the applicability of their work to all groups.

Each issue includes a mix of refereed research and practice papers, training updates, case studies, short reports, book reviews and a calendar of future events. Correspondence from readers is much welcomed, and it is hoped that these letters (edited where appropriate) will form a lively feature within the journal.

The views expressed in the papers in this volume are those of the authors and are not necessarily those of BASPCAN, the Editorial Board or the organizations to which the authors are affiliated.

Child Abuse Review published by John Wiley & Sons Ltd is the official journal for the British Association for the Study and Prevention of Child Abuse and Neglect whose members receive the journal as a membership entitlement. For membership details contact BASPCAN, 10 Priory Street, York, YO1 1EZ. Tel: +44 (0) 1904 613605. Fax: +44 (0) 1904 642239, www.baspcan.org.uk

Child Abuse Review Editorial Office:
Julia Walsh, Editorial Assistant, Newcomen Centre, Guy's Hospital, St Thomas Street, London SE1 9RT. Tel: +44 (0) 207 188 4532, Fax: +44 (0) 207 188 4629 Email: **julia.walsh@southwarkpct.nhs.uk**

Instructions to Authors
1. **Initial Manuscript Submission**. Submit five copies of the manuscript (including copies of tables and illustrations) to: Nicky Stanley, c/o Julia Walsh, Editorial Assistant, Child Abuse Review, Guy's, King's and St Thomas' School of Medicine, Newcomen Centre, Guy's Hospital, St Thomas Street, London SE1 9RT, Fax Number: +44 (0) 207 188 4629 or email to: **julia.walsh@southwarkpct.nhs.uk**.

Authors **must** also supply:
- an electronic copy of the final version (see section below),
- a Copyright Transfer Agreement with original signature(s) - without this we are unable to accept the submission, and
- permission grants - if the manuscript contains extracts, including illustrations, from other copyright works (including material from on-line or intranet sources) it is the author's responsibility to obtain written permission from the owners of the publishing rights to reproduce such extracts using the Wiley Permission Request Form. Permission grants should be submitted with the manuscript.

Submitted manuscripts should not have been previously published and should not be submitted for publication elsewhere while they are under consideration by Wiley. Submitted material will not be returned to the author unless specifically requested.

2. **Electronic submission**. The electronic copy of the final, revised manuscript must be sent to the Editor **together with** the paper copy. Disks should be PC or Mac formatted; write on the disk the software package used, the name of the author and the name of the journal. We are able to use most word processing packages, but prefer Word or WordPerfect.

Illustrations must be submitted in electronic format where possible. Save each figure as a separate file, in **TIFF** or **EPS** format preferably, and include the source file. Write on the disk the software package used to create them; we favor dedicated illustration packages over tools such as Excel or PowerPoint.

3. **Manuscript style**. The language of the journal is English. All submissions must have a title, be printed on one side of the paper, be double-line spaced and have a margin of 3cm all round. Illustrations and tables must be printed on separate sheets, and not be incorporated into the text. Their proposed location should be indicated in the text.

- The **title page** must list the full title, short title, and names and affiliations of all authors and a running headline. Give the full address, including email, telephone and fax, of the author who is to check the proofs.
- Include the name(s) of any **sponsor(s)** of the research contained in the Paper, along with **grant number(s)**.
- Supply an **abstract** of up to 200 words for all Papers, Case Studies and Brief Communications (optional). An abstract is a concise summary of the whole Paper, not just the conclusions, and is understandable without reference to the rest of the Paper. It should contain no citation to other published work.
- Include up to four **keywords** that describe your Paper, for indexing purposes.

Papers (excluding tables and references) should be between 3,000 and 5,000 words (Case Studies around 2,000 and Short Reports between 1,000 and 3,000). Authors should indicate the word-length of their manuscript at the end.

4. **Ethics, Confidentiality and Consent**. Authors must indicate how they addressed any ethical issues relating to the content of their paper, including the endorsement of any organization or group, such as a professional association or ethics committee.

Whenever publishing case material, if there is a possibility of identifying any individual, including clients or professionals, consideration needs to be given to informed consent. Where it is impossible or impractical to get informed consent, then care must be taken to ensure the case is truly anonymous and disguised, without compromising the validity of the substantive issues. Complete anonymity is difficult to achieve and informed consent should be obtained if there is any doubt. Consent for the publication of quotes from individuals (clients and professional) should also be obtained (e.g. at the time of a research interview). Consent is not necessary if material is already legitimately in the public domain. Authors should clearly state the approach taken in obtaining consent and the nature of any disguise should be described.

5. **Reference style**. References should be quoted in the text as name and year within brackets and listed at the end of the Paper alphabetically. Where reference is made to more than one work by the same author published in the same year, identify each citation in the text as

220

follows: (Collins, 1998a), (Collins, 1998b). Where three or more authors are listed in the reference list, please cite in the text as (Collins *et al.*, 1998).

All references must be complete and accurate. Online citations should include date of access. If necessary, cite unpublished or personal work in the text but do not include it in the reference list. References should be listed in the following style:

Conte JR, Schuerman JR. 1987. Factors associated with an increased impact of child sexual abuse. *Child Abuse and Neglect* **11**: 201-211.

Bentovim A, Elton A, Hildebrand J, Tranter A, Vizard E. 1988. *Child Sexual Abuse within the Family: Assessment and Treatment*. Butterworth: London.

Garbarino J. 1981. An ecological approach to child maltreatment. In *The Social Context of Child Abuse and Neglect*, Pelton H (ed). Human Sciences Press: New York; 17-44.

The Geriatric Website,1999. http:// www.wiley.com/oap/ [1 April 1999]

6. **Illustrations**. Supply each illustration on a separate sheet, with the lead author's name and the figure number, with the top of the figure indicated, on the reverse. Supply original **photographs**; photocopies or previously printed material will not be used. Line artwork must be high-quality laser output (not photocopies). Tints are not acceptable; lettering must be of a reasonable size that would still be clearly legible upon reduction, and consistent within each figure and set of figures. Supply artwork at the intended size for printing.

The cost of printing **color** illustrations in the journal will be charged to the author. If color illustrations are supplied electronically in either TIFF or EPS format, they **may** be used in the PDF of the article at no cost to the author, even if this illustration was printed in black and white in the journal. The PDF will appear on the *Wiley InterScience* site.

7. **Copyright**. To enable the publisher to disseminate the author's work to the fullest extent, the author must sign a Copyright Transfer Agreement, transferring copyright in the Paper from the author to the publisher, and submit the original signed agreement with the Paper presented for publication. A copy of the agreement to be used (which may be photocopied) can be found in the first issue of each volume of *Child Abuse Review*. Copies may also be obtained from the journal editor or publisher, or may be printed from this website.

8. **Further information**. Proofs will be sent to the author for checking. This stage is to be used only to correct errors that may have been introduced during the production process. Prompt return of the corrected proofs, preferably within two days of receipt, will minimize the risk of the Paper being held over to a later issue. 25 complimentary offprints will be provided to the author who checked the proofs, unless otherwise indicated. Further offprints and copies of the journal may be ordered. There is no page charge to authors.

Copyright Information

Child and Adolescent Mental Health

ADDRESS FOR SUBMISSION:

Udwin, Vostanis & Stallard, Editors
Child and Adolescent Mental Health
Assn for Child Psychology and Psychiatry
  ONLINE SUBMISSIONS ONLY
St. Saviour's House
39/41 Union Street
London, SE1 1SD
UK
Phone: +44 (0) 20 7403 7458
Fax: +44 (0) 20 7403 7081
E-Mail: camh@acpp.org.uk
Web: www.acpp.org.uk
Address May Change:

PUBLICATION GUIDELINES:

Manuscript Length: Less than 4000 words
Copies Required: Three
Computer Submission: Yes Web
Format: MS Word
Fees to Review: 0.00 US$

Manuscript Style:
    American Psychological Association

CIRCULATION DATA:

Reader: Practitioners
Frequency of Issue: 4 Times/Year
Copies per Issue: 3,001 - 4,000
Sponsor/Publisher: Association for Child
  Psychology & Psychiatry / Blackwell
  Publishers, Inc.
Subscribe Price: 40.00 US$ Individual
  108.00 US$ Institution
  28.00 Pounds Indv. & 75 Pounds Inst.

REVIEW INFORMATION:

Type of Review: Editorial Review
No. of External Reviewers: 2
No. of In House Reviewers: 0
Acceptance Rate: 50%
Time to Review: 2 - 3 Months
Reviewers Comments: Yes
Invited Articles: 0-5%
Fees to Publish: 0.00 US$

MANUSCRIPT TOPICS:

Adolescent Psychology; Child Psychology; Counseling Process; Developmental Psychology;
Educational Psychology; Family Counseling & Therapy; Learning & Conditioning;
Neuropsychology; Personality; Psychiatry; Psychological Testing; Sensation & Perception;
Social Psychology; Thinking & Cognition

MANUSCRIPT GUIDELINES/COMMENTS:

Editors
Orlee Udwin, Consultant Clinical Psychologist in Child Health, South London and Maudsley
(NHS) Trust, Mary Sheridan Centre, London, UK

Panos Vostanis, Professor of Child and Adolescent Psychiatry, University of Leicester, UK

Paul Stallard, Consultant Child Clinical Psychologist, Royal United Hospital, Bath, UK

Aims and Scope

Child and Adolescent Mental Health (formerly *Child Psychology & Psychiatry Review*) provides a forum for the exchange of clinical experience, ideas and research. Its principal aim is to foster good clinical practice. Wide-ranging in its coverage, *CAMH* includes studies of new theoretical developments, clinical case studies, descriptions of innovative techniques and new service developments. The Editors aim to publish original research of high quality relevant to all aspects of child and adolescent mental health.

In addition to original articles, the journal publishes commissioned reviews and includes special sections of broad based interest - Journal Monitor, Measurement Issues, Points of Law, Therapy Matters, Questions and Answers, Personal Profiles - as well as book reviews.

Readership

Clinical Psychologists, Developmental Psychologists, Psychiatrists, Psychotherapists, Educational Psychologists, Research Psychologists, Paediatricians, Social Workers, Nurses, Health Visitors, Students, General Practitioners, Research Officers, Teachers and Lecturers.

Submissions are invited. Clinical papers may take the form of single case studies, group studies, descriptions of innovative techniques, or novel service developments. Theoretical papers may inform on new developments in relevant fields. Original ideas and formulations will be particularly welcome. Research papers should contain clinically relevant empirical data. Studies may be modest in scope but ought to be well designed and papers need to highlight both their strengths and limitations. All papers should be set within the context of the relevant literature and draw out the implications for clinical practice. Full submission information can be found on the Submit Your Article page at the following website:

http://blackwellpublishers.co.uk/submit.asp?ref=1475-357X&site=1

Author Guidelines

1. Submission of a paper to *Child and Adolescent Mental Health* will be held to imply that it represents an original article, not previously published; that it is not being considered for publication elsewhere; and that if accepted for publication it will not be published elsewhere without the consent of the Editors. The copyright of articles accepted for publication in *CAMH* belongs to the Association for Child Psychology and Psychiatry.

2. Manuscripts should be submitted online. You will need your files in an electronic format, an Internet connection, a user ID and password for the site. Go to **http://acpp.manuscriptcentral.com** and Check for existing account if you have submitted to or reviewed for the journal before, or have forgotten your details. If you are new to the journal *Create a new account*. Alternatively, contributions, correspondence and a disk containing the manuscript can be sent to the Editors, *CAMH*, Association for Child Psychology and Psychiatry, St Saviour's House, 39/41 Union Street, London SE1 1SD, UK (Tel: +44 (0)20 7403 7458; Fax: +44 (0)20 7403 7081; Email: **camh@acpp.org.uk**).

3. Manuscripts should be double spaced and conform to the house style of *CAMH*. The first page of the manuscript should give the title, name(s) and address(es) of author(s), and an abbreviated title (running head) of up to 80 characters. Specify the author to whom any correspondence should be addressed.

Summary. Authors should include a brief **ABSTRACT** highlighting the main points of their article. This abstract should not exceed 100 words and should be typed on a separate sheet **double spaced**. **KEYWORDS** (3-6) should be given below the Abstract. Final accepted versions of commissioned reviews and papers should be sent on disk accompanied by a print-out. Diskettes should be 3.50" double sided, double density, preferably written in Word for Windows, or saved as/converted to ASCII files. Guidelines for Manuscripts Accepted for Publication, which specify instructions for typing manuscripts on disks, will be sent automatically to authors of articles which are provisionally accepted.

4. Papers submitted should be concise and written in English in a readily understandable style, avoiding sexist and racist language. Papers should not exceed 4000 words, excluding references and Tables. Occasionally, longer articles may be accepted after negotiation with the Editors. Authors should include a word count of their paper. Authors whose first language is not English may send a first language version of their paper along with the English version. Please note that this is to facilitate sub-editing and is not a translation service.

5. For referencing *CAMH* follows a slightly adapted version of the style used by *The Journal of Child Psychology and Psychiatry* (i.e. APA). References in running text should be quoted showing author(s) and date. For up to three authors, all surnames should be given on first citation; for subsequent citations or where there are more than three authors, 'et al.' should be used. A full reference list should be given at the end of the article, in alphabetical order.

References to journal articles should include: author's surnames and initials; year of publication; full chapter title; full book title; editors' initials and surnames; place of publication and publisher. Please see recent issues of *The Journal of Child Psychology and Psychiatry* for further details and examples.

6. **Tables**. These should be kept to a minimum and not duplicate what is in the text: they should be clearly set out and numbered.

7. **Figures**. Any figures, charts or diagrams should be submitted as camera-ready-copy (clear laser copy acceptable) with clear, easy to read titles or captions.

8. **Footnotes**. These should be avoided as much as possible, but if necessary use a superscript number or a number in brackets for footnote indicators in the text, and give footnotes at end of article, before References.

9. The Editors cannot accept responsibility for damage to, or loss of, papers submitted. Authors should keep copies of paper and disks; rejected manuscripts are not returned unless this is requested at the time of submission.

10. Authors of accepted papers receive one complementary copy of the relevant issue.

11. Whilst every effort is made by the Editors and ACPP to see that no inaccurate or misleading data, opinion or statement appears in *CAMH*, they wish to make it clear that the data and opinions appearing in the articles and advertisements herein are the sole

responsibility of the contributor or advertiser concerned. Accordingly, the ACPP, Editors and their respective editorial colleagues, employees, officers and agents accept no responsibility or liability whatsoever for the consequences of any such inaccurate or misleading data, opinion or statement.

12. **Copyright Assignment Form**. Authors will be required to assign copyright in their paper to Child Psychology and Psychiatry. Copyright assignment is a condition of publication and papers will not be passed to the publisher for production unless copyright has been assigned. To assist authors an appropriate copyright assignment form will be supplied by the editorial office. Alternatively, authors may like to download a copy of the form at **http://www.blackwellpublishing.com/pdf/CAMH_CAF.pdf** (Government employees need to complete the Author Warranty sections, although copyright in such cases does not need to be assigned.)

Child Development

ADDRESS FOR SUBMISSION:

Lynn S. Liben, Editor
Child Development
University of Michigan
3131 S. State St. Suite 302
Ann Arbor, MI 48108-1623
USA
Phone: 734-998-7310
Fax: 734-998-7282
E-Mail: cdev@umich.edu
Web: www.srcd.org/cd.html
Address May Change:

PUBLICATION GUIDELINES:

Manuscript Length: 25-40
Copies Required: Electronic
Computer Submission: Yes
Format: N/A
Fees to Review: 0.00 US$

Manuscript Style:
    American Psychological Association,
    Fifth Edition

CIRCULATION DATA:

Reader: Academics
Frequency of Issue: Bi-Monthly
Copies per Issue: 5,001 - 10,000
Sponsor/Publisher: Society for Research in
    Child Development / Blackwell
    Publishers, Inc.
Subscribe Price: 293.00 US$

REVIEW INFORMATION:

Type of Review: Blind Review
No. of External Reviewers: 2-4
No. of In House Reviewers: 0
Acceptance Rate: 21-30%
Time to Review: 2-4 Months
Reviewers Comments: Yes
Invited Articles: 21-30%
Fees to Publish: 0.00 US$

MANUSCRIPT TOPICS:
Child Psychology; Developmental Psychology; Educational Psychology; Exceptional Child;
Family Counseling & Therapy

MANUSCRIPT GUIDELINES/COMMENTS:

Notice to Contributors
Child Development publishes empirical, theoretical, review, applied, and policy articles
reporting research on child development. Published by the interdisciplinary Society for
Research in Child Development (SRCD), the journal welcomes relevant submissions from all
disciplines. Further information is available at **http://www.srcd.org/cd.html**.

Types of Articles
Child Development considers manuscripts in formats described below. Inquiries concerning
alternative formats should be addressed to the Editor prior to submission. All submissions are
expected to be no more than 40 manuscript pages, including tables, references, and figures
(but excluding appendices). Authors should provide a justification if the submission is
substantially longer. Unless the editor finds that justification compelling, the submission will
be returned to the author for shortening prior to editorial review.

Empirical articles comprise the major portion of the journal. To be accepted, empirical articles must be judged as being high in scientific quality, contributing to the empirical base of child development, and having important theoretical, practical, or interdisciplinary implications. Reports of multiple studies, methods, or settings are encouraged, but single-study reports are also considered. Empirical articles will thus vary considerably in length (approximately 8 to 40 manuscript pages); text and graphics should be as concise as material permits. All modes of empirical research are welcome.

Reviews focus on past empirical and/or on conceptual and theoretical work. They are expected to synthesize or evaluate a topic or issue relevant to child development, should appeal to a broad audience, and may be followed by a small number of solicited commentaries.

Essays describe original concepts, methods, trends, applications, and theories; these may also be accompanied by solicited commentaries.

Child Development and ... are articles that provide readers with tutorials about some new concept or academic specialty pertinent to research in child development. These papers should review the major definitions, methods, and findings of the concept or specialty and discuss past or potential links to child development.

From another perspective is a format in which papers on a focal topic, written by different authors, are published simultaneously. Papers represent diverse perspectives (e.g., authors whose work represents different populations; different disciplines; different theories, methods, or analytic tools). In some cases, calls for submissions on particular topics will be disseminated through SRCD (via e-mail or SRCD publications), and submissions will undergo normal editorial review. In some cases, a submitted manuscript (e.g., an empirical article) may be selected as a lead article for this format, with invited commentaries providing additional perspectives. The editors also welcome suggestions from readers for topics for this format.

Manuscript Submission

Please follow submission requirements carefully, as deviations may slow processing. *Child Development* will not consider for publication any manuscript under review elsewhere or substantially similar to a manuscript already published. At submission, please inform the Editor if the paper has been or is posted on a website. For more information on the SRCD policy on web publications, see website. Editors retain the right to reject manuscripts that do not meet established ethical standards.

Manuscripts should be submitted to **cdev@umich.edu** as an electronic attachment in a Word or WordPerfect file. The transmittal e-mail should contain the name(s) of the author(s) and affiliation(s), and the street address, telephone, fax, and electronic mail address of the corresponding author. A corresponding author's submission to *Child Development* implies that all co-authors have agreed to the content and form of the manuscript and that the ethical standards of SRCD have been followed (see the *Child Development* website or pp. 283-284 of the 2000 *SRCD Directory*). Any financial interest or conflict of interest must be explained to the Editor in the cover letter. The corresponding author is responsible for informing all co-authors, in a timely manner, of manuscript submission, editorial decisions, reviews, and revisions.

The manuscript file should be formatted with double spaced, 12-point type, and should include a single paragraph abstract of 100-120 words. Please follow all guidelines on format, style, and ethics provided in the *Publication Manual of the American Psychological Association* (5th ed.). Figures included with initial submissions will not be returned. Therefore, please submit only electronic files or copies of figures. Authors should keep a copy of all correspondence, files, and figures to guard against loss.

Manuscript Review
If you have not received acknowledgment within two weeks of transmission, please inquire at **cdev@umich.edu** or call (734) 998-7310. Each manuscript is handled by the Editor or an Associate Editor who consults with one or more Consulting Editors and/or ad hoc reviewers who have relevant expertise. To ensure blind review, cover sheets are removed before review; authors should avoid including any other information about identity or affiliation in submissions. Copies of the submission and associated correspondence are retained in the SRCD archives. For accepted manuscripts, authors are required to prepare a 300-500 layperson's summary for public dissemination purposes. Details are provided to authors as part of final processing.

There is no charge for publication in *Child Development* unless tabular or graphic materials exceed 10% of the total number of pages. Charges are also levied for changes in proofs other than correction of printer's errors. Any inquiries relating to charges or business matters (including reprint orders) should be addressed to Blackwell Publishers, *Child Development*, Production Coordinator, 350 Main Street, Malden, MA 02148, (781) 388-8200.

Inquiries and suggestions regarding editorial policy may be addressed to: Dr. Lynn S. Liben, Editor, Child Development, Department of Psychology, The Pennsylvania State University, University Park, PA 16802, **liben@psu.edu**. *Please do not send electronic or paper manuscripts to the above address.* Doing so will delay the processing of your manuscript.

Child Maltreatment: Journal of the American Prof. Soc. on the Abuse of Children

ADDRESS FOR SUBMISSION:

Steven J. Ondersma, Editor
Child Maltreatment: Journal of the
   American Prof. Soc. on the Abuse of
   Children
Wayne State University
School of Medicine
2761 E. Jefferson Ave
Detroit, MI 48207
USA
Phone: 313-577-4871
Fax: 313-993-1372
E-Mail: childmaltreatment@wayne.edu
Web: http://cmx.sagepub.com
Address May Change:

PUBLICATION GUIDELINES:

Manuscript Length: See Guidelines
Copies Required: Four
Computer Submission: Yes Email preferred
Format: MS Word
Fees to Review: 0.00 US$

Manuscript Style:
   American Psychological Association

CIRCULATION DATA:

Reader: Academics
Frequency of Issue: Quarterly
Copies per Issue: 3,001 - 4,000
Sponsor/Publisher: American Professional
   Society on the Abuse of Children
   (APSAC) / Sage Publications
Subscribe Price: 95.00 US$ Individual
   437.00 US$ Institution

REVIEW INFORMATION:

Type of Review: Blind Review
No. of External Reviewers: 3
No. of In House Reviewers: 0
Acceptance Rate:
Time to Review: 2-4 Months
Reviewers Comments: Yes
Invited Articles: 11-20%
Fees to Publish: 0.00 US$

MANUSCRIPT TOPICS:
Adolescent Psychology; Child Abuse; Child Neglect; Child Psychology

MANUSCRIPT GUIDELINES/COMMENTS:

Child Maltreatment: Journal of the American Professional Society on the Abuse of Children
Manuscript Length: 15 for brief reports, 30 for regular articles, 50 for reviews
Acceptance Rate: 13% first round; 40% ultimate (invited and regular submissions)

Child Maltreatment is the membership journal of the American Professional Society on the Abuse of Children (APSAC), the nation's largest multidisciplinary child maltreatment professional organization. The journal seeks to foster professional excellence in the field of child abuse and neglect by reporting the latest scientific information and technical innovations in a form which is immediately useful to practitioners and policy makers. An interdisciplinary journal, *Child Maltreatment* serves as a common ground for practitioners and researchers from mental health, child protection, medicine, law, and allied disciplines. *CM* emphasizes perspectives which have a rigorous scientific base and will inform policy, practice and research.

Child Maltreatment invites submission of the following types of manuscripts:
- Original quantitative empirical research. Most manuscripts are of this type.
- Integrative literature reviews or in-depth analyses.
- Research involving meta-analysis.
- Original qualitative, scholarly, policy, or legal research.
- Case presentations and program evaluations if they are presented as clearly illustrative of important theoretical issues, innovations, new phenomena, policies or laws, etc.
- Presentations of theories or models.
- Manuscripts describing technical or practice innovations and related issues or controversies
- Cross-cultural or multicultural research and analysis.
- Book or media reviews.
- Commentary on articles published in *Child Maltreatment*

The following types of manuscripts are generally not appropriate for *Child Maltreatment*:
- Topics only peripherally related to child abuse and neglect.
- Political commentary, journalism, testimonies or endorsements.
- Fiction, poetry, artwork, personal stories, biographies or autobiographies.
- Case presentations or program descriptions/evaluations not illustrative of new phenomena or important theoretical issues, etc.

Manuscripts should have an abstract of up to 150 words and follow stylistic elements of the *Publication Manual of the American Psychological Association* (5th Edition). Submissions should be limited to 30 typewritten double-spaced pages, including references, with the exception of major literature reviews which should be limited to 50 pages. Authors are reminded that manuscripts should be formatted to allow for anonymous peer review. Therefore, please include a second title page without author information and omit any identifying information (e.g. references to states, universities or organizations). If the study builds on earlier work which would identify the author, please hide the reference (e.g., "In our initial study from this project [reference withheld for review] we found......"). Endnotes, references, tables and figures should be on separate pages, and all figures should be camera ready. Submissions should be accompanied by a letter stating that the manuscript has neither been published, nor is under consideration elsewhere. If all or part of the same data has been published elsewhere, the authors should describe how the content of the submitted manuscript provides new information not available in previously published articles. For research projects involving human participants, please indicate in the letter whether or not the project was reviewed and approved by an IRB. Authors submitting manuscripts for a guest-edited section or submitting manuscripts invited by the journal should identify their manuscripts accordingly in the letter. Unless otherwise instructed, emailed submissions for both initial and revised manuscripts are preferred (**childmaltreatment@wayne.edu**).

Child Neuropsychology

ADDRESS FOR SUBMISSION:

M. Westerveld & J. Donders, Editors
Child Neuropsychology
ONLINE SUBMISSIONS ONLY
Phone:
Fax:
E-Mail: See Guidelines
Web: http://www.tandf.co.uk/journals
Address May Change:

PUBLICATION GUIDELINES:

Manuscript Length:
Copies Required: One
Computer Submission: Yes Disk, Email,
    Web
Format: MS Word/WordPerfect
Fees to Review: 0.00 US$

Manuscript Style:
    American Psychological Association

CIRCULATION DATA:

Reader: Academics
Frequency of Issue: 6 Times/Year
Copies per Issue:
Sponsor/Publisher: Taylor & Francis
Subscribe Price: 180.00 US$ Individual
    526.00 US$ Institution

REVIEW INFORMATION:

Type of Review:
No. of External Reviewers: 2-3
No. of In House Reviewers:
Acceptance Rate:
Time to Review: 4 - 6 Months
Reviewers Comments: Yes
Invited Articles:
Fees to Publish: 0.00 US$

MANUSCRIPT TOPICS:
Adolescent Psychology; Child Psychology; Neuropsychology

MANUSCRIPT GUIDELINES/COMMENTS:

Aims and Scope. The purposes of *Child Neuropsychology* are to (a) publish research on the neuropsychological effects of disorders which effect brain functioning in children and adolescents, (b) publish research on the neuropsychological dimension of development in childhood and adolescence and (c) promote the integration of theory, method and research findings in child/developmental neuropsychology.

The primary emphasis of *Child Neuropsychology* is to publish original empirical research. Theoretical and methodological papers and theoretically relevant case studies are welcome. Critical reviews of topics pertinent to child/developmental neuropsychology are encouraged. Special topics are also encouraged, including book and test reviews and reviews of relevant professional issues in *Child Neuropsychology*.

Manuscripts must be submitted through the journal's Scholar One website, **http://neuropsychology.manuscriptcentral.com**. Questions for the editor may be addressed to either **Westerm@msn.com** or **JDonders@mfbrc.com**. Book reviews can also be submitted to the editor at either address mentioned.

For authors without internet access who wish to submit to *Child Neuropsychology*, a copy on disk prepared in MS Word or WordPerfect is required. The disk must be clearly labeled with the authors' names, file name, and software program. A hardcopy printout that exactly matches the disk must be supplied. Each manuscript must be accompanied by a statement that it has not been published elsewhere and that it has not been submitted simultaneously for publication elsewhere. Authors are responsible for obtaining permission to reproduce copyrighted material from other sources and are required to sign an agreement for the transfer of copyright to the publisher. All accepted manuscripts, artwork, and photographs become the property of the publisher. All parts of the manuscript should be typewritten, double-spaced, with margins of at least one inch on all sides. Manuscript pages must be numbered consecutively throughout the paper. The text should be divided into the following sections: Introduction, Methods, Results, Discussion, Acknowledgements and References. The manuscript must be in accordance with the *APA Publication Manual*, 4th ed.

Authors should also supply a shortened version of the title suitable for the running head, not exceeding 50 character spaces. Each article should be summarized in an abstract of not more than 100 words. Avoid abbreviations, diagrams, and reference to the text in the abstract.

Special topics are also encouraged, including book and test reviews and reviews of relevant professional issues in *Child Neuropsychology*.

References. Cite in the text by author and date (Smith, 1983). Prepare reference list in accordance with the *APA Publication Manual*, 4th ed. Only references published in generally available journals or books will be accepted.

Examples:
Journal. Tsai, M., & Wagner, N. N. (1978). Therapy groups for women sexually molested as children. *Archives of Sexual Behaviour*, 7(6), 417-427.

Book. Millman, M. (1980). *Such a pretty face*. New York: W. W. Norton.

Contribution to a Book. Hartley, J. T., & Walsh, D. A. (1980). Contemporary issues in adult development of learning. In L. W. Poon (ed.), *Ageing in the 1980s* (pp. 239-252). Washington, DC: American Psychological Association.

Illustrations. Illustrations submitted (line drawings, halftones, photos, photomicrographs, etc.) should be clean originals or digital files. Digital files are recommended for highest quality reproduction and should follow these guidelines:
- 300 dpi or higher
- Sized to fit on journal page
- EPS, TIFF, or PSD format only
- Submitted as separate files, not embedded in text files

Color illustrations will be considered for publication; however, the author will be required to bear the full cost involved in their printing and publication. The charge for the first page with color is $900.00. The next three pages with color are $450.00 each. A custom quote will be provided for color art totaling more than 4 journal pages. Good-quality color prints should be provided in their final size. The publisher has the right to refuse publication of color prints deemed unacceptable.

Tables and Figures. Tables and figures (illustrations) should not be embedded in the text, but should be included as separate sheets or files. A short descriptive title should appear above each table with a clear legend and any footnotes suitably identified below. All units must be included. Figures should be completely labeled, taking into account necessary size reduction. Captions should be typed, double-spaced, on a separate sheet. All original figures should be clearly marked in pencil on the reverse side with the number, author's name, and top edge indicated.

Proofs. Page proofs are sent to the designated author using Taylor & Francis' EProof system. They must be carefully checked and returned within 48 hours of receipt. Offprints or copies of the journal may be ordered at this stage through the publisher.

Offprints/Reprints. The corresponding author of each article will receive one complete copy of the issue in which the article appears. Offprints of an individual article may be ordered from Taylor & Francis. Use the offprint order form included with page proofs. Up to 10 additional issue copies may also be ordered. If offprints are not ordered by the required date, reprint pricing goes into effect, and issue copies may not be ordered.

Child Psychiatry and Human Development

ADDRESS FOR SUBMISSION:

Kenneth J. Tarnowski, Editor
Child Psychiatry and Human Development
Florida Gulf Coast University
Department of Psychology
  ONLINE SUBMISSIONS ONLY
10501 FGCU Boulevard South
Fort Meyers, FL 33965-6565
USA
Phone: 239-590-7189
Fax: 239-590-7200
E-Mail: ktarnows@fgcu.edu
Web: www.wkap.nl
Address May Change:

PUBLICATION GUIDELINES:

Manuscript Length: 21-25
Copies Required: Three
Computer Submission: Yes Web
Format:
Fees to Review: 0.00 US$

Manuscript Style:
  See Manuscript Guidelines

CIRCULATION DATA:

Reader: Academics, Practitioners
Frequency of Issue: Quarterly
Copies per Issue: Less than 1,000
Sponsor/Publisher: Kluwer Academic
  Publishers
Subscribe Price:

REVIEW INFORMATION:

Type of Review: Editorial Review
No. of External Reviewers: 2
No. of In House Reviewers: 1
Acceptance Rate: 21-30%
Time to Review: 2 - 3 Months
Reviewers Comments: No Reply
Invited Articles: 0-5%
Fees to Publish: 0.00 US$

MANUSCRIPT TOPICS:
Abnormal Psychology; Adolescent Psychology; Alcoholism & Drug Addiction; Behavior Modification; Child Psychology; Developmental Psychology; Neuropsychology; Personality; Physiological Psychology; Psychiatry; Psychological Testing; Psychopathology

MANUSCRIPT GUIDELINES/COMMENTS:

Aims and Scope
Child Psychiatry and Human Development is an interdisciplinary international journal serving the groups represented by child and adolescent psychiatry, clinical child/pediatric/family psychology, pediatrics, social science, and human development. The journal publishes research on diagnosis, assessment, treatment, epidemiology, development, advocacy, training, cultural factors, ethics, policy, and professional issues as related to clinical disorders in children, adolescents, and families. The journal publishes peer-reviewed original empirical research, including case studies, in addition to substantive and theoretical reviews.

Online Manuscript Submission

Kluwer Academic Publishers now offers authors, editors and reviewers of *Child Psychiatry and Human Development* the use of our fully web-enabled online manuscript submission and review system. To keep the review time as short as possible, we request authors to submit manuscripts online to the journals editorial office. Our online manuscript submission and review system offers authors the option to track the progress of the review process of manuscripts in real time. Manuscripts should be submitted to: **http://chud.edmgr.com**

The online manuscript submission and review system for *Child Psychiatry and Human Development* offers easy and straightforward log-in and submission procedures. This system supports a wide range of submission file formats: for manuscripts - Word, WordPerfect, RTF, TXT and LaTex; for figures - TIFF, GIF, JPEG, EPS, PPT, and Postscript. PDF is not an acceptable file format.

Springer Open Choice

In addition to the normal publication process (whereby an article is submitted to the journal and access to that article is granted to customers who have purchased a subscription), Springer now provides an alternative publishing option: Springer Open Choice. A Springer Open Choice article receives all the benefits of a regular subscription-based article, but in addition is made available publicly through Springer's online platform SpringerLink. To publish via Springer Open Choice, upon acceptance please visit www.springeronline.com/openchoice to complete the relevant order form and provide the required payment information. Payment must be received in full before publication or articles will publish as regular subscription-model articles. We regret that Springer Open Choice cannot be ordered for published articles.

NOTE: In case you encounter any difficulties while submitting your manuscript online, please get in touch with the responsible Editorial Assistant.

Child Welfare

ADDRESS FOR SUBMISSION:

Julie Gwin, Editor
Child Welfare
Child Welfare League of America
440 First Street NW, Third floor
Washington, DC 20001-2085
USA
Phone: 202-942-0251
Fax: 202-638-4004
E-Mail: journal@cwla.org
Web: www.cwla.org/pubs
Address May Change:

PUBLICATION GUIDELINES:

Manuscript Length: 16-20
Copies Required: Four
Computer Submission: No
Format: N/A
Fees to Review: 0.00 US$

Manuscript Style:
     American Psychological Association

CIRCULATION DATA:

Reader: Practitioners
Frequency of Issue: Bi-Monthly
Copies per Issue: 5,000
Sponsor/Publisher: Child Welfare League
   of America/CWLA Press
Subscribe Price: 150.00 US$ Institution
   110.00 US$ Individual
   84.00 US$ Student

REVIEW INFORMATION:

Type of Review: Blind Review
No. of External Reviewers: 3
No. of In House Reviewers: 0
Acceptance Rate: 11-20%
Time to Review: 3-5 Months
Reviewers Comments: Yes
Invited Articles: 30%
Fees to Publish: 0.00 US$

MANUSCRIPT TOPICS:
Adoption & Foster Parenting; Child Welfare; Crime & Delinquency; Culture & Personality; Social Work

MANUSCRIPT GUIDELINES/COMMENTS:

Child Welfare is a bimonthly, peer-reviewed journal of policy, practice, and programs devoted to the needs of child welfare professionals and those in associated fields. The journal covers all aspects of child welfare as they affect the health, education, and psychosocial needs of children, offering theoretical concepts as well as practical ideas and strategies. It reports on innovations in practice, agency administration and board functions, staffing designs, training, legislation, research, and community development.

Child Welfare began publication in 1921 as a CWLA house organ and is the oldest specialized social service journal in existence. The journal goes to agencies, libraries, and individuals, reaching thousands of readers in the United States, Canada, and around the world.

Child Welfare has been an independent professional journal for many years but retains its connection with CWLA, which acts as the journal's publisher. Although *Child Welfare's* editorials conform to CWLA positions, papers submitted for review need not represent CWLA viewpoints, and published articles do not necessarily reflect CWLA philosophy. Authors need not be associated with a CWLA member agency.

Content

Child Welfare welcomes contributions, controversial or otherwise, that represent a responsible addition to the literature. All manuscripts are subject to a blind peer review process. Publication does not imply CWLA endorsement of the author's opinions.

Manuscripts accepted for publication in *Child Welfare* demonstrate a high quality of analysis of issues in the field and describe innovative programs or forms of practice. Papers are invited from all fields. Content should reflect aspects of work with children, youth, and their families.

Articles may focus on matters of policy, research, or other broad topics; emerging trend in working with children, youth, and families; material useful for training; or innovative programs that represent the direction in which the field is moving.

Child Welfare also publishes letters to the editor selected for relevance to the journal's content or for responsible critique of articles. In the latter case, the author of the original article is given the opportunity to reply. Letters are edited, and changes are subject to the writer's approval before publication.

Special Issues

Twice yearly, *Child Welfare* publishes special issues highlighting single subjects in child welfare and related fields. Past topics have included youth development; child day care; perspectives on serving African American children, youth, and families; substance abuse; special-needs adoptions; and kinship care. For information on upcoming special issues, including how to serve as a guest editor, contact the managing editor.

Format for submissions

Manuscripts submitted to *Child Welfare* for consideration should
- extend knowledge in the field of child and family welfare or related services;
- examine aspects of administration, casework, groupwork, community organization, teaching, research, or interpretation;
- explore facets of interdisciplinary approaches to the field; and
- cover issues of social policy that have a bearing on the welfare of children, youth, and families.

Submissions should conform to general standards of literacy and organization. Consult the *CWLA Style Guide* or *Publication Manual of the American Psychological Association, Fourth Edition* (APA).

Major manuscripts should be between 3,500 and 5,000 words in length - approximately 15 - 20 typewritten pages of about 250 words each. Some variability in length is permissible, depending on the topic. All manuscripts must be typed legibly, double-spaced throughout (including references, notes, illustrations, and quotations), on plain, white, 8 ½" x 11" paper, one side only, with approximately one-inch margins. Use a large, legible typeface, such as Times, 12 point.

A cover page, with the title of the paper; the author's name, academic degree, title, and affiliation; and a short, 75-word abstract, should accompany the manuscript. The author's name and affiliation should not appear on any other manuscript page. All identifying information is removed prior to peer review.

Authors should resist basing conclusions on one or a few cases, since material should illustrate rather than prove points. Authors are responsible for submitting titles that are short, clear, and stimulating.

Authors are strongly encouraged to use subheadings in organizing manuscripts. First-level headings should be typed in boldface, second-level headings in italics or underlined. All headings should be in upper- and lowercase, not all capitals.

Each table, illustration, or figure must be submitted on a separate sheet of paper, with placement indicated in the text. Avoid lengthy tables if possible. Several smaller tables are easier to read, analyze, and handle than one large table.

Tables and figures should be used only if necessary to comprehend the material; textual interpretation of data is often sufficient. To avoid overuse of tables, a footnote may suggest that readers contact the author for copies of tables, detailed statistical methodology, and so forth.

References and notes should be double-spaced and placed at the end of the manuscript. Again, refer to the *CWLA Style Guide* or APA for the proper format.

Authors are responsible for obtaining written permission to use any material - including text of more than 250 words in length, or any table, chart, figure, or graph - that has been previously copyrighted. CWLA reserves the right, on a case-by-case basis, to require authors to obtain written permission for shorter blocks of previously copyrighted material. Authors must also obtain permission to publish any case illustrations or other materials drawn from any agency. Authors should submit written permissions to *Child Welfare* with their revised manuscripts.

Authors must disguise all identifying information in case material. Nonessential identifying case information - such as specific names and addresses of individuals, organizations, and businesses - should always be changed. Changes to other information - such as nationalities, illnesses, or other details likely to identify individuals - frequently are advisable if the exact details are not of major importance. Substitutions of comparable significance are often possible.

Submission procedures
Submit four clean copies of the manuscript, in the format described above, to the managing editor. E-mail queries only (no submissions, please) to **journal@cwla.org**.

Each manuscript should be submitted with a telephone number for the lead author, as well as a current mailing address and an e-mail address if available. Correspondence will be addressed to the person who signs the cover letter. *Child Welfare* acknowledges submitted manuscripts by postcard immediately upon receipt.

Child Welfare does not accept manuscripts published elsewhere or under review by other periodicals, or material that has been extracted from previously published articles and is not so identified.

Peer review

All major manuscripts submitted to *Child Welfare* undergo a process of peer review. Identifying information is removed from manuscripts before they are sent to the peer review board. Items for the Readers' Forum are not submitted for review.

Child Welfare's editors may prescreen manuscripts to eliminate inappropriate submissions, including extremely long or short papers, those where plagiarism or libel is suspected, those whose subject has been overdone, those that are overly similar to others the author has published elsewhere, and those otherwise unsuitable for *Child Welfare*.

Three reviewers read each major manuscript: two peer reviewers and the senior editor. A list of peer review board members is published in each issue of *Child Welfare*. Manuscripts are assigned to reviewers, insofar as possible, according to each reviewer's expertise and interest. Reviewers disqualify themselves, or the editors may disqualify a reviewer, if a paper's subject or authorship creates any conflict of interest for them. Reviewers themselves may submit manuscripts without prejudice; their manuscripts remain anonymous during the review process.

Reviewers may make one of the following recommendations on a manuscript:
- accept for publication,
- accept with revision or rewrite by the author,
- rewrite and resubmit for review, or
- reject.

Once reviewers reach a decision on a manuscript, the senior editor notifies authors regarding review comments and decisions. Allow at least 12 weeks for completion of the review process.

Rejected manuscripts

A manuscript is rejected for publication when two or more reviewers recommend rejection. Insofar as possible, authors will be clearly informed why a manuscript is rejected.

Rejected manuscripts are returned only when authors so request and provide an SASE with sufficient postage. Rejected manuscripts remain on file at *Child Welfare* for one year from the date of rejection.

Acceptance

All manuscripts accepted for publication in *Child Welfare* require some revision. Upon acceptance of a manuscript, the author will receive author agreement, copyright release, and biographical information forms, and a copy of the edited manuscript for revision.

No manuscript will be published until the author has returned all agreement forms, answered all editorial queries, reformatted references as requested, and provided two clean paper copies of the manuscript, as well as an up-to-date electronic version on computer disk. Electronic versions may be e-mailed in certain circumstances; authors should first check with the editors.

Although all published manuscripts must conform to certain CWLA style requirements, the editors of *Child Welfare* strive to preserve the author's meaning and the essential flavor of the author's writing style. In reviewing the edited manuscript, authors should proofread carefully, restore meaning that has been unintentionally injured, and answer all queries. Once the author has approved and returned a manuscript, further alterations are accepted only in limited circumstances.

Copyright

Authors must be the sole owners of their material and will be required to sign an agreement transferring ownership rights to CWLA. As copyright holder, CWLA has exclusive right to publish and distribute articles appearing in *Child Welfare* in English and any translations and in any medium, including but not limited to reprints; photocopies; microfilm; and electronic media such as computer disk, CD-ROM, and the Internet.

Reprints

Except in special issues of the journal, a reprint request line appears at the end of every published article. *Child Welfare* expects authors to honor requests for single copies of their articles. Authors may have reprints prepared themselves; when they wish, however, *Child Welfare* can have reprints prepared and sent to authors (minimum quantity 100). Authors receive a price list and order form with their notification of acceptance. Authors may forward requests for large quantities of copies to the CWLA editorial offices. Requests received by authors for permission to reprint articles published in *Child Welfare* should be forwarded to the managing editor.

Publication schedule

Child Welfare is published bimonthly, on the first of the month, in January (January/February issue), March (March/April issue), May (May/June issue), July (July/August issue), September (September/ October issue), and November (November/December issue).

CWLA Style Requirements

In preparing manuscripts for publication, the CWLA editorial staff conforms punctuation, capitalization, number forms, and other matters of style to CWLA usage and format; corrects word usage, spelling, and grammar; eliminates repetition and unnecessary words; and edits for clarity. In addition to social work professionals, CWLA publications are read by lay people connected with the field and by members of other disciplines; authors should therefore avoid technical jargon as much as possible. Readability is the goal.

Essential Resources for Authors

CWLA generally follows the *Publication Manual of the American Psychological Association, Fourth Edition* (APA) for most points of style. CWLA does part with APA, however, on certain matters of form. To maintain uniformity of style in CWLA materials, authors of accepted manuscripts may receive the *CWLA Style Guide*.

When APA does not offer a solution, CWLA refers to *The Chicago Manual of Style, 14th Edition,* as its secondary style reference. CWLA also relies on *Words into Type, Third Edition,* and Strunk and White's *The Elements of Style,* Fourth Edition.

For questions regarding compound words - when to hyphenate and when to spell compounds open or closed - CWLA's chosen authority is *One Word, Two Words, Hyphenated?* (1998 Edition), by Mary Louise Gilman and published by the National Court Reporters Association, Vienna, Virginia.

For all other matters of spelling, CWLA's accepted authorities are *Merriam-Webster's Collegiate Dictionary,* 10th Edition, and Houghton-Mifflin's *American Heritage Dictionary of the English Language,* Fourth Edition. When dictionaries disagree, however, and if the *CWLA Style Guide* does not offer a solution, *One Word, Two Words* is the final authority for compound constructions, and *Merriam-Webster* is the final authority for all other spelling questions.

Differences in Style

Although the *CWLA Style Guide* is the preferred form for all publications, different publications may have slight variations in style. *Child Welfare* and professional titles published by CWLA Press follow a more scholarly style. *Children's Voice* books published by Child & Family Press, and CWLA Press titles targeted at a broader reader-ship often follow a less formal style. Because of space limitations, CWLA newsletters may also follow a less formal style.

Preparing Manuscripts in Electronic Form

CWLA produces its publications on a Macintosh desktop publishing system. To avoid publication delays caused by program or format incompatibilities, authors should conform their documents to the following guidelines.

Word Processing

All documents, whether prepared in DOS, Windows, or Macintosh environments, should be saved in either Microsoft Word or WordPerfect formats. Whenever possible, save Windows and DOS documents in a Mac format. If you must use a different program or format, contact the CWLA Publications Department to check compatibility. Clearly indicate on the disk or in a cover letter the software and operating system used.

Disk Format

For best results, use new, 1.44 MB, high-density, 3.5-inch diskettes. Name brand disks generally are more reliable than generics.

Indicate on the disk or in a cover letter the software and operating system used to create the disk files. Include a list of all documents on the disk. Give each file a unique, informative, name, such as "Chap1," "References," or "Notes."

Use updated virus protection software to en-sure both the diskette and your own computer are virus-free before copying files to the diskette. Do not write-protect your disk, password protect the files, or use any kind of document security, encryption, or protection features. Do not use any kind of data compression on your files without first checking with the CWLA Publications Department.

Do not use editing or revision settings in any software at any point in the creation of your document without first checking with the CWLA Publications Department. Even if you turn off editing and revision settings before saving the document for the final time, such settings sometimes corrupt the document.

General Formatting Instructions

Refrain from trying to make the document look "typeset." The CWLA Publications Department will handle all layout, design, and typesetting. The simpler your document is, the easier it is to open and translate.

Use a typeface common to both Windows and Macintosh systems, such as Times, Times New Roman, Courier, or Helvetica. "Exotic" typefaces can cause problems and delays. CWLA's designers will select appropriate typefaces and styles for all final published works.

Set all type flush left. Do not justify type. Insert only a single space after all punctuation. Use only a single tab to indent the beginning of a paragraph. Avoid using the tab key beyond that. Do not place material in multiple columns.

If a paragraph has to be indented at both sides (such as for block-quoted material), use the tab ruler to change the margin settings to provide the indent. Do not insert tabs and returns at the beginning and end of each line in the paragraph. Consult your word processing program's instruction manual for information on resetting margins with the tab ruler.

If changing the margin settings becomes problematic, leave the paragraph as is and insert notes to let the editor know where the indented material begins and ends (for example, "begin block quote" and "end block quote here").

Leave hyphenation settings turned off. Don't force a hyphenation by placing a hyphen and a return at the end of a line to break a word and achieve a better line length. Hyphens are acceptable at the end of a line only if they naturally occur in the word - that is, only if the word is a hyphenated compound word. Editors and book designers will hyphenate as appropriate when the book or article is typeset.

Do not insert hard returns at the end of a line - only at the end of a paragraph. Do not place a hard page break at the end of each manuscript page.

Formatting Book and Article Manuscripts

Each chapter of a book, regardless of length, should be in a separate document, as should each appendix and the references. The front matter of a book (title page, contents, acknowledgments) can be in one document. Short introductions and prefaces can be included with the front matter. Lengthy introductions and prefaces, however, should be in separate documents.

An article for *Child Welfare* or *Children's Voice* can usually be in one document. For longer articles, check with the Publications Department first.

Except for page numbers, do not use headers or footers in your document. For books, begin page numbering at page 1 for each chapter.

Chapter titles and headings

Set chapter titles in bold, and center on the page. Set in upper and lowercase type, capitalizing only the first letter of important words.

Set first-level headings in bold, upper and lower case type, flush left, on a line by them-selves. Place one extra line space above each first-level head.

Set second-level headings in italics, upper and lower case, flush left, on a line by themselves. Place one extra line space above each second-level head.

Set third-level headings in underlined type, followed by a period. Capitalize only the first word in third-level heads. Place one extra line space above each third-level head.

Avoid subheadings beyond the third level; the subheads become complex and hard to follow.

Lists and block quotes

Do not use your word processing program's automatic bullet or numbered list feature. For a bullet list, insert an asterisk, followed by a single tab, before each item. For a numbered list, use a number in parentheses, or a number and a period, followed by a single tab or single character space, before each item.

Quoted material of 40 words or more should be set as a block quote, with indents on both sides, as explained on page 25.

Tables, Figures, and Graphics

Do not include tables, figures, graphs, photos, or other graphics in the manuscript's word processing files. Rather, each table, figure, or other graphic should be in its own document. Leave insertion notes at appropriate places in the text ("Insert Table 1 here," "Figure 2 goes here," and so on). Include paper printouts of all tables, figures, and graphics. Always specify the computer program used to create the graphics.

Tables should be set in Excel or in Microsoft Word's table function. Avoid using other word processor's table functions, table editors, or spreadsheet software to create tables. If you are not able to use Word or Excel, check with the CWLA Publications Department first before creating tables.

As with document text, keep the formatting simple in tables and figures. Use bold type for main headings, italics for additional headings, and regular Roman type for the rest of the table or figure.

Creating computer-generated graphics is not necessary. In most instances, CWLA's designers will need to recreate graphic elements to con-form to the finished publication's typography. Hand-drawn or sketched graphics are acceptable as long as they clearly show what is needed in the finished graphic.

Endnotes and Footnotes

For submitted manuscripts, CWLA prefers citations in text, with references at the end of a chapter, article, or book, rather than footnotes or endnotes. Even with desktop publishing soft-ware, placing multiple notes at the bottom of a page causes difficulties in typesetting.

CWLA will set notes and references at the end of an authored book, at the end of a chapter in an edited book in which chapters have different authors, or at the end of an article published in such periodicals as *Child Welfare* or *Children's Voice.* An occasional, individual explanatory footnote is permissible when it must appear with the text in a particular chapter or article.

In either event, the preferred format for a manuscript submitted on disk is for all notes and references to appear at the end of each document. The automatic footnote-endnote function - in Microsoft Word or WordPerfect only - may be used if absolutely necessary, but it should be set for endnotes rather than footnotes. If you are using word processing software other than Micro-soft Word or WordPerfect, contact the Publications Department before using any footnote or endnote feature.

For specific endnote styles, refer to APA or the *CWLA Style Guide.*

Childhood

ADDRESS FOR SUBMISSION:

Karin Ekberg, Managing Editor
Childhood
Norwegian U. of Science and Technology
Norwegian Centre for Child Research
Editorial Office
N-7491
Trondheim,
Norway
Phone: +47 73 59 62 44/40
Fax: +47 73 59 62 39
E-Mail: karin.ekberg@svt.ntnu.no
Web: www.sagepub.uk
Address May Change:

PUBLICATION GUIDELINES:

Manuscript Length: 26-30
Copies Required: Three
Computer Submission: Yes
Format: MS Word
Fees to Review: 0.00 US$

Manuscript Style:
    See Manuscript Guidelines

CIRCULATION DATA:

Reader: Academics
Frequency of Issue: Quarterly
Copies per Issue: Less than 1,000
Sponsor/Publisher: Sage Publications
Subscribe Price:

REVIEW INFORMATION:

Type of Review: Blind Review
No. of External Reviewers: 2
No. of In House Reviewers: 0
Acceptance Rate: 21-30%
Time to Review: 4 - 6 Months
Reviewers Comments: Yes
Invited Articles: 11-20%
Fees to Publish: 0.00 US$

MANUSCRIPT TOPICS:
Child Psychology; Developmental Psychology; Educational Psychology; Exceptional Child

MANUSCRIPT GUIDELINES/COMMENTS:

Description
Childhood is a major interdisciplinary forum for child research that spans divisions between geographical regions, disciplines, social and cultural contexts, and applied and basic research.

Interdisciplinary Scholarship
Childhood publishes articles, reviews and scholarly comment on theoretical issues which aim to foster increased awareness and understanding of the research on children's culture, economics, language, health and social networks, with an emphasis on their rights and position in society. Each issue of the journal draws on work from a variety of disciplines concerned with the study of children and childhood including sociology, health studies, anthropology, cultural studies, social policy and welfare, history, economics, education, psychology and development studies.

International in Scope

Childhood is a truly international journal. A dynamic team of editors from the United States, Norway, the United Kingdom and Brazil have brought together an impressive list of scholars and researchers from around the world. The result is a timely periodical committed to bringing you the very latest discussions of children and childhood from within a global context.

Submission Manuscript Guidelines

1. All contributions should be typewritten in English, and double-spaced on A4 paper with wide margins.

2. Wherever possible, manuscripts should be dated and accompanied by a disk, containing only the final version of the paper, stating the computer system and software used. Please supply simple text files (i.e. not formatted for page layout), and keep all notes at the end of the article.

3. Title, author's name and designation should be typed on a separate, easily detachable sheet.

4. The corresponding author should provide his/her name and full postal address, telephone and fax numbers, and email address if available.

5. *Articles* should be preceded by an abstract (80-100 words) of the main argument(s), and a maximum of five key words. Articles should not normally be more than 8000 words in length. Review articles should normally be between 700 and 1000 words. Authors should specify the exact length of their contribution.

6. *Text.* The Introduction (no heading) should clearly state the purpose of the article, give only strictly pertinent references, and not review the subject extensively. Material and methods, and Results, must be presented in logical sequence in the text, with text and illustrations emphasizing only important observations. The Discussion should emphasize new and important observations of the study and conclusions there from. Do not repeat in detail data from results. Include implications of the findings and their limitations, and relate observations to other relevant studies.

7. *Acknowledgements* should be made only of people who have made a substantial contribution. Authors are responsible for obtaining written permission from all acknowledgements by name, as readers may infer their endorsement.

8. *References.* The Harvard system of referencing should be used. This entails providing a full bibliography in alphabetical order at the end of the article, e.g.:

Boswell, J. (1988) *The Abandonment of Children.* Harmondsworth: Penguin.

Burman, E. and P. Smith (1995) 'The Abnormal Distribution of Development: Policies for Southern Women and Children', *Gender, Place and Culture* 2(1): 21-37.

References to, or quotations from, these texts and articles should be followed by the author's name and year of publication of the text/article in brackets, e.g.

Burman (1995) appears to be saying that . . .

9. *Quotations*. All direct quotations of 35 words or more should be indented, but double-spaced.

10. *Notes*. Where notes are necessary, these should appear at the end of the text and before the bibliography.

11. *Tables* should be presented on separate sheets of paper at the end of the article, and should carry short descriptive titles. Their position within the text should be clearly indicated.

12. *Figures* should be of a reproducible standard, clearly numbered, and accompanied by explanatory numbered captions typed on a separate sheet. Their position within the text should be clearly indicated.

13. *Assessment procedures*. Articles are subject to the usual process of anonymous review. Articles are read by two people, in addition to one of the Editors.

14. *Proofs*. Authors will be sent proofs for checking and correction.

15. *Offprints*. Authors will receive 25 offprints of the article plus one copy of the journal on publication.

16. *Copyright*. Before publication, authors are requested to grant an exclusive publishing licence to SAGE Publications, which has the right to sub-license, subject to retaining their right to re-use the material in other publications written or edited by themselves and due to be published at least one year after initial publication in this Journal.

Editorial Address
Three copies of articles (accompanied by a disk wherever possible) should be submitted to:

Karin Ekberg, Managing Editor
Childhood Editorial Office
Norwegian Centre for Child Research
Norwegian University of Science and Technology
N-7491 Trondheim, Norway
Phone: +47 73 59 62 44/40, Fax: +47 73 59 62 39; Email: **karin.ekberg@svt.ntnu.no**

Books for review and all correspondence about reviews should also be sent to the above address.

Clinical Child and Family Psychology Review

ADDRESS FOR SUBMISSION:

Ronald Prinz, Thomas Ollendick, Editors
Clinical Child and Family Psychology
   Review
   SUBMISSION BY INVITATION ONLY
University of South Carolina
Department of Psychology
Columbia, SC 29208
USA
Phone: 803-777-7143
Fax: 803-777-5502
E-Mail: prinz@sc.edu
Web: www.kluweronline.com
Address May Change:

PUBLICATION GUIDELINES:

Manuscript Length:
Copies Required:
Computer Submission:
Format:
Fees to Review: 0.00 US$

Manuscript Style:
      American Psychological Association

CIRCULATION DATA:

Reader:
Frequency of Issue:
Copies per Issue:
Sponsor/Publisher: Kluwer
   Academic/Plenum Publishers
Subscribe Price:

REVIEW INFORMATION:

Type of Review:
No. of External Reviewers:
No. of In House Reviewers:
Acceptance Rate:
Time to Review:
Reviewers Comments:
Invited Articles:
Fees to Publish: 0.00 US$

MANUSCRIPT TOPICS:

Adolescent Psychology; Child Psychology; Community Psychology; Developmental
Psychology; Educational Psychology; Exceptional Child; Family Counseling & Therapy;
Psychiatry; Psychopathology

MANUSCRIPT GUIDELINES/COMMENTS:

Aims & Scope

This quarterly, peer-reviewed journal is the new vehicle for topics and issues covered in the
prestigious book series Advances in Clinical Child Psychology. Led by the series editors, the
journal will continue to identify important and new developments and provide in-depth
reviews on current thought and practices.

Providing an international interdisciplinary forum, *Clinical Child and Family Psychology
Review* publishes original research reviews, conceptual and theoretical papers, and related
work in the broad area of the behavioral sciences that pertains to infants, children, adolescents,
and families. Contributions originate from a wide array of disciplines including, but not

limited to, psychology (clinical, community, developmental, family, school), medicine (family practice, pediatrics, psychiatry), public health, social work, and education. Topical content includes science and application and covers facets of etiology, assessment, description, treatment/intervention, prevention, methodology, and public policy.

Contributions are by invitation only. The Editors, in consultation with the Editorial Board, invite highly qualified experts to contribute original papers on topics of timely interest and significance. Although solicited, all manuscripts are peer-reviewed and edited. Suggestions for topics and potential authors are welcome.

1. Manuscripts (by invitation only), in triplicate and in English, and editorial inquiries should be submitted to the Editors:

Ronald J. Prinz, Ph.D.
Department of Psychology
University of South Carolina
Columbia, South Carolina 29208
e-mail: **prinz@sc.edu**

Thomas H. Ollendick, Ph.D.
Department of Psychology
Virginia Polytechnic Institute and State University
Blacksburg, Virginia 24061-0355
e-mail: **tho@vt.edu**

Contributions are by invitation only. Suggestions for topics and potential authors are welcome and should be submitted to the Editors.

2. Submission is a representation that the manuscript has not been published previously and is not currently under consideration for publication elsewhere. A statement transferring copyright from the authors (or their employers, if they hold the copyright) to Plenum Publishing Corporation will be required before the manuscript can be accepted for publication. The Editors will supply the necessary forms for this transfer. Such a written transfer of copyright, which previously was assumed to be implicit in the act of submitting a manuscript, is necessary under the U.S. Copyright Law in order for the publisher to carry through the dissemination of research results and reviews as widely and effectively as possible.

3. Type double-spaced on one side of 8 ½ × 11 inch white paper using generous margins on all sides, and submit the original and two copies (including copies of all illustrations and tables). All copies must be dark, sharp, and clear. Computer-generated manuscripts must be of letter quality (not dot-matrix).

4. A title page is to be provided and should include the title of the article, author's name (no degrees), author's affiliation, and suggested running head. The affiliation should comprise the department, institution (usually university or company), city, and state (or nation) and should be typed as a footnote to the author's name. The suggested running head should be less than 80 characters (including spaces) and should comprise the article title or an abbreviated version thereof. For office purposes, the title page should include the complete mailing address,

telephone number, fax number, and e-mail address of the one author designated to review proofs.

5. An abstract is to be provided, preferably no longer than 100-200 words.

6. A list of 4-5 key words is to be provided directly below the abstract. Key words should express the precise content of the manuscript, as they are used for indexing purposes.

7. All acknowledgments (including those for grant and financial support) should be typed in one paragraph (so-headed) on a separate page that directly precedes the References section.

8. Tables should be numbered (with Arabic numerals) and referred to by number in the text. Each table should be typed on a separate sheet of paper. Center the title above the table, and type explanatory footnotes (indicated by superscript lowercase letters) below the table.

9. Illustrations (photographs, drawings, diagrams, and charts) are to be numbered in one consecutive series of Arabic numerals. The captions for illustrations should be typed on a separate sheet of paper. All illustrations must be complete and final, i.e., camera-ready. Photographs should be large, glossy prints, showing high contrast. Drawings should be high-quality laser prints or should be prepared with India ink. Either the original drawings or good-quality photographic prints are acceptable. Artwork for each figure should be provided on a separate sheet of paper. Identify figures on the back with author's name and number of the illustration. Electronic artwork submitted on disk should be in the TIFF or EPS format (1200 dpi for line and 300 dpi for half-tones and gray-scale art). Color art should be in the CYMK color space. Artwork should be on a separate disk from the text, and hard copy **must** accompany the disk.

10. List references alphabetically at the end of the paper and refer to them in the text by name and year in parentheses. References should include (in this order): last names and initials of all authors, year published, title of article, name of publication, volume number, and inclusive pages. The style and punctuation of the references should conform to strict APA style-illustrated by the following examples:

Journal Article
Romano, J. M., Turner, J. A., & Jensen, M. P. (1997). The family environment in chronic pain patients: Comparison to controls and relationship to patient functioning. *Journal of Clinical Psychology in Medical Settings*, 4, 383-395.

Book
Schlinger, H. D., Jr. (1995). *A behavior analytic view of child development.* New York: Plenum Press.

Contribution to a Book
Daugherty, T. K., & Shapiro, S. K. (1994). Behavior checklists and rating forms. In T. H. Ollendick, N. J. King, & W. Yule (Eds.), *International handbook of phobic and anxiety disorders in children and adolescents* (pp. 331-347). New York: Plenum Press.

11. Footnotes should be avoided. When their use is absolutely necessary, footnotes should be numbered consecutively using Arabic numerals and should be typed at the bottom of the page to which they refer. Place a line above the footnote, so that it is set off from the text. Use the appropriate superscript numeral for citation in the text.

12. In general, the journal follows the recommendations of the 1994 *Publication Manual of the American Psychological Association* (Fourth Edition), and it is suggested that contributors refer to this publication.

13. After a manuscript has been accepted for publication and after all revisions have been incorporated, manuscripts should be submitted to the Editor's Office as hard copy accompanied by electronic files on disk. Label the disk with identifying information -- software, journal name, and first author's last name. The disk *must* be the one from which the accompanying manuscript (finalized version) was printed out. The Editor's Office cannot accept a disk without its accompanying, matching hard-copy manuscript.

14. **The journal makes no page charges**. Reprints are available to authors, and order forms with the current price schedule are sent with proofs.

15. **Springer Open Choice**. In addition to the normal publication process (whereby an article is submitted to the journal and access to that article is granted to customers who have purchased a subscription), Springer now provides an alternative publishing option: Springer Open Choice. A Springer Open Choice article receives all the benefits of a regular subscription-based article, but in addition is made available publicly through Springer's online platform SpringerLink. To publish via Springer Open Choice, upon acceptance please visit www.springeronline.com/openchoice to complete the relevant order form and provide the required payment information. Payment must be received in full before publication or articles will publish as regular subscription-model articles. We regret that Springer Open Choice cannot be ordered for published articles.

Clinical Child Psychology and Psychiatry

ADDRESS FOR SUBMISSION:

John Leventhal, North American Editor
Clinical Child Psychology and Psychiatry
Yale University
School of Medicine
Section of Paediatrics
333 Cedar Street, PO Box 208064
New Haven, CT
USA
Phone: 203-688-2468
Fax: 203-785-3932
E-Mail: john.leventhal@yale.edu
Web: www.sagepub.com
Address May Change:

PUBLICATION GUIDELINES:

Manuscript Length: Up to 7500 words
Copies Required: Four
Computer Submission: Yes Disk & Email
Format: PC Compatible
Fees to Review: 0.00 US$

Manuscript Style:
    American Psychological Association

CIRCULATION DATA:

Reader: Practitioners
Frequency of Issue: Quarterly
Copies per Issue: 1,001 - 2,000
Sponsor/Publisher: Sage Publications
Subscribe Price:

REVIEW INFORMATION:

Type of Review: Blind Review
No. of External Reviewers: 3
No. of In House Reviewers: 0
Acceptance Rate: 40-50%
Time to Review: 2 - 3 Months
Reviewers Comments: Yes
Invited Articles: 0-5%
Fees to Publish: 0.00 US$

MANUSCRIPT TOPICS:
Adolescent Psychology; Child Psychology; Clinical Journal/ Clinically Focused Research;
Exceptional Child; Psychiatry; Psychotherapy

MANUSCRIPT GUIDELINES/COMMENTS:

Aims and Scope
Clinical Child Psychology and Psychiatry brings together clinically oriented work of the
highest distinction from an international and multidisciplinary perspective, offering
comprehensive coverage of clinical and treatment issues across the range of treatment
modalities. The journal is interested in advancing theory, practice and clinical research in the
realm of child and adolescent psychology and psychiatry and related disciplines. The journal
directs its attention to matters of clinical practice, including related topics such as the ethics of
treatment and the integration of research into practice.

Multidisciplinary in approach, the journal includes work by, and is of interest to, child psychologists, psychiatrists and psychotherapists, nurses, social workers and all other professionals in the fields of child and adolescent psychology and psychiatry.

Instruction To Authors

The Editor apologizes for the apparent pedantry of these instructions, but adherence to them will ensure rapid and efficient processing of your contributions, and will enhance the article itself.

Peer review process. The Editor will screen manuscripts for their overall fit with the aims and scope of the journal. Those that fit will be further reviewed by two or more independent reviewers. Papers will be evaluated by the Editorial Board and refereed in terms of merit, readability and interest. Unsolicited manuscripts will not be returned to the author.

Submission of MSS. Four copies of each manuscript, **typed in double spacing throughout**, and on one side only of white A4 or US standard size paper, and a copy on disk (preferably PC compatible) should be sent to the Editor at the address given below. All pages should be numbered. Email submissions are encouraged.

Format of MSS. Each manuscript should contain the following, in the correct order.

(a) Title page to include the title of the paper, full name of each author, current professional position and work context, and indicators of which author will be responsible for correspondence. A word count should also be included.

(b) Abstract. should not exceed 200 words (150 for preference); up to **5 key words to be listed alphabetically on the same page**. This page should carry the title of the paper but not the author name(s).

(c) Main text. not usually to exceed 7500 words and to be clearly organized, with a clear hierarchy of headings and subheadings (3 weights maximum).

(d) References. Citation of references follows APA (American Psychological Association) style. References cited in the text should read thus: Brown (1955, pp. 63-64); (Brown, 1995, pp. 63-64; Green & Brown, 1992, p. 102, Table 3). The letters a, b, c, etc., should distinguish citations of different works by the same author in the same year (Black, 1989a, 1989b).

All references cited in the text should appear in an alphabetical list, after the Notes section.

(e) Figures, tables, etc. should be numbered consecutively, carry descriptive captions and be clearly cited in the text. Keep them separate from the text itself, but indicate an approximate location on the relevant text page. Line diagrams should be presented as camera-ready copy on glossy paper (b/w, unless to be reproduced - by arrangement - in colour) and, if possible, on disk as EPS files (all fonts embedded) or TIFF files, 800 dpi - b/w only. For scanning, photographs should preferably be submitted as clear, glossy, unmounted b/w prints with a good range of contrast or on disk as TIFF files, 300 dpi.

(f) Author biographies. On a separate sheet provide a one-paragraph biobibliographical note for each author - up to 100 words for a single author, but none to exceed 65 words in a multi-authored paper.

Style. Use a clear and readable style, avoiding jargon. If technical terms must be included, define them when first used. Use plurals rather than he/she, (s)he, his or hers: 'If a child is unhappy, he or she. . .' is much better expressed as 'When children are unhappy, they. . .'.

Spelling. British or American spellings may be used ('z' versions of British spellings preferred to 's' versions, as given in the *Oxford English Dictionary*).

Punctuation. Use single quotation marks, with double inside single. Present dates in the form 9 May 1996. Do not use points in abbreviations, contractions or acronyms (e.g. DC, USA, DR, UNESCO).

Covering letter. Attach to every submission a letter confirming that all authors have agreed to the submission and that the article is not currently being considered for publication by any other journal. The name, address, telephone and fax number and email address of the corresponding author should always be clearly indicated.

Disks. On acceptance of your MS for publication you will be asked to supply a disk (preferably PC compatible) of the final version.

Copyright. Before publication authors are requested to assign copyright to Sage Publications, subject to retaining their right to reuse the material in other publications written or edited by themselves and due to be published preferably at least one year after initial publication in the Journal.

Mailing. Address MSS to the Editor: Bernadette Wren, Consultant Clinical Psychologist, Child and Family Department, Tavistock Clinic, 120 Belsize Lane, London NW3 5BA, UK. Email: **BWren@tavi-port.nhs.uk**

North America: Prof. John Leventhal, Yale University, Section of Paediatrics, School of Medicine, 333 Cedar Street, PO Box 208064, New Haven, Connecticut. Tel: 001 203 688 2468 Fax: 001 203 785 3932. Email: **John.Leventhal@Yale.Edu**

Books for review should be sent to: Rudi Dallos, Clinical Teaching Unit, University of Plymouth, 5 Rowe Street, Drake Circus, Plymouth, PL4 8AA, UK

Clinical Gerontologist

ADDRESS FOR SUBMISSION:

L Thompson & D Gallagher Thompson, Eds
Clinical Gerontologist
PO Box 3926
Los Altos, CA 94024-0926
USA
Phone: 650-400-8171 or 650-400-8172
Fax: 650-625-0915
E-Mail: larrywt@stanford.edu
Web: www.haworthpressinc.com
Address May Change:

PUBLICATION GUIDELINES:

Manuscript Length: 20-25 double-spaced
Copies Required: Four
Computer Submission: No
Format: N/A
Fees to Review: 0.00 US$

Manuscript Style:
    American Psychological Association

CIRCULATION DATA:

Reader: Academics, Practitioners
Frequency of Issue: Quarterly
Copies per Issue: 1,001 - 2,000
Sponsor/Publisher: Haworth Press, Inc.
Subscribe Price: 60.00 US$ Individual
    150.00 US$ Institution
    450.00 US$ Library

REVIEW INFORMATION:

Type of Review: Blind Review
No. of External Reviewers: 2 or 3
No. of In House Reviewers: 2
Acceptance Rate: 50%
Time to Review: 2 - 3 Months
Reviewers Comments: Yes
Invited Articles: 25-30%
Fees to Publish: 0.00 US$

MANUSCRIPT TOPICS:

Abnormal Psychology; Adulthood; Alcoholism & Drug Addiction; Behavior Modification; Family Counseling & Therapy; Gerontology; Psychiatry; Psychological Testing; Psychopathology

MANUSCRIPT GUIDELINES/COMMENTS:

Topics Include. Issues of concern for professionals in Clinical Gerontology, Geropsychology, Geropsychiatry, Social Work, Nursing, Occupational Therapy, Pharmacy, Physical Therapy and other Allied Health Disciplines: e.g., Alcoholism & Drug Addiction; Behavior Modification; Family Counseling & Therapy; Dementias and other Psychopathology; Psychological Assessment; Long Term Care; End-of-Life Concerns; Ethnic Minorities and Cultural Diversity

About the Journal

The superlative journal of aging and mental health, *Clinical Gerontologist* presents timely material relevant to the needs of mental health professionals and all practitioners who deal with the aged client. The journal is designed for psychologists, physicians, nurses, social workers, and counselors (family, pastoral, and vocational) who work with the problems commonly found in later life, including:

- Adjustments to changing roles
- Dementia
- Caregivers
- Depression
- Hypochondriasis
- Paranoia

Here is an excellent and informative resource for mental health professionals and practitioners who work with elderly clients. There. All articles in this practitioners' journal feature timely, practical material relevant and applicable to the assessment and management of mental disorders in later life.

Each issue provides insightful articles on current topics. The editor selects articles for both scholarship and relevance to the practitioner to ensure that the articles are among the best in the field. Authors report research, present illustrative case material, and review the field's literature. A unique column in *Clinical Gerontologist* is "Clinical Comments." This section features brief observations and specific suggestions from practitioners which avoid elaborate research designs or long lists of unrelated references. This section is a unique opportunity for you to learn about the valuable clinical work of your peers in a short, concise format.

Additional features of the journal are book reviews and media and software reviews. The combination of in-depth scholarly articles with direct relevance to daily practice, clinical reports, and reviews of books and computer programs in the field, keep you up-to-date on the latest developments. Whether you are a physician, psychologist, nurse, social worker, or clergy by training, *Clinical Gerontologist* provides the information you need for your continued excellence in mental health work with the aged.

Instructions for Authors
1. **Original Articles Only**. Submission of a manuscript to this Journal represents a certification on the part of the author(s) that it is an original work, and that neither this manuscript nor a version of it has been published elsewhere nor is being considered for publication elsewhere.

2. **Manuscript Length**. Your manuscript may be approximately **12 to 25 typed pages**. Sentences should be double-spaced (including references and abstract). **Clinical comments** are brief reports of illustrative cases limited to 4 pages; Reviews of books and other media are limited to 2 pages. Lengthier manuscripts may be considered, but only at the discretion of the Editor. Sometimes, lengthier manuscripts may be considered if they can be divided up into sections for publications in successive Journal issues.

3. **Manuscript Style**. References, citations, and general style of manuscripts for this Journal should follow the APA style (as outlined in the latest edition of the *Publication Manual of the American Psychological Association*). References should be double-spaced and placed in alphabetical order. Attention should be given to avoid sexist language.

If an author wishes to submit a paper that has been already prepared in another style, he or she may do so. However, if the paper is accepted (with or without reviewer's alterations), the author is fully responsible for retyping the manuscript in the correct style as indicated above. Neither the Editor nor the Publisher is responsible for re-preparing manuscript copy to adhere to the Journal's style.

4. Manuscript Preparation

Margins. Leave at least a one-inch margin on all four sides.

Paper. Use clean, white 8 ½" x 11" bond paper.

Number of copies. 4 (the original plus three photocopies).

Cover page. Important—staple a cover page to the manuscript, indicating only the article title (this is used for anonymous refereeing).

Second "title page". Enclose a regular title page but do not staple it to the manuscript. Include the title again, plus:

- full authorship
- an ABSTRACT of about 100 words. (Below the abstract provide 3–10 key words for index purposes).
- a header or footer on each page with abbreviated title and pg number of total (e.g., pg 2 of 7)
- an introductory footnote with authors' academic degrees, professional titles, affiliations, mailing and e-mail addresses, and any desired acknowledgment of research support or other credit.

5. Return Envelopes.
When you submit your four manuscript copies, also include:

- a 9" x 12" envelope, self-addressed and stamped (with sufficient postage to ensure return of your manuscript);
- a regular envelope, stamped and self-addressed. This is for the Editor to send you an "acknowledgement of receipt" letter.

6. Spelling, Grammar, and Punctuation.
You are responsible for preparing manuscript copy which is clearly written in acceptable, scholarly English and which contains no errors of spelling, grammar, or punctuation. Neither the Editor nor the Publisher is responsible for correcting errors of spelling and grammar. The manuscript, after acceptance by the Editor, must be immediately ready for typesetting as it is finally submitted by the author(s). Check your paper for the following common errors:

- dangling modifiers
- misplaced modifiers
- unclear antecedents
- incorrect or inconsistent abbreviations

Also, check the accuracy of all arithmetic calculations, statistics, numerical data, text citations, and references.

7. Inconsistencies Must Be Avoided.
Be sure you are consistent in your use of abbreviations, terminology, and in citing references, from one part of your paper to another.

8. **Preparation of Tables, Figures, and Illustrations**. Any material that is not textual is considered artwork. This includes tables, figures, diagrams, charts, graphs, illustrations, appendices, screen captures, and photos. Tables and figures (including legend, notes, and sources) should be no larger than 4 ½ X 6 ½ inches. Type styles should be Helvetica (or Helvetica narrow if necessary) and no smaller than 8 point. We request that computer-generated figures be in black and white and/or shades of gray (preferably no color, for it does not reproduce well). Camera-ready art must contain no grammatical, typographical, or format errors and must reproduce sharply and clearly in the dimensions of the final printed page (4 ½ x 6 ½ inches). Photos and screen captures must be on disk as a TIF file, or other graphic file format such as JPEG or BMP. For rapid publication we must receive black-and-white glossy or matte positives (white background with black images and/or wording) in addition to files on disk. Tables should be created in the text document file using the software's Table feature.

9. **Submitting Art**. Both a printed hard copy and a disk copy of the art must be provided. We request that each piece of art be sent in its own file, on a disk separate from the disk containing the manuscript text file(s), and be clearly labeled. We reserve the right to (if necessary) request new art, alter art, or if all else has failed in achieving art that is presentable, delete art. If submitted art cannot be used, the Publisher reserves the right to redo the art and to change the author for a fee of $35.00 per hour for this service. The Haworth Press, Inc. is not responsible for errors incurred in the preparation of new artwork. Camera-ready artwork must be prepared on separate sheets of paper. Always use black ink and professional drawing instruments. On the back of these items, write your article title and the journal title lightly in soft-lead pencil (please do not write on the face of art). In the text file, skip extra lines and indicate where these figures are placed. Photos are considered part of the acceptable manuscript and remain with the Publisher for use in additional printings.

10. **Electronic Media**. Haworth's in-house typesetting unit is able to utilize your final manuscript material as prepared on most personal computers and word processors. This will minimize typographical errors and decrease overall production time. Please send the first draft and final draft copies of your manuscript to the journal Editor in print format for his/her final review and approval. After approval of your final manuscript, please submit the final approved version both on printed format ("hard copy") and floppy diskette. On the outside of the diskette package write:
1) the brand name of your computer or word processor
2) the word processing program and version that you used
3) the title of your article, and
4) the file name.

Note: Disk and hard copy must agree. In case of discrepancies, it is The Haworth Press' policy to follow hard copy. Authors are advised that no revisions of the manuscript can be made after acceptance by the Editor for publication. The benefits of this procedure are many with speed and accuracy being the most obvious. We look forward to working with your electronic submission which will allow us to serve you more efficiently.

11. **Alterations Required by Referees and Reviewers**. Many times a paper is accepted by the Editor contingent upon changes that are mandated by anonymous specialist referees and members of the Editorial Board. If the Editor returns your manuscript for revisions, you are

responsible for retyping any sections of the paper to incorporate these revisions (if applicable, revisions should also be put on disk).

12. **Typesetting**. You will not be receiving galley proofs of your article. Editorial revisions, if any, must therefore be made while your article is still in manuscript. The final version of the manuscript will be the version you see published. Typesetter's errors will be corrected by the production staff of The Haworth Press. Authors are expected to submit manuscripts, disks, and art that are free from error.

13. **Reprints**. The senior author will receive two copies of the journal issue and 25 complimentary reprints of his or her article. The junior author will receive two copies of the journal issue. These are sent several weeks after the journal issue is published and in circulation. An order form for the purchase of additional reprints will also be sent to all authors at this time. (Approximately 4-6 weeks is necessary for the preparation of reprints.) Please do not query the Journal's Editor about reprints. All such questions should be sent directly to The Haworth Press, Inc., Production Department, 37 West Broad Street, West Hazleton, PA 18202. To order additional reprints (minimum: 50 copies), please contact The Haworth Document Delivery Center, 10 Alice Street, Binghamton, NY 13904-1580; 1-800-342-9678 or Fax (607) 722-6362.

14. **Copyright**. Copyright ownership of your manuscript must be transferred officially to The Haworth Press, Inc. before we can begin the peer-review process. The Editor's letter acknowledging receipt of the manuscript will be accompanied by a form fully explaining this. All authors must sign the form and return the original to the Editor as soon as possible. Failure to return the copyright form in a timely fashion will result in a delay in review and subsequent publication.

Clinical Neuropsychologist (The)

ADDRESS FOR SUBMISSION:

Russell M. Bauer & Jerry J. Sweet, Eds.
Clinical Neuropsychologist (The)
  ONLINE SUBMISSIONS ONLY
Phone:
Fax:
E-Mail: See Guidelines
Web: http://www.tandf.co.uk/journals
Address May Change:

PUBLICATION GUIDELINES:

Manuscript Length:
Copies Required:
Computer Submission: Yes Email
Format: MS Word or WordPerfect
Fees to Review: 0.00 US$

Manuscript Style:
  American Psychological Association

CIRCULATION DATA:

Reader: Academics
Frequency of Issue: Quarterly
Copies per Issue:
Sponsor/Publisher: Taylor & Francis
Subscribe Price: 169.00 US$ Individual
  420.00 US$ Institution

REVIEW INFORMATION:

Type of Review:
No. of External Reviewers: 2-3
No. of In House Reviewers:
Acceptance Rate:
Time to Review: 4 - 6 Months
Reviewers Comments: Yes
Invited Articles:
Fees to Publish: 0.00 US$

MANUSCRIPT TOPICS:
Abnormal Psychology; Neuropsychology

MANUSCRIPT GUIDELINES/COMMENTS:

Aims and Scope. *The Clinical Neuropsychologist* (*TCN*) provides in-depth discussions of matters relevant to the practicing clinical neuropsychologist. Because clinical neuropsychology is a rapidly expanding discipline, there is a need for airing of empirical data, models, concepts, and positions pertaining to educational, clinical, and professional issues. *TCN* is designed to provide a forum for such presentation and discussions.

Submission of Manuscripts. Manuscripts must be submitted through the journal's Scholar One website **http://neuropsychology.manuscriptcentral.com.**

Questions for the editor may be addressed to: Russell M. Bauer at **rbauer@hp.ufl.edu** or to Jerry J. Sweet at **j-sweet@northwestern.edu.**

Each manuscript must be accompanied by a statement that it has not been published elsewhere and that it has not been submitted simultaneously for publication in another source. Authors are responsible for obtaining permission to reproduce copyrighted material from other sources and are required to sign an agreement for the transfer of copyright to the publisher. All accepted manuscripts, artwork, and photographs become the property of the publisher.

Authors are responsible for disclosing any funding sources and financial interests that could create a potential conflict of interest (see volume 18, page 1).

All parts of the manuscript should be typewritten, double-spaced, with margins of one inch on all sides. Manuscript pages should be numbered consecutively throughout the paper. Authors should also supply a shortened version of the title suitable for the running head, not exceeding 50 character spaces. Each article should be summarized in an abstract of not more than 100 words. In the abstract, abbreviations, diagrams, and reference to the text should be avoided.

Reference style. In the text cite by author and date (Smith, 1983). Prepare reference list in accordance with the *APA Publication Manual*, 5th ed. Examples include:

Journal. Tsai, M., & Wagner, N. N. (1978). Therapy groups for women sexually molested as children. *Archives of Sexual Behaviour*, 7, 417-427.

Book. Millman, M. (1980). *Such a pretty face*. New York: W. W. Norton.

Contribution to a Book. Hartley, J. T., & Walsh, D. A. (1980). Contemporary issues in adult development of learning. In L. W. Poon (Ed.), *Ageing in the 1980s* (pp. 239-252). Washington, DC: American Psychological Association.

Illustrations. Illustrations submitted (line drawings, halftones, photos, photomicrographs, etc.) should be clean originals or digital files. Digital files are recommended for highest quality reproduction and should follow these guidelines:
* 300 dpi or higher
* Sized to fit on journal page
* EPS, TIFF, or PSD format only
* Submitted as separate files, not embedded in text files

Color illustrations will be considered for publication; however, the author will be required to bear the full cost involved in their printing and publication. The charge for the first page with color is $900.00. The next three pages with color are $450.00 each. A custom quote will be provided for color art totaling more than 4 journal pages. Good-quality color prints should be provided in their final size. The publisher has the right to refuse publication of color prints deemed unacceptable.

Tables and Figures. Tables and figures (illustrations) should not be embedded in the text, but should be included as separate sheets or files. A short descriptive title should appear above each table with a clear legend and any footnotes suitably identified below. All units of measurement must be included. Figures should be completely labeled, taking into account necessary size reduction. Captions should be typed, double-spaced, on a separate sheet. All original figures should be clearly marked in pencil on the reverse side with the number, author's name, and top edge indicated.

Proofs. Page proofs are sent to the designated author using Taylor & Francis' EProof system. They must be carefully checked and returned within 48 hours of receipt.

Offprints/Reprints. The corresponding author of each article will receive one complete copy of the issue and 25 offprints in which the article appears. Offprints of an individual article may be ordered from Taylor & Francis. Use the offprint order form included with page proofs. Up to 10 additional issue copies may also be ordered. If offprints are not ordered by the required date, reprint pricing goes into effect, and issue copies may not be ordered.

Clinical Nursing Research

ADDRESS FOR SUBMISSION:

Patricia Hayes & Marilyn Wood,Co-Editors
Clinical Nursing Research
University of Alberta
Faculty of Nursing
3-107 Clinical Sciences Building
Edmonton, Alberta, T6G 2G3
Canada
Phone: 780-492-1037
Fax: 780-492-2551
E-Mail: susan.sanfordblades@ualberta.ca
Web: www.sagepub.com
Address May Change:

PUBLICATION GUIDELINES:

Manuscript Length: 16-20
Copies Required: One
Computer Submission: Yes Email preferred
Format: MS Word (PC Compatible)
Fees to Review: 0.00 US$

Manuscript Style:
American Psychological Association,
5th Edition

CIRCULATION DATA:

Reader: Academics, Practitioners, Nurse
Researchers, and Graduate Students
Frequency of Issue: Quarterly
Copies per Issue: Less than 1,000
Sponsor/Publisher: Sage Publications
Subscribe Price: 76.00 US$ Individual
320.00 US$ Institution
92.00 US$ Indv.& $336 Inst. - Foreign

REVIEW INFORMATION:

Type of Review: Blind Review
No. of External Reviewers: 3
No. of In House Reviewers: 2
Acceptance Rate: 53%
Time to Review: 2 - 3 Months
Reviewers Comments: Yes
Invited Articles: 0-5%
Fees to Publish: 0.00 US$

MANUSCRIPT TOPICS:
Abnormal Psychology; Adolescent Psychology; Adulthood; Alcoholism & Drug Addiction; As Applied by Nurses to Patient (Client) Care; Child Psychology; Family Counseling & Therapy; Gerontology; Psychological Testing

MANUSCRIPT GUIDELINES/COMMENTS:

Description
Clinical Nursing Research addresses issues of clinical research that are meaningful to practicing nurses, providing an international forum to:
1. Encourage discussion among clinical practitioners.
2. Enhance clinical practice by pinpointing potential clinical applications of the latest scholarly research.
3. Disseminate research findings of particular interest to practicing nurses

A Vital Resource for Clinicians and Researchers. Whether you're a clinician concerned with improving the quality of your work or a researcher involved in clinical investigations, *Clinical Nursing Research* is one of your most important resources.

An Indispensable Reference for Students. In *Clinical Nursing Research*, graduate and undergraduate students alike have access to a rich source of research ideas and studies that can be directly related to clinical settings.

Pertinent Features Keep You Up-to-Date. *Clinical Nursing Research* offers the following special features and articles that concentrate on nursing practice:

- *Research Articles*. Presentations of current research, with discussions on the applicability of its findings to the clinical setting.
- *Internationally Refereed Feature Articles*. This section encourages contributions from various continents and enhances the network potential of *Clinical Nursing Research* throughout the international community. It includes commentaries by referees on continents other than that of the article's author(s). Referees' comments examine the use of research findings in their own environments and identify possible cultural biases or health-care issues that could diminish the universal applicability of the findings.
- *Research Briefs*. Short research reports that focus on various aspects of practice.
- *Replication Studies*. Unique to *Clinical Nursing Research*, these studies replicate existing research and compare the findings, providing valuable information for clinicians committed to introducing research findings into their practice.
- *Letters*. Correspondence from clinicians and consumers of research requesting studies in particular areas and documenting the results of using research findings in clinical practice.

Journal Submission Guidelines

Manuscripts should focus on the patient as subject. Although there are no restrictions as to research design or methods used, an essential addition to all studies is a section on the applicability of the research findings to the clinical setting. Authors submitting manuscripts do so with the understanding that, if the manuscript is accepted for publication, copyright will transfer to Sage.

1. **General Instructions**. All portions of the manuscript, including the abstract, notes, quotations, appendixes, tables, and reference list, must be typed double-spaced and left-justified (ragged right margins), with minimum one-inch margins. Number all pages, including the title page and reference list. Include the title on the first page of the text. As this is a refereed journal, authors' names must not appear anywhere in the manuscript other than on the title page. Treat acknowledgements as footnotes and include them on a separate page entitled "Notes" at the end of the manuscript.

2. **Manuscript Length**. The text for a research article should be approximately *6,200* words; the manuscript should not exceed *20* pages, including references. Research briefs and replication studies are limited to 8 manuscript pages.

3. **Title Page**. A separate title page must include the title (in not more than eight words), the authors' names, titles, current addresses (including postal or zip code) and telephone and FAX numbers, and their affiliations as they should appear in print. Provide three to five key words for indexing purposes.

4. **Abstract**. The abstract should be a single paragraph summary of the manuscript typed on a separate page. It should be concise (not more than 150 words) and complete in itself. Include the study's purpose, methodology, major results, and application if appropriate.

5. **Style**. Refer to the *Publication Manual of the American Psychological Association* (APA Style Manual), 5th Edition, and pay particular attention to the sections on sexist language and reference style. All references documented in the reference section must be cited in the text; similarly, all text citations must appear in the reference list.

6. **Copyright and Releases**. Include a typed covering letter with your submission, which states that the author(s) is submitting the manuscript to *Clinical Nursing Research* exclusively. Authors submitting manuscripts do so with the understanding that, if the paper is accepted for publication, copyright belongs to the publisher. The senior author will be required to sign a Transfer of Copyright form when the manuscript is accepted for publication.

7. **Tables and Figures**. All figures and those tables with 17 or more columns must be camera-ready. Submit black and white photographs of your figures, or original line drawings. Group tables and figures at the end of the manuscript; do not embed them within the text itself, and do not include more than one table on each page. Limit the total number of tables and figures to three.

8. **Permissions**. Include proof of written permission for all quotations which require permission or exceed *300* words in length, and for all tables and figures from sources for which the author does not hold the copyright.

9. **Submission**. Submit your manuscript in a Word document via email, to:
   susan.sanfordblades@ualberta.ca.

PRESENTATION FORMATS FOR CLINICAL NURSING RESEARCH
Research Reports and Briefs
Research reports submitted to *Clinical Nursing Research* should follow the following format. The journal's audience includes clinical practitioners as well as researchers, so please ensure that your writing style is simple and understandable. (Refer to Tornquist, E. M., Funk, S. G., & Champagne, M. T. (1989). Writing research reports for clinical audiences. Western journal of Nursing Research, 11(5), 576-582.) You will not necessarily use the following headings in your manuscript; choose subtitles which are appropriate for your study.

1. The **Introduction** summarizes what the study is about, in one paragraph.

2. The **Problem** includes the background and rationale for the study, the conceptual framework, and a summary of the literature on which the study was based. Choose a subtitle appropriate to this section's content.

3. The section documenting the **Purpose of the Study** will include the research questions, hypotheses, and specific aims or objectives as appropriate.

4. Label and describe the specific **Design** used in your study.

5. Describe the target population, the **Sample**, and how the subjects were selected for the study. Include the number of subjects in the sample.

6. In the **Methods** section, clearly describe procedures, protocols, instruments, and process. Discuss instruments' reliability and validity.

7. Under **Data Analysis**, provide sufficient detail to facilitate a clear understanding of your analysis techniques.

8. Provide a descriptive account of the major **Findings**, as well as of tests of significance, etc.

9. In the **Discussion**, assess the meaning of your findings for the reader. Discuss the study's strengths and weaknesses.

10. The **Application** section is of critical importance to the journal. Discuss how the findings apply to nursing practice, and outline their immediate or potential use in the clinical setting. Advise the reader of how much confidence can be placed in the results, and include recommendations for replication of parts or all of the study before application. Emphasize the ways in which your study validates previous work.

Replication Studies
Follow the same guidelines, including the following:

1. Clearly identify the study under replication; include a detailed reference to the original publication, the number of replications reported, and the modifications made. Report changes of location that could have cultural and environmental influences on the study. Record consultation(s) with the author(s) of the original study in the Notes section.

2. The literature review can be limited to an update of the original work. Identify differences from the original study that could affect the findings, and indicate the extent of the replication without repeating the original work.

Clinical Psychology Review

ADDRESS FOR SUBMISSION:

Alan S. Bellack & Michel Hersen, Editors
Clinical Psychology Review
CBTS, 737 W. Lombard St Suite 551
Baltimore, MD 21201
USA
Phone: 410-706-0893
Fax: 410-706-0934
E-Mail: abellack@umaryland.edu
Web: authors.elsevier.com
Address May Change:

PUBLICATION GUIDELINES:

Manuscript Length: 30+
Copies Required: Three
Computer Submission: Yes
Format: MS Word
Fees to Review: 0.00 US$

Manuscript Style:
American Psychological Association

CIRCULATION DATA:

Reader: Academics
Frequency of Issue: 8 Times/Year
Copies per Issue: 1,001 - 2,000
Sponsor/Publisher: Elsevier
Subscribe Price: 0.00 US$

REVIEW INFORMATION:

Type of Review: Editorial Review
No. of External Reviewers: 2
No. of In House Reviewers: 0
Acceptance Rate: 21-30%
Time to Review: 4 - 6 Months
Reviewers Comments: Yes
Invited Articles: 6-10%
Fees to Publish: 0.00 US$

MANUSCRIPT TOPICS:
Abnormal Psychology; Behavior Modification; Child Psychology

MANUSCRIPT GUIDELINES/COMMENTS:

Aims and Scope
Clinical Psychology Review publishes substantive reviews of topics germane to clinical psychology. Its purpose is to help clinical psychologists keep up-to-date on relevant issues outside of their immediate areas of expertise by publishing scholarly but readable reviews. Papers cover diverse issues including: psychopathology, psychotherapy, behavior therapy, behavioral medicine, community mental health, assessment, and child development.

Reviews on other topics, such as psychophysiology, learning therapy, and social psychology, often appear if they have a clear relationship to research or practice in clinical psychology. Integrative literature reviews and summary reports of innovative ongoing clinical research programs are also sometimes published. Reports on individual research studies are not appropriate.

Submission Requirements. All manuscripts should be submitted to Alan S. Bellack, The University of Maryland at Baltimore, Department of Psychiatry, 737 W. Lombard St., Suite 551, Baltimore, MD 21201, USA. Submit three (3) high-quality copies of the entire manuscript; the original is not required. Allow ample margins and type double-space throughout. Papers should not exceed 50 pages (including references). One of the paper's authors should enclose a letter to the Editor, requesting review and possible publication; the letter must also state that the manuscript has not been previously published and has not been submitted elsewhere. One author's address (as well as any upcoming address change), telephone and *fax* numbers, and *E-mail address* (if available) should be included; this individual will receive all correspondence from the Editor and Publisher.

Papers accepted for *Clinical Psychology Review* may not be published elsewhere in any language without written permission from the author(s) and publishers. Upon acceptance for publication, the author(s) must complete a transfer of Copyright Agreement form.

Computer Disks. Authors are encouraged to submit a 3.5" HD/DD computer disk to the editorial office. Please observe the following criteria: (1) Send only hard copy when first submitting your paper. (2) When your paper has been refereed, revised if necessary, and accepted, send a disk containing the final version with the final hard copy. If the disk cannot be converted, the hard copy will be used. (3) Specify what software was used, including which release, e.g., WordPerfect 6.0a. (4) Specify what computer was used (IBM compatible PC, Apple Macintosh, etc.). (5) The article file should include all textual material (text, references, tables, figure captions, etc.) and separate illustration files, if available. (6) The file should follow the general instructions on style/arrangement and, in particular, the reference style of this journal as given in the Instructions to Contributors. (7) The file should be single-spaced and should use the wrap-around end-of-line feature, i.e., returns at the end of paragraphs only. Place two returns after every element such as title, headings, paragraphs, figure and table call-outs. (8) Keep a backup disk for reference and safety.

Title Page. The title page should list (1) the article; (2) the authors' names and affiliations at the time the work was conducted; (3) a concise running title; and (4) an unnumbered footnote giving an address for reprint requests and acknowledgements.

Abstract. An abstract should be submitted that does not exceed 200 words in length. This should be typed on a separate page following the title page.

Keywords. Authors should include up to six keywords with their article. Keywords should be selected from the APA list of index descriptors, unless otherwise agreed with the Editor.

Style and References. Manuscripts should be carefully prepared using the *Publication Manual of the American Psychological Association*, 4th ed., 1994, for style. The reference section must be double spaced, and all works cited must be listed. Avoid abbreviations of journal titles and incomplete information.

Reference Style for Journals
Raymond, M.J. (1964). The treatment of addiction by aversion conditioning with apomorphine. *Behaviour Research and Therapy, 3,* 287-290.

For Books
Barlow, D.H., Hayes S.C., & Nelson, R.O. (1984). *The scientist practitioner: Research and accountability in clinical and educational settings.* Elmsford, NY: Pergamon.

Tables and Figures. Do not send glossy prints, photographs or original artwork until acceptance. Copies of all tables and figures should be included with each copy of the manuscript. Upon acceptance of a manuscript for publication, original, camera-ready photographs and artwork must be submitted, unmounted and on glossy paper. Photocopies, blue ink or pencil are not acceptable. Use black India ink and type figure legends on a separate sheet. Write the article title and figure number lightly in pencil on the back of each.

Page Proofs and Offprints. Page proofs of the article will be sent to the corresponding author. These should be carefully proofread. Except for typographical errors, corrections should be minimal, and rewriting the text is not permitted. Corrected page proofs must be returned within 48 hours of receipt. Along with the page proofs, the corresponding author will receive a form for ordering offprints and full copies of the issue in which the article appears. Twenty-five (25) free offprints are provided; orders for additional offprints must be received before printing in order to qualify for lower publication rates. All coauthor offprint requirements should be included on the offprint order form.

Author Queries. For queries relating to the submission of articles (including electronic submission), the status of accepted articles through Online Article Status Information System (OASIS), author Frequently Asked Questions, and other queries elating to Elsevier Science, please consult http://www.elsevier.com/locate/authors/ For all other queries please e-mail Elsevier Author Support at: authorsupport@elsevier.ie

Copyright. Publications are copyrighted for the protection of the authors and the publisher. A Transfer of Copyright Agreement will be sent to the author whose manuscript is accepted. The form must be completed and returned to the publisher before the article can be published.

Clinical Social Work Journal

ADDRESS FOR SUBMISSION:

Carolyn Saari, Editor
Clinical Social Work Journal
Loyola University Chicago
School of Social Work
820 N. Michigan Avenue
Chicago, IL 60611
USA
Phone: 312-915-7018
Fax: 312-915-7645
E-Mail: csaari@luc.edu
Web: www.wkap.nl
Address May Change:

PUBLICATION GUIDELINES:

Manuscript Length: 21-25
Copies Required: Three
Computer Submission: Yes Web
Format:
Fees to Review: 0.00 US$

Manuscript Style:
    American Psychological Association

CIRCULATION DATA:

Reader: Practitioners
Frequency of Issue: Quarterly
Copies per Issue: 4,001 - 5,000
Sponsor/Publisher: Clinical Social Work
    Federation / Kluwer Academic Publishers
Subscribe Price:

REVIEW INFORMATION:

Type of Review: Blind Review
No. of External Reviewers: 2
No. of In House Reviewers: 0
Acceptance Rate: 21-30%
Time to Review: 4 - 6 Months
Reviewers Comments: Yes
Invited Articles: 0-5%
Fees to Publish: 0.00 US$

MANUSCRIPT TOPICS:

Culture & Personality; Gender Roles; Human Relations; Human Sexuality; Motivation; Psychodynamic Psychotherapy Primarily; Psychology of Women

MANUSCRIPT GUIDELINES/COMMENTS:

Aims & Scope

Clinical Social Work Journal, sponsored by the Clinical Social Work Federation, is devoted exclusively to the publication of original peer-reviewed papers on clinical social work theory and practice. This interdisciplinary journal disseminates diverse articles that provide a cross-fertilization of timely ideas and concepts in the field. The journal endeavors to broaden the understanding and skill of the clinical social work practitioner or educator concerned with individuals, couples, families and groups.

1. Manuscripts, in English, should be submitted to the Editor's Office via the journal's web-based online manuscript submission and peer-review system: **http://csow.edmgr.com**

Inquiries regarding journal policy, manuscript preparation, and other such general topics should be sent to the Editor:

Carolyn Saari, Ph.D.
Editor, Clinical Social Work Journal
8 Eastwood Drive
Jaffrey, NH 03452
E-mail: **carolynsaa@msn.com**

The online system offers easy straightforward log-in and submission; supports a wide range of submission file formats [Word, WordPerfect, RTF, TXT, and LaTeX for manuscripts; TIFF, GIF, JPEG, EPS, PPT, and Postscript for figures (artwork)]; eliminates the need to submit manuscripts as hard-copy printouts, disks, and/or e-mail attachments; enables real-time tracking of manuscript status by author; and provides help should authors experience any submission difficulties (click on "Contact Us" from the toolbar).

2. Submission is a representation that the manuscript has not been published previously and is not currently under consideration for publication elsewhere. A statement transferring copyright from the authors (or their employers, if they hold the copyright) to Kluwer Academic/Human Sciences Press will be required before the manuscript can be accepted for publication. The Editor will supply the necessary forms for this transfer. Such a written transfer of copyright, which previously was assumed to be implicit in the act of submitting a manuscript, is necessary under the U.S. Copyright Law in order for the publisher to carry through the dissemination of research results and reviews as widely and effectively as possible.

3. Type double-spaced on one side of 8½ × 11 inch white paper using generous margins on all sides. The entire manuscript, including quotations, references, figure-caption list, and tables, should be double-spaced. Manuscript length, except under unusual circumstances, should not exceed 20 double-spaced pages.

4. A title page is to be provided and should include the title of the article, author's name (with degree), author's affiliation, and suggested running head. The affiliation should comprise the department, institution (usually university or company), city, and state (or nation) and should be typed as a numbered footnote to the author's name. The suggested running head should be less than 80 characters (including spaces) and should comprise the article title or an abbreviated version thereof. The title page should also include the complete mailing address, telephone number, and e-mail address of the one author designated to review proofs.

5. An abstract is to be provided, preferably no longer than 50–100 words.

6. A list of 3–5 key words is to be provided directly below the abstract. Key words should express the precise content of the manuscript, as they are used for indexing purposes.

7. Illustrations (photographs, drawings, diagrams, and charts) are to be numbered in one consecutive series of Arabic numerals. The captions for illustrations should be typed on a separate sheet of paper. Photographs should be large, glossy prints, showing high contrast. Drawings should be high-quality laser prints or should be prepared with India ink. Either the

original drawings or good-quality photographic prints are acceptable. Artwork for each figure should be provided on a separate sheet of paper. Identify figures on the back with author's name and number of the illustration. Electronic artwork submitted on disk should be in TIFF or EPS format (1200 dpi for line and 300 dpi for halftones and gray-scale art). Color art should be in the CYMK color space. Artwork should be on a separate disk from the text, and hard copy must accompany the disk.

8. Tables should be numbered (with Arabic numerals) and referred to by number in the text. Each table should be typed on a separate sheet of paper. Center the title above the table, and type explanatory footnotes (as indicated by superscript lowercase letters) below the table.

9. List references alphabetically at the end of the paper and refer to them in the text by name and year in parentheses. References should include (in this order): last names and initials of all authors, year published, title of article, name of publication, volume number, and inclusive pages. The style and punctuation of the references should conform to strict APA style – illustrated by the following examples:

Journal Article
Martin, J.S., Petr, C.G., & Kapp, S.A. (2003). Consumer satisfaction with children's mental health services. *Child and Adolescent Social Work Journal*, 20, 211-226.

Book
Allen, D.M. (1991). *Deciphering motivation in psychotherapy*. New York: Plenum Press.

Contribution to a Book
Fine, S., & Gilbert, M. (1993). Short-term group therapy with depressed adolescents. In R. A. Wells and V. J. Giannetti (Eds.), *Casebook of the brief psychotherapies* (pp. 375-387). New York: Plenum Press.

10. Footnotes should be avoided. When their use is absolutely necessary, footnotes should be numbered consecutively using Arabic numerals and should be typed at the bottom of the page to which they refer. Place a line above the footnote, so that it is set off from the text. Use the appropriate superscript numeral for citation in the text.

11. In general, the journal follows the recommendations of the 2001 *Publication Manual of the American Psychological Association* (Fifth Edition), and it is suggested that contributors refer to this publication.

12. After a manuscript has been accepted for publication and after all revisions have been incorporated, manuscripts should be submitted to the Editor's Office as hard copy accompanied by electronic files on disk. Label the disk with identifying information – software, journal name, and first author's last name. **The disk *must* be the one from which the accompanying manuscript (finalized version) was printed out**. The Editor's Office cannot accept a disk without its accompanying matching hard-copy manuscript. [This point does not apply to manuscripts in the online system.]

13. The **journal makes no page charges**. Reprints are available to authors, and order forms with the current price schedule are sent with proofs.

14. **Springer Open Choice**. In addition to the normal publication process (whereby an article is submitted to the journal and access to that article is granted to customers who have purchased a subscription), Springer now provides an alternative publishing option: Springer Open Choice. A Springer Open Choice article receives all the benefits of a regular subscription-based article, but in addition is made available publicly through Springer's online platform, SpringerLink. To publish via Springer Open Choice, upon acceptance please visit www.springeronline.com/openchoice to complete the relevant order form and provide the required payment information. Payment must be received in full before publication or articles will publish as regular subscription-model articles. We regret that Springer Open Choice cannot be ordered for published articles.

Cognition and Emotion

ADDRESS FOR SUBMISSION:

Craig Smith, Editor
Cognition and Emotion
c/o Journals Editorial Assistant
Psychology Press Ltd.
27 Church Road
Hove, East Sussex, BN3 2FA
UK
Phone: (0) 1273 225007
Fax: (0) 1273 205612
E-Mail: craig.a.smith@Vanderbilt.edu
Web: http://www.tandf.co.uk/journals
Address May Change:

CIRCULATION DATA:

Reader: Academics
Frequency of Issue: 8 Times/Year
Copies per Issue:
Sponsor/Publisher: Taylor & Francis
Subscribe Price: 368.00 US$ Individual
    998.00 US$ Institution

PUBLICATION GUIDELINES:

Manuscript Length:
Copies Required: One
Computer Submission: Yes Disk, Email
Format: MS Word, RTF, PDF
Fees to Review: 0.00 US$

Manuscript Style:
    American Psychological Association

REVIEW INFORMATION:

Type of Review:
No. of External Reviewers: 2-3
No. of In House Reviewers:
Acceptance Rate:
Time to Review:
Reviewers Comments: Yes
Invited Articles:
Fees to Publish: 0.00 US$

MANUSCRIPT TOPICS:
Abnormal Psychology; Social Psychology; Thinking & Cognition

MANUSCRIPT GUIDELINES/COMMENTS:

Note to Authors. Please make sure your contact address information is clearly visible on the outside of all packages you are sending to Editors.

Manuscript Submission
Manuscripts are invited for submission. Please note that authors are encouraged to submit papers electronically to expedite the peer review process. Please email your paper, saved in a standard document format type such as Word, Rich Text Format, or PDF, to **reviews@psypress.co.uk**. Alternatively, if you wish to submit a hard copy, please send one copy of the manuscript AND a disk version to: Journals Editorial Assistant, Psychology Press Ltd, 27 Church Road, Hove, East Sussex, BN3 2FA, UK. Tel: (0)1273 225007, Fax: (0)1273 205612.

Your covering email/letter must include full contact details (including email), and the title of your article.

All manuscripts should be submitted in American Psychological Association (APA) format following the latest edition of *Publication Manual of the APA* (currently 5th edition).

The publishers **strongly encourage** the submission of final, accepted manuscripts on disk (accompanied by hard copy). For guidelines for presentation of final manuscripts on disk please see http://www.tandf.co.uk/journals/authors/electronic.asp

Copyright. It is a condition of publication that authors vest or license copyright in their articles, including abstracts, in Psychology Press Ltd. This enables us to ensure full copyright protection and to disseminate the article, and the journal, to the widest possible readership in print and electronic formats as appropriate. Authors may, of course, use the material elsewhere after publication providing that prior permission is obtained from Taylor & Francis Ltd. Authors are themselves responsible for obtaining permission to reproduce copyright material from other sources. To view the 'Copyright Transfer Frequently Asked Questions please visit www.tandf.co.uk/journals/copyright.asp.

Journal Production Editor: **kirsten.buchanan@psypress.co.uk**

Format
Typescripts. The style and format of the typescripts should conform to the specifications given in the *Publication Manual of the American Psychological Association* (5th edition).

Typescripts should be **double spaced** on **one side** only of A4 paper, with adequate margins, and numbered throughout. The title page of an article should contain only:
(1) the title of the paper, the name(s) and address(es) of the author(s);
(2) a short title not exceeding 40 letters and spaces, which will be used for page headlines;
(3) name and address of the author to whom correspondence and proofs should be sent;
(4) your telephone, fax and e-mail numbers, as this helps speed of processing considerably.

Abstract. An abstract of 100-150 words should follow the title page on a separate sheet.

Headings. Indicate headings and subheadings for different sections of the paper clearly. Do not number headings.

Acknowledgements. These should be as brief as possible and typed on a separate sheet at the beginning of the text.

Permission to quote. Any direct quotation, regardless of length, must be accompanied by a reference citation that includes a page number. Any quote over six manuscript lines should have formal written permission to quote from the copyright owner. It is the author's responsibility to determine whether permission is required from the copyright owner and, if so, to obtain it. (See the bottom of the page for a template of a letter seeking copyright permission.)

Footnotes. These should be avoided unless absolutely necessary. Essential footnotes should be indicated by superscript figures in the text and collected on a separate sheet at the end of the manuscript.

Reference citations within the text. Use authors' last names, with the year of publication in parentheses after the last author's name, e.g., "Jones and Smith (1987)"; alternatively, "(Brown, 1982; Jones & Smith, 1987; White, Johnson, & Thomas, 1990)". On first citation of references with three to six authors, give all names in full, thereafter use first author "et al.". If more than one article by the same author(s) in the same year is cited, the letters a, b, c, etc. should follow the year.

Reference list. A full list of references quoted in the text should be given at the end of the paper in alphabetical order of authors' surnames (or chronologically for a group of references by the same authors), commencing as a new sheet, typed double spaced. Titles of journals and books should be given in full, e.g.:

Books
Baddeley, A. D. (1999). *Essentials of human memory*. Hove, UK: Psychology Press.

Chapter in edited book
Plomin, R., & Dale, P. S. (2000). Genetics and early language development: A UK study of twins. In D. V. M. Bishop & L. B. Leonard (Eds.), *Speech and language impairments in children: Causes, characteristics, intervention and outcome* (pp. 35-51). Hove, UK: Psychology Press.

Journal article
Schwartz, M. F., & Hodgson, C. (2002). A new multiword naming deficit: Evidence and interpretation. *Cognitive Neuropsychology*, 19, 263-288.

Tables. These should be kept to the minimum. Each table should be typed double spaced on a separate sheet, giving the heading, e.g., "Table 2", in Arabic numerals, followed by the legend, followed by the table. Make sure that appropriate units are given. Instructions for placing the table should be given in parentheses in the text, e.g., "(Table 2 about here)".

Figures. Figures should only be used when essential. The same data should not be presented both as a figure and in a table. Where possible, related diagrams should be grouped together to form a single figure. Figures should be drawn to professional standards and it is recommended that the linear dimensions of figures be approximately twice those intended for the final printed version. Each of these should be on a separate page, not integrated with the text. Figures will be reproduced directly from originals supplied by the author(s). These must be of good quality, clearly and completely lettered. Make sure that axes of graphs are properly labelled, and that appropriate units are given. Photocopies will reproduce poorly, as will pale or broken originals. Dense tones should be avoided, and never combined with lettering. Half-tone figures should be clear, highly-contrasted black and white glossy prints.

Black and white figures are included free of charge. Colour figures are not normally acceptable for publication in print -- however, it may be possible both to **print** in black and white and to **publish online** in colour. Colour figures will only be printed by prior arrangement between the editor(s), publisher and author(s); and authors may be asked to share the costs of inclusion of such figures.

The figure captions should be typed in a separate section, headed, e.g., "Figure 2", in Arabic numerals. Instructions for placing the figure should be given in parentheses in the text, e.g., "(Figure 2 about here)". More detailed Guidelines for the Preparation of Figure Artwork are available from the publisher: Psychology Press Ltd, 27 Church Road, Hove, East Sussex BN3 2FA, UK (Email: **kirsten.buchanan@psypress.co.uk**).

Statistics. Results of statistical tests should be given in the following form:

"... results showed an effect of group, $F(2, 21) = 13.74$, $MSE = 451.98$, $p < .001$, but there was no effect of repeated trials, $F(5, 105) = 1.44$, $MSE = 17.70$, and no interaction, $F(10, 105) = 1.34$, $MSE = 17.70$."

Other tests should be reported in a similar manner to the above example of an F -ratio. For a fuller explanation of statistical presentation, see pages 136-147 of the *APA Publication Manual* (5th ed.). For guidelines on presenting statistical significance, see pages 24-25.

Abbreviations. Abbreviations that are specific to a particular manuscript or to a very specific area of research should be avoided, and authors will be asked to spell out in full any such abbreviations throughout the text. Standard abbreviations such as RT for reaction time, SOA for stimulus onset asynchrony or other standard abbreviations that will be readily understood by readers of the journal are acceptable. Experimental conditions should be named in full, except in tables and figures.

After Acceptance f Publication in the Journal
Proofs. Page proofs will be emailed to the corresponding author as a PDF attachment to check for typesetting accuracy. No changes to the original typescript will be permitted at this stage. A list of queries raised by the copy editor will also be emailed. Proofs should be returned promptly **with the original copy-edited manuscript and query sheet**.

Early electronic offprints (e-prints). Specified corresponding authors will receive their article by email as a complete PDF. This allows the author to print up to 50 copies, free of charge, and disseminate them to colleagues. In many cases, this facility will be available up to two weeks prior to print publication of the article. One copy of the journal issue in which their paper appears will be sent by post to all specified corresponding authors free after print publication. Paper offprints can still be purchased by authors if they complete the enclosed offprint order form and return with payment together with their corrected proofs.

Copyright Permission
Contributors are required to secure permission for the reproduction of any figure, table, or extensive (more than six manuscript lines) extract from the text, from a source which is copyrighted -- or owned -- by a party other than Psychology Press Ltd or the contributor.

This applies both to direct reproduction or "derivative reproduction" -- when the contributor has created a new figure or table which derives **substantially** from a copyrighted source.

The following form of words can be used in seeking permission:

Dear [COPYRIGHT HOLDER]

I/we are preparing for publication an article entitled
[STATE TITLE]
to be published by Psychology Press Ltd in *Cognition and Emotion*.

I/we should be grateful if you would grant us permission to include the following materials:
[STATE FIGURE NUMBER AND ORIGINAL SOURCE]
We are requesting non-exclusive rights in this edition and in all forms. It is understood, of course, that full acknowledgement will be given to the source.

Please note that Psychology Press Ltd are signatories of and respect the spirit of the STM Agreement regarding the free sharing and dissemination of scholarly information.

Your prompt consideration of this request would be greatly appreciated.

Yours faithfully

Volume contents and author index. The list of contents and the author index for the whole of the year's issues are published in the last issue of the year of each journal. For *Cognition and Emotion*, this is issue 8 (November).

Cognitive and Behavioral Neurology

ADDRESS FOR SUBMISSION:

Murray Grossman, Editor
Cognitive and Behavioral Neurology
University of Pennsylvania
School of Medicine
Department of Neurology - 2 Gibson
3400 Spruce St
Philadelphia, PA 19104-4283
USA
Phone:
Fax: 215-349-8464
E-Mail: cbn@mail.med.upenn.edu
Web: cbn@lww.com
Address May Change:

PUBLICATION GUIDELINES:

Manuscript Length: 11-15
Copies Required: Four
Computer Submission: Yes
Format: MS Word
Fees to Review: 0.00 US$

Manuscript Style:
    Other, See Website

CIRCULATION DATA:

Reader: Academics, Physicians
Frequency of Issue: Quarterly
Copies per Issue: 1,001 - 2,000
Sponsor/Publisher: Behavioral and
    Cognitive Neurology Society
Subscribe Price: 0.00 US$

REVIEW INFORMATION:

Type of Review: Editorial Review
No. of External Reviewers: 2
No. of In House Reviewers: 1
Acceptance Rate: 21-30%
Time to Review: 2 - 3 Months
Reviewers Comments: Yes
Invited Articles: 0-5%
Fees to Publish: 0.00 US$

MANUSCRIPT TOPICS:
Cognitive Neuroscience; Gerontology; Neuropsychology; Psychiatry; Psychobiology;
Thinking & Cognition

MANUSCRIPT GUIDELINES/COMMENTS:

Scope
The journal focuses on hypothesis-generating case studies, hypothesis-testing experimental studies examining the neural basis for cognition and affect, and exploratory therapeutic trials. The journal welcomes contributions from all sources on any subject pertinent to cognitive neurology, neuropsychology, or neuropsychiatry. Each contribution will be reviewed by at least two peers and will be judged on the basis of its scientific merit, timeliness, and readability. Priority will be given to papers of multidisciplinary interest and to articles that provide original data on theoretical concepts, basic brain processes, or major clinical issues.

Manuscript Submission

A submitted manuscript must be an original contribution not previously published (except as an abstract or preliminary report), must not be under consideration for publication elsewhere, and, if accepted, must not be published elsewhere in similar form, in any language, without the consent of Lippincott Williams & Wilkins. Each person listed as an author is expected to have participated in the study to a significant extent. Although the editors and referees make every effort to ensure the validity of published manuscripts, the final responsibility rests with the authors, not with the Journal, its editors, or the publisher.

Patient anonymity and informed consent. It is the author's responsibility to ensure that a patient's anonymity be carefully protected and to verify that any experimental investigation with human subjects reported in the manuscript was performed with informed consent and following all the guidelines for experimental investigation with human subjects required by the institution(s) with which all the authors are affiliated. Authors should mask patients' eyes and remove patients' names from figures unless they obtain written consent from the patients and submit written consent with the manuscript.

Copyright. All authors must sign a copy of the Journal's "Authorship Responsibility, Financial Disclosure, and Copyright Transfer" form and submit it with the original manuscript.

Permissions. Authors must submit written permission from the copyright owner (usually the publisher) to use direct quotations, tables, or illustrations that have appeared in copyrighted form elsewhere, along with complete details about the source. Any permissions fees that might be required by the copyright owner are the responsibility of the authors requesting use of the borrowed material, not the responsibility of Lippincott Williams & Wilkins.

Preparation of Manuscript

Manuscripts that do not adhere to the following instructions will be returned to the corresponding author for technical revision before undergoing peer review. Neither the journal editors nor the publisher will proofread a manuscript. Authors must carefully proofread a manuscript prior to submission.

General Format. Submit manuscripts in English in quadruplicate (one original and three copies) and printed on standard 8½ × 11-inch (21 × 28-cm) paper with at least a 1-inch (2.5 cm) margin on all sides. Double space all copy, including legends, footnotes, tables, and references, and print on one side of the sheet only. An electronic version of the manuscript also must be submitted on disk. Indicate the format on the label. If a manuscript is accepted for publication, the authors must then submit the final, accepted version of the manuscript on disk.

Title page. Include on the title page (a) complete manuscript title; (b) authors' full names, highest academic degrees, and affiliations; (c) name and address for correspondence, including fax number, telephone number, and e-mail address; (d) address for reprints if different from that of corresponding author; and (e) sources of support that require acknowledgment.

Structured abstract and key words. Limit the abstract to 200 words. Do not cite references in the abstract. Limit the use of abbreviations and acronyms. Use the following subheads: Objective, Background, Method, Results, and Conclusions. Provide three to five key words.

Text. Organize the manuscript into four main headings: Introduction, Materials and Methods, Results, and Discussion. Define abbreviations at first mention in text and in each table and figure. If a brand name is cited, supply the manufacturer's name and address (city and state/country). Acknowledge all forms of support, including pharmaceutical and industry support, in an Acknowledgments paragraph.

Abbreviations. For a list of standard abbreviations, consult the Council of Biology Editors Style Guide (available from the Council of Science Editors, 9650 Rockville Pike, Bethesda, MD 20814) or other standard sources. Write out the full term for each abbreviation at its first use unless it is a standard unit of measure.

References. The authors are responsible for the accuracy of the references. Key the references (double-spaced) at the end of the manuscript. Cite the references in text in the order of appearance. Cite unpublished data, such as papers submitted but not yet accepted for publication or personal communications, in parentheses in the text. If there are more than three authors, name only the first three authors and then use et al. Refer to the List of Journals Indexed in Index Medicus for abbreviations of journal names, or access the list at: http://www.nlm.nih.gov/tsd/serials/lji.html. Sample references are given below:

Journal article
1. Galynker II, Cohen LJ, Cai J. Negative symptoms in patients with major depressive disorder: a preliminary study. *Neuropsychiatr Neuropsychol Behav Neurol* 2000;13:171–6.

Book chapter
2. Delis DC, Lucas JA, Kopelman MD. Memory. In: Fogel BS, Schiffer RB, Rao SM, eds. *Synopsis of neuropsychiatry.* Philadelphia: Lippincott Williams & Wilkins, 2000;169–91.

Entire book
3. Kellman RM, Marentette LJ. *Atlas of craniomaxillofacial fixation.* Philadelphia: Lippincott Williams & Wilkins, 1999.

Software
4. *Epi Info* [computer program]. Version 6. Atlanta: Centers for Disease Control and Prevention; 1994.

Online journal
5. Miyamoto O, Auer RN. Hypoxia, hyperoxia, ischemia, and brain necrosis. *Neurology* [serial online] 2000;54:362–71. Available at: www.neurology.org. Accessed February 23, 2000.

Database
6. *CANCERNET-PDQ* [database online]. Bethesda, MD: National Cancer Institute; 1996. Updated March 29, 1996.

World Wide Web

7. Gostin LO. Drug use and *HIV/AIDS* [JAMA HIV/AIDS Web site]. June 1, 1996. Available at: http://ama-assn.org/special/hiv/ethics. Accessed June 26, 1997.

Figures. Cite figures consecutively in the text, and number them in the order in which they are discussed. Write the first author's last name, the figure number and figure part (1A, 1B, 1C), and an arrow to indicate the top edge of the figure on a label pasted to the back of each figure. Submit all artwork in quadruplicate in camera-ready form; illustrations should be glossy prints or high-quality, laser-printed illustrations. Photocopies are unacceptable. Lettering should be large enough that it will remain legible after figure reduction; typewritten or unprofessional lettering is unacceptable. Figure parts (A, B, C) may be left unlabeled (but clearly marked on back) for professional placement by the Journal's printer.

Figure legends. Legends must be submitted for all figures. They should be brief and specific, and they should appear on a separate page after the references. Use scale markers in the image for electron micrographs, and indicate the type of stain.

Color figures. The journal accepts for publication color figures that will enhance an article. Authors who submit color figures will receive an estimate of the cost for color reproduction. If they decide not to pay for color reproduction, they can request that the figures be converted to black and white at no charge.

Digital figures. Electronic art should be created/scanned and saved and submitted as either a TIFF (tagged image file format), an EPS (encapsulated postscript) file, or a PPT (Power Point) file. Line art must have a resolution of at least 1200 dpi (dots per inch), and electronic photographs—radiographs, CT scans, and so on—and scanned images must have a resolution of at least 300 dpi. If fonts are used in the artwork, they must be converted to paths or outlines or they must be embedded in the files. Color images must be created/scanned and saved and submitted as CMYK files. All electronic art must be accompanied by high-resolution laser prints of the images. Files can be submitted on a 3½-inch high-density disk, a CD-ROM, or an Iomega Zip disk. Please note that artwork generated from office suite programs such as Corel Draw and MS Word and artwork downloaded from the Internet (JPEG or GIFF files) cannot be used.

Tables. Create tables using the table creating and editing feature of your word processing software (eg, Word, WordPerfect). Do not use Excel or comparable spreadsheet programs. Group all tables at the end of the manuscript, or supply them together in a separate file. Cite tables consecutively in the text, and number them in that order. Key each on a separate sheet, and include the table title, appropriate column heads, and explanatory legends (including definitions of any abbreviations used). Do not embed tables within the body of the manuscript. They should be self-explanatory and should supplement, rather than duplicate, the material in the text.

Style. Pattern manuscript style after the *American Medical Association Manual of Style* (9th edition). *Stedman's Medical Dictionary* (27th edition) *and Merriam Webster's Collegiate Dictionary* (10th edition) should be used as standard references. Refer to drugs and therapeutic agents by their accepted generic or chemical names, and do not abbreviate them. Use code numbers only when a generic name is not yet available. In that case, supply the chemical name and a figure giving the chemical structure of the drug is required. Copyright or trade names of drugs should be capitalized and placed in parentheses after the name of the drug. Names and locations (city and state in USA; city and country outside USA) of manufacturers of drugs, supplies, or equipment cited in a manuscript are required to comply with trademark law and should be provided in parentheses. Units of measure should be expressed in the metric system, and temperatures should be expressed in degrees Celsius. Conventional units should be written as SI units as appropriate.

Address for manuscript submission. Send the manuscript with a cover letter that includes the corresponding author's e-mail address and full mailing address to Murray Grossman, M.D., Cognitive and Behavioral Neurology, Department of Neurology - 3 W. Gates, University of Pennsylvania Medical Center, 3400 Spruce Street, Philadelphia, PA 19104; tel: (215) 349-8463; fax: (215) 349-8464; e-mail: **nnbn@mail.med.upenn.edu** (please see the checklist at the end of these Instructions before mailing manuscripts).

The editorial office will acknowledge receipt of your manuscript and will give you a manuscript number for your reference. Address all inquiries regarding manuscripts not yet accepted or published to the Journal's editorial office.

After Acceptance

Disk submission. Authors must submit an electronic version of the final accepted manuscript along with a printout of the final accepted manuscript. Electronic files should be submitted in a standard word processing format; Microsoft Word (or Corel WordPerfect) is preferred. Although conversions can be made from other word processing formats, the vagaries of the conversion process may introduce errors. Do not submit ASCII text files. Do not use automatic numbering or footnotes for references. The Journal does not assume responsibility for errors in the conversion of customized software, newly released software, and special characters. Authors preparing manuscripts on Macintosh computers should not use the Fast Save option. Each submitted disk must be clearly labeled with the name of the author, item title, Journal title, word processing program and version, and file name used. The disk should contain only one file—the final version of the accepted manuscript.

Electronic page proofs and corrections. Corresponding authors will receive electronic page proofs to check the copyedited and typeset article before publication. Portable document format (PDF) files of the typeset pages and support documents (e.g., reprint order form) will be sent to the corresponding author via e-mail. Complete instructions will be provided with the e-mail for downloading and printing the files and for faxing the corrected pages to the publisher. Those authors without an e-mail address will receive traditional page proofs.

It is the author's responsibility to ensure that there are no errors in the proofs. Changes that have been made to conform to journal style will stand if they do not alter the authors' meaning. Only the most critical changes to the accuracy of the content will be made. Changes that are stylistic or are a reworking of previously accepted material will be disallowed. The publisher reserves the right to deny any changes that do not affect the accuracy of the content. Authors may be charged for alterations to the proofs beyond those required to correct errors or to answer queries. Electronic proofs must be checked carefully and corrections faxed within 24 to 48 hours of receipt, as requested in the cover letter accompanying the page proofs.

Reprints. Authors will receive a reprint order form and a price list with the page proofs. Reprint requests should be faxed to the publisher with the corrected proofs, if possible. Reprints are normally shipped 6 to 8 weeks after publication of the issue in which the item appears. Contact the Reprint Department, Lippincott Williams & Wilkins, 351 W. Camden Street, Baltimore, MD 21201 with any questions.

Publisher's contact. Fax corrected page proofs, reprint order forms, and any other related materials to Doug Miller, The Sheridan Press, 450 Fame Avenue,, Hanover, PA 17331.

Manuscript Submission Checklist

1. Four copies of complete manuscript
2. Four sets of clearly labeled figures
3. Cover letter
4. Title page
5. Abstract
6. References double-spaced in AMA style
7. Corresponding author designated, and full mailing address included, in cover letter and on title page
8. E-mail address of corresponding author included in cover letter and on title page
9. Permission to reproduce copyrighted materials or signed patient consent forms
10. Acknowledgments listed for grants and technical support
11. Materials packed in extra-strength envelope
12. Manuscript Authorship Responsibility, Financial Disclosure, and Copyright Transfer form signed by each author
13. Disk and high-quality print of electronic art
14. Disk containing final version of manuscript after acceptance by the editorial office

Cognitive Neuropsychiatry

ADDRESS FOR SUBMISSION:

A. S. David & P. W. Halligan, Editors
Cognitive Neuropsychiatry
c/o Journals Editorial Assistant
Psychology Press Ltd.
27 Church Road,
Hove, East Sussex, BN3 2FA
UK
Phone: (0) 1273 225007
Fax: (0) 1273 205612
E-Mail: See Guidelines
Web: http://www.tandf.co.uk/journals
Address May Change:

PUBLICATION GUIDELINES:

Manuscript Length:
Copies Required: One
Computer Submission: Yes Disk, Email
Format: MS Word, RTF, PDF
Fees to Review: 0.00 US$

Manuscript Style:
  American Psychological Association

CIRCULATION DATA:

Reader: Academics
Frequency of Issue: 5 Times/Year
Copies per Issue:
Sponsor/Publisher: Taylor & Francis
Subscribe Price: 202.00 US$ Individual
  412.00 US$ Institution

REVIEW INFORMATION:

Type of Review:
No. of External Reviewers: 2-3
No. of In House Reviewers: 0
Acceptance Rate:
Time to Review: 2-6 Months
Reviewers Comments: Yes
Invited Articles:
Fees to Publish: 0.00 US$

MANUSCRIPT TOPICS:
Abnormal Psychology; Neuropsychology; Thinking & Cognition

MANUSCRIPT GUIDELINES/COMMENTS:

Editor's Email Addresses: **HALLIGANPW@cardiff.ac.uk** & **a.david@iop.kcl.ac.uk**

Note to Authors. Please make sure your contact address information is clearly visible on the outside of all packages you are sending to Editors.

Manuscript Submission
Copyright. It is a condition of publication that authors vest or license copyright in their articles, including abstracts, in Psychology Press Ltd. This enables us to ensure full copyright protection and to disseminate the article, and the journal, to the widest possible readership in print and electronic formats as appropriate. Authors may, of course, use the material elsewhere after publication providing that prior permission is obtained from Taylor & Francis Ltd. Authors are themselves responsible for obtaining permission to reproduce copyright

material from other sources. To view the 'Copyright Transfer Frequently Asked Questions' please visit www.tandf.co.uk/journals/copyright.asp.

Manuscripts are invited for submission. Please note that authors are encouraged to submit papers electronically to expedite the peer review process. Please email your paper, saved in a standard document format type such as Word, Rich Text Format, or PDF, to **reviews@psypress.co.uk**. Alternatively, if you wish to submit a hard copy, please send one copy of the manuscript AND a disk version to: Journals Editorial Assistant, Psychology Press Ltd, 27 Church Road, Hove, East Sussex, BN3 2FA, UK. Tel: (0)1273 225007, Fax: (0)1273 205612.

Your covering email/letter must include full contact details (including email), the title of the journal to which you are submitting, and the title of your article.

All manuscripts should be submitted in American Psychological Association (APA) format following the latest edition of *Publication Manual of the APA* (currently 5th edition).

Authors may request blind refereeing. In this case, it is the responsibility of the author to prepare his or her manuscript such that after detachment of the title page no clues remain as to authorial identities.

The publishers strongly encourage the submission of final, accepted manuscripts on disk (accompanied by matching hard copy). For guidelines for presentation of final manuscripts on disk please see http://www.tandf.co.uk/journals/authors/electronic.asp.

Journal Production Editor: **kirsten.buchanan@psypress.co.uk**

Format
Typescripts. The style and format of the typescripts should conform to the specifications given in the *Publication Manual of the American Psychological Association* (5th ed.). Typescripts should be double spaced on one side only of A4 paper, with adequate margins, and numbered throughout. The title page of an article should contain only:
1. the title of the paper, the name(s) and address(es) of the author(s);
2. a short title not exceeding 40 letters and spaces, which will be used for page headlines;
3. name and address of the author to whom correspondence and proofs should be sent;
4. your telephone, fax and e-mail numbers, as this helps speed of processing considerably;
5. up to six keywords.

Structured Abstracts. Authors submitting papers should note that the journal uses Structured Abstracts. There is good evidence that Structured Abstracts are clearer for readers and facilitate better appropriate indexing and citation of papers.

The Structured Abstract should be between 50-200 words and their essential features are given below. Note in particular that any clinical implications should be clearly stated.

Introduction. Describe the background to the study, hypotheses, aims, objectives, research questions, etc.

Methods. Include outline of the methodology and design of experiments; materials employed and subject/participant numbers with basic relevant demographic information; the nature of the analyses performed.

Results. Outline the important and relevant results of the analyses.

Conclusions. State the basic conclusions and implications of the study. State, clearly and usefully, if there are implications for management, treatment or service delivery.

Headings. Indicate headings and subheadings for different sections of the paper clearly. Do not number headings.

Acknowledgements. These should be as brief as possible and typed on a separate sheet at the beginning of the text.

Permission to quote. Any direct quotation, regardless of length, must be accompanied by a reference citation that includes a page number. Any quote over six manuscript lines should have formal written permission to quote from the copyright owner. It is the author's responsibility to determine whether permission is required from the copyright owner and, if so, to obtain it. (See the bottom of the page for a template of a letter seeking copyright permission.)

Footnotes. These should be avoided unless absolutely necessary. Essential footnotes should be indicated by superscript figures in the text and collected on a separate sheet at the end of the manuscript.

Reference citations within the text. Use authors' last names, with the year of publication in parentheses after the last author's name, e.g., "Jones and Smith (1987)"; alternatively, "(Brown, 1982; Jones & Smith, 1987; White, Johnson, & Thomas, 1990)". On first citation of references with three to six authors, give all names in full, thereafter use first author "et al.". If more than one article by the same author(s) in the same year is cited, the letters a, b, c, etc., should follow the year.

Reference list. A full list of references quoted in the text should be given at the end of the paper in alphabetical order of authors' surnames (or chronologically for a group of references by the same authors), commencing as a new sheet, typed double spaced. Titles of journals and books should be given in full, e.g.:

Books
Baddeley, A. D. (1999). *Essentials of human memory*. Hove, UK: Psychology Press.

Chapter in edited book
Plomin, R., & Dale, P. S. (2000). Genetics and early language development: A UK study of twins. In D. V. M. Bishop & L. B. Leonard (Eds.), *Speech and language impairments in children: Causes, characteristics, intervention and outcome* (pp. 35-51). Hove, UK: Psychology Press.

Journal article
Schwartz, M. F., & Hodgson, C. (2002). A new multiword naming deficit: Evidence and interpretation. *Cognitive Neuropsychology*, 19, 263-288.

Tables. These should be kept to the minimum. Each table should be typed double spaced on a separate sheet, giving the heading, e.g., "Table 2", in Arabic numerals, followed by the legend, followed by the table. Make sure that appropriate units are given. Instructions for placing the table should be given in parentheses in the text, e.g., "(Table 2 about here)".

Figures. Figures should only be used when essential. The same data should not be presented both as a figure and in a table. Where possible, related diagrams should be grouped together to form a single figure. Figures should be drawn to professional standards and it is recommended that the linear dimensions of figures be approximately twice those intended for the final printed version. Each of these should be on a separate page, not integrated with the text. Figures will be reproduced directly from originals supplied by the author(s). These must be of good quality, clearly and completely lettered. Make sure that axes of graphs are properly labelled, and that appropriate units are given. Photocopies will reproduce poorly, as will pale or broken originals. Dense tones should be avoided, and never combined with lettering. Half-tone figures should be clear, highly-contrasted black and white glossy prints.

Black and white figures are included free of charge. Colour figures are not normally acceptable for publication in print -- however, it may be possible both to **print** in black and white and to **publish online** in colour. Colour figures will only be printed by prior arrangement between the editor(s), publisher and author(s); and authors may be asked to share the costs of inclusion of such figures.

The figure captions should be typed in a separate section, headed, e.g., "Figure 2", in Arabic numerals. Instructions for placing the figure should be given in parentheses in the text, e.g., "(Figure 2 about here)". More detailed Guidelines for the Preparation of Figure Artwork are available from the publisher: Psychology Press Ltd, 27 Church Road, Hove, East Sussex BN3 2FA, UK (Email: **kirsten.buchanan@psypress.co.uk**).

Statistics. Results of statistical tests should be given in the following form:
"... results showed an effect of group, $F(2, 21) = 13.74$, $MSE = 451.98$, $p < .001$, but there was no effect of repeated trials, $F(5, 105) = 1.44$, $MSE = 17.70$, and no interaction, $F(10, 105) = 1.34$, $MSE = 17.70$."

Other tests should be reported in a similar manner to the above example of an F -ratio. For a fuller explanation of statistical presentation, see pages 136-147 of the *APA Publication Manual* (5th ed.). For guidelines on presenting statistical significance, see pages 24-25.

Abbreviations. Abbreviations that are specific to a particular manuscript or to a very specific area of research should be avoided, and authors will be asked to spell out in full any such abbreviations throughout the text. Standard abbreviations such as RT for reaction time, SOA for stimulus onset asynchrony or other standard abbreviations that will be readily understood by readers of the journal are acceptable. Experimental conditions should be named in full, except in tables and figures.

After Acceptance of Publication in the Journal

Proofs. Page proofs will be emailed to the corresponding author as a PDF attachment to check for typesetting accuracy. No changes to the original typescript will be permitted at this stage. A list of queries raised by the copy editor will also be emailed. Proofs should be returned promptly **with the original copy-edited manuscript and query sheet**.

Early electronic offprints (e-prints). Specified corresponding authors will receive their article by email as a complete PDF. This allows the author to print up to 50 copies, free of charge, and disseminate them to colleagues. In many cases, this facility will be available up to two weeks prior to print publication of the article. One copy of the journal issue in which their paper appears will be sent by post to all specified corresponding authors free after print publication. Paper offprints can still be purchased by authors if they complete the enclosed offprint order form and return with payment together with their corrected proofs.

Copyright Permission

Contributors are required to secure permission for the reproduction of any figure, table, or extensive (more than six manuscript lines) extract from the text, from a source which is copyrighted -- or owned -- by a party other than Psychology Press Ltd or the contributor.

This applies both to direct reproduction or "derivative reproduction" -- when the contributor has created a new figure or table which derives substantially from a copyrighted source.

The following form of words can be used in seeking permission:

Dear [COPYRIGHT HOLDER]

I/we are preparing for publication an article entitled
[STATE TITLE]
to be published by Psychology Press Ltd in *Cognitive Neuropsychiatry*.

I/we should be grateful if you would grant us permission to include the following materials:
[STATE FIGURE NUMBER AND ORIGINAL SOURCE]
We are requesting non-exclusive rights in this edition and in all forms. It is understood, of course, that full acknowledgement will be given to the source.

Please note that Psychology Press Ltd are signatories of and respect the spirit of the STM Agreement regarding the free sharing and dissemination of scholarly information.

Your prompt consideration of this request would be greatly appreciated.

Yours faithfully

Volume contents and author index. The list of contents and the author index for the whole of the year's issues are published in the last issue of the year of each journal. For Cognitive Neuropsychiatry, this is issue 5 (November).

Cognitive Neuropsychology

ADDRESS FOR SUBMISSION:

Alfonso Caramazza, Editor
Cognitive Neuropsychology
c/o Journals Editorial Assistant
Psychology Press Ltd.
27 Church Road
Hove, East Sussex, BN3 2FA
UK
Phone: (0) 1273 225007
Fax: (0) 1273 205612
E-Mail: caram@wjh.harvard.edu
Web: http://www.tandf.co.uk/journals
Address May Change:

PUBLICATION GUIDELINES:

Manuscript Length:
Copies Required: One
Computer Submission: Yes Disk, Email
Format: MS Word, RTF, PDF
Fees to Review: 0.00 US$

Manuscript Style:
American Psychological Association

CIRCULATION DATA:

Reader: Academics
Frequency of Issue: 8 Times/Year
Copies per Issue:
Sponsor/Publisher: Taylor & Francis
Subscribe Price: 399.00 US$ Individual
1238.00 US$ Institution

REVIEW INFORMATION:

Type of Review:
No. of External Reviewers: 2-3
No. of In House Reviewers: 0
Acceptance Rate:
Time to Review: 2-6 Months
Reviewers Comments: Yes
Invited Articles:
Fees to Publish: 0.00 US$

MANUSCRIPT TOPICS:
Neuropsychology; Thinking & Cognition

MANUSCRIPT GUIDELINES/COMMENTS:

Aims and Scopes. The basic aim of this journal is to promote the study of cognitive processes from a neuropsychological perspective. Cognition will be understood very broadly, as including perception, attention, object recognition, planning, language, thinking, memory and action, for example. Any neuropsychological work bearing upon our understanding of normal cognitive processes would be directly appropriate for the journal. Neuropsychological disorders of cognition arising at any stage of the life span-both developmental disorders and disorders associated with ageing, as well as traumatic disorders, for example-will be of interest. Also relevant will be any studies of cognition in normal subjects which may shed some light upon the nature of disorders of cognition, as well as studies of rehabilitation of such disorders in which a cognitive-neuropsychological perspective is adopted. Papers need not be reports of the author's experimental research: theoretical contributions, critical reviews of the literature, and commentaries on papers published in previous issues of the journal would also be appropriate.

The journal will also publish in-depth critical reviews of books dealing with any aspect of *Cognitive Neuropsychology*. There is no requirement that reviewed books be contemporary. Any book whose importance for *Cognitive Neuropsychology* is sufficiently clear may be reviewed in the journal, no matter how long ago the book was published. Anyone interested in submitting a book review to the journal should contact the Book Reviews Editor, Professor Tim Shallice, Institute of Cognitive Neuroscience, University College London, Alexandra House, 17 Queen Square, London, WC1N 3AR, UK.

Finally, it is intended that the journal will occasionally reprint important papers that have already appeared elsewhere, but which are likely to have escaped the notice of most cognitive neuropsychologists, either because the papers were published long ago, or in languages other than English. Suggestions as to papers which deserve reprinting for these reasons may be sent to Professor A. W. Ellis (Department of Psychology, University of York, Heslington, York YO1 5DD, UK).

Methodological Considerations
Papers should in general satisfy methodological standards expected of publications on normal cognitive processes in such journals as the *Journal of Experimental Psychology or Cognitive Psychology*, as well as satisfying requirements appropriate for neuropsychological publications in journals such as *Brain* (e.g., where studies of neuropsychological patients are reported, efforts should be made to provide a clear background description of the general neurological and neuropsychological status of the patient).

The importance of single case studies for the resolution of theoretical issues is acknowledged, and methodologically adequate single case studies are welcomed. In reports of such studies, the nature of a patient's deficits should be documented in quantitative terms (a simple syndrome label is insufficient). The level of detail required here depends upon the specific hypothesis being tested. Essentially what is needed is documentation of the presence of specified deficits and preserved capacities as these are related to particular hypotheses.

In reports of group studies, criteria for selecting and for grouping patients must be detailed and explicit, and related to the particular hypotheses being tested. The designation of a group of patients simply as "Broca's aphasics", for example, would not be sufficient. A set of patients classified as Broca's aphasics can be extremely heterogeneous, and any conclusions reached in such a study may, in fact, be true for only a few of the patients in this group. One way around this problem is to treat each patient as an individual, i.e., carry out single case studies. Another is to provide explicit evidence of homogeneity of the group in a group study.

Submissions
Manuscripts are invited for submission. Please note that authors are encouraged to submit papers electronically to expedite the peer review process. Please email your paper, saved in a standard document format type such as Word, Rich Text Format, or PDF, to **reviews@psypress.co.uk**. Alternatively, if you wish to submit a hard copy, please send one copy of the manuscript AND a disk version to: Journals Editorial Assistant, Psychology Press Ltd, 27 Church Road, Hove, East Sussex, BN3 2FA, UK. Tel: (0)1273 207411, Fax: (0)1273 205612.

Your covering email/letter must include full contact details (including email), the title of the journal to which you are submitting, and the title of your article.

All manuscripts should be submitted in American Psychological Association (APA) format following the latest edition of *Publication Manual of the APA* (currently 5th edition).

Authors may request blind refereeing. In this case, it is the responsibility of the author to prepare his or her manuscript such that after detachment of the title page no clues remain as to authorial identities.

Each paper submitted to the Editor will be assigned to an appropriate member of the Board of Editors, who will thenceforth have full editorial responsibility for the paper, and will obtain and transmit to authors reviews from at least two independent reviewers.

The publishers **strongly encourage** the submission of final, accepted manuscripts on disk (accompanied by matching hard copy). For guidelines for presentation of final manuscripts on disk please see http://www.tandf.co.uk/journals/authors/electronic.asp.

Copyright. It is a condition of publication that authors vest or license copyright in their articles, including abstracts, in Psychology Press Ltd. This enables us to ensure full copyright protection and to disseminate the article, and the journal, to the widest possible readership in print and electronic formats as appropriate. Authors may, of course, use the material elsewhere after publication providing that prior permission is obtained from Taylor & Francis Ltd. Authors are themselves responsible for obtaining permission to reproduce copyright material from other sources. To view the 'Copyright Transfer Frequently Asked Questions please visit www.tandf.co.uk/journals/copyright.asp.

Journal Production Editor: **kate.moysen@psypress.co.uk**

Format
Typescripts. The style and format of the typescripts should conform to the specifications given in the *Publication Manual of the American Psychological Association* (5th ed.). Typescripts should be double spaced on one side only of A4 paper, with adequate margins, and numbered throughout. The title page of an article should contain only:
1. the title of the paper, the name(s) and address(es) of the author(s);
2. a short title not exceeding 40 letters and spaces, which will be used for page headlines;
3. name and full contact address of the author to whom correspondence and proofs should be sent;
4. your telephone, fax and email details, as this helps speed of processing considerably.

Abstract. An abstract of 100-150 words should follow the title page on a separate sheet.

Headings. Indicate headings and subheadings for different sections of the paper clearly. Do not number headings.

Acknowledgements. These should be as brief as possible and typed on a separate sheet at the beginning of the text.

Permission to quote. Any direct quotation, regardless of length, must be accompanied by a reference citation that includes a page number. Any quote over six manuscript lines should have formal written permission to quote from the copyright owner. It is the author's responsibility to determine whether permission is required from the copyright owner and, if so, to obtain it. (See the bottom of the page for a template of a letter seeking copyright permission.)

Footnotes. These should be avoided unless absolutely necessary. Essential footnotes should be indicated by superscript figures in the text and collected on a separate sheet at the end of the manuscript.

Reference citations within the text. Use authors' last names, with the year of publication in parentheses after the last author's name, e.g., "Jones and Smith (1987)"; alternatively, "(Brown, 1982; Jones & Smith, 1987; White, Johnson, & Thomas, 1990)". On first citation of references with three to six authors, give all names in full, thereafter use first author "et al.". If more than one article by the same author(s) in the same year is cited, the letters a, b, c, etc., should follow the year.

Reference list. A full list of references quoted in the text should be given at the end of the paper in alphabetical order of authors' surnames (or chronologically for a group of references by the same authors), commencing as a new sheet, typed double spaced. Titles of journals and books should be given in full, e.g.:

Books
Baddeley, A. D. (1999). *Essentials of human memory*. Hove, UK: Psychology Press.

Chapter in edited book
Plomin, R., & Dale, P. S. (2000). Genetics and early language development: A UK study of twins. In D. V. M. Bishop & L. B. Leonard (Eds.), *Speech and language impairments in children: Causes, characteristics, intervention and outcome* (pp. 35-51). Hove, UK: Psychology Press.

Journal article
Schwartz, M. F., & Hodgson, C. (2002). A new multiword naming deficit: Evidence and interpretation. *Cognitive Neuropsychology, 19*, 263-288.

Tables. These should be kept to the minimum. Each table should be typed double spaced on a separate sheet, giving the heading, e.g., "Table 2", in Arabic numerals, followed by the legend, followed by the table. Make sure that appropriate units are given. Instructions for placing the table should be given in parentheses in the text, e.g., "(Table 2 about here)".

Figures. Figures should only be used when essential. The same data should not be presented both as a figure and in a table. Where possible, related diagrams should be grouped together to form a single figure. Figures should be drawn to professional standards and it is recommended that the linear dimensions of figures be approximately twice those intended for the final printed version. Each of these should be on a separate page, not integrated with the text. Figures will be reproduced directly from originals supplied by the author(s). These must be of good quality, clearly and completely lettered. Make sure that axes of graphs are properly labelled, and that appropriate units are given. Photocopies will reproduce poorly, as will pale or broken originals. Dense tones should be avoided, and never combined with lettering. Half-tone figures should be clear, highly-contrasted black and white glossy prints.

Black and white figures are included free of charge. Colour figures are not normally acceptable for publication in print-however, it may be possible both to **print** in black and white and to **publish online** in colour. Colour figures will only be printed by prior arrangement between the editor(s), publisher and author(s); and authors may be asked to share the costs of inclusion of such figures. The figure captions should be typed in a separate section, headed, e.g., "Figure 2", in Arabic numerals. Instructions for placing the figure should be given in parentheses in the text, e.g., "(Figure 2 about here)". More detailed Guidelines for the preparation of figure artwork are available from the publisher: Psychology Press Ltd, 27 Church Road, Hove, East Sussex BN3 2FA, UK (Email: **kate.moysen@psypress.co.uk**).

Statistics. Results of statistical tests should be given in the following form:

"... results showed an effect of group, $F(2, 21) = 13.74$, $MSE = 451.98$, $p < .001$, but there was no effect of repeated trials, $F(5, 105) = 1.44$, $MSE = 17.70$, and no interaction, $F(10, 105) = 1.34$, $MSE = 17.70$."

Other tests should be reported in a similar manner to the above example of an F -ratio. For a fuller explanation of statistical presentation, see pages 136-147 of the APA Publication Manual (5th ed.). For guidelines on presenting statistical significance, see pages 24-25.

Abbreviations. Abbreviations that are specific to a particular manuscript or to a very specific area of research should be avoided, and authors will be asked to spell out in full any such abbreviations throughout the text. Standard abbreviations such as RT for reaction time, SOA for stimulus onset asynchrony or other standard abbreviations that will be readily understood by readers of the journal are acceptable. Experimental conditions should be named in full, except in tables and figures.

After Acceptance of Publication in the Journal
Proofs. Page proofs will be emailed to the corresponding author as a PDF attachment to check for typesetting accuracy. No changes to the original typescript will be permitted at this stage. A list of queries raised by the copy editor will also be emailed. Proofs should be returned promptly **with the original copy-edited manuscript and query sheet**.

Early electronic offprints (e-prints). Specified corresponding authors will receive their article by email as a complete PDF. This allows the author to print up to 50 copies, free of charge, and disseminate them to colleagues. In many cases, this facility will be available up to two weeks prior to print publication of the article. One copy of the journal issue in which their paper appears will be sent by post to all specified corresponding authors free after print publication. Paper offprints can still be purchased by authors if they complete the enclosed offprint order form and return with payment together with their corrected proofs.

Copyright Permission
Contributors are required to secure permission for the reproduction of any figure, table, or extensive (more than six manuscript lines) extract from the text, from a source which is copyrighted-or owned-by a party other than Psychology Press Ltd or the contributor.

This applies both to direct reproduction or "derivative reproduction" -- when the contributor has created a new figure or table which derives substantially from a copyrighted source.

The following form of words can be used in seeking permission:

Dear [COPYRIGHT HOLDER]

I/we are preparing for publication an article entitled
[STATE TITLE]
to be published by Psychology Press Ltd in *Cognitive Neuropsychology*.

I/we should be grateful if you would grant us permission to include the following materials:
[STATE FIGURE NUMBER AND ORIGINAL SOURCE]
We are requesting non-exclusive rights in this edition and in all forms. It is understood, of course, that full acknowledgement will be given to the source.

Please note that Psychology Press Ltd are signatories of and respect the spirit of the STM Agreement regarding the free sharing and dissemination of scholarly information.

Your prompt consideration of this request would be greatly appreciated.

Yours faithfully

Volume contents, cumulative author index, and subject index. The list of contents for the whole of the year's issues are published in the last issue of the year. Also, the Cumulative Author Index for Volume 1 onwards, and the Cumulative Subject Index for Volume 16 onwards, are both published in the last issue of the year. For *Cognitive Neuropsychology*, this is issue 8 (December).

Cognitive Psychology

ADDRESS FOR SUBMISSION:

Gordon Logan, Editor
Cognitive Psychology
Editorial Office
525 B Street, Suite 1900
San Diego, CA 92101-4495
USA
Phone: 619-669-6417
Fax: 619-699-6800
E-Mail: cogpsy@elsevier.com
Web:
Address May Change:

PUBLICATION GUIDELINES:

Manuscript Length: 30+
Copies Required: Five
Computer Submission: Yes Encouraged
Format:
Fees to Review: 0.00 US$

Manuscript Style:
    See Manuscript Guidelines

CIRCULATION DATA:

Reader: Academics
Frequency of Issue: 8 Times/Year
Copies per Issue: No Reply
Sponsor/Publisher: Academic Press
Subscribe Price: 475.00 US$ US & Canada
    520.00 US$ All Other Countries
    US$ Deep Discounts Available

REVIEW INFORMATION:

Type of Review: Editorial Review
No. of External Reviewers: 3
No. of In House Reviewers: 0
Acceptance Rate: 11-20%
Time to Review: 4 - 6 Months
Reviewers Comments: Yes
Invited Articles: 0-5%
Fees to Publish: 0.00 US$

MANUSCRIPT TOPICS:
Developmental Psychology; Educational Psychology; Learning & Conditioning;
Neuropsychology; Social Psychology; Thinking & Cognition

MANUSCRIPT GUIDELINES/COMMENTS:

Notice to Contributors
The publishers wish to call your attention to the following instructions for preparing manuscripts for *Cognitive Psychology*: Format and style of manuscript should conform to the conventions specified in the *Publication Manual of the American Psychological Association* (1200 Seventeenth Street, N.W., Washington, D.C. 20036; 1983 Revision), with the exceptions listed below. Please note that it is the responsibility of the author that manuscripts for *Cognitive Psychology* conform to the requirements of this journal.

Cognitive Psychology publishes original empirical, theoretical, and tutorial papers, methodological articles, and critical reviews dealing with memory, language processing, perception, problem solving, and thinking. This journal emphasizes work on human cognition. Papers dealing with relevant problems in such related areas as social psychology, developmental psychology, linguistics, artificial intelligence, and neurophysiology also are welcomed provided that they are of direct interest to cognitive psychologists and are written so as to be understandable by such readers. Minor or very specialized studies are seldom accepted.

All manuscripts should be submitted to:
Dr. Gordon Logan
Editorial Office
Cognitive Psychology
525 B Street, Suite 1900
San Diego, CA 92101-4495 USA

Original papers only will be considered. Manuscripts are accepted for review with the understanding that the same work has not been published, that it is not under consideration for publication elsewhere, and that its submission for publication has been approved by all of the authors and by the institution where the work was carried out; further, that any person cited as a source of personal communications has approved such citation. Written authorization may be required at the Editor's discretion. Articles and any other material published in *Cognitive Psychology* represent the opinions of the author(s) and should not be construed to reflect the opinions of the Editor(s) and the Publisher.

Authors submitting a manuscript do so on the understanding that if it is accepted for publication, copyright in the article, including the right to reproduce the article in all forms and media, shall be assigned exclusively to the Publisher. The Copyright Transfer Agreement, which may be copied from the pages following the Information for Authors or found on the journal home page listed here, should be signed by the appropriate person(s) and should accompany the original submission of a manuscript to this journal. The transfer of copyright does not take effect until the manuscript is accepted for publication.

A manuscript submitted for publication is judged by three main criteria: (a) appropriateness of the subject matter for this journal; (b) significance of its contribution to knowledge; and (c) clarity and conciseness of writing. No changes in a manuscript may be made once it has been accepted and is in press.

Form. Type at least double-spaced throughout, including tables, footnotes, references, and figure captions, with 1 inch margins on all sides. **Submit five complete copies**. Each copy *must* include all figures and tables.

Number the pages consecutively. *Page 1* should contain the article title, author(s) name(s), and affiliation; at the bottom of the page type a short title, not exceeding 35 characters and spaces, and the name and complete mailing address (including zip code) of the person to whom proofs should be sent. The address of correspondence should be given as a footnote to the appropriate author's name. *Page 2* should contain a short abstract, approximately 100 to 150 words in length. *Key Words* should be listed immediately after the abstract.

Headings. The organization of the paper must be clearly indicated by appropriate headings and subheadings.

Abbreviations. Do not use final periods with units of measure that are abbreviated (cm, s, kg, etc.) in text or in tables, except for "in." (inch).

Symbols. Underline letters that represent mathematical symbols; these will be set in *italic* type.

Equations. Number displayed equations consecutively, with the number placed in parentheses to the extreme right of the equation. Refer to numbered equations as Equation 1 or say "the first equation." Punctuate equations to conform to their place in the syntax of the sentence.

Footnotes. Use only when absolutely necessary, in which case type the footnotes consecutively, double-spaced, on a separate sheet of paper in the order of their appearance in the text. Use Arabic numbers 1, 2, etc. In the text, refer to footnotes by superscript 1, 2, etc.

Tables. Number tables consecutively with Arabic numerals in order of their appearance in the text. Type each table, double-spaced throughout, on a separate sheet; avoid vertical rules. Supply a short descriptive title below the table number. Type table footnotes, lettered *a, b,* etc., at the end of the table. For further information, see the *Publication Manual,* pages 83–94.

Illustrations. All illustrations are considered as figures, and must be supplied in finished form, ready for reproduction. Pages 94-105 of the *Publication Manual* describe concisely the proper preparation of line drawings and photographs. Plan figures to fit the proportion of the printed page (allowing for the legend under the figure), and take care that lettering on the original is large enough to be legible after a reduction of 50–60%.

Number the figures with Arabic numerals in order of mention in the text. Supply descriptive legends (captions) for all figures. Type these (double-spaced throughout) consecutively on a separate sheet of paper.

Illustrations in color can be accepted only if the authors defray the cost.

References. Cite references in the text by surname of the author, followed by year of publication.

> Smith (1982) found that . . .
> Contrary results (Brown, 1984) have been . . .

When a reference has two authors, cite both names, as (Harris & Cooper, 1980). When more than two are involved, cite the surnames of all authors, with the date, at first mention, but in subsequent citations of the same reference give the surname of the first author followed by et al. and the year, as

> (Colberg, Matthews, & Cooper, 1983) *first mention*
> (Colberg et al., 1983) *second mention*

In citing more than one publication by the same author or authors in the same year, add suffixes a, b, c, etc. after the year, as (Smith 1982a) and repeat the letter identification in the bibliography, at the end of the reference.

Under the heading REFERENCES, arrange the literature citations in the text in alphabetical order according to the surname of the first author. Do not abbreviate journal names; write them out in full. Full information on forms of literature citations may be found on pages 107-117 of the *Publication Manual.*

The following examples show style of capitalization and punctuation for journal articles, books, and edited books:

Biggs, J. B., & Collis, K. F. (1982). *Evaluating the quality of learning: The SOLO taxonomy.* New York: Academic Press.

Donchin, E., Ritter, W., & McCallum, C. (1978). Cognitive psychophysiology: The endogenous components of the ERP. In E. Calloway, P. Teuting, & S. Koslow (Eds.), *Brain event-related potentials in man* (pp. 349-441). New York: Academic Press.

Siegler, R. S., & Robinson, M. (1982). The development of numerical understandings. In H. W. Reese & L. P. Lipsitt (Eds.), *Advances in child development and behavior* (Vol. 16). New York: Academic Press.

Wilkinson, A. C. (1984). Children's partial knowledge of the cognitive skill of counting. *Cognitive Psychology,* 16, 28-64

[Use underline for journal names and book titles only.]

Author's alterations in excess of 10% of the cost of composition will be charged to the author.

Reprints. 50 reprints of each article will be supplied free of charge. Additional reprints can be ordered on the form accompanying the proofs.

Electronic Submission. Manuscripts may be submitted to *Cognitive Psychology* after all revisions have been incorporated and the manuscript has been accepted for publication. A hard-copy printout of the manuscript that exactly matches the electronic file must be supplied. The manuscript will be edited according to the style of the journal, and the proofs must be read carefully by the author. Complete instructions for electronic submission can be found on the Electronic Submission page.

Preparation of Electronic Files
Academic Press (AP) encourages all of its authors to prepare and transmit their manuscripts and associated materials electronically. **Please see the Information for Authors (IFA) section of the appropriate journal (either online or in print) for details regarding required formatting and whether electronic submission is acceptable when the manuscript is initially submitted for review or only upon acceptance.** Paper copies of each version of the manuscript are still required. Electronic versions must be transmitted in conjunction with and must exactly match the hard copy, including the abstract, key words, footnotes, references, tables, and figures. This guide describes how to prepare an electronic manuscript for transmission to AP.

Electronic manuscripts can be transmitted via FTP, e-mail, or computer disk. Electronic manuscripts should be accompanied by the appropriate number of hard copies, each time a version is transmitted.

New Submissions

AP encourages transmission of new submissions in PDF, DVI, or PostScript unless otherwise noted in the journal's Information for Authors (IFA) section. Although submission in these formats is preferred, transmission of new submissions as word-processing files or TeX is also acceptable. Files created in layout programs such as Adobe FrameMaker or PageMaker, QuarkXPress and Corel Ventura are unacceptable. Be advised that some journals also require the transmission of the manuscript at the time it has been accepted (see the journal's IFA section for details). Hard-copy printouts exactly matching the electronic file must be supplied. For the exact number of copies required see the IFA section of the appropriate journal. When submitting a revised version of a manuscript, please provide the file electronically along with a new hard copy of the revised manuscript. See the Electronic Artwork section below for instructions on preparing electronic artwork.

PDF Files

Adobe Portable Document Format (PDF) is a universal file format that preserves all of the fonts, formatting, colors, and graphics of any source document, regardless of the application and platform used to create it. PDF files are compact and can be shared, viewed, navigated, and printed exactly as intended by anyone with a free Adobe Acrobat Reader. You can convert any document to Adobe PDF using proprietary software including Adobe Acrobat.

DVI Files

Authors are requested to send Device Independent (DVI) files of their TeX or LaTeX files at initial submission as this will facilitate the review process. Please see the TeX Files section below for specific instructions for formatting the TeX file.

PS Files

Adobe PostScript files (PS) can be created from any application capable of printing files, provided a PostScript printer driver is used. Authors are encouraged to use PostScript Level 2, use ADSC structuring, include all fonts in the file and save it in ASCII rather than binary format.

AP requests PDF, DVI and PS submissions for review purposes only; they cannot be effectively edited and are unusable during the post acceptance production stage.

Accepted Manuscripts

AP strongly encourages authors to submit an electronic version of their accepted manuscript, as this will significantly speed the processing of the manuscript. Please bear in mind that this electronic version must exactly match the final hard copy that was accepted. Acceptable formats for this final transmission stage are described below. AP cannot use PDF, DVI, or PostScript files at this stage because they do not allow editing of the text. Files created in layout programs such as Adobe FrameMaker or PageMaker, QuarkXPress and Corel Ventura are unacceptable. Artwork should not be embedded within the manuscript. It must be supplied in electronic files separate from the manuscript file. See the Electronic Artwork section below for instructions on preparing electronic artwork.

Word-Processing Files

Most word-processing packages are acceptable; however, AP prefers that authors use a recent version of Microsoft Word or Corel WordPerfect. Manuscripts saved with formatting intact are preferred. Rich-text format (.rtf extension) is acceptable, but plain text (.txt extension) files are discouraged. For some journals, it may be acceptable or preferable to prepare manuscripts in TeX; please see TeX Files (below) for instructions. Regardless of the software and file format used, one hard copy of the accepted version of the manuscript must be supplied.

Symbols and foreign characters can be set with word-processing software by altering typefaces to a corresponding font that displays the appropriate character. Use the Symbol font for Greek characters whenever possible. When special characters are unavailable, please note them on the hard-copy printout as not appearing properly in the electronic file. Do so by circling or making notes in the left margin.

Use the automatic word-processing wraparound feature and not hard returns (¶) for line breaks within a paragraph. Only use hard returns at the end of each paragraph and after heads. Use only one space between words and sentences. Use appropriate characters: do not use a lowercase "l" for a one or an "o" for a zero. Do not use double-byte characters for special symbols. Do not use automated bulleting, numbering, or internal linking.

The elements of the electronic file should be ordered so that all non-text elements, e.g., running title, figure legends, and footnotes, are out of the text stream. The running title should be placed above the article or chapter title, and the footnotes should be placed after the figure legends at the end of the manuscript. Do not use the footnote function of the software. Thus, the order should be running title, title, author(s), affiliation(s) including e-mail addresses, abstract, key words, text elements, references, figure legends, footnotes. Incorporate the above-listed components into one file.

AP may set tables from electronic files, typeset them conventionally, or scan them as art. Therefore, when providing tables electronically, please place them in a file separate from the manuscript.

Use the software's spell-checking and page-numbering capabilities before final transmission. Do not embed artwork into a word-processing file. See the Electronic Artwork section below for instructions on preparing electronic artwork.

TeX Files

TeX and LaTeX files are acceptable for electronic transmission provided they comply with the guidelines below. Deviation from these rules may cause inaccuracies in the article or a delay in publication, or may even result in the LaTeX file being discarded altogether so that the article is typeset conventionally.

AP prefers that authors prepare TeX manuscripts using LaTeX(2e). Use of specialized versions of TeX other than LaTeX, plain TeX, or AMSTeX or extensive use of packages or custom macros may render the electronic file unusable.

The most important thing to keep in mind while preparing a file for submission or publication is that it should be kept as simple as possible. Extensive formatting could render the file unusable to the typesetter. For this reason, restrict manual formatting to equations; page formatting will be done by the typesetter. Avoid manual coding of line breaks (except in displays), figure placement, and vertical and horizontal spacing. Such coding is difficult for typesetters to remove and increases the risk of errors in typesetting.

AP Preprint Class File and Templates
Where available, AP encourages authors who wish to use LaTeX(2e) to use our preprint style files. Check the journal home page to verify whether such files are available. The use of AP style files will speed the typesetting process and reduce the chance of typographical errors resulting from resetting text. However, AP does not require that submissions be prepared using our files. LaTeX manuscripts created without AP templates may be submitted if prepared according to the guidelines given below.

General TeX Guidelines
In order to enable the publisher to bring the article into the uniform layout and style of the journal in which it will appear, authors are kindly requested to follow the suggestions below.

So far as the journal style is concerned, if you can observe such matters as how references are cited (in parentheses or brackets, by numbers or by name and date), how equations are numbered and cited, how reference lists are styled, and how chemical terms (for example) are styled, this will be helpful. Such matters as single column vs. double column, or the typographic style of the section heads, are not important; the typesetter will impose the correct style for these in any case.

Extensive formatting could render the file unusable to the typesetter. Please use the usual LaTeX environments and sectioning commands, rather than explicit layout commands such as \hspace, \vspace, \large, \centering, etc. Also, do not redefine the page layout parameters. For this reason, restrict manual formatting to equations; page formatting will be done by the typesetter.

Do not be concerned with bad line breaks, page breaks, or under full or overfull boxes. These issues will be resolved during final production.

Custom macro definitions should be placed in the preamble of the article, and not at any other place in the document. Such custom definitions, i.e., definitions made using the commands \newcommand, \renewcommand, \newenvironrnment, or \renewenvironment, should be used with great care. Sensible, restricted usage of private definitions is encouraged. Large macro packages should be avoided. Definitions that are not used in the article should be omitted. Do not change existing environments, commands, or other standard parts of LaTeX.

It is preferable for you as the author to set the line breaks in equations, rather than having possibly undesirable breaks added during the production process. If you are not using Academic Press style files, check the printed width of your journal, and check that each equation will fit within that width. If you are using an AP style file, the text width will be set for the journal, and any equations that extend beyond the right margin will be obvious.

Lists should be produced with the usual itemize and enumerate environments. The itemize environment is used for unnumbered lists and the enumerate environment for numbered lists. The layout will be adjusted to match the journal style in the production process.

If you use BiBTeX, remember to send your .bbl file (not the .bib file). At this time, Academic Press does not provide bibstyles for our journals; please use one of the commonly available styles that closely resembles the format for your journal.

When you are done creating your LaTeX file, add the command \listfiles to the preamble, and run LaTeX again. In the log file, you will see a list of every file used in the typesetting process. If any of the listed files are not part of the basic LaTeX installation or not available on CTAN, please find those files on your local system and submit them along with your .tex file.

Submit the text of your manuscript as a single file whenever possible. If there are other files such as figures, tables, or style files, put all of the files into one archive file before submission.

TeX Figure and Table Guidelines
Use the LaTeX picture commands or other LaTeX drawing programs only for simple diagrams, as the quality is not acceptable for final typesetting.

Figures should be supplied as separate files, in .eps or .tif format, to ensure the best graphic output. Hard-copy printouts of the artwork, of reproduction quality, must be included with the printed manuscript. (For more information, see Electronic Artwork1 below.)

Floats such as figures and tables will be repositioned during our production process. Do not spend too much effort in adjusting float placement. Do ensure that each float is clearly cited in the text, and our typesetters will ensure that the figure is placed in the optimal position, as near to the first citation as possible.

Use of vertical lines within tables is strongly discouraged. Tables may be submitted within the main text of the manuscript or as separate tex files \input to the main file.

If you have further questions about TeX files, please see our TeX FAQ.

Electronic Artwork
In the interest of quality and accuracy, AP prefers to use author-supplied electronic artwork for all figures and complex tables. Each individual figure or graphic must be supplied as a separate, stand-alone file. Figure and table files must be named with their respective numbers and graphic types such as *SmithFig1.tif, SmithFig2a.tif, SmithTable1.eps,* etc. Long file names are acceptable.

Only EPS and TIFF file formats are considered acceptable; TIFF is preferred. Artwork submitted in TIFF should adhere to the following resolution settings: half tones (color/grayscale): 300 dpi; line art (black and white), and mixed images (halftones with text or line art): 600 to 1200 dpi. If it is necessary to import graphics from a vector-based drawing program (e.g., Adobe Illustrator) into a raster-based program (e.g., Adobe PhotoShop) in order to produce a TIFF file, a resolution of at least 600 dpi is required for quality reproduction.

Color artwork should be transmitted as CMYK color. RGB images must be converted to CMYK and all necessary color adjustments must be made prior to the transmission of the files. Authors must supply AP with a color-correct CMYK printout of all color electronic art.

When creating your figures, use font sizes and line weights that will reproduce clearly and accurately when figures are sized to the appropriate column width. The minimum line weight is 1/2 point (thinner lines will not reproduce well). Eliminate all excess white space from the borders of each figure. Do not include figure legends or other extraneous text in a graphic file; figure legends should be provided as text, placed after the reference section in the main manuscript file.

A hardcopy printout that **exactly** matches the electronic version of all artwork must be supplied.

All figures and complex tables not transmitted in electronic form must be sent as high-quality, camera-ready hard copies.

Transmission of Electronic Materials
Authors are requested to include in their electronic submission a cover letter and all ancillary materials.

Transmission of electronic files is quicker and more reliable if the files are first compressed or encoded. Files created using most popular compression/encoding schemes from the Windows, Macintosh and UNIX platforms are acceptable. Acceptable formats include:

ZIP, SIT, BIN, HQX, CAB, TAR, TGZ, TAZ, TZ, GZ, Z, UU, UUE, XXE, B64, BHX, MIM

All other formats, including LZH, ARJ, ARC, and self-extracting archives (EXE and SEA), are not acceptable.

Important. Please choose unique, descriptive file names. File names should include the corresponding author's last name, or the manuscript number (if available), or else the production number (if available). Examples: *SmithFig3.eps, DBIO2001-0439Fig1.tif,* or *DBIO4212Text.doc.* Upon successful completion of an FTP transmission, authors must send an e-mail message to the journal as notification that the files have been posted. The journal e-mail address uses the same journal abbreviation as the folder name prefixed to @acad.com (for example, jcat@acad.com for *Journal of Catalysis*). If you are unsure of the e-mail address, please see the IFA section of the appropriate journal. In the body of the e-mail, please include the name of the journal to which the manuscript has been transmitted, the title of the manuscript, the names of all the authors, the type of computer used to create the files, the type of software and version number used to create the files, and a list of all file names.

FTP

Because FTP (file transfer protocol) is fast, reliable, and convenient, AP considers it the preferred method for authors to transmit their electronic files. To access the proper location, authors log on anonymously to our FTP server at ftp://ftp.harcourtbrace.com/ and navigate to pub/academic press/saved. Within the "saved" directory are folders for most of our titles, named with the standard abbreviation for the journal. If you are unsure of the standard abbreviation, please see the Information for Authors section of the appropriate journal. Within each journal directory is a folder called "incoming." On some systems, it will appear as if access to the incoming folder is "denied"; this will not prevent correct transmission of the files. Anonymous users have write-only access to the incoming folder and will not be able to see anything inside, including their own materials. Alternatively, authors can place their files directly under the journal folder. Files placed here will not be protected and may be viewed by other anonymous users.

If you have not created a single archive file including all materials and you plan to transmit multiple files, you are strongly advised to create a new folder, appropriately named in accordance with the recommendations above, within the "incoming" folder on the FTP site.

E-mail

Manuscript files can be transmitted via e-mail if the total file size of all attached files does not exceed 2 megabytes. Address the e-mail to the journal and supply the information requested for FTP submission. If you are unsure of the e-mail address, please see the IFA section of the appropriate journal.

Storage Media

Although we prefer receiving files via the Internet, we also accept materials on 3.5-inch high-density (not double-density) disks, CD-ROMs, 100-MB Zip disks, 1-GB Jaz disks, and SyQuest disks (44, 88, or 200 MB). Disks should be formatted for DOS/Windows or Macintosh. Because we can access disks formatted for some, but not all, versions of UNIX, we strongly discourage transmission on UNIX disks. **Note on the disk label the operating system, software, file format, and version numbers used to create the disk: e.g., Windows 95 - Word 97; Windows 98 - WordPerfect 9; MacOS 8.6 - Word 98**. If you submit your electronic materials on one of these media, we recommend using the special packaging materials available and shipping them via a reputable express courier service.

We regret that storage media cannot be returned.

Cognitive Science

ADDRESS FOR SUBMISSION:

Robert Goldstone, Editor
Cognitive Science
Indiana University
Psychology Department
1101 East Street
Bloomington, IN 47405-7007
USA
Phone: 812-855-4853
Fax:
E-Mail: cogscij@indiana.edu
Web: www.cognitivesciencesociety.org
Address May Change: 12/31/2005

PUBLICATION GUIDELINES:

Manuscript Length: 30+
Copies Required: Electronic
Computer Submission: Yes Required
Format: See Guidelines
Fees to Review: 0.00 US$

Manuscript Style:
    American Psychological Association

CIRCULATION DATA:

Reader: Academics
Frequency of Issue: Bi-Monthly
Copies per Issue: 2,001 - 3,000
Sponsor/Publisher: Cognitive Science
    Society / Lawrence Erlbaum Associates,
    Inc.
Subscribe Price: 90.00 US$ Non Members
    65.00 US$ Cognitive Science Society

REVIEW INFORMATION:

Type of Review: Editorial Review
No. of External Reviewers: 3
No. of In House Reviewers: 0
Acceptance Rate: 11-20%
Time to Review: 2 - 3 Months
Reviewers Comments: Yes
Invited Articles: 6-10%
Fees to Publish: 0.00 US$

MANUSCRIPT TOPICS:
Neuropsychology; Psychobiology; Thinking & Cognition

MANUSCRIPT GUIDELINES/COMMENTS:

Topics Include
Anthropology, Artificial Intelligence, Biology, Computer Science, Education, Linguistics, Neuroscience, Philosophy and Psychology

Submission Information for Authors
Cognitive Science is a bimonthly journal for the multidisciplinary study of minds and other intelligent systems. It publishes articles on cognition from perspective in artificial intelligence, education, linguistics, neuroscience, philosophy, psychology, and anthropology of multidisciplinary concern. Editorial decisions are made on the basis of content, rather than discipline or author, and papers in all areas of cognitive science are welcome. Research reports which are specifically written for a multidisciplinary audience are given the highest priority. Papers which are very general or speculative, which constitute parametric refinements of well-known ideas, or which are accessible to only a narrow or discipline-

specific audience, will be given very low priority and may be returned to authors without formal review.

The following kinds of articles are appropriate for the journal: (a) theories or theoretical analyses of knowledge representation, cognitive processes, and brain theory; (b) experimental or ethnographic studies relevant to theoretical issues in cognitive science; (c) descriptions of intelligent programs that exhibit or model some human ability; (d) design proposals for cognitive models; (e) protocol or discourse analysis of human cognitive processing; (f) discussions of new problem areas or methodological issues in cognitive science; and (g) short theoretical notes or rebuttals. The journal will publish four categories of articles. *Regular articles* are approximately 30 published pages (12,000 words). *Extended articles* have a target length of approximately 45 pages (18,000 words), and are expected to present particularly noteworthy research that cannot be adequately described within the constraints of a regular article. *Brief reports* have a target length of about 10 pages (4,000 words). *Letters to the editor* will typically consist of approximately 2-3 page (1,000 words) commentaries to articles, responses to commentaries, and discussion items of general relevance to the cognitive science community.

Original articles only will be considered. Submission of an article is understood to imply that the article is original and unpublished, is not being considered for publication elsewhere, and will not be submitted elsewhere while it is under review by *Cognitive Science*. Distribution of a prepublication draft in paper or electronic form is not considered as prior publication, as long as the distributed article is clearly identified as a prepublication draft. Following publication, authors are entitled to distribute copies of their article for personal use, either on paper or electronically, through their own personal mailing or website, or through mailing or the website of an agency by which they are employed, but permission of the Cognitive Science Society is required to reproduce published papers in other sources, including electronic archives.

Cognitive Science uses a web-based submission and review process, Editorial Manager. Authors should log onto **http://www.editorialmanager.com/cogsci/** for instructions on how to register and submit manuscripts online. Paper copies of submissions are no longer acceptable. When submitting their manuscripts to Editorial Manager, authors will need to provide an electronic version of their manuscript and abstract, a set of keywords chosen from a set of classifications, and a category designation for their manuscript (letter to the editor, brief report, regular article, or extended article). Authors may send queries concerning the submission process, manuscript status, or journal procedures to the editorial office at **cogscij@indiana.edu**.

Illustrations. Color figures can now be reproduced on **www.leaonline.com** at no additional charge, regardless of whether or not these illustrations are reproduced in color in the printed version. In situations where figures make essential use of color, the journal also has the capacity to publish a limited number of color figures in the printed version. In these cases, costs incurred will be the author's responsibility. For further information on the preparation of electronic artwork, please see:
  https://www.erlbaum.com/shop/tek9.asp?pg=products&specific=0364-0213

Please note: Because of technical complications that can arise by converting color figures to 'gray scale' (for printed version should you not opt for color in print) please also submit usable black and white prints corresponding to all the color illustrations. For manuscripts submitted online, a file of a black and white version of each color should be uploaded, in addition to the color figure file.

Manuscripts should conform to APA 5th edition as specified in the *Publication Manual of the American Psychological Association* with the exceptions and considerations listed below. Authors may be asked to re-format manuscripts that do not conform to the following guidelines prior to editorial evaluation.

Preparation of Manuscript
Please double-space all material. Manuscripts should have 1-in. margins on all sides. Number pages consecutively with the title page as page 1 and include a brief abstract of 100 to 150 words as page 2. In departure from APA format, we accept and encourage submissions in which tables, figures, and figure captions are integrated into the text body rather than separated into sections. However, if authors choose to integrate these materials, they will still need to separate them for the version of the manuscript sent to the publisher. All tables and other end-of-paper matter except art should be numbered.

Figures
Figures must be supplied in electronic format and should be of sufficiently high resolution to appear sharp and artifact-free when printed. All figures must be in a form suitable for reproduction. Ideally, we would like authors to submit their figures in the actual final size. The maximum size allowed for this journal is 5½ by 7¼ inches (to allow room for the legend). Color illustrations are only available for the printed version of the journal. Figures captions should appear on a list separate from the text or on the figures themselves. The word "Figure" should always appear as Fig. in text and in legends.

Numbering of Figures and Tables
Each figure and table must be mentioned in the text and must be numbered consecutively using Arabic numerals in the order of its appearance in the text. On the reverse side of every figure write the name of the author and the figure number, unless figures are integrated with the text. A brief title should be typed directly above each table. Tables do not need any legends, and any explanations or clarifications of tabular material should be indicated as a footnote to the table by means of lower case letters.

References
Contributors should refer to the *APA Publication Manual* for the correct listing of references in the text and reference list. All references must be closely checked in text and lists to determine that dates and spellings are consistent. Please note that the names of all authors should be given in the list of references, and "et al." used only in the text. Examples for books, journals, and conference proceedings follow:

Reisen, A.H. (1966). Sensory deprivation. In E. Stellar & J.M. Sprague (Eds.), *Progress in physiological psychology* (Vol. 1). New York: Academic Press.

310

Atkinson, R.C., & Shiffrin, R.M. (1971). The control of short-term memory. *Scientific American,* 225, 82-90.

Keane, M.T.(1995). On order effects in analogical mapping: Predicting human error using IAM. In J.D. Moore & J.F. Lehman (Eds.), *Proceedings of the Seventeenth Annual Conference of the Cognitive Science Society* (pp. 449-454). Mahwah, NJ:Erlbaum.

Spelling, Terminology, and Abbreviations
American spelling, rather than British, is preferred. The Third Edition of *Webster's Unabridged Dictionary* is the standard reference work when in doubt. Please try to avoid jargon and, wherever possible, abbreviations that are not commonly accepted.

Permissions
Contributors are responsible for obtaining permission from copyright owners if they use an illustration, table, or lengthy quote from material that has been published elsewhere. Contributors should write to both the publisher and author of material they are seeking permission to reproduce.

Reprints
The only opportunity contributors have to order offprints is when page proofs are returned.

Please submit to **http://cogsci.edmgr.com**

Acceptable Formats
Word, WordPerfect, TXT, RTF, LaTeX2e, AMSTeX, TIFF, GIF, JPEG, EPS, Postscript, PICT, Excel and Powerpoint

Cognitive, Affective, & Behavioral Neuroscience

ADDRESS FOR SUBMISSION:

John Jonides, Editor
Cognitive, Affective, & Behavioral
   Neuroscience
University of Michigan
Department of Psychology
525 E. University Avenue
Ann Arbor, MI 48109-1109
USA
Phone: 734-764-0192
Fax: 734-994-7157
E-Mail: See Guidelines
Web: www.psychonomic.org/cabn
Address May Change: 12/31/2006

PUBLICATION GUIDELINES:

Manuscript Length: 26-30
Copies Required: One
Computer Submission: Yes Email
Format: PDF
Fees to Review: 0.00 US$

Manuscript Style:
    American Psychological Association

CIRCULATION DATA:

Reader: Academics
Frequency of Issue: Quarterly
Copies per Issue: 1,001 - 2,000
Sponsor/Publisher: Psychonomic Society
Subscribe Price: 75.00 US$ Individual
   172.00 US$ Institution
   39.00 US$ Student

REVIEW INFORMATION:

Type of Review: Editorial Review
No. of External Reviewers: 2-3
No. of In House Reviewers: No Reply
Acceptance Rate: N/A
Time to Review: 2-3 Months
Reviewers Comments: Yes
Invited Articles: N/A
Fees to Publish: 0.00 US$

MANUSCRIPT TOPICS:
Affective Neuoscience; Cognitive Neuroscience; Learning & Conditioning; Neuropsychology;
Psychobiology

MANUSCRIPT GUIDELINES/COMMENTS:

Manuscript Submission
Cognitive, Affective, & Behavioral Neuroscience publishes review and primary research
articles concerned with behavior and brain processes in humans, both normal participants and
patients with brain injury. In addition, articles that use animal models to address cognitive or
affective processes involving behavioral, invasive, or imaging methods are also strongly
encouraged. Articles will be appropriate to the journal if they cover topics relating to
cognition such as perception, attention, memory, language, problem-solving, and reasoning or
topics concerning emotional processes and affective states such as fear, anxiety, anger, and
surprise. In all cases, the editors will give highest priority to papers that report a combination
of behavioral and neuroscientific methods to address these research topics; we also invite
synthetic papers that make use of computational and other approaches to modeling.

312

Primary research articles should be limited to approximately 10,000 words, and review articles should be limited to 15,000 words (in each case, plus figures and tables). Consult the 'Guidelines for Authors' for details.

This journal is published by the Psychonomic Society under the direction of its Publications Committee (Chair, 2002: Stephen E. Palmer).

For submission questions: **contact the editor**.

Manuscripts. A PDF version of the full manuscript, including tables and figures, must be sent to John Jonides **jjonides@umich.edu** and Jennifer Scott **scottjen@umich.edu** as an attachment at the time of submission (use Adobe Acrobat to create this file). This PDF file will be sent to reviewers of the manuscript, so it must be complete. Also, a message should be sent to **jjonides@umich.edu** and **scottjen@umich.edu** at the time of submission that lists the title of the paper, the authors, the abstract, and a list of suggested reviewers. Hard copies of the paper in text format will be required later in the process if the paper is suitable for publication.

Manuscripts should be packaged with care to avoid damage or loss in the mail. It is suggested that a padded envelope be used, especially if the package must cross any borders.

On the title page, include your address, telephone number, and e-mail address. Manuscripts must be double-spaced throughout (2.5 to 3 lines to the inch with 1.5-in. margins). Include an abstract of no more than 150 words in the form used by the American Psychological Association. Manuscripts should adhere to the conventions concerning references, manuscript format, tables etc. described in the *Publication Manual of the American Psychological Association* (4th ed.), except that in the abbreviation of physical units, the style of the American Institute of Physics should be followed. When in doubt, consult a recent issue of any Psychonomic journal.

In all contributions describing research with animals, authors are required to specify the light: dark cycle under which the animals were maintained, as well as the time in the cycle at which the experimentation was carried out. For contributions describing research with humans or other animals, there must be a stipulation that procedures adhere to generally accepted practices for experimental research on the respective species. The Editor expects that human and animal subjects will be treated ethically; mistreatment of subjects is grounds for rejection of a manuscript.

With final acceptance of a manuscript, please submit a hard copy of the manuscript as well as a computer disk with the manuscript in ASCII (text only) format, together with files containing figures (Macintosh Photoshop, Illustrator, and QuarkXpress are the most reliable; however, EPS, PICT, TIFF, or JPEG formats are often sufficient). Hard copies of figures should include graphics and lettering that are clear and sharp enough to accommodate probable reduction for publication, with special attention given to both detail and figure-ground contrast. Color figures are acceptable; the cost of publishing each color figure, borne by the author, is $500 (exceptions to this price in the case of hardship may be made by approval of the Editor). The disk copy and hard copy must match exactly. For details, see the Psychonomic Society Publications Guidelines for Authors on pp. 85–87 of Vol. 2 or call the Publications Office at 512-462-2442.

Copyright and Permission. Authors must secure from both the Psychonomic Society and the author of reproduced material written permission to quote text of more than 500 words or to reproduce two or more tables or figures from any article published in this journal, except for the few that are in the public domain. The Psychonomic Society normally grants permission contingent upon the author's permission, a complete citation of source, and payment of a $10 fee per article from which material is taken. The fee only is waived for authors who wish to use their own material commercially.

Permission from the Society is waived for authors who wish to reproduce a single table or figure, provided the author's permission is obtained and full credit is given to the Psychonomic Society and the author through a complete citation. (If written permission is requested for commercial use of a single table or figure, the $10 fee will be assessed.) Permission and fees are waived for authors who wish to reproduce their own material for personal use, and for others to make single or multiple copies of single articles for personal, noncommercial scholarly, or nonprofit, educational classroom use. Extensive use of copy privileges in such a way as to substitute for a subscription to this journal is not intended or permitted.

Libraries and other users are permitted to photocopy beyond the limits of U.S. copyright law provided that the applicable fee is paid through the Copyright Clearance Center, 222 Rosewood Dr., Danvers, MA 01923. Phone: (978) 750-8400. Fax: (978) 750-4470.

Permission through the Academic Permissions Service of the CCC, or written permission from the Psychonomic Society, is required for all other kinds of copying such as copying for resale, for general distribution, for advertising or promotional purposes, or for creating new collective works.

GUIDELINES FOR AUTHORS

General Information
Manuscript Format. Manuscripts should, in general, adhere to the conventions described in the *Publication Manual of the American Psychological Association* (4th ed.), except in the abbreviation of physical units, for which the style of the American Institute of Physics is followed. When in doubt, consult a recent issue of a Psychonomic Society journal. See also the Psychonomic Society Publications *Guidelines for References*.

Printed Manuscript. The printed manuscript, including the abstract, references, and notes, must be double-spaced *throughout* (2.5 - 3 lines per inch), with 1.5-in. margins.

In addition to the main text, manuscripts (both hard copy and disk) should include: Title page-with:
A.   title, author name(s) and affiliation(s),
B.   mailing address, telephone number, and e-mail address of the author contact, and

C. a suggested running head; abstract of 100-150 words; author's note; list of figure captions; references – complete and correct (with all journal names written out); note(s) – if needed; table(s) – if needed; appendix(es) and listing(s) – if needed. These sections should begin on separate pages, and the pages should be numbered consecutively from the abstract on. Approximate locations of the figures should be noted within the text (e.g. "Figure 1 about here"). *The figures should also be on separate pages.*

Permissions. It is the author's responsibility to determine from the copyright owner whether or not permission is required for quoting text or for reproducing or adapting all or part of a table or figure from a copyrighted source. Authors must obtain any necessary written permission and enclose a copy with the submitted or revised manuscript.

Proof. A copy of the edited manuscript will not be included when proof is sent to the author. It is therefore incumbent upon the author to read and mark the proof *carefully*. Please use a pen to mark proof, print all comments clearly, and always include a mark in the margin next to the change.

Reprints. Reprints should be ordered when the proof is returned to the Publications Office. Institutional purchase orders can follow later, but the *number* of reprints desired should be indicated when the proof is returned.

For general questions regarding publication, call or e-mail the Publications Office at (512) 462-2442; cinnamon@psychonomic.org or jbellquist@psychonomic.org. For questions regarding computer disks and figures, see below.

Computer Disks
After a manuscript has been conditionally accepted and a revision requested, authors must also submit a disk containing the text that *agrees exactly* with the latest printed revision sent to the editor. These are to be sent either to the journal editor or to the Publications Office, according to requirements of each journal. If any further changes or additions are to be made, please send to the Publications Office a letter that lists the further changes, or, if the changes are extensive, a revised disk and a revised printed version of the manuscript with the changes indicated.

Disk Label - Indicate the following on the disk label:
1. Disk type: PC or Macintosh.
2. Software used and version number.
3. Document name, and whether graphics (figures) are included.
4. Our production number, if known; if not, the editor's manuscript number (if neither is known, use first author's surname).

Disk Contents - On the disk itself, include the following:
1. **An ASCII or text only document of the manuscript**. From this document, all printing/formatting commands other than paragraph breaks will have been deleted. This is especially important if you work in TEX or LATEX. (Note: Many word processing programs define ASCII as "text only"; e.g., in Microsoft Word, simply save the document as "text only.")

2. **A document in your word processor format** (i.e., .doc for MS Word, .wpd, for Word Perfect, etc.). This includes the hidden printing/formatting commands (e.g., for running heads, page numbers, italics, etc.) that produce the printed version of the manuscript.

3. **Graphics.** Please provide documents for all figures and illustrations composed on computers, in addition to camera-ready versions. Please refer to FIGURES section.

Please call or e-mail the Publications Office if you have questions regarding typesetting or computer disks (512-462-2442; dgrenier@psychonomic.org).

Tables

The *Publication Manual of the American Psychological Association* (4th ed., pp. 120-141) gives excellent instructions for constructing tables. The following will emphasize areas that are particularly important and will explain Psychonomic journal departures from APA style.

General. Make sure the table is necessary. Small tables with few entries can often be dealt with just as effectively in a line or two of text. Do not combine two tables of dissimilar format into one table (e.g., if sections A and B of Table 1 are not of similar format, section A should be Table 1 and section B, Table 2). However, do combine small tables of identical format with few entries (i.e., provide one table with, say, four columns and four rows, one for each experiment, rather than four tables of four columns and one row giving data for each of four experiments).

Keep the material as simple and straightforward as possible. Double-space all tables for easy editing and typesetting. Number all tables in the order in which they are mentioned in the text. Make sure all tables are mentioned in the text.

Table Arrangement. Instead of a column of 0.00 plus or minus .00 entries, use two columns with separate appropriate headings (e.g., M and SE or SD). Arrange tables so that similar numbers fall into separate columns. That is, if possible, do not mix, in one column, such numbers as 0000, 00.00, .0000.

Avoid unnecessary repetitions throughout the table. Columns with the same numerical entries throughout the table or throughout sections of the table can be put in footnotes (e.g., "In Condition 1, $n = 20$ for each group; in Condition 2, $n = 30$ for each group"). Units of measurement can simply be abbreviated in headings –"RTs (in msec)"- or explained in footnotes ("RTs are given in milliseconds").

Other Requirements. Define all measurements used for values in the table (e.g., "Thresholds are given in decibels"). Define (or avoid using) all abbreviations. Do not use material in tables that should normally be placed in figures (e.g., graphic objects, photographic reproductions). Define, in the table footnotes, all asterisks, daggers, and other symbols used. General footnotes (denoted by "Note-...") qualify, explain, or provide information relating to the table as a whole or to a major section of the table (e.g., a column or a group of columns). Specific footnotes (denoted by *, †, ‡, etc.) relate to individual entries or give probability levels. Do not use asterisks, daggers, and other symbols to denote anything other than footnotes pertaining to particular entries in the body of the table. Psychonomic journals do not normally use superscripted footnotes (raised a, b, c, etc.) in tables.

All major words of table titles and column headings should be capitalized. Column headings refer *only* to entries in the column(s) below them. A column heading may *never* refer to other column headings to its right across the top of the table.

Do not print a table in a visible "cellular" format: Vertical rules are *never* used in Psychonomic journals; horizontal rules are never used within the body of the table.

Figures
High-quality hard (printed) copies, preferably on glossy stock, must be provided for all figures. Hard copies are necessary for proofing and/or scanning. Photocopies are not acceptable. Each figure should be clearly identified on the back with the figure number and author's name. The top of each figure should be clearly indicated.

Figure captions should be included on a separate sheet of the manuscript, not with the figure itself.

Figures should be between 3 in. (18 picas) and 6.5 in. (39 picas) wide. Figures similar in configuration should be of similar size. Type sizes should be proportional to the figure size. Type sizes should vary by no more than 4 points within a figure. Helvetica and Times at 10 points are the preferred fonts. Graph fills or symbols should be easily distinguished from one another. Do not use similar shades of gray in bar graphs.

Digital figures should be high resolution (300 dpi or higher), submitted on either 3.5-in. or Zip disks. The following file formats are preferable: TIFF, EPS, JPEG, or PICT. Figures created in Photoshop or Illustrator, or figures saved as Windows Metafiles and imported into Word documents are acceptable. Figures created in Microsoft Word, hand drawn originals (except when appropriate), and Excel documents are not acceptable. Do not compress files to save memory.

With rare exceptions, Psychonomic journal figures are printed in black and white. Color figures should be converted to black and white or grayscale before submission. Check any converted color figures for clarity and contrast before you submit them.

Refer to the *Publication Manual of the American Psychological Association* (4th ed., pp. 141-163) for additional guidelines on the preparation of figures.

If any changes are to be made in a figure, a new, corrected version must be submitted to the Publications Office.

E-mail **molly@psychonomic.org** with figure questions or concerns.

Visit **www.psychonomic.org** for updates in the guidelines.

Communication Education

ADDRESS FOR SUBMISSION:

Don Rubin, Editor
Communication Education
University of Georgia
110 Terrell Hall
Athens, GA 30602-1725
USA
Phone: 706-542-3247
Fax: 706-542-3245
E-Mail: ComEd@uga.edu
Web: http://www.tandf.co.uk/journals
Address May Change: 12/31/2005

PUBLICATION GUIDELINES:

Manuscript Length: 26-30
Copies Required: Three
Computer Submission: Yes Disk
Format: MS Word, RTF
Fees to Review: 0.00 US$

Manuscript Style:
    American Psychological Association

CIRCULATION DATA:

Reader: Academics
Frequency of Issue: Quarterly
Copies per Issue:
Sponsor/Publisher: National
    Communication Association / Taylor &
    Francis
Subscribe Price: 52.00 US$ Individual
    200.00 US$ Institution

REVIEW INFORMATION:

Type of Review: Blind Review
No. of External Reviewers: 2
No. of In House Reviewers: 1
Acceptance Rate: 11-20%
Time to Review: 2 - 3 Months
Reviewers Comments: Yes
Invited Articles: 0-5%
Fees to Publish: 0.00 US$

MANUSCRIPT TOPICS:
Instruction in Communication; Psycholinguistics

MANUSCRIPT GUIDELINES/COMMENTS:

Website. www.arches.uga.edu/~comed

Call for Manuscripts for Issues of *Communication Education* to be published in the years 2003-2005

Communication Education publishes original scholarship bearing on the intersections of communication, instruction, and human development. Within this broad purview, it welcomes diverse disciplinary, conceptual, and methodological perspectives, especially scholarship in the following areas:

- Classroom discourse
- Life-span development of communication competence
- Mediating instructional communication with technology
- Diverse backgrounds of learners and teachers in instructional interaction
- Interaction in informal education and in varied instructional settings

- Learning outcomes associated with instructional communication practices across disciplines
- Learning outcomes and processes in the discipline of communication studies
- Rhetorical and organizational aspects of communication among educational agencies, among policy-makers, and among their stakeholders

Manuscripts submitted to *Communication Education* must subscribe to the National Communication Association Code of Professional Ethics for Authors. (Please see the website: http://www.natcom.org/policies/Internal/code_of_professional_ethics.htm or write NCA, 1765 N Street NW, Washington, DC 20036). These guidelines enjoin authors to use inclusive and nondefamatory language. In addition, submissions should be accompanied by a cover letter attesting that the author has met professional standards for any of the following principles as may apply. (1) The manuscript is original work and proper publication credit is accorded to all authors. (2) Simultaneous editorial consideration of the manuscript at another publication venue is prohibited. (3) Any publication history of the manuscript is disclosed, indicating in particular whether the manuscript or another version of it has been presented at a conference, or published electronically, or whether portions of the manuscript have been published previously. (4) Duplicate publication of data is avoided; or if parts of the data have already been reported, then that fact is acknowledged. (5) All legal, institutional, and professional obligations for obtaining informed consent from research participants and for limiting their risk are honored. (6) The scholarship reported is authentic.

Full-length manuscripts of articles reporting empirical research, critical analyses, historical scholarship, or theoretic expositions should conform to the *Style Manual of the American Psychological Association*, 5th edition (2001). Article manuscripts should generally not exceed 30 double-spaced pages, except in cases in which "thick description" of qualitative data may require it. Authors are asked to submit three manuscript copies along with an electronic file on disk. (Rich Text Format is preferred for the electronic copy.) To facilitate masked review, the author's identity should not be discernible in the text, except on the title page. The title page should also state the history of the manuscript (i.e., whether it has been previously presented at a conference or derives from a thesis or dissertation) and any author acknowledgements. Authors should mail these materials to Don Rubin, Editor, Communication Education, 110 Terrell Hall, The University of Georgia, Athens, GA 30602-1725 [e-mail: **ComEd@uga.edu**].

Communication Education also solicits briefer manuscripts of approximately 2000 words for a section entitled **The Scholarship of Teaching and Learning in Communication (SOTL/Com)**. SOTL/Com builds upon the movement in education studies and policy that began with the Carnegie Foundation's 1990 manifesto Scholarship Reconsidered. **SOTL/Com** recognizes that teaching communication is a form of scholarship, just as is the scholarship of discovery or of critical analysis. Submissions for **SOTL/Com** will explore questions about student learning in relationship to a particular teaching practice or innovation. Typically these questions will be posed by teachers about their own teaching. The work will be driven by questions about how an instructional communication practice influenced the teaching and learning of a particular subject in a particular setting. Subject matter and setting are not limited to communication classes, but may range across disciplines and across types of institutions. The motivation for the inquiry must be well grounded in theory and research.

Manuscripts for **SOTL/Com** will report appropriate quantitative or qualitative assessments of student learning outcomes. Results will be discussed in light of the focal question about student learning, and also in a manner that contributes to a growing understanding of the interplay between communication and education. In keeping with the rigorous standards for **SOTL/Com**, all submissions to this section will be subjected to masked peer review. Submit manuscripts for **SOTL/COM** in electronic form (RTF format preferred) to Associate Editor Ann L. Darling, Department of Communication, 255 South Central Campus Drive, University of Utah, Salt Lake City, UT 84112 [e-mail: **Ann.darling@m.cc.utah.edu**].

In addition, *Communication Education* publishes reviews of books and nonprint media on a broad range of topics related to communication and education. Reviews should not exceed 1000 words, although longer essay reviews of several related works may be considered. The journal does not generally print reviews of course textbooks. Submission of both reviews and books to be considered for review are invited. Review manuscripts (2 print copies and one copy on computer disk in RTF format) and materials should be mailed to Nancy Rost Goulden, Department of Speech Communication, Theatre, and Dance, Nichols 101, Kansas State University, Manhattan, KS 66506 [e-mail: **nag@ksu.edu**].

Proposals for themed issues will be reviewed by members of the Editorial Advisory Board.

Communication Research

ADDRESS FOR SUBMISSION:

Pamela J. Shoemaker, Co-Editor
Communication Research
Syracuse University
S.I. Newhouse Sch. of Public Communicat.
215 University Place
Syracuse, NY 13244-2100
USA
Phone: 315-443-1422
Fax: 315-443-1107
E-Mail: commres@sunmail.syr.edu
Web: sagepub.com/ejournals
Address May Change:

PUBLICATION GUIDELINES:

Manuscript Length: 26-30
Copies Required: Four
Computer Submission: No
Format: N/A
Fees to Review: 0.00 US$

Manuscript Style:
American Psychological Association

CIRCULATION DATA:

Reader: Academics
Frequency of Issue: 6 Times/Year
Copies per Issue: Less than 1,000
Sponsor/Publisher: Sage Publications
Subscribe Price: 88.00 US$ Individual
500.00 US$ Institution
112.00 US$ Indv., $524 Inst./Non-US

REVIEW INFORMATION:

Type of Review: Blind Review
No. of External Reviewers: 2-3
No. of In House Reviewers: 0-1
Acceptance Rate: 6-10%
Time to Review: 2 - 3 Months
Reviewers Comments: Yes
Invited Articles: 0-5%
Fees to Publish: 0.00 US$

MANUSCRIPT TOPICS:
Mass Communication; Psycholinguistics

MANUSCRIPT GUIDELINES/COMMENTS:

Important, In-Depth Research and Scholarship
Communication processes are a fundamental part of virtually every aspect of human social life. *Communication Research* publishes articles that explore the processes, antecedents, and consequences of communication in a broad range of societal systems. These include:

- mass media
- interpersonal
- health
- political
- new technology
- organization
- intercultural
- family

Communication Research takes you to the cutting-edge of research and theory in all areas within the field of communication. It serves as the international forum aimed at the academic or professional interested in current research in communication and its related fields.

Diverse, Challenging and Enlightening

Communication Research publishes peer-reviewed articles that develop theory, report research and describe new developments in methodology - articles that advance our understanding of human communication processes. The pages of *Communication Research* have a wide range of topics including computer-mediated communication, non-verbal communication, news reporting and public opinion, popular culture, the impact of media, gender differences, and conflict resolution.

Journal Submission Guidelines

The editorial goal of *Communication Research* is to offer a special opportunity for reflection and change in the new millennium. To qualify for publication, research should, first, be explicitly tied to some form of communication; second, be theoretically driven with results that inform theory; third, use the most rigorous empirical methods; and fourth, be directly linked to the most important problems and issues facing humankind. Our criteria do not privilege any particular context; indeed, we believe that the key problems facing humankind occur in close relationships, groups, organizations, and cultures. Hence, we hope to publish research conducted across a wide variety of levels and units of analysis.

The co-editors and editorial board make every effort to review manuscripts thoroughly and promptly. One of the co-editors initially determines whether the content of the manuscript is appropriate for the journal and whether there is sufficient publication potential to proceed with anonymous reviews. Manuscripts that do not pass this initial screening are returned immediately. If a manuscript is sent out for the review process it is typically completed in six weeks. Authors are encouraged to obtain and incorporate editorial advice of their colleagues prior to submitting their work to *Communication Research*.

Manuscripts should be prepared in accordance with the *Publication Manual of the American Psychological Association,* 5th edition (2001). In particular, the entire manuscript should be double spaced, and manuscripts should have one and a half inch margins on all four sides. Tables should be clear and understandable independent of the text. Figures should be sent camera ready, clear, and legible when reduced. References should be carefully edited to ensure consistency with APA guidelines. Reliability estimates should be provided for measures. Effect size estimates should accompany reports of all statistically significant differences. Submissions should include current addresses, phone and fax numbers, and e-mail addresses of all authors as well as author biographies of 100 words maximum for all authors. In addition, we request an abstract of no more than 150 words. We require that authors report standard deviations with means and that authors report measures of strength of association with tests of significance. Authors are responsible for gaining permission for including any copyrighted material that needs permission, including quotations of more than 300 words.

A copy of the final revised manuscript on a computer disk should be included with the final revised hard copy. Submission of a manuscript implies commitment to publish in the journal.

Authors submitting manuscripts to the journal should not simultaneously submit them to another journal, nor should manuscripts have been published elsewhere in substantially similar form or with substantially similar content. Authors in doubt about what constitutes prior publication should consult the editor.

Four copies of submitted manuscripts should be sent to Pamela J. Shoemaker, Co-editor, Communication Research, S.I. Newhouse School of Public Communications, Syracuse University, 215 University Place, Syracuse, New York 13244-2100.

Communication Research Reports

ADDRESS FOR SUBMISSION:

Lisa Sparks, Editor
Communication Research Reports
George Mason University
Department of Communication
MS3D6
Fairfax, VA 22030
USA
Phone: 703-993-3774
Fax: 703-993-1096
E-Mail: lsparks@gmu.edu
Web:
Address May Change:

PUBLICATION GUIDELINES:

Manuscript Length: 11-15
Copies Required: Three
Computer Submission: Yes Email
Format: Word for Windows
Fees to Review: 0.00 US$

Manuscript Style:
  American Psychological Association

CIRCULATION DATA:

Reader: Academics
Frequency of Issue: Quarterly
Copies per Issue: 2,001 - 3,000
Sponsor/Publisher: Eastern Communication
  Association
Subscribe Price: 35.00 US$ Individual

REVIEW INFORMATION:

Type of Review: Blind Review
No. of External Reviewers: 2
No. of In House Reviewers: 0
Acceptance Rate: 11-20%
Time to Review: 2 - 3 Months
Reviewers Comments: Yes
Invited Articles: 0-5%
Fees to Publish: 0.00 US$

MANUSCRIPT TOPICS:

Communication; Culture & Personality; Decision Making Theory; Gender Roles; Group
Dynamics; Human Relations; Industry & Organization; Motivation; Negotiating Process

MANUSCRIPT GUIDELINES/COMMENTS:

Communication Research Reports publishes brief empirical articles (about 2500 words not
counting references or tables; approximately 10 double spaced pages or less including
references) on a wide variety of topics pertaining to human communication. Appropriate
topics include studies of small group, relational, political, persuasive, organizational,
nonverbal, mass, interpersonal, intercultural, instructional, health, aging/lifespan, family, and
computer mediated communication.

Authors should provide a sentence to a paragraph outlining the theoretical framework guiding
the brief empirical report. In sum, theoretical rationale should receive modest coverage in the
research report (1-2 paragraphs) along with a brief review of the representative literature on
the topic, with the main portion of the paper devoted to a thorough reporting and interpretation
of the results.

Manuscripts Preparation

After removing all identifiers in the properties of the document, authors should submit one electronic double-spaced copy of the manuscript in MS Word (preferred) or WordPerfect to conforming to the 5th edition of the *American Psychological Association Style Manual* and should also submit a hard copy to the editor at the address below. A detachable cover sheet must contain: (1) the title of the manuscript; (2) the author's name, address, and institutional affiliation; and (3) the author's phone number and e-mail address. The first page of the manuscript must include the title and a 50-100 word abstract. Manuscripts should be emailed and mailed to:

Lisa Sparks, Editor-Elect
Communication Research Reports
George Mason University, MS3D6
Department of Communication
Fairfax, VA 22030
Phone: (703) 993-3774
Fax: (703) 993-1096
Email: **lsparks@gmu.edu**

The final version of a manuscript accepted for publication must be submitted and formatted in Word (6.0 or above) to the editor via email.

Review Policy

Manuscripts will be blind-reviewed by at least two members of the editorial board whose evaluations will provide the basis for the publication decision. *Communication Research Reports* is committed to completing the review process as rapidly as possible, ideally within three months of the manuscript's receipt. Manuscripts that do not conform to the mission of the journal, or that do not comply with submission guidelines, will not be reviewed. No manuscript can be previously published or under consideration in any other journal at the time of submission.

Consulting Psychology Journal: Practice and Research

ADDRESS FOR SUBMISSION:

Richard Diedrich, Editor
Consulting Psychology Journal: Practice
  and Research
PO Box 555
Marshfield Hills, MA 02051-0555
USA
Phone: 781-837-7543
Fax: 781-837-7543
E-Mail: rcdiedrich@hotmail.com
Web: http://www.apa.org
Address May Change:

CIRCULATION DATA:

Reader: Practitioners
Frequency of Issue: Quarterly
Copies per Issue: 1,001 - 2,000
Sponsor/Publisher: Division 13 of
  American Psychological Association
Subscribe Price: 62.00 US$ Individual
  108.00 US$ Institution

PUBLICATION GUIDELINES:

Manuscript Length: 21-25
Copies Required: Three
Computer Submission: Yes Disk w/
  hardcopies
Format: 3-1/2 DOS Format
Fees to Review: 0.00 US$

Manuscript Style:
  American Psychological Association

REVIEW INFORMATION:

Type of Review: Blind Review
No. of External Reviewers: 2
No. of In House Reviewers: 1
Acceptance Rate: 60%
Time to Review: 2 - 3 Months
Reviewers Comments: Yes
Invited Articles: 11-20%
Fees to Publish: 0.00 US$

MANUSCRIPT TOPICS:
Consultation; Counseling Process; Family Counseling & Therapy

MANUSCRIPT GUIDELINES/COMMENTS:

Mission and Purpose
Consulting Psychology Journal: Practice and Research is published by the Educational Publishing Foundation in collaboration with the Division of Consulting Psychology of the American Psychological Association (Division 13). The mission of this journal is to facilitate the exchange of knowledge and ideas regarding the field of consultation to the community of psychologists and others interested in consultation. *Consulting Psychology Journal* publishes articles in the following areas:
a.   theoretical/conceptual articles with implications for application to consulting;
b.   original research regarding consultation;
c.   in-depth reviews of the research and literature in specific areas of consultation practice;
d.   case studies that demonstrate the application of innovative consultation methods/strategies, that highlight critical or often overlooked issues for consultation, or that have unusual features that would be of general interest to other consultants;
e.   articles on consultation practice development; and

f.　articles addressing the unique issues encountered by consulting psychologists in applying their knowledge and skill to the problems of clients. *Consulting Psychology Journal: Practice and Research* also publishes special topic issues with guest editors on a regular basis. Topics for these issues are suggested by the members of Division 13.

Send manuscripts and diskettes to Richard Diedrich, P.O. Box 555, Marshfield Hills, MA 02051-0555.

Manuscript Submission Guidelines

Manuscripts should be submitted on 3½-in. DOS-formatted floppy disks as well as on 8½ x 11-in. paper (three copies), double-spaced format. Authors should prepare manuscripts according to the *Publication Manual of the American Psychological Association* (5th ed.). Original, camera-ready artwork for figures is required. Original color figures can be printed in color provided the author agrees to pay half of the associated production costs.

Authors are required to obtain and provide to APA all necessary permissions to reproduce any copyrighted work, including, for example, test instruments and other test materials or portions thereof.

APA policy prohibits an author from submitting the same manuscript for concurrent consideration by two or more publications. Manuscripts and computer disks will not be returned, so authors are strongly encouraged to retain copies.

APA requires authors to reveal any possible conflict of interest in the conduct and reporting of research (e.g., financial interests in a test or procedure, financing by pharmaceutical companies for drug research).

Masked Review

Manuscripts accepted by the Editor are submitted to a masked review by members of the Editorial Review Board. To ensure anonymity, each manuscript should contain a separate title page with authors' names and affiliations, and these should not appear anywhere else on the manuscript. Reviewers are instructed to provide comments that will help authors revise and improve their manuscripts. The final decision regarding publication will be made by the Editor in consultation with the reviewers regarding the manuscript's quality, importance, and relevancy.

Schedule and Submission Deadlines

Manuscripts for articles are accepted at any time. Authors should expect the review/revision process to take 6 to 9 months. Deadlines for submission of advertisements, divisional news, letters to the editor, etc., are January 1, April 1, June 1, and September 15 for the Winter, Spring, Summer, and Fall issues, respectively.

Contemporary Educational Psychology

ADDRESS FOR SUBMISSION:

Patricia Alexander, Editor
Contemporary Educational Psychology
University of Maryland
Dept. of Human Development
Benjamin Bldg.
College Park, MD 20742
USA
Phone: 301-405-6493 or 301-405-2821
Fax: 301-405-2891
E-Mail: palexand@umd.edu
Web: www.elsevier.com/locate/yceps
Address May Change:

PUBLICATION GUIDELINES:

Manuscript Length: 30+
Copies Required: Four + 1 Disk Copy
Computer Submission: No
Format: MS Word or WordPerfect
Fees to Review: 0.00 USS

Manuscript Style:
    American Psychological Association

CIRCULATION DATA:

Reader: Academics
Frequency of Issue: Quarterly
Copies per Issue: No Reply
Sponsor/Publisher: Elsevier, San Diego, CA
Subscribe Price: 0.00 USS

REVIEW INFORMATION:

Type of Review: Blind Review
No. of External Reviewers: 3
No. of In House Reviewers: 0
Acceptance Rate: 11-15%
Time to Review: 2 - 3 Months
Reviewers Comments: Yes
Invited Articles: 0-5%
Fees to Publish: 0.00 USS

MANUSCRIPT TOPICS:

Child Psychology; Counseling Process; Educational Psychology; Exceptional Child; Family
Counseling & Therapy; Psychological Testing

MANUSCRIPT GUIDELINES/COMMENTS:

Contemporary Educational Psychology publishes articles that involve the application of
psychological theory and science to the educational process. Of particular relevance are
descriptions of, research reviews of, and the presentation of theory designed to either explicate
or enhance the educational process. The journal publishes quantitative, qualitative, and single-
subject design studies that involve the application of psychological science to an important
educational process, issue, or problem.

The journal does not limit its scope to any age range. Articles dealing with the education of
preschoolers, K-12 children, adults, and the elderly are all relevant if they apply psychological
theory and science to the process of education. Likewise, articles that make a substantial
contribution to the understanding of individual differences in the process of learning are also
appropriate. The journal does not focus on a particular educational setting. Articles applying

psychological theory and research methods in school settings, industry, or other formal or informal settings involving adults or children are relevant, assuming they are judged in the review process to advance the science of education.

Submission of Manuscripts

Manuscripts must be written in English and should be submitted in quadruplicate along with an electronic copy of the manuscript prepared as a Word or Rich Text File (RTF) on a computer disk to:

Contemporary Educational Psychology
Patricia Alexander, Editor
University of Maryland
Department of Human Development
Benjamin Building
College Park, MD 20742-1131, USA

The Editor can also be reached at:
Patricia Alexander
Telephone (301)405-2821; Fax: (301)405-2891; E-mail: **pa34@umail.umd.edu**

Manuscripts are accepted for review with the understanding that the same work has not been and is not currently submitted elsewhere, and that it will not be submitted elsewhere prior to the journal's making an editorial decision. At the time of submission, authors must notify the Editor if any part of the data on which their article depends has been published elsewhere. Moreover, it must be the case that submission of the article for publication has been approved by all of the authors and by the institution where the work was carried out; further, that any person cited as a source of personal communications has approved such citation. Written authorization may be required at the Editor's discretion. Articles and an other material published in *Contemporary Educational Psychology* represent the opinions of the author(s) and should not be construed to reflect the opinions of the Editor or the Publisher.

Upon acceptance of an article, authors will be asked to transfer copyright (for more information on copyright, see http://authors.elsevier.com). This transfer will ensure the widest possible dissemination of information. A letter will be sent to the corresponding author confirming receipt of the manuscript. A form facilitating transfer of copyright will be provided after acceptance.

If excerpts from other copyrighted works are included, the author(s) must obtain written permission from the copyright owners and credit the source(s) in the article. Elsevier has preprinted forms for use by authors in these cases: contact Elsevier Global Rights Department, P.O. Box 800, Oxford OX5 1DX, UK; phone: (+44) 1865 843830, fax: (+44) 1865 853333, e-mail: permissions@elsevier.com.

Electronic Transmission of Accepted Manuscripts. Authors are requested to transmit the text and art of the manuscript in electronic form via either computer disk or e-mail, after all revisions have been incorporated and the manuscript has been accepted for publication. Submission as an e-mail attachment is acceptable provided that all files are included in a single archive the size of which does not exceed 2 megabytes (**pa34@umail.umd.edu**). Hardcopy printouts of the manuscript and art must also be supplied. The manuscript will be edited according to the style of the journal, and authors must read the proofs carefully.

Type of Articles That *CEP* Publishes
The journal publishes three types of articles: Research Studies, Brief Research Reports, and Reviews.

Research Studies report a quantitative, qualitative, or single-subject design study. Articles that contain multiple studies are seen as particularly desirable contributions. For quantitative studies, authors should report effect sizes. Methods for calculating and interpreting effect sizes are presented in *Contemporary Educational Psychology* in Volume 25 (Number 3) on pages 241-286.*Brief Research Reports* are relatively short articles that provide a needed replication of a previous research effort or that extend the boundaries of earlier research. Brief Research Reports are initially submitted as full Research Studies and identified as Brief Research Reports during the review process.

Review Articles are primarily based on other published work and include reviews of existing literature, methodological reviews of research in a particular area, or theoretical presentations that advance or clarify psychological theory or science as it applies to education.

Preparation of the Manuscript
Manuscripts should be prepared on 8.5 x 11-inch or A4 white paper, using double spacing throughout. Authors are requested to follow the instructions given in the most recent edition of the *Publication Manual of the American Psychological Association*. Four copies of the manuscript should be submitted; each copy must include all figures and tables. Each page of the manuscript should be numbered consecutively.

The title page (p. 1) should contain the article title, authors' names and complete affiliations, footnotes to the title, and the address for manuscript correspondence (including e-mail address and telephone and fax numbers).

The second page (p. 2) should contain only the article title and footnotes to the title. These items should be placed in the same position as they were on the title page.

The abstract (p. 3) must be a single paragraph that summarizes the main findings of the paper in less than 150 words. After the abstract a list of up to 10 keywords that will be useful for indexing or searching should be included.

References in the text should be cited by author's surname and the year of publication, e.g., Hum (1994); Hum et al. (1993); Hum and St. Clair (1993, p. 128) (for references to a specific page); Hum & St. Clair (1993) (ampersand for references in parentheses). If more than one paper was published by the same author in a given year, the correct style is Smith (1985a) and Smith (1985b). References cited in the text should be listed alphabetically and typed double-spaced at the end of the article. Journal titles should be written out in full according to the form followed in the most recent edition of the *Publication Manual of the American*

330

Psychological Association. Personal communications should be cited as such in the text and should not be included in the reference list. Please note the following examples:

Gagne, R. M., & Driscoll, M. P. (1988). *Essentials of learning for instruction.* Englewood Cliffs, NJ: Prentice-Hall.

Griffin, M. M., & Griffin, B. W. (1995, April). *An investigation of the effects of reciprocal peer tutoring on achievement, self-efficacy, and test anxiety.* Paper presented at the Annual Meeting of the National Consortium for Instruction and Cognition, San Francisco, CA.

Kulhavy, R. W., Schwartz, N. H., & Peterson, S. (1986). Working memory: The encoding process. In G. D. Phye & T. Andre (Eds.), *Cognitive classroom learning: Understanding, thinking, and problem solving* (pp. 115-140). Orlando, FL: Academic Press.

Zeidner, M., & Schleyer, E. J. (1999). The big-fish-little-pond effect for academic self-concept, test anxiety, and school grades in gifted children. *Contemporary Educational Psychology,* 24, 305-329.

Figures should be in a finished form suitable for publication. Number figures consecutively with Arabic numerals, and indicate the top and the authors on the back of each figure. Lettering on drawings should be professional quality or generated by high-resolution computer graphics and must be large enough to withstand appropriate reduction for publication. Please visit our Web site at http://authors.elsevier.com/artwork for detailed instructions on preparing electronic artwork.

If, together with your accepted article, you submit usable color figures, then Elsevier will ensure, at no additional charge, that these figures will appear in color on the Web (e.g., ScienceDirect and other sites) regardless of whether these illustrations are reproduced in color in the printed version. For color reproduction in print, you will receive information regarding the costs from Elsevier after receipt of your accepted article. For further information on the preparation of electronic artwork, please see http://authors.elsevier.com/artwork.

Please note: Because of technical complications that can arise in converting color figures to "gray scale" (for the printed version should you not opt for color in print), please submit in addition usable black-and-white prints corresponding to all the color illustrations.

Tables should be numbered consecutively with Arabic numerals in order of appearance in the text. Type each table double-spaced on a separate page with a short descriptive title typed directly above and with essential footnotes below. Authors should submit complex tables as camera-ready copy.

Preparation of Supplementary Material
Elsevier now accepts electronic supplementary material to support and enhance your scientific research. Supplementary files offer additional possibilities for publishing supporting applications, movies, animation sequences, high-resolution images, background datasets, sound clips, and more. Supplementary files supplied will be published online alongside the electronic version of your article in Elsevier Web products, including ScienceDirect

(http://www.sciencedirect.com). To ensure that your submitted material is directly usable, please provide the data in one of our recommended file formats. Authors should submit the material in electronic format together with the article and supply a concise and descriptive caption for each file. Please note, however, that supplementary material will not appear in the printed journal. Files can be stored on 3?-inch diskette, ZIP disk, or CD (either MS-DOS or Macintosh). For more detailed instructions, please visit our Author Gateway at http://authors.elsevier.com, click on "Artwork instructions," and then click on "Multimedia files."

Proofs
PDF proofs will be sent by e-mail to the corresponding author. To avoid delay in publication, only necessary changes should be made, and corrections should be returned promptly. Authors will be charged for alterations that exceed 10% of the total cost of composition.

Reprints
Twenty-five reprints will be provided to the corresponding author free of charge. Additional reprints may be ordered. A reprint order form will accompany your proofs.

Author Inquiries
For inquiries relating to the submission of articles (including electronic submission where available) please visit the Elsevier Author Gateway at http://authors.elsevier.com. The Author Gateway also provides the facility to track accepted articles and set up e-mail alerts to inform you of when an article's status has changed, as well as detailed artwork guidelines, copyright information, frequently asked questions, and more. Contact details for questions arising after acceptance of an article, especially those relating to proofs, are provided after registration of an article for publication.

Contemporary Family Therapy

ADDRESS FOR SUBMISSION:

William C. Nichols, Editor
Contemporary Family Therapy
755 West Lake Drive
Athens, GA 30606
USA
Phone: 706-549-5890
Fax:
E-Mail: nicholsw@aol.com
Web: www.wkap.nl
Address May Change:

CIRCULATION DATA:

Reader: Practitioners, Academics
Frequency of Issue: Quarterly
Copies per Issue: Less than 1,000
Sponsor/Publisher: Kluwer Academic Press
   (Human Sciences Press)
Subscribe Price: 88.00 US$ Individual
   565.00 US$ Institution

PUBLICATION GUIDELINES:

Manuscript Length: 21-25
Copies Required: No Hardcopy
Computer Submission: Yes Disk, Prefer
   Email
Format: MS Word
Fees to Review: 0.00 US$

Manuscript Style:
   American Psychological Association

REVIEW INFORMATION:

Type of Review: Blind Review
No. of External Reviewers: 1-2
No. of In House Reviewers: 1-2
Acceptance Rate: 35%
Time to Review: 2 - 3 Months
Reviewers Comments: No Reply
Invited Articles: 0-5%
Fees to Publish: 0.00 US$

MANUSCRIPT TOPICS:
Family Counseling & Therapy; Not Counseling

MANUSCRIPT GUIDELINES/COMMENTS:

Topics Include. Related family topics, including family development, divorce, remarriage, etc.

Aims & Scope
Contemporary Family Therapy: An International Journal presents the latest developments in theory, research and practice pertaining to family therapy with an emphasis on examining families within the broader socio-economic and ethnic matrices of which families and their members are a part. Demonstrating that the therapeutic relationship is most effective when family, individual, and society are seen as interacting systems, the journal examines essential factors which include family value systems, social class, and racial, religious, and ethnic backgrounds.

Author Instructions
1. Authors may query the editor at **nicholsw@aol.com** regarding electronic submission.

Manuscripts should be in English and should be checked for content *and* style (correct spelling, punctuation, and grammar; accuracy and consistency in the citation of figures, tables, and references; stylistic uniformity of entries in the References section; etc.). Page proofs (of accepted manuscripts) are sent to the designated author for proofreading and checking. Typographical errors are corrected; authors' alterations are generally not allowed.

2. Submission is a representation that the manuscript has not been published previously and is not currently under consideration for publication elsewhere. A statement transferring copyright from the authors (or their employers, if they hold the copyright) to Human Sciences Press, Inc. will be required before the manuscript can be accepted for publication. The Editor will supply the necessary forms for this transfer. Such a written transfer of copyright, which previously was assumed to be implicit in the act of submitting a manuscript, is necessary under the U.S. Copyright Law in order for the publisher to carry through the dissemination of research results and reviews as widely and effectively as possible.

3. Type double-spaced on one side of 8-½ × 11 inch white paper using generous margins on all sides, and submit the original and two copies (including copies of all illustrations and tables).

4. A title page is to be provided and should include the title of the article and author's name (no degrees). Under a dividing line near the bottom of the page, provide each author's name, highest earned degree, current professional position and address, the name and address to which reprint requests should be directed, and any appropriate acknowledgments. The title page should also include the complete mailing address, telephone number, and email address of the one author designated to review proofs.

5. An abstract is to be provided, preferably no longer than 100 words.

6. A list of 3-5 key words is to be provided directly below the abstract. Key words should express the precise content of the manuscript, as they are used for indexing purposes.

7. Illustrations (photographs, drawings, diagrams, and charts) are to be numbered in one consecutive series of Arabic numerals. The captions for illustrations should be typed on a separate sheet of paper. Photographs should be large, glossy prints, showing high contrast. Drawings should be prepared with india ink. Either the original drawings or good-quality photographic prints are acceptable. Identify figures on the back with author's name and number of the illustration.

8. Tables should be numbered (with Arabic numerals) and referred to by number in the text. Each table should be typed on a separate sheet of paper. Center the title above the table, and type explanatory footnotes (if any) below the table.

9. List references alphabetically at the end of the paper and refer to them in the text by name and year in parentheses. References should include (in this order): last names and initials of *all* authors, year published, title of article, name of publication, volume number, and inclusive pages. In general, the style and punctuation of the references should conform to APA style - illustrated by the following examples:

334

Journal Article
Hicks, M. W., & Cornille, T. A. (1993). Treating jealousy as a system dynamic in recovering alcoholic families: An application of the social network model of recovery. *Contemporary Family Therapy,15*, 381-393.

Book
Liberman, R. P., Wheeler, E. G., de Visser, L. A. J. M., Kuehnel, J., & Kuehnel, T. (1980). *Handbook of marital therapy: A positive approach to helping troubled relationships.* New York: Plenum Press.

Contribution to a Book
Nichols, W. C. (1989). A family systems approach. In C. R. Figley (Ed.), *Treating stress in families* (pp. 67-96). New York: Brunner/Mazel.

10. Footnotes should be avoided. When their use is absolutely necessary, footnotes should be numbered consecutively using Arabic numerals and should be typed at the bottom of the page to which they refer. Place a line above the footnote, so that it is set off from the text. Use the appropriate superscript numeral for citation in the text.

11. In general, the journal follows the recommendations of the 1994 *Publication Manual of the American Psychological Association* (Fourth Edition), and it is suggested that contributors refer to this publication.

12. **The journal makes no page charges**. Reprints are available to authors, and order forms with the current price schedule are sent with proofs.

13. More detailed guidelines may be obtained from the Editor.

Counseling and Values

ADDRESS FOR SUBMISSION:

Christopher Sink, Editor
Counseling and Values
Seattle Pacific University
School of Education
3307 3rd Avenue West
Seattle, WA 98119
USA
Phone: 206-281-2453
Fax: 206-281-2756
E-Mail: csink@spu.edu
Web:
Address May Change:

PUBLICATION GUIDELINES:

Manuscript Length: 10-20
Copies Required: Three
Computer Submission: No
Format: N/A
Fees to Review: 0.00 US$

Manuscript Style:
American Psychological Association

CIRCULATION DATA:

Reader: Academics, Counselors
Frequency of Issue: 3 Times/Year
Copies per Issue: 2,300
Sponsor/Publisher: Professional Association
Subscribe Price: 41.00 US$ Individual
    50.00 US$ Institution

REVIEW INFORMATION:

Type of Review: Blind Review
No. of External Reviewers: 2
No. of In House Reviewers: 0
Acceptance Rate: 15-20%
Time to Review: 2 - 3 Months
Reviewers Comments: Yes
Invited Articles: 0-5%
Fees to Publish: 0.00 US$

MANUSCRIPT TOPICS:

Abnormal Psychology; Adolescent Psychology; Adulthood; Alcoholism & Drug Addiction;
Counseling Process; Developmental Psychology; Educational Psychology; Gerontology;
Learning & Conditioning; Personality; Psychological Testing; Research Methods & Statistics;
Social Psychology; Spirituality; Thinking & Cognition

MANUSCRIPT GUIDELINES/COMMENTS:

Topics Include. Spiritual, Ethical, Religious and Values Issues as these relate to Counseling,
Counseling Theory and Counselor Preparation

The Association for Spiritual, Ethical and Religious Values in Counseling (ASERVIC) is one
of 17 divisions of the American Counseling Association. Originally the National Catholic
Guidance Conference, ASERVIC was chartered in 1974. ASERVIC is devoted to
professionals who believe that spiritual, ethical, religious, and other human values are
essential to the full development of the person and to the discipline of counseling.

To Contact ASERVIC: ASERVIC, A Division of the American Counseling Association, 5999 Stevenson Avenue, Alexandria, VA 22304-3300, 1-800-347-6647

ASERVIC's Journal is *Counseling and Values*.

Counseling and Values is a professional journal of theory, research and informed opinion concerned with relationships among counseling, ethics, philosophy, psychology, religion, personal and social values and spirituality. *Counseling and Values'* mission is to promote free intellectual inquiry across these domains. Its vision is to attract a diverse readership reflective of a growing diversity in the membership of ASERVIC and to effect change leading to the continuing growth and development of a more genuinely civil society. *Counseling and Values* welcomes theoretical, philosophical, empirical or methodological manuscripts dealing with significant moral, ethical, religious, spiritual and values issues as these relate to counseling and related mental health work. Manuscripts must be submitted in triplicate along with a disk in Word or via email with the editor's prior consent.

Journal Editor
Christopher Sink, Ph.D., LMHC, Professor and Chair
Department of School Counseling, School of Education, Seattle Pacific University
3307 3rd Ave West, Seattle, WA 98119
Phone: 206 281-2453 (W), Fax: 206 281-2756; Email: **csink@spu.edu**

GUIDELINES FOR AUTHORS
Articles
Manuscripts should be well organized and concise so that the development of ideas is clear. Avoid dull, clichéd writing and use of jargon.

- Authors are required to submit a disk of the current revised copy in MS Word.
- Provide an abstract of the article of approximately 100 words. Do not use footnotes. Most footnote material can be incorporated into the body of the manuscript.
- Manuscripts are typically between 10 and 20 pages, typewritten, and double spaced. This does not include title page, abstract, and references.
- Double space all material, including direct quotations and references.
- Authors' names, positions, and places of employment should appear only on the title page. Authors' names should not appear on the manuscript.
- Manuscript style is that of the fifth edition of the *Publication Manual of the American Psychological Association* (available from APA, 750 First St. N.E., Washington, DC 20002-4242). All items cited in articles should be listed as references. Reference notes are not used. Provide page numbers for direct quotations.
- Authors should not submit more than three tables or two figures with each manuscript. Include only essential data and combine tables where possible. Tables should be typed on separate pages. Figures (graphs, illustrations, line drawings) should be supplied as camera-ready art (prepared by a commercial artist). Figure captions should be attached to the art and will be set in the appropriate type.
- Authors should reduce bias in language against persons on the basis of gender, sexual orientation, racial or ethnic group, disability, or age by referring to the guidelines in the fifth edition of the *APA Publication Manual*.

- Manuscripts must be submitted in the original and two clear copies. If you wish to have your manuscript returned, you must include a stamped, self-addressed envelope.
- Never submit material for concurrent consideration by another periodical. Manuscripts that meet the guidelines and are appropriate for the focus of the journal are ordinarily submitted to a blind review by the Editorial Board members. Two or 3 months may elapse between acknowledgment of receipt of a manuscript and notification of its disposition. After publication of an article, each author receives a copy of the journal.

Forum

- *Forum* articles will be published in concert with preannounced special topic(s) subject headings. Please consult ACA's newspaper *Counseling Today* for special topic(s) to be addressed in future issues.
- Reactions to editorials, articles, and other *Forum* subjects will be considered for publication in this section as space is available. The editor reserves the right to edit and abridge responses published as reactions to original articles.
- All other guidelines for articles apply to *Forum*.

Issues and Insights

- Philosophical and practical applications of first person narratives that are written in accordance with *APA Publication Manual* standards for publication will be featured.
- Manuscripts must be clearly referenced and represent an author's attempt to offer fresh information.
- "New" counseling interventions and accompanying "techniques that work" will be considered for publication in this section.
- All other guidelines for articles apply *to Issues and Insights*.

Send all manuscripts and correspondence to: Christopher Sink, Ph.D., LMHC, Professor and Chair, Department of School Counseling, School of Education, Seattle Pacific University, 3307 3rd Ave West, Seattle, WA 98119, Phone: 206 281-2453 (W), FAX: 206 281-2756, Email: **csink@spu.edu**

Counseling Psychologist (The)

ADDRESS FOR SUBMISSION:

Robert T. Carter, Editor
Counseling Psychologist (The)
Columbia University
Teachers College
Dept of Counseling & Clinical Psychology
525 West 120th Street, Box 32
New York, NY 10027
USA
Phone: 212-678-3346
Fax: 212-678-8205
E-Mail: tcpjournal@tc.columbia.edu
Web: www.div17.rg/tcp/guidelines
Address May Change: 1/1/2009

CIRCULATION DATA:

Reader: Academics
Frequency of Issue: 6 Times/Year
Copies per Issue: No Reply
Sponsor/Publisher: Amer. Psychological
   Association (APA Divison 17) / Sage
   Publications
Subscribe Price: 86.00 US$ Individual
   495.00 US$ Institution

PUBLICATION GUIDELINES:

Manuscript Length: 30+
Copies Required: Six
Computer Submission: No
Format: N/A
Fees to Review: 0.00 US$

Manuscript Style:
   American Psychological Association

REVIEW INFORMATION:

Type of Review: Blind Review
No. of External Reviewers: 3+
No. of In House Reviewers: 0
Acceptance Rate: 6-10%
Time to Review: 1 - 2 Months
Reviewers Comments: Yes
Invited Articles: 0-5%
Fees to Publish: 0.00 US$

MANUSCRIPT TOPICS:

Adulthood; Alcoholism & Drug Addiction; Behavior Modification; Counseling Process;
Counseling Psychology; Family Counseling & Therapy; Gerontology; Personality;
Psychological Testing; Research Methods & Statistics

MANUSCRIPT GUIDELINES/COMMENTS:

GUIDELINES FOR SUBMITTING MAJOR CONTRIBUTION PROPOSALS

Perhaps one of the hallmarks of *The Counseling Psychologist* (*TCP*) is the thematic format of
the journal, introduced in 1969 by John Whiteley. The basic format is to have one or more
papers constituting a Major Contribution on a single topic, followed by reaction papers from a
diverse group of colleagues to stimulate additional thought. Given the manuscript length of
the Major Contributions, most often potential authors engage in a two-step review process.
First, they submit a proposal for a Major Contribution (approximately 15 pages), and if the
proposal is approved, full-length manuscripts are subsequently developed and reviewed for
acceptability (see details below). In a few exceptional cases, potential authors may have

already complete, full length manuscripts; these authors can submit their manuscripts directly for editorial review.

Proposal Format
The proposal format is to consist of three sections typed on 8.5 x 11 paper, double-spaced, in American Psychological Association (APA) style.

I. Proposed Content and Structure
Section I is approximately a five page overview of the following five points, preferably addressed point by point.

1. A one-paragraph description of the content domain of the Major Contribution.

2. Specific goals of the Major Contribution. The goals should include some level of conceptual, empirical, and methodological contributions to either research, practice, and training activities of interest to counseling psychologists. Critical literature reviews are encouraged. Authors are especially encouraged to submit a package of shorter articles. For example, the lead article might be primarily a conceptual article, with the next two articles each providing empirical support for some part of the conceptual model identified in the first article. A fourth article might build on the other three articles by discussing practice implications. Collectively, the package of articles in such a Major Contribution would integrate theory, science, and practice. Whether through one extended manuscript or package of shorter articles, the best proposals will *explicitly* (a) integrate theory, practice, and science; (b) discuss implications for specific populations, such as women, men, ethnic minorities, non-ethnic minorities (gay, lesbian, bisexual), and various educational levels, social classes, and nationalities; (c) establish a historical context for the Major Contribution; and (d) address major societal problems.

3. A brief rationale explaining *why* and *how* both the content and specific goals above are important for counseling psychologists at this time.

4. one-paragraph description of the proposed structure of the Major Contribution. The most common structures are (a) one Major Contribution followed by reactions, and (b) three or four interrelated papers to form a Major Contribution, followed by reactions. The complete manuscript, whether consisting of one or more papers, including references but excluding reactions, can range from 70 to 120 double-spaced typed pages. Given the general shortage of journal space, concise manuscripts are valued.

5. Specify the amount of time needed to prepare the proposed Major Contribution.

II. Detailed Outline of the Proposed Major Contribution
Section II is a summary of the proposed paper(s) that constitute the Major Contribution (approximately 10 pages). The purpose of this section is to allow the author(s) to provide specific details about the proposed structure and content of the proposal discussed in Section I. Inclusion of some citations is encouraged.

III. References
Section III is a listing of the references utilized in Sections I and II.

Review and Implementation Process
Proposals for Major Contributions involve at least the six steps below; the review process for completed manuscripts submitted for review consists of at least the last three steps below (steps 4-6).

1. For proposals, the editor will make a prompt review of the suitability of the proposal for distribution to the editorial board. If the proposal is found inappropriate or incomplete, it will be returned promptly to the author with recommendations regarding submission. Once a proposal is complete, it will be sent out to members of the *TCP* editorial board for ratings and comments. The editor, after receiving responses, will provide feedback to the author within approximately 2 months after receipt of the proposal. This communication will specify a decision about whether to proceed, or whether any additional information or development is needed before a final decision can be made.

2. Any substantial deviations from the approved proposal must be cleared with the editor.

3. A date for completion of the paper(s) and an approximate publication date will be established. A failure to meet the established deadline will result in loss of position in the publishing schedule, possibly resulting in a delay in publication of a year or more.

4. When the completed manuscript(s) is received, it will be reviewed by at least two editorial board consultants, at least one ad hoc reviewer, and the editor. Editorial feedback will be provided within 6 to 8 weeks of receipt of the manuscript. If appropriate, the author(s) will be allowed up to 8 weeks to make revisions and still retain their original place in the publication sequence. Delays in making acceptable revisions could again result in long delays in subsequent publication.

5. If the manuscript is reviewed favorably for publication, the author(s) will be asked to submit a list of possible respondents. The editor will review these suggestions, consult with content experts (including *TCP* board members) and then discuss with the author(s) the editor's decision.

6. Once a first draft has been received and is judged to be acceptable with only minor revisions, *respondents will be contacted by the editor*. Reactants will be allowed 6 to 8 weeks for preparing their reactions.

Manuscript Preparation and Ethical Issues
Issues pertaining to the preparation of the proposal/manuscript for a Major Contribution, as well as all ethical considerations, are identical to those indicated in the Forums guidelines.

Submission of Proposals/Manuscripts
Authors should:
a.   submit 12 copies of proposals for Major Contributions *or*
b.   6 copies of manuscripts for one of the Forums to the Editor.

GUIDELINES FOR SUBMITTING MANUSCRIPTS TO THE FORUMS

An important component of *The Counseling Psychologist* are the forums that facilitate the discussion of conceptual, empirical, and methodological issues in specific domains. Each forum has one or more features, as described below.

The Professional Forum is for articles that examine a wide range of professional issues in counseling psychology such as (but not limited to) education and training, professional roles, professional development, licensure, organizational and political issues within the profession, the impact of social issues and national policies on counseling psychology, and ethical/legal issues.

The Scientific Forum is for articles that (a) examine methodological issues, (b) are critical reviews of the literature, and (c) are an integration of conceptual and empirical approaches to enhance theory development.

The Special Populations Forum is for articles that build on the Division of Counseling Psychology's commitment to enhance awareness, sensitivity, knowledge, and practice about a broad range of culturally diverse populations. More specifically, this forum provides opportunities to integrate conceptual, empirical, and methodological issues in conducting research and practice with populations that vary in gender, ethnicity, age, lifestyle, and religious values.

The Legacies and Traditions Forum is for articles that document the personal and professional lives of early pioneers whose work has shaped our profession. In a way, each article represents an oral history of the profession. Pioneers must be at least 60 years of age and have made major contributions to the field of counseling psychology through science and/or practice activities. All inquiries regarding the suitability of a person, selection criteria, and selection process for this forum should be sent to the series coeditors:

Nadya A. Fouad, Ph.D. Nancy Downing Hansen, Ph.D.
Dept. of Educational Psychology 2028 Evergreen Drive
733 Enderis Hall, Box 413 Fort Collins, CO 80521
Univ. of Wisconsin-Milwaukee U.S.A.
Milwaukee, WI 53201

The International Forum is a deliberate attempt to increase the visibility of international contributions to counseling in a variety of ways: (a) to promote awareness, knowledge, and skill for international and intercultural counseling activities among Division 17 members, (b) to promote professional relations and communication between Division 17 members and the larger international community of professional counselors, and (c) to provide an opportunity to share information on international and intercultural counseling issues.

Articles might focus on:
- counseling persons in an international population;
- counseling strategies unique to an international setting;
- problems in adapting counseling to an international setting;
- reviews of literature on counseling in non-English speaking countries;

- analysis of results from international counseling conferences;
- ethical and professional issues in international counseling;
- methods of counselor training in other countries.

All inquiries regarding this forum should be sent to the series coeditors:
Frederick Leong, Ph.D., David Blustein, Ph.D.
Dept. of Psychology Dept. of Counseling Psychology
The Ohio State University Boston College
142 Townsend Hall Campion Hall 315
Columbus, OH 43210 Chestnut Hill, MA 02467

Around the Winter Roundtable is for major invited addresses focusing on multicultural issues relevant to counseling psychology from the Winter Roundtable of Multicultural Psychology and Education. This forum is edited by:
Robert T. Carter, Ph.D.
Teachers College
Columbia University
Box 32
New York, NY 10027

The Comments Forum is for brief comments on articles published in the journal. Based on both Fowler (1991) and Stone (1994), the following guidelines have been established for the comments section:
- Manuscripts submitted as comments should not exceed five double-spaced pages.
- All comments are reviewed.
- Comments on comments are rarely accepted.
- Rejoinder from an author whose article is being commented on will be reviewed, if warranted.
- Unsolicited rejoinders (from other than the original author) are rarely accepted.
- Readers are encouraged to write directly to the author with comments that do not fit our guidelines or do not require a broad audience.
- Comments should be submitted no later than three months after the publication on which the comment is made.

Any exceptions to the above guidelines are made only if they significantly and substantially add to the discussion or provide corrections of points of facts.

In Memoriam is to honor those psychologists who have made significant contributions to counseling psychology. Past presidents of Division 17 and Leona Tyler Award winners are all recognized. In addition, selection of distinguished past contributors is on a case-by-case basis, with assistance from an advisory committee composed of the past president, president, and president-elect of Division 17.

Manuscript Preparation and Ethical Issues
Manuscripts sent to *The Counseling Psychologist* for editorial review should be prepared according to the *Publication Manual of the American Psychological Association*, Fourth

Edition (APA, 750 First Street, NE, Washington, DC 20002-4242). All parts of the manuscript must be typed double-spaced on 8.5 x 11 paper. Authors are advised to use language that is free from sexist, racist, or ethnic bias; heterosexism; bias toward people with disabilities; ageism, and other kinds of bias. All manuscripts should include an abstract on a separate page that contains no more than 150 words. Tables are to be included when necessary to depict the results. Tables, figures, abstracts, and captions are to be prepared on separate pages and must conform to the *Publication Manual of the APA*. *The Counseling Psychologist* uses a blind review system whenever possible; all manuscripts will be reviewed anonymously such that the identity of the author will be unknown to reviewers both during and after the review process; authors submitting manuscripts for review should identify themselves only on a removable cover sheet and nowhere else on the manuscript.

Authors are expected to adhere to the APA Ethical Guidelines in conducting all phases of their investigation and manuscript preparation. In particular, it is important that all ethical issues regarding treatment of research participants be carefully examined and actions taken in accordance with the APA Ethical Guidelines. Moreover, it is important that every person who contributed to the project is acknowledged in the Author Notes in accordance with APA policy, or as an author.

In preparing and submitting manuscripts, authors are expected to report data and results that are both honest and accurate. Such practices as submitting a previously published manuscript for review, and submitting the same manuscript to various journals at the same time should not be exercised. Piecemeal or fragmented publications from a single study is discouraged unless there is a clear benefit to scientific communication. Multiple reports from a large data set must include reference to prior reports, and make clear the degree of sample overlap. In all cases of multiple reports from the same data set, authors should inform the editor as well as explicitly note any overlap in the report. Upon receipt of any manuscript for review, authors will be asked to sign a form indicating adherence to APA Ethical Guidelines as well as the issues identified above.

Authors submitting manuscripts are protected by common law against the unauthorized use of their unpublished work. Specifically, an unpublished manuscript is considered to be a confidential or privileged paper. Reviewers will be asked to destroy or return the manuscript after their review is completed; in addition, reviewers will be asked not to circulate, quote, cite, or refer to the unpublished work in any way unless specific permission is granted by the author.

Manuscript Submissions
All manuscripts (including the *International Forum* as well as the *Legacies and Traditions Forum*) should be submitted with an original plus five copies to the Editor. Inquiries can be addressed to the editor at the above address.

References
Fowler, R. D. (1991). Statement of editorial policy. *American Psychologist*, 46, 3-5.

Stone, G. L. (1994). Comment on comments. *The Counseling Psychologist*, 22, 5.

Creativity Research Journal

ADDRESS FOR SUBMISSION:

Mark A. Runco, Editor
Creativity Research Journal
California State University
EC 105
PO Box 6868
Fullerton, CA 92834
USA
Phone: 714-278-3376
Fax: 714-278-3314
E-Mail: runco@exchange.fullerton.edu
Web: www.erlbaum.com
Address May Change:

PUBLICATION GUIDELINES:

Manuscript Length: 15-40
Copies Required: Five
Computer Submission: Yes
Format: See Manuscript Guidelines
Fees to Review: 0.00 US$

Manuscript Style:
     American Psychological Association

CIRCULATION DATA:

Reader: Academics, Organizational, Social,
   and Experimental Psychologists
Frequency of Issue: Quarterly
Copies per Issue: 1,001 - 2,000
Sponsor/Publisher: Lawrence Erlbaum
   Associates
Subscribe Price: 55.00 US$ Individual
   260.00 US$ Institution
   49.50 US$ / $234.00 for Electronic

REVIEW INFORMATION:

Type of Review: Blind Review
No. of External Reviewers: 2
No. of In House Reviewers: 2
Acceptance Rate: 11-20%
Time to Review: 2 - 3 Months
Reviewers Comments: Yes
Invited Articles: 6-10%
Fees to Publish: 0.00 US$

MANUSCRIPT TOPICS:
Art; Decision Making Theory; Education; Experimental Psychology; Group Dynamics; Industry & Organization; Motivation; Personality

MANUSCRIPT GUIDELINES/COMMENTS:

Topics Include. Behavioral, clinical, cognitive, developmental, educational, historical, personality or psychometric research on Creativity and related topics (e.g., Innovation, Originality, the Arts, Aesthetics, Entrepreneurship, Problem solving, Brainstorming, Giftedness).

Editorial Scope
This well-established journal publishes high quality, scholarly research capturing the full range of approaches to the study of creativity – behavioral, clinical, cognitive, cross-cultural, developmental, educational, genetic, organizational, psychoanalytic, psychometric, and social. Interdisciplinary research is also published, as is research within specific domains such as art and science, as well as on critical issues such as aesthetics, genius, imagery, imagination, incubation, insight, intuition, metaphor, play, and problem finding and solving. Integrative

literature reviews and theoretical pieces that appreciate empirical work are welcome, but purely speculative articles will not be published.

Audience. Behavioral, clinical, cognitive, developmental, and educational psychologists, and others interested in the study of creativity.

Instructions to Contributors
Manuscript Preparation. Prepare manuscripts according to the *Publication Manual of the American Psychological Association* (5th ed., 1994; American Psychological Association, P.O. Box 2710, Hyattsville, MD 20784), especially with regard to reference lists and text citations. Follow "Guidelines to Reduce Bias in Language" (*APA Manual*, pp. 46-60). Report exact probabilities (e.g., p = .03) and effect sizes. Using 8½ x 11-in. non-smear paper and 1-in. margins, type all components double-spaced and in the following order: title page (p. 1), abstract (p. 2), text (including quotations), references, appendices, footnotes, tables, and figure captions. On page 1, type article title, author name(s) and affiliation(s), running head (abbreviated title, no more than 45 characters and spaces), author notes and acknowledgments, submission date (month, day, and year on original manuscript and on any revisions), and name and address of the person to whom requests for reprints should be addressed; on page 2, type an abstract of 150 to 200 words. Indent all paragraphs. Use footnotes sparingly. Attach photocopies of all figures. Number all manuscript pages (including photocopies of figures). Cover Letter, Permissions, Credit Lines:

In a cover letter, include the contact author's complete mailing address, e-mail address, and telephone and fax numbers. State that the manuscript includes only original material that has not been published and that is not under review for publication elsewhere. Authors are responsible for all statements made in their work and for obtaining permission to reprint or adapt a copyrighted table or figure or to quote at length from a copyrighted work. Authors should write to original author(s) and original publisher to see if permission is required and to request nonexclusive world rights in all languages to use the material in the current article and in future editions. Include copies of all permissions and credit lines with the manuscript. (See p. 140 of the *APA Manual* for samples of credit lines.)

Manuscript Submission. Prepare manuscript on a word processor and submit five (5) high quality printouts to the Editor, Mark A. Runco, EC 105, Calif State Univ, PO Box 6868, Fullerton, CA 92834, USA. E-mail: **runco@exchange.fullerton.edu**. Manuscripts are not returned. Accepted Manuscripts and Computer Disk Submission: After manuscripts are accepted, authors are asked to sign and return copyright-transfer agreements and submit uniquely labeled, highly legible, camera-ready figures (use Times Roman font for text appearing in figures). It is the responsibility of the contact author to ascertain that all co-authors approve the accepted manuscript and concur with its publication in the journal. Submit a disk containing two files: word-processor and ASCII versions of the manuscript. File content must match the printed manuscript exactly, or there will be a delay in publication. Disks are not returned. Production Notes: Files are copyedited and typeset into page proofs. Authors read proofs to correct errors and answer editors' queries. Authors may order reprints at that time.

Crime & Delinquency

ADDRESS FOR SUBMISSION:

Elizabeth Piper Deschenes, Editor
Crime & Delinquency
California State University, Long Beach
Department of Criminal Justice
1250 Bellflower Blvd.
Long Beach, CA 90840-4603
USA
Phone: 562-985-8567
Fax: 562-985-8086
E-Mail: See Guidelines
Web: http://cad.sagepub.com
Address May Change:

PUBLICATION GUIDELINES:

Manuscript Length: 26-30
Copies Required: Five
Computer Submission: Not at this time
Format: N/A
Fees to Review: 10.00 US$

Manuscript Style:
    American Psychological Association

CIRCULATION DATA:

Reader: Academics
Frequency of Issue: Quarterly
Copies per Issue: 1,001 - 2,000
Sponsor/Publisher: National Council on
    Crime and Delinquency
Subscribe Price: 105.00 US$ Indv Print
    667.20 US$ Inst. Print
    See Website - more details

REVIEW INFORMATION:

Type of Review: Blind Review
No. of External Reviewers: 3
No. of In House Reviewers: 2
Acceptance Rate: 11-20%
Time to Review: 1 - 2 Months
Reviewers Comments: Yes
Invited Articles: 0-5%
Fees to Publish: 0.00 US$

MANUSCRIPT TOPICS:

Alcoholism & Drug Addiction; Behavior Modification; Crime & Delinquency;
Psychopathology; Research Methods & Statistics

MANUSCRIPT GUIDELINES/COMMENTS:

Manuscripts should be submitted to *Crime & Delinquency*, Elizabeth Piper Deschenes, Editor,
Department of Criminal Justice, California State University, Long Beach, 1250 Bellflower
Blvd., Long Beach, CA 90840-4603. Please submit five copies, not to exceed 30 typed,
double-spaced pages, with notes, references, tables, and figures (the latter two to be held to a
minimum) on separate pages. Include a 100-word abstract and key words. Author's name and
a brief statement indicating author's current position and affiliation should appear on a
separate title page. References should follow the guidelines indicated in the *Publication
Manual of the American Psychological Association* (5th ed.). Please include a check for
$10.00 to Crime & Delinquency for the reviewing fee. A copy of the final revised manuscript
saved on an IBM-compatible disk should be included with the final revised hard copy. Email:
jour-crimndel@csulb.edu or **libby@csulb.edu**

Criminal Justice and Behavior

ADDRESS FOR SUBMISSION:

Curt R. Bartol, Editor
Criminal Justice and Behavior
Castleton State College
Department of Psychology
Castleton, VT 05735
USA
Phone: 802-468-1405
Fax: 802-468-3020
E-Mail: curt.bartol@castleton.edu
Web: www.sagepub.com
Address May Change: 4/30/2008

PUBLICATION GUIDELINES:

Manuscript Length: 21-25
Copies Required: Three
Computer Submission: See Guidelines
Format: MS Word, Windows Platform
Fees to Review: 0.00 US$

Manuscript Style:
        American Psychological Association

CIRCULATION DATA:

Reader: Academics, Practitioners
Frequency of Issue: Bi-Monthly
Copies per Issue: 2,001 - 3,000
Sponsor/Publisher: American Association
    for Correctional Psychology (AACP) /
    Sage Publications
Subscribe Price: 84.00 US$ Individual
    551.00 US$ Institution

REVIEW INFORMATION:

Type of Review: Blind Review
No. of External Reviewers: 3
No. of In House Reviewers: 1
Acceptance Rate: 6-10%
Time to Review: 2 - 3 Months
Reviewers Comments: Yes
Invited Articles: 6-10%
Fees to Publish: 0.00 US$

MANUSCRIPT TOPICS:
Behavior Modification; Classification Systems; Correctional Psychology; Criminal
Behaviour; Forensics; Police Psychology; Prevention; Psychiatry; Psychopathy; Risk
Assessment; Social Psychology; Treatment; Victiminology

MANUSCRIPT GUIDELINES/COMMENTS:

About the Journal
For over 30 years *Criminal Justice and Behavior* has published timely, well-conceived and
lively scholarship. *Criminal Justice and Behavior* advances the knowledge and expertise of
professionals and academics involved in forensic psychology, with a concentration on
correctional psychology.

A peer-reviewed scholarly publication, *Criminal Justice and Behavior* (*CJ&B*) publishes
issues confronting today's professionals and academics in corrections, criminology, and
forensic psychology. *CJ&B* covers:
- classification and treatments of offenders
- causes of delinquent and criminal behavior
- prevention, intervention, and treatment programs

- education and training
- effectiveness of different sanctions
- offender and offensive characteristics
- psychology of policing
- psychology and law issues

In addition to the scholarly excellence of the contributions you'll find in *Criminal Justice and Behavior* you'll also see a representation of extraordinary diversity - of subject matter, of professional discipline and affiliation, and of nationality. Published submissions have come from countries as varied as the UK, United States, Canada, Spain, Australia, Sweden, Germany, Norway, Israel, and the Netherlands.

Criminal Justice and Behavior's broad range of coverage is the result of an editorial mandate to expand the journal's editorial board and pool of reviewers to draw on a wider range of expertise. *CJ&B* brings you research and analyses in forensic psychology from behavioral science scholars with diverse professional affiliations, including:

- police psychology
- criminal justice administration
- family studies/research
- public administration
- sociology and anthropology
- psychiatry
- forensic science
- law/legal studies
- public policy
- community health

Comprehensive Coverage

Criminal Justice and Behavior brings you original research, theoretical contributions, and information on innovative programs and practices, as well as critical reviews of literature or theory on topics central to criminal justice and behavior. In the pages of the journal you'll find:

Articles. To keep you at the very forefront of correctional and forensic psychology the journal fosters, *Criminal Justice and Behavior* publishes high-quality scholarship concerning the interface between the behavioral sciences and the criminal justice system. Empirical research is emphasized, and theoretical and integrative review articles are also featured.

Commentaries. To present you with a wide variety of opinions and experiences, journal commentaries are often solicited on articles that are particularly thought-provoking in their implications or that can be further illuminated by an additional perspective.

Book Reviews. The journal includes stimulating reviews on recently published books to help you stay current on the best and most important resources in the field.

Notes for Authors

Manuscripts should be submitted in triplicate to Curt R. Bartol PhD, Editor, *Criminal Justice and Behavior,* Department of Psychology, Castleton State College, Castleton, VT 05735.

Direct questions concerning manuscript submissions to:
   CJB@Castleton.edu or **Curt.Bartol@Castleton.edu**

Manuscripts must be typewritten double-spaced with tables, charts, footnotes, and references on separate pages. The format described in the *Publication Manual of the American Psychological Association* (5th edition) should be followed.

Culture, Medicine and Psychiatry

ADDRESS FOR SUBMISSION:

Anne E. Becker & Peter Guarnaccia, Eds.
Culture, Medicine and Psychiatry
Harvard Medical School
Department of Social Medicine
641 Huntington Avenue, 2nd Floor
Boston, MA 02115
USA
Phone: 617-432-0716
Fax: 617-432-2565
E-Mail: cmp@hms.harvard.edu
Web: www.springeronline.com/
Address May Change:

PUBLICATION GUIDELINES:

Manuscript Length: 21-45
Copies Required: No Reply
Computer Submission: Yes
Format: Electronic in MS Word
Fees to Review: 0.00 US$

Manuscript Style:
  Chicago Manual of Style, American
  Anthropologist Style

CIRCULATION DATA:

Reader: Academics
Frequency of Issue: Quarterly
Copies per Issue: No Reply
Sponsor/Publisher: Department of Social
  Medicine, Harvard Medical
  School/Springer Academic Publishers
Subscribe Price: 353.00 US$ Individual
  327.00 US$ Institution
  109.00 US$ SMA, SPA, APA &
  Students

REVIEW INFORMATION:

Type of Review: Editorial Review
No. of External Reviewers: 2
No. of In House Reviewers: 1
Acceptance Rate: N/A
Time to Review: 4 - 6 Months
Reviewers Comments: Yes
Invited Articles: 25%
Fees to Publish: 0.00 US$

MANUSCRIPT TOPICS:
Culture & Personality; Culture and Medicine; Culture and Psychiatry

MANUSCRIPT GUIDELINES/COMMENTS:

Aims & Scope
Culture, Medicine and Psychiatry is an international and interdisciplinary forum for the publication of work in three interrelated fields: medical and psychiatric anthropology, cross-cultural psychiatry, and related cross-societal and clinical epidemiological studies. The journal publishes original research as well as cross-cultural case formulations. Interdisciplinary work which bridges anthropological and medical perspectives and methods which are clinically relevant are particularly welcome, as is research on the cultural context of normative and deviant behavior, including the anthropological, epidemiological and clinical aspects of the subject.

Culture, Medicine and Psychiatry also fosters systematic and wide-ranging examinations of the significance of culture in health care, including comparisons of how the concept of culture is operationalized in anthropological and medical disciplines.

With the increasing emphasis on the cultural diversity of society, which finds its reflection in many facets of our day to day life, including health care, *Culture, Medicine and Psychiatry* is required reading in anthropology, psychiatry and general health care libraries.

Author Instructions
Articles should be submitted to the Editors-in-Chief:
> Anne E. Becker, M.D., Ph.D.
> Department of Social Medicine
> Harvard Medical School
> 641 Huntington Avenue
> Boston, MA 02115
> U.S.A.
> Email: **cmp@hms.harvard.edu**
> or
> Peter Guarnaccia, Ph.D.
> **cmp@hms.harvard.edu**

Articles should be submitted as either a Microsoft Word or Rich Text file, double-spaced in 12 point, Times New Roman font, with at least 1 inch margins on all sides and the right-hand margin not justified. Pages should be numbered, beginning with the title page.

All manuscripts should follow the style of the 'American Anthropologist' with the following amendment. Double quotes should be used for direct quotations, and single quotes for quotations within quotations, for words set off for 'emphasis', and for literal translations of foreign language words and phrases (translations intended mainly for the reader's convenience, in manuscripts where the emphasis is not on linguistic data, should appear in parentheses). Manuscripts must be submitted electronically.

No page charges are levied on authors or their institutions.

Current Anthropology

ADDRESS FOR SUBMISSION:

Benjamin S. Orlove, Editor
Current Anthropology
University of California
Dept. of Environmental Science & Policy
One Shields Avenue
Davis, CA 95616-6101
USA
Phone: 530-754-6101
Fax: 530-754-6114
E-Mail: curranth@ucdavis.edu
Web: www.journals.uchicago.edu/ca/
Address May Change:

PUBLICATION GUIDELINES:

Manuscript Length: Depends on Type
Copies Required: Three
Computer Submission: Yes
Format: MS Word or PDF
Fees to Review: 0.00 US$

Manuscript Style:
    Chicago Manual of Style

CIRCULATION DATA:

Reader: Academics
Frequency of Issue: 5 Times/Year
Copies per Issue: 4,001 - 5,000
Sponsor/Publisher: Wenner-Gren
    Foundation / University of Chicago Press
Subscribe Price: 48.00 US$ Individual
    170.00 US$ Institution
    25.00 US$ Student/$35 Retired

REVIEW INFORMATION:

Type of Review: Editorial Review
No. of External Reviewers: 3+
No. of In House Reviewers: 1
Acceptance Rate: 0-15%
Time to Review: 4 - 6 Months
Reviewers Comments: Yes
Invited Articles: 0-5%
Fees to Publish: 0.00 US$

MANUSCRIPT TOPICS:

Culture & Personality; Decision Making Theory; Gender Roles; Group Dynamics; Human Relations; Human Sexuality; Psychology of Women; Sports & Leisure

MANUSCRIPT GUIDELINES/COMMENTS:

Information for Contributors

Current Anthropology is a transnational journal devoted to research on humankind. The journal defines such research in the broadest possible way, to encompass all scholarship on human cultures and on the human, or closely related, species. It therefore makes a strong commitment to a comprehensive view of anthropology and provides a forum for active scholarly critique as a major means by which to achieve this view. To this end, all major articles undergo the CA★ treatment: commentators, selected internationally, write critiques that appear in the same issue as the article, along with a reply from the author. The journal also publishes research reports, book reviews, interviews, critical comments, and other anthropological news items.

Current Anthropology hopes to build up a comprehensive anthropology by publishing analytic, theoretical, or synthetic articles that communicate significantly to the largest number of anthropologists and to scholars in related disciplines. One way for articles to achieve this breadth is to span disciplinary and subdisciplinary boundaries. Another way is to provide essential knowledge to anthropologists in the other subdisciplines. The journal will not publish articles incapable of reaching a broad international audience through one means or another.

Current Anthropology, in its very name, makes a commitment to publish articles contributing to current debates in anthropology and related disciplines. Articles should be at the forefront of present-day scholarship and may take controversial positions; they may even be speculative at times, as long as their intention is to bring important questions into scholarly debate.

Current Anthropology is published in a print and an electronic version. The journal intends to pioneer the use of the new forms of scholarly publication permitted by the Internet at the same time as maintaining the exacting standards it observes in print. The electronic version is expected to become part of the permanent record of scholarship in anthropology and to provide as valuable a resource as the print journal has been over the past 40 years.

General Guidelines for Submissions
Current Anthropology publishes scholarship in several formats. *Major articles* with commentaries – those that receive the CA★ treatment – must make theoretical or methodological interventions into current controversies within anthropology, broadly construed. Most major papers are 50 manuscript pages or fewer in length and must be accompanied by abstracts of 200 words or fewer. Reports present research findings of theoretical significance to anthropology, and this significance must be made clear in the text. Reports are usually about 15 manuscript pages in length, including references, and they do not require abstracts. Major papers and reports should also be provided with a list of four key words by which they may be indexed. One key word should give the subdisciplinary designation most appropriate to the article, and another should give an appropriate geographical designation.

Current Anthropology also publishes two forums as means of stimulating debate: the *Forum on Anthropology in Public* concerns the involvement of anthropology in public issues or the interactions of anthropology with the wider society, and the *Forum on Theory in Anthropology* presents contending arguments on theoretical issues of importance to anthropology. Papers written for the forums are usually about 20 manuscript pages in length. A final format, the *Commentary*, consists of overviews and statements of position by senior anthropologists. Commentaries are usually by invitation of the editor, and they are about 15 pages in length.

Authors may not submit a new major-article or report manuscript until two years after the publication of their last one. *Current Anthropology* does not consider more than one submission at a time for any author.

The books listed in "Books Received" are those sent to *Current Anthropology* by publishers. The books reviewed in the journal are chosen from among those received at the editorial

354

office. Book reviews are by invitation of the editor only, and unsolicited book reviews will not be considered.

The Wenner-Gren Foundation for Anthropological Research sponsors *Current Anthropology* in order to create a worldwide community of scholars that transcends national borders and parochial intellectual orientations. This community of scholars forms the Associates of *Current Anthropology*, who serve as contributors, commentators, and referees, as well as advisors to the editor. Authors also may submit the names and addresses of possible reviewers.

Current Anthropology requires the assignment of copyright to the Wenner-Gren Foundation for Anthropological Research for major articles, reports, forums, and commentaries. Although copyright to other contributions remains with their authors, it is understood that, in return for publication, the journal has the nonexclusive right to publish the contribution and the continuing right, without limit, to include the contribution as part of any reprinting of the issue in whole or in part, by any means and in any format, including computer-assisted storage and read-out.

Articles published in *Current Anthropology* are in the English language only. However, manuscripts may be submitted in other languages, and funds exist for making translations into English. This means that authors need not translate their articles into English before submitting them and that authors will be able to revise their papers, should they be accepted, using their native tongue. Contributions submitted for review should not have been published in any form or language. Manuscripts should be double-spaced, in 12 pt. font, and all pages should be numbered. References cited should be listed alphabetically, double- spaced, at the end of the paper. Please submit one original copy; the journal would welcome 3 additional copies for review purposes. Electronic submission is encouraged. In-text citations should take the following form: (Sahlins 1961:323). The form for the listing of references is as follows:

Journals
HUGHES-FREELAND, FELICIA. 1997. Consciousness in performance: A Javanese theory. *Social Anthropology* 5:55-68.

Books
KAPLAN, MATTHEW, ATSUKO KUSANO, ICHIRO TSUJI, AND SHIGERU HISAMICHI. 1998. *Intergenerational programs: Support for children, youth, and elders in Japan*. Albany: State University of New York Press.

Sections of Books
LEHMAN, F. AND K. WITZ. 1974. "Prolegomena to a formal theory of kinship," in *Genealogical mathematics*. Edited by P. Ballonoff, pp. 111-34. The Hague: Mouton.

Footnotes, numbered in sequence throughout the paper, should be gathered together and typed double-spaced at the end. Acknowledgments, if any, should constitute the first footnote (the identifying number being attached to the title of the paper). For review purposes authors should submit clear photocopies of all tables, figures, and photos rather than the originals. A diskette is required only when the manuscript has been accepted and is submitted in final form. When submitted in final form for publication, tables should be typed on separate sheets, titled, numbered with Arabic numerals, and cited in the text. Figures should also be numbered and cited in the text. Photographs should have glossy finish and high contrast. Drawings should be in India ink on white paper. Legends for all figures should be typed, double-spaced, on a separate sheet of paper.

Electronic Version and Enhancements

Online versions of articles will include all elements of the print version, but they may also contain the enhancements that electronic publication permits. These enhancements are meant to expand the scholarly significance of the article and constitute a new treatment referred to as CA+. Articles enhanced for electronic publication may contain any of the following additions to the original text: sound files, color photographs, color-enhanced graphics, maps (with zoom capability), supporting texts, multiple abstracts, or additional data, as well as links to related articles, official documents, and other relevant sites on the Internet.

Online enhancements for electronic publication should be submitted in these forms:

- Short sound files should be submitted in WAV or AIFF format. MP3 files will be accepted as well so long as the sound quality is adequate.
- Photographs and other graphics may be submitted at present in print or slide form, and the journal will digitize them. However, digital files are preferable and should be supplied in TIFF, EPS, or Photoshop format. Digital files should be accompanied by camera-ready hard copies in case the graphic files are unusable. Current Anthropology prefers that contributors provide high-resolution files without downsampling or lossy compression (e.g., converting the image to JPEG format).
- Additional data may be submitted in a variety of formats, including delimited text, Data Interchange Format (DIF), or spreadsheet files.

As with printed matter, the editor must give approval to any and all enhancements to the electronic version. The copyright agreement between authors and the Wenner-Gren Foundation covers both print and electronic publication.

Copying

The code on the first page of an article indicates the copyright owner's consent that copies of the article be made beyond those permitted by Sections 107 and 108 of the U.S. Copyright Law, provided that the copies are made only for personal or internal use of specific clients and provided that the copier pay the stated per-copy fee through the Copyright Clearance Center, Inc., Operations Center, P. O. Box 765, Schenectady, N.Y. 12301, U.S.A. Permission for other kinds of copying, such as copying for general distribution, for advertising or promotional purposes, for creating new collective works, or for resale, may be requested from the Permissions Department, University of Chicago Press, 1427 E. 60th St., Chicago, Ill. 60637, U.S.A. If no code appears on the first page of an article, permission to reprint it may be obtained only from the author. Multiple copies of past and present articles, in units of 100, may be ordered from the Journals Division, University of Chicago Press, 1427 E. 60th St., Chicago, Ill. 60637, U.S.A. Single tear-sheets are supplied by the Institute for Scientific Information, 325 Chestnut St., Philadelphia, Pa. 19106, U.S.A. Microfilms and xerographic copies may be obtained from ProQuest Information and Learning, 300 N. Zeeb Rd., P.O. Box 1346, Ann Arbor, Mich. 48106-1346, U.S.A.

356

Communications concerning editorial matters, including books for review and requests to reprint or translate, should be addressed to:

Benjamin S. Orlove, Editor
Current Anthropology
Department of Environmental Science and Policy
University of California
One Shields Avenue
Davis, CA., 95616-8576 USA
Phone: 530-754-6101; Fax: 530-754-6114; Email: **currenth@ucdavis.edu**
URL: **http://www.journals.uchicago.edu/CA/journal/**

Death Studies

ADDRESS FOR SUBMISSION:

Robert A. Neimeyer, Editor
Death Studies
University of Memphis
Department of Psychology
Memphis, TN 38152
USA
Phone: 901-678-4680
Fax: 901-678-2147
E-Mail: neimeyer@memphis.edu
Web: http://www.tandf.co.uk/journals
Address May Change:

PUBLICATION GUIDELINES:

Manuscript Length: 21-25
Copies Required: Four
Computer Submission: Yes Email
Format: Prefer MS Word
Fees to Review: 0.00 US$

Manuscript Style:
    American Psychological Association

CIRCULATION DATA:

Reader: Academics
Frequency of Issue: 10 Times/Year
Copies per Issue:
Sponsor/Publisher: Brunner Routledge
    (Taylor & Francis)
Subscribe Price: 169.00 US$ Individual
    447.00 US$ Institution

REVIEW INFORMATION:

Type of Review: Blind Review
No. of External Reviewers: 3
No. of In House Reviewers: 1
Acceptance Rate: 21-30%
Time to Review: 2 - 3 Months
Reviewers Comments: Yes
Invited Articles: 0-5%
Fees to Publish: 0.00 US$

MANUSCRIPT TOPICS:
Death and Dying; Gerontology; Grief; Suicidology

MANUSCRIPT GUIDELINES/COMMENTS:

Aims and Scope. Now published eight times each year, this acclaimed journal provides refereed papers on significant research, scholarship, and practical approaches in the fast growing areas of bereavement and loss, grief therapy, death attitudes, suicide, and death education. It provides an international interdisciplinary forum in which a variety of professionals share results of research and practice, with the aim of better understanding the human encounter with death and assisting those who work with the dying and their families.

Readership. Professionals in a wide variety of settings, including colleges and universities, hospitals, hospices, and counseling centers, who are interested in the major topics in the field of death and dying.

Instructions for Authors
Note to Authors. Please make sure your contact address information is clearly visible on the outside of all packages you are sending to Editors.

358

Submission of Manuscripts

Original and four copies of the manuscript should be submitted to the Editor, Robert A. Neimeyer, Department of Psychology, University of Memphis, Memphis, TN 38152.

In addition to these four paper copies, authors are strongly encouraged to submit manuscripts on disk. The disk should be prepared using MS Word or WordPerfect and should be clearly labeled with the authors' names, file name, and software program. Each manuscript must be accompanied by a statement that it has not been published elsewhere and that it has not been submitted simultaneously for publication elsewhere. Authors are responsible for obtaining permission to reproduce copyrighted material from other sources and are required to sign an agreement for the transfer of copyright to the publisher. All accepted manuscripts, artwork, and photographs become the property of the publisher.

All parts of the manuscript should be typewritten, double-spaced, with margins of at least one inch on all sides. Number manuscript pages consecutively throughout the paper. Authors should also supply a shortened version of the title suitable for the running head, not exceeding 50 character spaces. Each article should be summarized in an abstract of no more that 100 words. Avoid abbreviations, diagrams, and reference to the text.

Manuscripts, including tables, figures, and references, should be prepared in accordance with the *Publication Manual of the American Psychological Association* (Fourth Edition, 1994). Copies of the manual can be obtained from the Publication Department, American Psychological Association, 750 First Street NE, Washington, DC 20002-4242; phone (202) 336-5500.

A Microsoft Word author template file, which also includes more detailed instructions in its **"Read Me"** file, can be downloaded from "Instructions for Authors" web page.

Illustrations. Illustrations submitted (line drawings, halftones, photos, photomicrographs, etc.) should be clean originals or digital files. Digital files are recommended for highest quality reproduction and should follow these guidelines:
- 300 dpi or higher
- sized to fit on journal page
- EPS, TIFF, or PSD format only
- submitted as separate files, not embedded in text files

Tables and Figures. Tables and figures should not be embedded in the text, but should be included as separate sheets or files. A short descriptive title should appear above each table with a clear legend and any footnotes suitably identified below. All units must be included. Figures should be completely labeled, taking into account necessary size reduction. Captions should be typed, double-spaced, on a separate sheet. All original figures should be clearly marked in pencil on the reverse side with the number, author's name, and top edge indicated.

Proofs. One set of page proofs is sent to the designated author. Proofs should be checked and returned within 48 hours.

Dementia and Geriatric Cognitive Disorders

ADDRESS FOR SUBMISSION:

Victoria Chan-Palay, Editor-in-Chief
Dementia and Geriatric Cognitive Disorders
S. Karger AG
Editorial Office
PO Box
CH-4009 Basel,
Switzerland
Phone: +41-61-306-1356
Fax: +41-61-306-1434
E-Mail: e.lawrence@karger.ch
Web: www.karger.com
Address May Change:

PUBLICATION GUIDELINES:

Manuscript Length: 11-15
Copies Required: Three
Computer Submission: No
Format: N/A
Fees to Review: 0.00 US$

Manuscript Style:
    Chicago Manual of Style

CIRCULATION DATA:

Reader: Academics, Practitioners, and
    Libraries
Frequency of Issue: Bi-Monthly
Copies per Issue: Less than 1,000
Sponsor/Publisher: Karger Publishers
Subscribe Price: 211.00 US$ Individual
    1056.00 US$ Institution
    60.00 US$ Indv.& $90 Inst.-Electronic

REVIEW INFORMATION:

Type of Review: Blind Review
No. of External Reviewers: 2
No. of In House Reviewers: 1
Acceptance Rate: No Reply
Time to Review: 1 Month or Less
Reviewers Comments: Yes
Invited Articles: 6-10%
Fees to Publish: 0.00 US$

MANUSCRIPT TOPICS:
Alzheimeis; Dementia; Gerontology

MANUSCRIPT GUIDELINES/COMMENTS:

As a unique forum devoted exclusively to the study of cognitive dysfunction, *Dementia and Geriatric Cognitive Disorders* concentrates on Alzheimer's and Parkinson's disease, Huntington's chorea and other neurodegenerative diseases. The journal draws from diverse related research disciplines such as psychogeriatrics, neuropsychology, clinical neurology, morphology, physiology, genetic molecular biology, pathology, biochemistry, immunology, pharmacology and pharmaceutics. Strong emphasis is placed on the publication of research findings from animal studies which are complemented by clinical and therapeutic experience to give an overall appreciation of the field.

Submission. Only original papers written in English are considered and should be sent to:
    Prof. V. Chan-Palay, S. Karger AG, Editorial Office Dementia and Geriatric Cognitive Disorders, P.O. Box, CH–4009 Basel (Switzerland), Tel. +41 61 306 1437, Fax +41 61 306 1434, E-mail: **e.lawrence@karger.ch**

Mailing address for courier deliveries only:
Allschwilerstr. 10
CH–4055 Basel (Switzerland)

Papers from USA/Canada to be sent to:
S. Karger Publishers, Inc.
Editorial Office Dementia and Geriatric Cognitive Disorders
26 West Avon Road
P.O. Box 529
Farmington, CT 06085 (USA)

Manuscripts, together with a disk, should be submitted in triplicate (with three sets of illustrations of which one is an original), typewritten double-spaced on one side of the paper, with a wide margin. The manuscript should match the file on disk exactly. For details refer to Disk Submission. Editorial work and copy-editing will be executed from the disk version of your manuscript.

Conditions
All manuscripts are subject to editorial review. Manuscripts are received with the explicit understanding that they are not under simultaneous consideration by any other publication. Submission of an article for publication implies the transfer of the copyright from the author to the publisher upon acceptance. Accepted papers become the permanent property of *Dementia and Geriatric Cognitive Disorders* and may not be reproduced by any means, in whole or in part, without the written consent of the publisher. It is the author's responsibility to obtain permission to reproduce illustrations, tables, etc. from other publications. The manuscripts should be accompanied by a statement by the submitting author certifying that all the authors have read the papers and have agreed to be listed as authors. A similar statement should be appended for the names of colleagues who are acknowledged in footnotes as having contributed to or criticized the paper. For papers involving human subjects, adequate documentation should be provided to certify that appropriate ethical safeguards and protocols have been followed. Animal experiments should include a clear description of the method of anesthesia and killing.

Arrangement
All pages should be consecutively beginning numbered with the title page, then the text, acknowledgements, references and legends to figures. Two types of manuscripts will be considered:

1. *Original Research Articles.* An Abstract, Introduction, Materials and Methods, Results, and Discussion sections are required. The literature review should be succinct. There are no restrictions on the number of pages or figures.

2. *Review Articles* in which a specific field is reviewed through an exhaustive literature survey. An Abstract is required. A Materials and Methods section and a Results section are not required. There are no restrictions on the number of pages or figures. Preliminary notes are not desired.

Title page. The first page of each paper should indicate the title, the authors' names, and the institute where the work was conducted. A short title for use as running head as well as the full address of the author to whom correspondence should be sent are also required.

Full address. The exact postal address complete with postal code must be given at the bottom of the title page. Please also supply phone and fax numbers, as well as your e-mail address.

Key words. For indexing purposes, a list of 3-10 key words in English is essential. Try to use key words such as found in the headings of *Index Medicus*.

Abstract. The first page of the text should include an abstract of up to 10 lines.

Small type. Paragraphs which can or must be set in smaller type (case histories, test methods, etc.) should be indicated with a 'p' (petit) in the margin on the left-hand side.

Footnotes. Avoid footnotes. When essential, they are numbered consecutively and typed at the foot of the appropriate page.

Abbreviations. Abbreviations should not be used excessively in the text. Only standard abbreviations should be used. Nonstandard abbreviations of terms that are used frequently in the text should be explained by the term written out completely and followed immediately by the abbreviation in parentheses, for example: 'increase in norepinephrine (NE) content ...'.

Tables and illustrations. Tables and illustrations (both numbered in Arabic numerals) should be prepared on separate sheets. Tables require a heading and figures a legend, also prepared on a separate sheet. For the reproduction of illustrations, only good drawings and original photographs can be accepted; negatives or photocopies cannot be used. Due to technical reasons, figures with a screen background should not be submitted. When possible, group several illustrations on one block for reproduction (max. size 181 x 223 mm) or provide crop marks. On the back of each illustration, indicate its number, the author's name, and 'top' with a soft pencil.

Color Illustrations

Up to 6 color illustrations per page can now be integrated within the text at the reduced price of CHF 660.– / USD 545.00 per page. Color illustrations are reproduced at the author's expense.

References

In the text identify references by Arabic numerals [in square brackets]. Material submitted for publication but not yet accepted should be noted as 'unpublished data' and not be included in the reference list. The list of references should include only those publications which are cited in the text. Do not alphabetize; number references in the order in which they are first mentioned in the text. The surnames of the authors followed by initials should be given. There should be no punctuation other than a comma to separate the authors. Cite all authors, 'et al' is not sufficient. Abbreviate journal names according to the *Index Medicus* system. (Also see

362

International Committee of Medical Journal Editors: Uniform requirements for manuscripts submitted to biomedical journals. N Engl J Med 1997;336:309-315.)

a. *Papers published in periodicals:* Alzheimer A: Über eine eigenartige Erkrankung der Hirnrinde. Neurol Centralbl 1907;18:177–179. Goldgaber D, Lerman MI, McBride OW, Saffiotti U, Gajdusek DC: Characterization and chromosomal localization of a cDNA encoding brain amyloid of Alzheimer's disease. Science 1987;235:877–884.

b. *Monographs:* Matthews DE, Farewell VT: Using and Understanding Medical Statistics, ed 3, revised. Basel, Karger, 1996.

c. *Edited books:* Esiri MM: Typical and atypical viruses in the aetiology of senile dementia of the Alzheimer type; in Ulrich J (ed): Histology and Histopathology of the Aging Brain. Interdiscipl Top Gerontol. Basel, Karger, 1988, vol 25, pp 119-139.

Page Charges

The publisher of *Dementia and Geriatric Cognitive Disorders* would like to extend to authors and contributors of each paper accepted for publication in the journal the opportunity to subscribe annually at the very reduced rate of CHF 150.- / USD 120.00 plus postage. This offer is limited to one year, after that it will be transformed to a personal subscription. This arrangement is intended to increase readership around the world, and to avoid page charges. This charge will be added to the invoice normally sent for other charges, such as reprints, etc. If there is no possibility for cooperation in this form, it will be necessary for the publisher to charge the author(s) CHF 68.- / USD 60.00 per printed page of their paper. The publisher and the Editor-in-Chief of *Dementia and Geriatric Cognitive Disorders* thank you for your understanding and cooperation in this matter and look forward to a continued healthy development of the journal.

Galley Proofs

Unless otherwise indicated, galley proofs are sent to the first-named author and should be returned with the least possible delay. Alterations made in galley proofs, other than the correction of printer's errors, are charged to the author. No page proofs are supplied.

Reprints

Order forms and a price list are sent with the galley proofs. Orders submitted after the issue is printed are subject to considerably higher prices.

Development and Psychopathology

ADDRESS FOR SUBMISSION:

Dante Cicchetti, Editor
Development and Psychopathology
University of Rochester
Director, Mt. Hope Family Center
Department of Psychology
187 Edinburgh Street
Rochester, NY 14608
USA
Phone: 585-275-2991
Fax: 585-454-2972
E-Mail: mhfc@netacc.net
Web:
Address May Change:

PUBLICATION GUIDELINES:

Manuscript Length: 30+
Copies Required: Five
Computer Submission: No
Format: N/A
Fees to Review: 0.00 US$

Manuscript Style:
    American Psychological Association

CIRCULATION DATA:

Reader: Academics
Frequency of Issue: Quarterly
Copies per Issue: 1,001 - 2,000
Sponsor/Publisher: Cambridge University
    Press
Subscribe Price: 85.00 US$ Individual
    207.00 US$ Institution-Electronic only
    220.00 US$ Inst. - Print + Electronic

REVIEW INFORMATION:

Type of Review: Blind Review
No. of External Reviewers: 3+
No. of In House Reviewers: 0
Acceptance Rate: 11-20%
Time to Review: 2 - 3 Months
Reviewers Comments: Yes
Invited Articles: 31-50%
Fees to Publish: 0.00 US$

MANUSCRIPT TOPICS:
Developmental Psychology; Psychiatry; Psychopathology

MANUSCRIPT GUIDELINES/COMMENTS:

This multidisciplinary journal is devoted to the publication of original, empirical, theoretical and review papers which address the interrelationship of normal and pathological development in adults and children. It is intended to serve and integrate the emerging field of developmental psychopathology which strives to understand patterns of adaptation and maladaptation throughout the lifespan. This journal is of interest to psychologists, psychiatrists, social scientists, neuroscientists, pediatricians, and researchers.

Development and Psychopathology strongly encourages contributions from a wide array of disciplines because an effective developmental approach to psychopathology necessitates a broad synthesis of knowledge. Manuscripts will be considered that address, for example, the causes and effects of genetic, ontogenetic, biochemical, cognitive, or socioeconomic factors in developmental processes with relevance to various risk or psychopathological conditions. The journal also seeks articles on the processes underlying the adaptive and maladaptive outcomes in populations at risk for psychopathology.

Manuscript Review Policy

Manuscripts will have a blind review by at least two scholars. Every effort will be made to notify authors within 90 days of submission concerning the reviewers' recommendations and comments. Manuscripts will be promptly published upon acceptance. *Development and Psychopathology* has no page charges.

Manuscript Submission

Four copies of each manuscript should be submitted to:

Dante Cicchetti, PhD, Department of Psychology
Director, Mt. Hope Family Center, University of Rochester
187 Edinburgh Street, Rochester, NY 14608, U.S.A.

Manuscript Preparation and Style

General. All manuscripts must be typed on 8.5 x 11" or A4 white bond paper with ample margins on all sides. The entire manuscript-including abstract, tables, and references-must be double-spaced. Manuscript pages must be numbered consecutively. Language of publication: English.

Style and Manuscript Order. Follow the general style guidelines set forth in the *Publication Manual of the American Psychological Association* (3rd ed.). The Editor may find it necessary to return manuscripts for reworking or retyping that do not conform to requirements. Manuscripts must be arranged in the following order:

Title Page (page 1). To facilitate blind review, all indication of authorship must be limited to this page; other pages must only show the short title plus page number at the top right. On the title page include (a) full article title; (b) name and affiliations of all authors; (c) mailing address and telephone number of the lead author; (d) address of where to send offprints, if different from the lead author; (e) short title of less than 50 characters.

Abstract Page (page 2). Include (a) full article title; (b) abstract of no more than 200 words; (c) up to 5 keywords for indexing and information retrieval.

Acknowledgments (page 2). These should be placed below the abstract. Use this section to indicate grant support, substantial assistance in the preparation of the article, or other author notes.

Text (page 3). Use a 5-character paragraph indent. Do not hyphenate words at the end of lines. Do not justify right margins.

References. Bibliographic citations in the text must include the author's last name and date of publication, and may include page references. Examples of in-text citation styling are: Brown (1983), Ingram (1976, 54-55), Smith and Miller (1966), (Smith & Miller, 1966), (Peterson, Danner, & Flavell, 1972), and subsequently (Peterson et al., 1972). If more than one, citations must be in *alphabetical* order. Every in - text citation must be included in the reference section; every reference must be cited in the text. Examples of reference styling are:

Journal Article
Sroufe, L. A., & Rutter, M. (1984). The domain of developmental psychopathology. *Child Development, 55*, 17-29.

Book
Piaget, J. (1962). Play, dreams, and imitation in childhood. New York: Norton.

Chapter in an Edited Book
Cicchetti, D., & Pogge-Hesse, P. (1982). Possible contributions of the study of organically retarded persons to developmental theory. In E. Zigler & D. Balla (Eds.), *Mental retardation: The developmental difference controversy* (pp. 277-318). Hillsdale, NJ: Erlbaum.

Appendix (optional). Use only if needed. May be useful for review, but not appropriate for publication.

Tables. Tables must appear as a unit following the reference section. Each table should be typed double-spaced on a separate sheet, numbered consecutively with an Arabic numeral, and given a short title. (Example: Table 5. Comparisons on language variables.) All tables must be cited in the text.

Figures. Figures must appear as a unit following the tables. Each figure must be numbered consecutively with an Arabic numeral and a descriptive legend. Legends must be typed together, double-spaced, on a separate sheet preceding the artwork. (Example: Figure 3. Progress in language development.) Figures must be supplied no larger than 8 x 10", be black and white, and be ready for photographic reproduction.

Diagrams must be professionally rendered or computer generated. All labels and details must be clearly printed and large enough to remain legible at a 50% reduction. Artwork should be identified by figure number and short title and be carefully packaged in a protective envelope. All figures must be cited in the text.

Copyediting and Page Proofs
The publisher reserves the right to copyedit manuscripts to conform to journal style. The lead author will receive page proofs for correction of typographical errors only. No rewriting of the original manuscript as submitted is allowed in the proof stage. Authors must return proofs to Cambridge within 48 hours of receipt or approval will be assumed.

Offprints
The lead author will receive 25 free article offprints of his or her article. A form accompanying page proofs allows the lead author to order complete copies of the issue and/or purchase of additional offprints. All coauthor offprint requirements must be included on this form. Orders received after the issue is printed are subject to a 50% reprint surcharge.

366

Copyright and Originality
It is a condition of publication that all manuscripts submitted to this journal have not been published and will not be simultaneously submitted or published elsewhere. Authors of articles published in the journal assign copyright to Cambridge University Press (with certain rights reserved) and you will receive a copyright assignment form for signature on acceptance of your paper. Government authors whose articles were created in the course of their employment must so certify in lieu of copyright transfer. Authors are responsible for obtaining written permission from the copyright owners to reprint any previously published material included in their article.

Developmental Neuropsychology

ADDRESS FOR SUBMISSION:

Dennis L. Molfese, Editor
Developmental Neuropsychology
University of Louisville
Dept. of Psychological & Brain Sciences
315 Life Sciences
Belknap Campus
Louisville, KY 40292
USA
Phone: 502-852-8274
Fax: 502-852-8904
E-Mail: dlmolfese@mac.com
Web: www.erlbaum.com
Address May Change:

PUBLICATION GUIDELINES:

Manuscript Length: 26-30
Copies Required: Four
Computer Submission: No
Format:
Fees to Review: 0.00 US$

Manuscript Style:
      American Psychological Association

CIRCULATION DATA:

Reader: Academics
Frequency of Issue: Bi-Monthly
Copies per Issue: Less than 1,000
Sponsor/Publisher: Lawrence Erlbaum
   Associates, Inc.
Subscribe Price:
   See Website

REVIEW INFORMATION:

Type of Review: Blind Review
No. of External Reviewers: 3
No. of In House Reviewers: 1
Acceptance Rate: 11-20%
Time to Review: 4 - 6 Months
Reviewers Comments: Yes
Invited Articles: 0-5%
Fees to Publish: 0.00 US$

MANUSCRIPT TOPICS:
Abnormal Psychology; Adolescent Psychology; Adulthood; Alcoholism & Drug Addiction;
Behavior Modification; Child Psychology; Developmental Psychology; Educational
Psychology; Exceptional Child; Experimental Psychology; Gerontology; Learning &
Conditioning; Neuropsychology; Personality; Physiological Psychology; Psychiatry;
Psychobiology; Psychological Testing; Psychopathology; Research Methods & Statistics;
Sensation & Perception; Social Psychology; Thinking & Cognition

MANUSCRIPT GUIDELINES/COMMENTS:

Content
Developmental Neuropsychology is devoted to exploring the relationships which exist
between brain and behavior across the life span. The journal will publish scholarly papers on
the appearance and development of behavioral functions such as language, perception, and
cognitive processes as they relate to brain functions and structures. Some examples of subjects
that would be appropriate for publications are studies of early cognitive behaviors in normal
and brain-damaged children, plasticity and recovery of function after early brain damage, the

development of complex cognitive and motor skills, and specific and nonspecific disturbances such as learning disabilities, mental retardation, schizophrenia, stuttering, developmental aphasia, and so forth. Appropriate gerontologic topics include neuropsychological analyses of normal age-related changes in brain and behavioral functions (e.g., in sensory, motor, cognitive, and adaptive abilities, studies of age-related diseases of the nervous system, and recovery of function in later life).

Empirical studies, research reviews, critical commentary, and book reviews will be published. By publishing both basic and clinical studies of the developing and the aging brain, the editors hope to encourage scholarly work that advances the understanding of the field of developmental neuropsychology.

Submissions
Contributors should submit four copies of manuscripts for review to Dennis L. Molfese, Editor, Developmental Neuropsychology, Department of Psychological and Brain Sciences, University, of Louisville, Life Sciences 315, Belknap Campus, Louisville, Kentucky 40292. Manuscripts should be highly legible copies and will not be routinely returned to authors.

Blind Review
To facilitate anonymous review, only the article title should appear on the first page of the manuscript. An attached cover page must contain the title, authorship, and an introductory footnote with professional titles, mailing addresses, and telephone number of the authors and any statements of credit or research support. Every effort should be made by the authors to see that the manuscript itself contains no clues to their identities.

Form
In order to accommodate the various forms of developmental neuropsychology that mark pertinent research in the areas described, articles of varied length will be published. Manuscripts should be prepared according to the guidelines established in the *Publication Manual of the American Psychological Association* (5th ed.). (Copies may be obtained from APA, 750 First Street, NE, Washington, DC 20002-4242.) Supply camera-ready originals or glossies of all figures.

Permissions
It is assumed that manuscripts submitted for review have not been published and are not presently under review for publication elsewhere. Contributors are responsible for obtaining permission from copyright owners if they use an illustration, table, or lengthy quote (100+ words) that has been published elsewhere. Contributors should write to both the publisher and the author of such material, requesting permission for its use.

Deviant Behavior

ADDRESS FOR SUBMISSION:

Craig J. Forsyth, Editor-in-Chief
Deviant Behavior
University of Louisiana at Lafayette
Department of Sociology & Anthropology
P O Box 40198
Lafayette, LA 70504-0198
USA
Phone: 337-482-5372
Fax: 337-482-5694
E-Mail: cjf5714@louisiana.edu
Web: http://www.tandf.co.uk/journals
Address May Change:

PUBLICATION GUIDELINES:

Manuscript Length: 1-25
Copies Required: Five
Computer Submission: No
Format: MS Word or WordPerfect
Fees to Review: 0.00 US$

Manuscript Style:
, American Sociological Association

CIRCULATION DATA:

Reader: Academics
Frequency of Issue: 6 Times/Year
Copies per Issue:
Sponsor/Publisher: Taylor & Francis
Subscribe Price: 147.00 US$ Individual
375.00 US$ Institution

REVIEW INFORMATION:

Type of Review: Blind Review
No. of External Reviewers: 3
No. of In House Reviewers: 1
Acceptance Rate: 11-20%
Time to Review: 2 - 3 Months
Reviewers Comments: Yes
Invited Articles: 0-5%
Fees to Publish: 0.00 US$

MANUSCRIPT TOPICS:
Abnormal Psychology; Alcoholism & Drug Addiction; Criminology; Deviant Behavior

MANUSCRIPT GUIDELINES/COMMENTS:

Aims and Scope
Deviant Behavior is the only journal that specifically and exclusively addresses social deviance. International and interdisciplinary in scope, it publishes refereed theoretical, descriptive, methodological, and applied papers. All aspects of deviant behavior are discussed, including crime, juvenile delinquency, alcohol abuse and narcotic addiction, sexual deviance, societal reaction to handicap and disfigurement, mental illness, and socially inappropriate behavior.

In addition, *Deviant Behavior* frequently includes articles that address contemporary theoretical and conceptual controversies, allowing the specialist in deviance to stay informed of ongoing debates.

The journal also publishes overview articles on particular aspects of deviance, updating the reader on research and theoretical developments.

Readership. Sociologists, criminologists, anthropologists, criminal justice professionals, social workers, counselors, therapists, and correctional and law enforcement administrators.

Instructions For Authors

Note to Authors. Please make sure your contact address information is clearly visible on the outside of all packages you are sending to Editors

Submission of Manuscripts

An original and four copies of the manuscript should be submitted to the Editor-in-Chief, Craig J. Forsyth, PhD, Department of Sociology and Anthropology, University of Louisiana, Lafayette, Louisiana 70504-0198. Authors are strongly encouraged to submit manuscripts on disk. The disk should be prepared using MS Word or WordPerfect and should be clearly labeled with the authors' names, file name, and software program. Each manuscript must be accompanied by a statement that it has not been published elsewhere and that it has not been submitted simultaneously for publication elsewhere. Authors are responsible for obtaining permission to reproduce copyrighted material from other sources and are required to sign an agreement for the transfer of copyright to the publisher. All accepted manuscripts, artwork, and photographs become the property of the publisher.

A Microsoft Word author template file, which also includes more detailed instructions in its "Read Me" file, can be downloaded from the "Instructions for Authors" web page.

All papers undergo a blind review. Authors shall be notified. All manuscripts submitted to *Deviant Behavior* from those serving as Board Members or Associate Editors of the journal undergo the same blind review process as do those submitted by other individuals. In addition, any manuscript submitted for review authored or co-authored by the Editor-in-Chief is handled by an independent Special Editor who coordinates a blind review process and makes the final decision as to the suitability of the manuscript(s) for publication in *Deviant Behavior*.

All parts of the manuscript should be typewritten, double-spaced, with margins of at least one inch on all sides. Number manuscript pages consecutively throughout the paper. Authors should also supply a shortened version of the title suitable for the running head, not exceeding 50 character spaces. Each article should be summarized in an abstract of no more than 100 words. Avoid abbreviations, diagrams, and reference to the text.

References

Should be listed at the end of the paper and refer only to material cited in the manuscript. They should be listed in alphabetical order and follow the current American Sociological Review style. In the text, reference citations should include author and year of publication (Brown 1978). Identify subsequent citations of the same source in the same way as the first, not using ibid., op. cit., or loc. cit. Give both last names for dual authors; for more than two, use "et al." in the text. When two authors have the same last name, use identifying initials in the text. For institutional authorship, supply minimum identification from the beginning of the complete citation (U.S. Bureau of the Census 1963, p. 117).

In the reference section, list all source citations by author, and within author by year of publication. The reference list must be complete and include all references in the text. The use of "et al" is not acceptable in the reference list; provide the names of all authors. If there is more than one reference to the same author and year, distinguish them by the letters "a," "b," etc. added to the year (Levy 1963a). Give the publisher's name in as brief a form as is fully intelligible. If the cited material is unpublished, use "forthcoming" with the name of journal or publisher; otherwise use "unpublished."

Books
Jud, Gerald J., Edgar W. Mills, Jr., and Genevieve Walters Burch. 1970. Ex-Pastors. Philadelphia: Pilgrim Press.

Periodicals
Conger, Rand. Forthcoming. "The Effects of Positive Feedback on Direction and Amount of Verbalization in a Social Setting." Pacific Sociological Review.

Collections
Davie, M. 1938. "The Pattern of Urban Growth." Pp. 133 161 in Studies in the Science of Society, edited by G. Murdock. New Haven: Yale University Press.

Illustrations
Illustrations submitted (line drawings, halftones, photos, photomicrographs, etc.) should be clean originals or digital files. Digital files are recommended for highest quality reproduction and should follow these guidelines:
- 300 dpi or higher
- sized to fit on journal page
- EPS, TIFF, or PSD format only
- submitted as separate files, not embedded in text files

Tables and Figures
Tables and figures should not be embedded in the text, but should be included as separate sheets or files. A short descriptive title should appear above each table with a clear legend and any footnotes suitably identified below. All units must be included. Figures should be completely labeled, taking into account necessary size reduction. Captions should be typed, double-spaced, on a separate sheet. All original figures should be clearly marked in pencil on the reverse side with the number, author's name, and top edge indicated.

Discourse Processes

ADDRESS FOR SUBMISSION:

Michael Schober, Editor
Discourse Processes
New School for Social Research
Department of Psychology, F 330
 ELECTRONIC SUBMISSIONS ONLY
65 Fifth Avenue
New York, NY 10003
USA
Phone: 212-220-5787
Fax: 121-989-0846
E-Mail: schober@newschool.edu
Web: See Guidelines
Address May Change:

PUBLICATION GUIDELINES:

Manuscript Length: 26-35
Copies Required: Electronic
Computer Submission: Yes
Format: N/A
Fees to Review: 0.00 US$

Manuscript Style:
       American Psychological Association

CIRCULATION DATA:

Reader: Academics
Frequency of Issue: 6 Times/Year
Copies per Issue: 1,001 - 2,000
Sponsor/Publisher: The Society for Text
    and Discourse
Subscribe Price: 100.00 US$ Individual
    405.00 US$ Institution Print Only
    See Website - More Details

REVIEW INFORMATION:

Type of Review: Editorial Review
No. of External Reviewers: 3
No. of In House Reviewers: 0
Acceptance Rate: 21-30%
Time to Review: 2 - 3 Months
Reviewers Comments: Yes
Invited Articles: 11-20%
Fees to Publish: 0.00 US$

MANUSCRIPT TOPICS:
Conversation; Discourse; Psycholinguistics; Reading; Sociolinguistics; Writing

MANUSCRIPT GUIDELINES/COMMENTS:

Discourse Processes is the official journal of The Society for Text and Discourse.

Discourse Processes is a multidisciplinary journal providing a forum for cross-fertilization of ideas from diverse disciplines sharing a common interest in discourse--prose comprehension and recall, dialogue analysis, text grammar construction, computer simulation of natural language, cross-cultural comparisons of communicative competence, or related topics. The problems posed by multi-sentence contexts and the methods required to investigate them, although not always unique to discourse, are sufficiently distinct so as to require an organized mode of scientific interaction made possible through the journal.

The journal accepts original experimental or theoretical papers that substantially advance understanding of the structure and function of discourse. Scholars working in the discourse area from the perspective of sociolinguistics, psycholinguistics, discourse psychology, text linguistics, ethno methodology and sociology of language, education, philosophy of language, computer science, and related sub-areas are invited to contribute. Newer methods and technologies for studying discourse processes in their full complexity can require new ways of presenting data and analyses.

Starting with Volume 39, the electronic version of Discourse Processes will allow access to multimedia (video and/or audio) content when it appropriately augments the presentation of a particular piece.

Submission
Submitted papers in most cases should not exceed 35 double-spaced pages, including figures and tables. Brief reports and, in rare instances, articles of monographic length will also be considered.

Submit five copies of the manuscript to the electronic submission system.

Manuscript Preparation
Manuscripts should be prepared according to the guidelines of the *Publication Manual of the American Psychological Association* (4th ed.). Double space all material, including title page, abstract, text, quotations, acknowledgments, references, appendixes, tables, figure captions, and footnotes. The title page should include the title of the manuscript; name and affiliations of all authors; name, address, phone and fax numbers, and e-mail address of the corresponding author; and a running head of no more than 48 letters and spaces. The second page should include the manuscript title and an abstract of 100 to 150 words. All figures must be camera ready. Authors should keep a copy of their manuscript to guard against loss.

Peer Review
To facilitate a prompt review of their articles, authors should submit a list of five possible reviewers, at least three of whom should be on the *Discourse Processes* Editorial Board. The address, email address and telephone number should be included for recommended reviewers who are not on the editorial board.

Permissions
Authors are responsible for all statements made in their work and for obtaining permission from copyright owners to use a lengthy quotation (500 words or more) or to reprint or adapt a table or figure published elsewhere. Authors should write to original author(s) and publisher of such material to request nonexclusive world rights in all languages for use in the article and in future editions. Provide copies of all permissions and credit lines obtained.

Production Notes
Accepted manuscripts are copyedited, the authors review copyediting, and the manuscripts are typeset into page proofs. Authors are asked to read proofs for typesetter's errors and other defects. Correction of typographical errors is made without charge; other alterations are to be prepaid by authors. Authors may order reprints of their articles only when they return page proofs.

Drug and Alcohol Dependence

ADDRESS FOR SUBMISSION:

Robert L. Balster, Editor-in-Chief
Drug and Alcohol Dependence
Virginia Commonwealth University
Medical College of Virginia
Room 760 Blackwell Smith Bldg.
410 N 12th St., PO Box 980310
Richmond, VA 23298-0310
USA
Phone: 804-828-8402
Fax: 804-827-0304
E-Mail: balster@hsc.vcu.edu
Web: www.ees.elsevier.com/dad
Address May Change:

PUBLICATION GUIDELINES:

Manuscript Length: 21-30
Copies Required: Electronic
Computer Submission: Yes
Format: N/A
Fees to Review: 0.00 US$

Manuscript Style:
See Manuscript Guidelines

CIRCULATION DATA:

Reader: Academics
Frequency of Issue: Monthly
Copies per Issue: No Reply
Sponsor/Publisher: College on Problems of
   Drug Dependence / Elsevier Science
   Publishing Co.
Subscribe Price: 208.00 US$ Individual
   See Website - More Details

REVIEW INFORMATION:

Type of Review: Editorial Review
No. of External Reviewers: 2-3
No. of In House Reviewers: 1
Acceptance Rate: 45%
Time to Review: 1 - 2 Months
Reviewers Comments: Yes
Invited Articles: 0-5%
Fees to Publish: 0.00 US$

MANUSCRIPT TOPICS:
Abnormal Psychology; Adolescent Psychology; Adulthood; Alcoholism & Drug Addiction; Behavior Modification; Developmental Psychology; Experimental Psychology; Family Counseling & Therapy; Gerontology; Learning & Conditioning; Neuropsychology; Personality; Physiological Psychology; Psychiatry; Psychobiology; Psychological Testing; Psychopathology; Research Methods & Statistics; Social Psychology; Thinking & Cognition

MANUSCRIPT GUIDELINES/COMMENTS:

Aims and Scope
Drug and Alcohol Dependence is an international journal devoted to publishing original research, scholarly reviews, commentaries, and policy analyses in the area of drug, alcohol and tobacco use and dependence. It is sponsored by the College on Problems of Drug Dependence (CPDD), the oldest scientific organization in the United States concerned with research on addiction. The goal of its editors is to promote mutual understanding of the many facets of drug abuse to the benefit of all investigators involved in drug and alcohol research, and to facilitate the transfer of scientific findings to successful treatment and prevention

practices. *Drug and Alcohol Dependence* is currently being distributed to all the members of CPDD.

Submission of Manuscripts

Drug and Alcohol Dependence now proceeds totally online via an electronic submission system. Mail submissions will not be accepted after November 1, 2004. By accessing the website, **www.ees.elsevier.com/dad** you will be guided stepwise through the creation and uploading of the various files. When submitting a manuscript to the Elsevier Editorial System (EES), authors need to provide an electronic version of their manuscript and any accompanying figures and tables. The author should select from a list of scientific classifications, which will be used to help the editors select reviewers with appropriate expertise, and an article type for their manuscript (full length report, review article, or short communication). Once the uploading is done, the system automatically generates an electronic (PDF) proof, which is then used for reviewing. All correspondence, including the Editor's decision and request for revisions, will be processed through the system and will reach the corresponding author by e-mail.

The submitting author will be required to state that *all authors* have been provided a copy of this submission and that they all affirm that it is not currently under review elsewhere and that all applicable subject protection guidelines and regulations were followed in the conduct of the research (see below). Page charges will not be requested.

Once a manuscript has successfully been submitted via the online submission system authors may track the status of their manuscript using the system (details will be provided by e-mail). If your manuscript is accepted by the journal, subsequent tracking facilities are available on Elsevier's Author Gateway, using the unique reference number provided by Elsevier and corresponding author name (details will be provided by e-mail). See Tracking Accepted Manuscript section.

Authors may send queries concerning the submission process, manuscript status, or journal procedures to the Editorial Offices at **dad@vcu.edu** (for North, South and Central American authors) or **dad@iop.kcl.ac.uk** (all other authors). For further details on how to submit online, please refer to the EES Tutorial for authors, available on www.ees.elsevier.com/dad/ or contact Elsevier's Author Support Department via the Author Gateway:
www.authors.elsevier.com/journal/drugalcdep

Preparation of Manuscripts

Manuscripts should be written in English.

Types of Papers

Full-length Reports reporting original results of research within the field of drug, alcohol and tobacco use and dependence.

Review Articles of specialized topics within the scope of the journal. Authors who plan to submit reviews to the journal are advised to contact one of the editors to discuss the suitability of the proposed topic.

Short Communications reporting on research that has progressed to the stage where a preliminary publication is appropriate. The maximum length allowed will be 1500 words plus references and illustrations. There should be not more than 2 illustrations (figure or tables).

Manuscript Submission Requirements
The online manuscript submission system will guide you when and how to submit the following required items:

- **Addresses for all of the authors** as they should appear in the publication and full contact details for the corresponding author (address, phone, FAX and E-mail)
- An **abstract** with a 200-word summary. Abstracts can be either unstructured or structured with specific sections describing the background, methods, results and conclusions.
- 3-6 **key words** for indexing.
- **The body of research reports** will generally include introduction, methods, results and discussion sections. Further subheadings are acceptable. Review papers should also use section headings and subheadings. Sections should be numbered using the 1., 1.1, 1.1.1, 2., 2.1 etc. system. Extensive use of footnoting is not encouraged.
- **Acknowledgments** must declare all sources of financial support (direct or indirect) for any part of the work presented. If there was no support from external sponsors, authors must state that the research was supported by internal funds only.
- **Figures** of good quality should be submitted online as a separate file. The lettering should be large enough to permit photographic reduction. The legends should be typed on a page separate from the figure. If there are multiple figures, the legends should be compiled together on one page (or more if necessary). Please refer to the generic Elsevier artwork instructions for more information:
  http://authors.elsevier.com/issn/artwork/03768716.
- **Tables** are to be uploaded, numbered consecutively (Table 1, Table 2, etc.) and to have a caption consistent with others in this journal.
- **Tables and figures** should be so constructed that they, together with their captions and legends, will be intelligible with minimal reference to the text
- **References** should be assembled beginning on a separate sheet. In the text they should be referred to by name and year (Harvard System). When referring to a work by more than two authors, the name of the first author should be given followed by et al. Examples of the correct format for citation within the text are (Jessor and Jessor, 1977) and (Chutuape et al., 2001). Personal communications and papers submitted for publication should be so indicated and appear with the source or author's name(s) in the text in parentheses. References should be listed alphabetically by first author and must consist of names and initials of all authors, year, title of paper, abbreviated title of journal, volume number and first and last page numbers of the paper. Abbreviations of journal titles should conform to those used by Index Medicus (http://www.nlm.nih.gov/tsd/serials/lji.html). References to journals, books and multi-author books should be in accord with the following examples:

Chutuape, M.A., Katz, E.C., Stitzer, M.L., 2001. Methods for enhancing transition of substance dependent patients from inpatient to outpatient treatment. Drug Alcohol Depend. 61, 137-143.

Jessor, R., Jessor, S.L., 1977. Problem Behaviour and Psychosocial Development: A Longitudinal Study of Youth. Academic Press, New York.

Smith, S.G., Davis, W.M., 1975. A method for chronic intravenous drug administration in the rat. In: Ehrenpreis, S., Neidle, A. (Eds.), Methods in Narcotics Research. Marcel Dekker, New York, pp. 3-21.

To cite material on the internet, the authors (if known), title of the page and the URL should be provided along with an <accessed on [date]> to indicate a date on which the cited material was present.

Supplementary Material

Elsevier now also accepts electronic supplementary material to support and enhance your scientific research. Supplementary files offer the author additional possibilities to publish additional text or data, , movies, animation sequences, high-resolution images, background datasets, sound clips and more. Supplementary files supplied will be published online alongside the electronic version of your article in Elsevier web products, including ScienceDirect: http://www.sciencedirect.com.

The article in the journal must be complete and fully comprehensible without reference to the Supplementary Material. The purpose of Supplementary Material is to provide additional and usually more detailed information for readers who are particularly interested in the study. Supplementary Material is not an integral part of a published paper; the suitability of the Supplementary Material is assessed by the editor but it is not subject to the peer review procedure as applied to articles in the journal. Supplementary Material may either accompany the first version of a manuscript submitted to the journal or in response to a request from an editor.

In order to ensure that your submitted material is directly usable, please ensure that data are provided in one of our recommended file formats. Authors should submit the material in electronic format together with the article and supply a concise and descriptive caption for each file. For further details on how to prepare these materials, please consult the Multi Media file on our Artwork Instructions homepage http://authors.elsevier.com/issn/artwork/03768716

Colour Reproduction

Drug and Alcohol Dependence is now also included in a new initiative from Elsevier: 'Colourful e-Products'. Through this initiative, figures that appear in black & white in print can appear in colour, online, in ScienceDirect at http://www.sciencedirect.com. There is no extra charge for authors who participate.

For colour reproduction in print, you will receive information regarding the costs from Elsevier after receipt of your accepted article. Please indicate your preference for colour in print or on the Web only. Because of technical complications which can arise by converting colour figures to "grey scale" (for the printed version should you not opt for colour in print) please submit in addition usable black and white versions of all the colour illustrations. For further information on the preparation of electronic artwork, please see:
    http://authors.elsevier.com/issn/artwork/03768716

378

Ethics of Experimentation
The journal and CPDD are committed to the protection of animal and human research subjects and ethical practices in science publishing. Studies submitted to *Drug and Alcohol Dependence* must have been conducted in accordance with the Declaration of Helsinki and/or with the Guide for the Care and Use of Laboratory Subjects as adopted and promulgated by the US National Institutes of Health and/or according to requirements of all applicable local and international standards. Studies that entail pain or distress will be assessed in terms of the balance between the distress inflicted and the likelihood of benefit, and must be of such a nature that their objectives could not have been achieved by using less stressful procedures. All authors must conform to the highest standards of ethical conduct in the submission of accurate data, acknowledging the work of others, and divulging potential conflicts of interests. Policies on the handling of evidence for scientific misconduct can be obtained from the editors.

Copyright Transfer
Upon acceptance of an article, you will be asked to transfer copyright (for more information on copyright see www.authors.elsevier.com/journal/drugalcdep). This transfer will ensure the widest possible dissemination of information. If excerpts from other copyrighted works are included in the submission, the author(s) must obtain written permission from the copyright owners and credit the source(s) in the article. Elsevier has preprinted forms for use by authors in these cases: contact Elsevier's Rights Department, Philadelphia, PA, USA: phone (+1) 215 238 7869, fax (+1) 215 238 2239, e-mail healthpermissions@elsevier.com.

Requests for materials from other Elsevier publications may also be completed on-line via the Elsevier homepage http://www.elsevier.com/locate/permissions.

Proofs and Page Charge
One set of proofs will be sent to the corresponding author. A form with queries from the copyeditor may accompany your proofs. Please answer all queries and make any corrections within 2 days of receipt. No alteration of the substance of the text, tables or figures will be allowed at this stage. Should there be no corrections, please confirm this.

Elsevier will do everything possible to get your article corrected and published as quickly and accurate as possible. In order to do this we need your help. When you receive the (PDF) proof of your article for correction it is important to ensure that all of your corrections are sent back to us in one communication. Subsequent corrections will not be possible, so please ensure your first sending is complete.

Tracking Accepted Manuscripts
After acceptance of your article by the journal, and following receipt of the files at Elsevier, authors can keep track of the progress of their accepted article, and set up e-mail alerts informing them of changes in their manuscript's status using the 'Track Your Paper' feature of Elsevier's Author Gateway (www.authors.elsevier.com/journal/drugalcdep). You will receive a unique reference code together with the acknowledgment e-mail from Elsevier sent upon receipt of your manuscript files in the Elsevier production system.

Authors in Japan Please Note
Upon request, Elsevier will provide authors with a list of people who can check and improve the English of their paper (before submission). Please contact our Tokyo office: Elsevier Japan, 4F Higashi-Azabu, 1-Chome Bldg, 1-9-15 Higashi-Azabu, Minato-ku, Tokyo 106-0044, Japan, Phone: (03)-5561-5032; Fax: (03)-5561-5045; e-mail: **jp.info@elsevier.com**

Reprints
A total of 25 reprints will be provided to the author(s) free of charge. Additional reprints can be ordered at prices shown on the reprint order form which will be sent to the corresponding author.

Drug and Alcohol Review

ADDRESS FOR SUBMISSION:

John B. Saunders, Editor
Drug and Alcohol Review
PO Box 88
St. Pauls, NSW 2031
Australia
Phone: +61 2 9385 0252
Fax: +61 2 9385 0222
E-Mail: apsad@unsw.edu.au
Web: http://www.tandf.co.uk/journals
Address May Change:

PUBLICATION GUIDELINES:

Manuscript Length: 11-15
Copies Required: Three
Computer Submission: Yes Email
Format: Word, English, Vancouver Rfrenc.
Fees to Review: 0.00 US$

Manuscript Style:
    See Manuscript Guidelines

CIRCULATION DATA:

Reader: Academics, Practitioners
Frequency of Issue: Bi-Monthly
Copies per Issue:
Sponsor/Publisher: APSAD / Taylor &
    Francis Group
Subscribe Price: 398.00 US$ Individual
    1406.00 US$ Institiution
    248.00 Pounds Indv. & 853 Pounds Inst.

REVIEW INFORMATION:

Type of Review: Peer Review
No. of External Reviewers: 3
No. of In House Reviewers: 1
Acceptance Rate: 70%
Time to Review: 4 - 6 Months
Reviewers Comments: Yes
Invited Articles: 6-10%
Fees to Publish: 0.00 US$

MANUSCRIPT TOPICS:
Alcoholism & Drug Addiction

MANUSCRIPT GUIDELINES/COMMENTS:

Drug and Alcohol Review is an international meeting ground for the views, expertise and experience of all those involved in the study of treatment of alcohol, tobacco and drug problems.

Contributors to the Journal examine and report on alcohol and drug abuse from a wide range of clinical, biomedical, psychological and sociological standpoints. *Drug and Alcohol Review* particularly encourages the submission of papers which have a harm reducation perspective. However, all philosophies will find a place in the Journal: the principal criterion for publication of papers is their quality.

Drug and Alcohol Review is published on behalf of the Australian Professional Society on Alcohol and Other Drugs (APSAD). Members of the Society receive the Journal as part of their annual subscription. Please contact the Society for details **www.apsad.org.au**.

Instructions For Authors

Instructions for authors can be viewed at http://www.tandf.co.uk/journals/authors/cdarauth.pdf

Note to Authors. Please make sure your contact address information is clearly visible on the outside of all packages you are sending to Editors.

All material submitted for publication is received on the understanding that it has not been published in whole or in part elsewhere and is not under consideration by any other journal. If any part of the material has been or is being published elsewhere the authors are obliged to state this in an accompanying letter and where necessary to provide permission from the copyright holder for reproduction of the material.

It is the usual practice of the *Drug & Alcohol Review* to refer papers for assessment by expert referees. All material is accepted on the understanding that it may be subject to editorial revision.

Manuscripts should be submitted to: Ms Jennifer McIntyre, Editorial Officer, Drug and Alcohol Review, PO Box 88, St Pauls NSW 2031, Australia, Tel: +61 2 9385 0252; Fax: +61 2 9385 0222. Enquiries can also be made by e-mail: **apsad@unsw.edu.au**

Papers are published in four sections:
(i) **Original Papers**, which are reports of new research findings that make a significant contribution to knowledge;
(ii) **Reviews and Commentaries**, which may be critical reviews of the literature or analyses of the philosophy, organisation and development of clinical, education or preventive strategies;
(iii) **Brief Communications**, which describe the preliminary findings of research in progress or a case report of particular interest; and
(iv) **Proceedings of Conferences**. These are published by prior arrangement with the editor and are not subject to the normal peer review process of the *Review*.

Original papers and reviews should not normally exceed 2500 words and brief communications should not exceed 1000 words.

Editorial articles are usually commissioned but unsolicited material may be considered. Authors should communicate with the editor in advance of submitting such material. **Letters to the editor** and **book reviews** are also welcomed.

Early Electronic Offprints

Corresponding authors can now receive their article by e-mail as a complete PDF. This allows the author to print up to 50 copies, free of charge, and disseminate them to colleagues. In many cases this facility will be available up to two weeks prior to publication. Or, alternatively, corresponding authors will receive the traditional 50 offprints. A copy of the journal will be sent by post to all corresponding authors after publication. Additional copies of the journal can be purchased at the author's preferential rate of £15.00/$25.00 per copy.

Electronic Submissions. Authors should submit their articles in both hard copy paper and electronic disk forms. It is essential that the hard copy (paper) version *exactly* matches the material on disk. Please print out one hard copy from the disk you are sending. Once accepted for publication, one printed copies of the final version of the article should be submitted together with the disk to the journal's editorial office. Save all files on a standard 3.5 inch high-density disk. We prefer to receive disks in Microsoft Word in a PC format, but can translate from most other common word processing programs as well as Macs. Please specify which program you have used. Do not save your files as "text only" or "read only".

Format for Submissions
One copy of each manuscript should be submitted and authors should retain at least one copy for reference. Manuscripts should be typed double-spaced on one side only of plain 297 x 210 mm (A4) paper with 3 cm margins on all sides. They should be prepared in accordance with the "Uniform requirements for manuscripts submitted to biomedical journals" (Vancouver Convention).The pages should be numbered and each part of the manuscript should begin on a new page in the following sequence: title page, abstract; text; acknowledgements; list of references; tables; legends to figures. Figures and other illustrations should be contained in an envelope attached to the manuscript.

The title page should carry:
- the title of the article, which should be concise but informative;
- initial or first name and middle initial, surname and qualification of the authors;
- the posts of each author at the time the work was done;
- name of department(s) and institution(s) where the work was undertaken;
- disclaimers, if any;
- name and address of author responsible for correspondence and handling requests for reprints.
- the title page should also carry key words.

Abstracts
From the January 2005 issue the *Drug and Alcohol Review* will require that abstracts of papers received for publication will be in a structured format. The *Review* recognises that different formats will be appropriate for the variety of papers the journal receives. Below is the approved format for:
(1) Research papers
(2) Review papers

Prospective authors may consult the Executive Editor or Editorial Officer if they are unsure of which format they should adopt or if the paper does not clearly fall into either of the above categories.

Research papers
Introduction and aims
Design and methods
Results
Discussion and conclusions

For papers reporting quantitative findings (e.g. from clinical or epidemiological studies), authors should include in the Design and methods section a statement about the setting, the participants and the measures employed. Reports of controlled trials should describe the intervention(s). Qualitative studies should include a statement about the setting, participants and the interview or observation techniques adopted.

Reviews
Issue
Approach
Key findings
Implications and conclusions

Papers on **policy development and evaluation** are welcome. Authors should adopt whichever of the above formats is most suitable for their purpose.

Text
The text of original papers should conform to the conventional structure for biomedical communications - introduction, methods (or patients and methods), results and discussion. The format of reviews and commentaries is likely to differ from this and authors should consult previous issues of the *Drug & Alcohol Review* for guidance.

Brief communications should in general conform to the format of original papers except that certain sections of the text may be combined if appropriate.

It is important to justify statements concerning results by describing the statistical methods employed and the results of the tests of statistical significance.

Drugs should be given their approved, not proprietary, names and the source of any new or experimental preparation should be given. Scientific measurements should be given in SI units with traditional units in parenthesis; exceptions are blood pressure which should be expressed in mm Hg and haemoglobin concentrations (g/dl). An explanation of all abbreviations should be given on the first occasion of their use, with the exception of abbreviations of certain standard units of measurement and statistical measures of variation such as SD and SEM which may be used without explanation.

Acknowledgement
The source(s) of support in the form of grants, equipment or drugs may be stated in the acknowledgement section. Acknowledgement should be made only of those persons who have made substantive contributions to the study.

References
References should be numbered consecutively in the order in which they are first mentioned in the text. References in the text, tables and legends to figures should be identified by Arabic numerals. References should be listed in numerical order at the end of the paper beginning on a new page. The Vancouver System of referencing should be used. For journal articles the names and then initials of all authors (up to six) should be given; commas should follow the

last initials of each author but internal stops should be omitted. When there are seven or more authors list only the first three and then add **et al**. Following this should come the full title of the article, then the title of the journal abbreviated according to the style used in Index Medicus, the year of publication, volume number and first and last page number in that order.

Examples of the Vancouver system are as follows:

Rose G. International trends in cardiovascular disease: implications for prevention and treatment. Aust NZJ Med 1984;14:375-80.

Henderson S, Byrne DG, Duncan-Jones P. Neurosis and the social environment. Sydney: Academic Press, 1981.

Weinstein L, Swartz MN. Pathogenic properties of invading microorganisms. In: Sodeman WA Jr, Sodeman WA, eds. Pathologic physiology: mechanisms of disease. Philadelphia, PA: WB Saunders, 1974:457-72.

For details of the appropriate way of citing other publications authors should refer to the examples reproduced in the British Medical Journal 1982, 12 June;284:1766-1779; the Medical Journal of Australia 1982;2:590-6; and Australian Alcohol/Drug Review 1985;4:5-13. Authors should try to avoid using abstracts as references. References to "unpublished observations" and "personal communication" should be made in the text of the article as such, and should not be numbered or included in the list of references. Manuscripts accepted but not yet published may be referenced as usual, in the list of references, the journal should be named and the phrase "in press" should follow.

Tables
Each table should be typed doubled-spaced on a separate sheet. Tables should be numbered consecutively and a brief title of each should be provided. Explanatory matter should be placed in footnotes. If data are used from another published or unpublished paper the original source should be cited.

Figures and Illustrations
Figures and other illustrations must be good quality, unmounted glossy prints or original line artwork usually 127x173 mm (5" by 7"), but no larger than 203x254 mm (8" by 10"). They should be cited in the text in consecutive order. Two copies of each should be provided with the manuscript. Letters, numbers and symbols should be clear and even throughout and of sufficient size that, when reduced for publication each item will still be legible. Titles and detailed explanations of each figure/illustration should be listed in numerical sequence beginning on a separate page under the heading "Legends to Figures". Each figure/illustration should have a label affixed to its back indicating the number of the figure, the names of the authors and the top of the figure. Authors should not write on the back of the figures, nor alter, annotate or bend them. If a figure/illustration has been published the original source should be acknowledged and written permission from the author and the copyright holder to reproduce the figure should accompany the manuscript.

Early Childhood Research Quarterly

ADDRESS FOR SUBMISSION:

Karen Diamond, Editor
Early Childhood Research Quarterly
Purdue University
Child Development and Family Studies
101 Gates Rd.
West Lafayette, IN 47907-2020
USA
Phone: 765-494-0942
Fax: 765-496-1144
E-Mail: kdiamond@purdue.edu
Web: www.elsevier.com
Address May Change:

PUBLICATION GUIDELINES:

Manuscript Length: 30+
Copies Required: Five
Computer Submission: Yes Email
    w/hardcopies
Format: MS Word, RTF
Fees to Review: 0.00 US$

Manuscript Style:
    American Psychological Association,
    5th Edition

CIRCULATION DATA:

Reader: Academics
Frequency of Issue: Quarterly
Copies per Issue: No Reply
Sponsor/Publisher: National Association for
    the Education of Young Children
    (NAEYC) / Elsevier Science
Subscribe Price: 123.00 US$ Individual
    296.00 US$ Institution
    40.00 US$ NAEYC Member

REVIEW INFORMATION:

Type of Review: Blind Review
No. of External Reviewers: 3
No. of In House Reviewers: 1
Acceptance Rate: 11-20%
Time to Review: 2 - 3 Months
Reviewers Comments: Yes
Invited Articles: 0-5%
Fees to Publish: 0.00 US$

MANUSCRIPT TOPICS:
Developmental Psychology; Early Childhood; Exceptional Child

MANUSCRIPT GUIDELINES/COMMENTS:

Sponsored by the National Association for the Education of Young Children, *Early Childhood Research Quarterly* includes articles presenting significant research and scholarship on all topics related to the care and education of children from birth through 8 years. Articles reflect the interdisciplinary nature of the field and of the National Association for the Education of Young Children. The Quarterly is published by Elsevier Sciences.

Five complete copies of manuscripts from 15-40 pages in length should be submitted to Dr. Karen E. Diamond, Department of Child Development and Family Studies, CDFS Building, 101 Gates Rd., Purdue University, W. Lafayette, IN 47907-2020.

Manuscripts are accepted for review with the understanding that the same work has not been and will not be published nor is presently submitted elsewhere, and that all person listed as authors have given their approval for the submission of the paper; further, that any person cited as a source of personal communication has approved such citation. Written authorization may be required at the Editor's discretion. Articles and other material published in *Early Childhood Research Quarterly* represent the opinions of the authors and should not be construed to reflect the opinion of the Editor, the Publisher, or the Sponsor.

Authors submitting a manuscript do so on the understanding that, if it is accepted for publication, copyright in the article, including the right to reproduce the article in all forms and media, shall be assigned exclusively to the Publisher. The Publisher will not refuse any reasonable request by the author for permission to reproduce any of his or her contributions to the Quarterly. Responsibility for accuracy of the material in the manuscript, including appropriate reference to related work, lies entirely with the authors.

In submitting a manuscript please keep in mind the Following instructions:

1. **Manuscript Preparation**. Manuscripts should be typewritten, double-spaced, with one-inch margins on all sides. Articles should be concise and in English. Page I should contain the article title, author(s), affiliation(s), a short form of the title (less that 55 characters including letters and spaces), and the name, telephone number, and complete mailing address of the author to whom correspondence should be sent. Page 2 should contain a short abstract (100-150 words for a report of an empirical study; 70-100 words for a review or theoretical article).

2. **Style**. The style guidelines of the *Publication Manual of the American Psychological Association*, (5th. ed.) should be followed, especially for reference lists and text citations or sources. American, not British, spelling and punctuation should be used.

3. **Review**. Since the manuscripts are submitted for blind review, all identifying information should be removed from the body of the paper.

4. **Table and Figures**. Tables and figures should be completely understandable independent of the text. Each table and figure must be mentioned in the text, given a title, and consecutively numbered with Arabic numerals. Authors must provide good-quality originals of all figures, to be directly reproduced for publication. Originals must be legible after reduction to a maximum size of 4 ½ inches wide by 7 ½ inches high. Graphs and charts must be professionally prepared and may be submitted as original black ink drawings or as sharp black-and-white photographic reproduction. Color originals, which will be published in black and white, are discouraged.

5. **Footnotes**. Footnotes should be used sparingly and indicated by consecutive numbers in text. Acknowledgments, grant numbers, or other credits should be given as a separate, asterisked footnote.

6. **References**. All sources cited in the text must be included in the reference list, and vice versa.

7. **Permissions**. Copies of any letters granting permission to reproduce illustrations, tables, or lengthy quoted passages should be included with the manuscript.

8. **Corrections**. Authors are expected to correct and return proof page to the Publisher within a week of receipt. Authors are responsible for the cost of change, additions, or corrections other than the Printer's or Publisher's errors, although the Publisher may waive such charges.

9. **Reprints**. Reprints must be ordered when page proofs are returned to the Publisher. Availability of article reprints for back issues cannot be guaranteed.

Eating Disorders: The Journal of Treatment and Prevention

ADDRESS FOR SUBMISSION:

Leigh Cohn, Editor-in-Chief
Eating Disorders: The Journal of Treatment
    and Prevention
PO Box 2238
Carlsbad, CA 92018
USA
Phone: 760-434-7533
Fax: 760-434-5476
E-Mail: gurze@aol.com
Web: http://www.tandf.co.uk/journals
Address May Change:

PUBLICATION GUIDELINES:

Manuscript Length: 18-25
Copies Required: Five
Computer Submission: Yes
Format: N/A
Fees to Review: 0.00 US$

Manuscript Style:
    American Psychological Association

CIRCULATION DATA:

Reader: Practitioners
Frequency of Issue: 5 Times/Year
Copies per Issue:
Sponsor/Publisher: Routledge Journals
    (Taylor and Francis)
Subscribe Price: 72.00 US$ Individual
    158.00 US$ Institution

REVIEW INFORMATION:

Type of Review: Editorial Review
No. of External Reviewers: 30
No. of In House Reviewers: 0
Acceptance Rate: 60%
Time to Review: 2 - 3 Months
Reviewers Comments: Yes
Invited Articles: 21-30%
Fees to Publish: 0.00 US$

MANUSCRIPT TOPICS:
Adolescent Psychology; Alcoholism & Drug Addiction; Behavior Modification; Eating Disorders; Exceptional Child; Family Counseling & Therapy; Prevention

MANUSCRIPT GUIDELINES/COMMENTS:

Aims and Scope
As the incidence and awareness of eating disorders continues to rise, it has become apparent that there is a need for a comprehensive source detailing the multidisciplinary approaches to the treatment and education of this growing problem. *Eating Disorders* places itself in the epicenter of this innovative work.

Now in its 13th year, *Eating Disorders* is contemporary and wide ranging. It takes a fundamentally practical, humanistic, compassionate view of clients and their presenting problems. You'll find a multidisciplinary perspective that considers the essential cultural, social, familial, and personal elements that not only foster eating-related problems, but also furnish clues that facilitate the most effective possible therapies and treatment approaches.

A distinguished international editorial board ensures that *Eating Disorders* will continuously reflect the variety of current theories and treatment approaches in the eating disorders arena. From anorexia nervosa to bingeing to yo-yo dieting, editors and contributors explore eating disorders from a number of exciting, sometimes unexpected, and always thought-provoking angles.

Regular features of the journal include:

* Q & A
* Book Reviews
* How I Practice
* The Last Word

Readership
Psychiatrists, psychologists, college counselors, marriage and family counselors, dieticians, nutritionists, social workers, and professionals at eating disorder treatment facilities.

Instructions for Authors
Note to Authors. Please make sure your contact address information is clearly visible on the outside of all packages you are sending to Editors.

Submission of Manuscripts
Authors preparing manuscripts should follow the *Publication Manual for the American Psychological Association* (4th edition). Address all editorial communications to:

Mr. Leigh Cohn, Editor-in-Chief, Eating Disorders: The Journal of Treatment and Prevention
P.O. Box 2238, Carlsbad, CA 92018
Tel: (760) 434-7533, Fax: (760) 434-5476; Email: **gurze@aol.com**
or
5145 B Avenida Encina, Carlsbad, CA 92008

Four hardcopy printouts of the manuscript or an electronic file must be supplied. Each manuscript must be accompanied by a statement that it has not been published elsewhere and that it has not been submitted simultaneously for publication elsewhere. Authors are responsible for obtaining permission to reproduce copyrighted material from other sources and are required to sign an agreement for the transfer of copyright to the publisher. Following acceptance for publication, the authors should provide a copy of the manuscript on disk. The disk should be prepared using MS Word or WordPerfect and should be clearly labeled with the authors' names, file name, and software program. All accepted manuscripts, artwork, and photographs become the property of the publisher.

All parts of the manuscript should be typewritten, double-spaced, with margins of at least one inch on all sides. Number manuscript pages consecutively throughout the paper. Authors should also supply a shortened version of the title suitable for the running head, not exceeding 50 character spaces. Each article should be summarized in an abstract of not more that 100 words. Avoid abbreviations, diagrams, and reference to the text.

A Microsoft Word author template file, which also includes more detailed instructions in its "Read Me" file, can be downloaded from the web page.

Illustrations

Illustrations submitted (line drawings, halftones, photos, photomicrographs, etc.) should be clean originals or digital files. Digital files are recommended for highest quality reproduction and should follow these guidelines:

- 300 dpi or higher
- sized to fit on journal page
- EPS, TIFF, or PSD format only
- submitted as separate files, not embedded in text files

Tables and Figures

Tables and figures should not be embedded in the text, but should be included as separate sheets or files. A short descriptive title should appear above each table with a clear legend and any footnotes suitably identified below. All units must be included. Figures should be completely labeled, taking into account necessary size reduction. Captions should be typed, double-spaced, on a separate sheet. All original figures should be clearly marked in pencil on the reverse side with the number, author's name, and top edge indicated.

Educational and Psychological Measurement

ADDRESS FOR SUBMISSION:

Xitao Fan, Editor
Educational and Psychological
   Measurement
University of Virginia
Curry School of Education
405 Emmet Street South
Charlottesville, VA 22903-2495
USA
Phone: 434-243-8906
Fax: 434-924-1384
E-Mail: epm_uva@virginia.edu
Web: www.people.virginia.edu/~xf8d
Address May Change:

PUBLICATION GUIDELINES:

Manuscript Length: N/A
Copies Required: Four
Computer Submission: No
Format: N/A
Fees to Review: 0.00 US$

Manuscript Style:
   American Psychological Association

CIRCULATION DATA:

Reader: Academics
Frequency of Issue: Bi-Monthly
Copies per Issue: 2,001 - 3,000
Sponsor/Publisher: Sage Publications
Subscribe Price: 120.00 US$ Individual
   599.00 US$ Institution

REVIEW INFORMATION:

Type of Review: Blind Review
No. of External Reviewers: 2-3
No. of In House Reviewers: 1-2
Acceptance Rate: 20% -/+
Time to Review: About 6 Months
Reviewers Comments: Yes
Invited Articles: 0-5%
Fees to Publish: 0.00 US$

MANUSCRIPT TOPICS:

Educational Psychology; Experimental Psychology; Personality; Psychological Testing;
Research Methods & Statistics; Tests, Measurement & Evaluation

MANUSCRIPT GUIDELINES/COMMENTS:

Notes for Authors

Educational and Psychological Measurement is open to (a) discussions of problems in the field of the measurement individual differences; (b) reports of research on the development and use of tests and measurements in education, industry, and government; (c) measurement models (e.g., IRT family models) and quantitative techniques/methods, especially those relevant for measurement professionals (e.g., factor analysis, structural equation modelin, various techniques applicable in research about individual differences); (d) descriptions of testing programs being used for various purposes; and (e) reports that are pertinent to the measurement field, such as suggestions of new types of items or improved methods of treating test data.

392

Manuscript Submission. Four copies (three of which are blind copies), together with an IBM-formatted disk (or CD) that contains the electronic file of the manuscript (Microsoft Word or Acrobat PDF file format; only one electronic file for each manuscript), should be sent to: Xitao Fan, EPM Editor, Curry School of Education, University of Virginia, 287 Ruffner Hall, 405 Emmet Street South, Charlottesville, VA 22903-2495.

For all submissions, the corresponding author must provide both his/her postal mailing address and e-mail address. Manuscripts should follow the general guidelines in the 5th edition of the *Publication Manual of the American Psychological Association*. Manuscripts should comply with the general requirements in the author guidelines presented in the lead of issue 4 of volume 54 of the journal (Winter, 1994, pp. 837-847) and in supplementary "guidelines editorials" published on an occasional basis (e.g., August, 1995, pp. 525-534; April 1996, pp. 197-208; and August , 2001, pp. 517-531). Copies of these guideline editorials are available on the World Wide Web at http://www.people.virginia.edu/~xf8d. Authors are also strongly encouraged to review the recommendations of the APA Task Force on Statistical Inference, published in the August 1999 issue of American Psychologist (http://www.apa.org/journals/amp/amp548594.html).

Various Author Guidelines editorials are available on the Web via:
   http://www.people.virginia.edu/~xf8d/

Educational Assessment

ADDRESS FOR SUBMISSION:

Joan Herman, Editor
Educational Assessment
Nat'l Center for Research on Evaluation,
   Standards, and Student Testing
GSE&IS Bldg., 3rd Fl, Box 951522
300 Charles E. Young Drive North
Los Angeles, CA 90095-1522
USA
Phone: 310-794-9157
Fax: 310-825-3883
E-Mail: herman@cse.ucla.edu
Web: www.erlbaum.com
Address May Change:

PUBLICATION GUIDELINES:

Manuscript Length: 26-30+
Copies Required: Four
Computer Submission: Yes
Format: MS Word (preferred); WordPerfect
Fees to Review: 0.00 US$

Manuscript Style:
   American Psychological Association

CIRCULATION DATA:

Reader: Academics
Frequency of Issue: Quarterly
Copies per Issue: Less than 1,000
Sponsor/Publisher: Lawrence Erlbaum
   Associates
Subscribe Price: 35.00 US$ Individual
   255.00 US$ Institution

REVIEW INFORMATION:

Type of Review: Blind Review
No. of External Reviewers: 3
No. of In House Reviewers: 1
Acceptance Rate: 21-30%
Time to Review: 4 - 6 Months
Reviewers Comments: Yes
Invited Articles: 11-20%
Fees to Publish: 0.00 US$

MANUSCRIPT TOPICS:
Assessment and Measurement; Educational Psychology; Educational Testing

MANUSCRIPT GUIDELINES/COMMENTS:

Topics Include. Classroom assessment and use of assessment for planning and decision making

Editorial Scope. The journal publishes original research and scholarship on the assessment of individuals, groups, and programs in educational settings. It includes theory, methodological approaches and empirical research in the appraisal of the learning and achievement of students and teachers, young children and adults, and novices and experts. The journal reports on current large-scale testing practices, discusses alternative approaches, presents scholarship on classroom assessment practices and includes assessment topics debated at the national level. It welcomes both conceptual and empirical pieces and encourages articles that provide a strong bridge between theory and/or empirical research and the implications for educational policy and/or practice.

Audience. Researchers; assessment developers; subject matter and curriculum specialists; federal, state, district and school administrators responsible for assessment; educational policymakers.

INSTRUCTIONS TO CONTRIBUTORS
Manuscript Submission
Only articles written in English will be considered. Submit four copies of your manuscript to the Editor: Joan Herman, National Center for Research on Evaluation, Standards, and Student Testing (CRESST), 300 Charles E. Young Drive North GSE&IS Building, 3rd Floor, Mailbox 951522, Los Angeles, CA 90095-1522 Phone: 310-794-9157, E-mail: **herman@cse.ucla.edu**

Prepare manuscripts according to the *Publication Manual of the American Psychological Association* (4th ed.). Type all components of the manuscript double-sided, including title page, abstract, text, quotes, acknowledgements, references, appendices, tables, figure captions, and footnotes. An abstract of 100 to 150 words should be typed on a separate page. Authors must follow the "Guidelines to Reduce Bias in Language," on pages 46-60 of the *APA Manual*. Four photocopies of the illustrations and the original illustrations should accompany the manuscript. All manuscripts submitted will be acknowledged promptly. Authors should keep a copy of their manuscripts to guard against loss.

Blind Review
To facilitate anonymous review, only the article title should appear on the first page of the manuscript. An attached cover page must contain the title; authorship; authors' affiliations; any statements of credit or research support; and authors; mailing addresses, phone and fax numbers, and e-mail addresses. Every effort should be made by the authors to see that the manuscript itself contains no clues to their identities.

Permissions
Authors are responsible for all statements made in their work and for obtaining permission from copyright owners to reprint or adapt a table or figure or to reprint a quotation of 500 words or more. Authors should write to original author(s) and publisher to request nonexclusive world rights in all languages to use the material in the article and in future editions. Provide copies of all permissions and credit lines obtained.

Regulations
In a cover letter, authors should state that the findings reported in the manuscript are original and have not been published previously and that the manuscript is not being simultaneously submitted elsewhere. Authors should also state that they have complied with American Psychological Association ethical standards in the treatment of their samples.

Production Notes
After a manuscript is accepted for publication, its author is asked to provide a computer disk containing the manuscript file. Files are copyedited and typeset into page proofs. Authors read proofs to correct errors and answer editors' queries.

Educational Psychologist

ADDRESS FOR SUBMISSION:

Philip H. Winne & Lyn Corno, Co-Editors
Educational Psychologist
Simon Fraser University
Faculty of Eductation
Burnaby, BC, V5A 1S6
Canada
Phone: 604-291-4858
Fax: 604-291-3203
E-Mail: winne@sfu.ca
Web:
Address May Change: 12/31/2005

PUBLICATION GUIDELINES:

Manuscript Length: 21-25
Copies Required: Five
Computer Submission: No
Format:
Fees to Review: 0.00 US$

Manuscript Style:
American Psychological Association

CIRCULATION DATA:

Reader: Academics
Frequency of Issue: Quarterly
Copies per Issue: 2,001 - 3,000
Sponsor/Publisher:
Subscribe Price: 50.00 US$ Individual
    Free to Div. 15 APA Members

REVIEW INFORMATION:

Type of Review: Blind Review
No. of External Reviewers: 2
No. of In House Reviewers: 1
Acceptance Rate: 21-30%
Time to Review: 2 - 3 Months
Reviewers Comments: Yes
Invited Articles: 31-50%
Fees to Publish: 0.00 US$

MANUSCRIPT TOPICS:
Educational Psychology

MANUSCRIPT GUIDELINES/COMMENTS:

Editorial Scope
The scholarly essays, reviews, critiques, and theoretical and conceptual articles featured in this exceptional journal contribute to understanding issues, problems, and research concerning all aspects of educational psychology. From meta-analyses of experiments probing the effectiveness of instructional methods to historical analyses of theories and research techniques, the journal provides insightful explorations of new educational concepts and accepted educational practices. The journal, however, does not publish articles whose primary purpose is to report the methods and results of an empirical study.

Audience. Educational Psychologists, researchers, teachers, administrators, and policymakers.

Instructions To Contributors

Submission of Manuscripts. Manuscripts must be prepared in accordance with the following instructions.

Follow APA Style. Authors should follow *the Publication Manual of the American Psychological Association* (5th ed.) in preparing manuscripts for submission to this journal. All manuscripts must be prefaced by an abstract of 100-150 words on a separate sheet. All manuscript pages, including reference lists and tables, must be typed double-spaced. All figures must be camera ready. Authors should comply with "Guidelines to Reduce Bias in Language" as printed in the *Publication Manual*. Manuscripts that fail to conform to APA-style guidelines will be returned to the author(s).

Prepare For Blind Peer Review. All articles appearing in the *EP* are peer reviewed. Because the reviewers have agreed to participate in a blind reviewing system, authors submitting manuscripts are requested to include with each copy of the manuscript a cover sheet that shows the title of the manuscript, the names of the authors, the authors' institutional affiliations, the mailing address, the date the manuscript is submitted, and a running head. The first page of the manuscript should omit the authors' names and affiliations but should include the title of the manuscript and the date it is submitted. Footnotes containing information pertaining to the authors' identities or affiliations should be placed on separate pages. Every effort should be made by authors to see that the manuscript itself contains no clues to their identities.

Screen for Appropriateness. By submitting manuscripts to the *Educational Psychologist*, authors are confirming that the manuscripts have not been published and are not under consideration for publication elsewhere. Prior to submission, authors should determine whether their manuscripts correspond to the journal's statement of purpose--to publish essays, critiques, and articles of a theoretical/conceptual nature that contribute to our understanding of the issues, problems, and research associated with the field of educational psychology. Articles consistent with the journal's purpose include critical, integrative reviews of educational psychology research; conceptual or theoretical syntheses or analyses of educational psychology research; scientifically documented digests of educational psychology research relevant to policy issues; and documented, scholarly essays of general interest to the educational psychology community. Consistent with the journal's mission to serve as a forum for important ideas in educational psychology, articles of varying lengths and covering all aspects of educational psychology will be considered, including articles focusing on implications for educational theory, research, practice, or policy. Articles that report mainly the results of an empirical study (e.g., would be appropriate for the *Journal of Educational Psychology*) or articles that are intended mainly as practical guides (without research documentation) are inappropriate for the *EP* and will be returned to the authors. In addition to publishing regular articles, the journal publishes special issues that are devoted to important themes in educational psychology and keynote reviews with published peer commentary. Authors interested in the latter formats are requested to contact the editor prior to submitting a proposal for a special issue or keynote review.

Follow Copyright Laws. Authors are responsible for obtaining and providing written permission from copyright owners for reprinting previously published illustrations, tables, or lengthy quotes (500 or more words). Authors are responsible for the accuracy of the material in their manuscripts.

Submit Five Copies. Send five copies of your manuscripts (an original and four duplicates) to: Philip H. Winne and Lyn Corno, Coeditors, Educational Psychologist, Faculty of Education, Simon Fraser University, Burnaby, British Columbia, Canada V5A 1S6. Authors should keep a copy of the manuscript to guard against loss in the mail. After a manuscript is accepted for publication, its author is asked to provide a computer disk containing the manuscript file. Files are copyedited and typeset into page proofs. Authors read proofs to correct errors and answer editors' queries.

Emotion

ADDRESS FOR SUBMISSION:

R.J. Davidson, K.R. Scherer, Co-Editors
Emotion
University of Wisconsin - Madison
Dept of Psychology & Waisman Center
1500 Highland Avenue
Madison, WI 53705-2280
USA
Phone: 608-265-2062
Fax: 608-265-8682
E-Mail: rjdavids@facstaff.wisc.edu
Web: www.apa.org/journals/emo.html
Address May Change: 12/31/2006

PUBLICATION GUIDELINES:

Manuscript Length: 30+
Copies Required: Two
Computer Submission: Yes
Format: MSWord, WdPerfect, Adobe
    Acrobat
Fees to Review: 0.00 US$

Manuscript Style:
    American Psychological Association

CIRCULATION DATA:

Reader: Academics
Frequency of Issue: Quarterly
Copies per Issue: No Reply
Sponsor/Publisher: American Psychological
    Association
Subscribe Price:

REVIEW INFORMATION:

Type of Review: Editorial Review
No. of External Reviewers: 3
No. of In House Reviewers: 0
Acceptance Rate: 21-30%
Time to Review: 2 - 3 Months
Reviewers Comments: Yes
Invited Articles: No Reply
Fees to Publish: 0.00 US$

MANUSCRIPT TOPICS:

Abnormal Psychology; Adolescent Psychology; Adulthood; Alcoholism & Drug Addiction; Child Psychology; Developmental Psychology; Experimental Psychology; Family Counseling & Therapy; Gerontology; Learning & Conditioning; Neuropsychology; Personality; Physiological Psychology; Psychiatry; Psychobiology; Psychological Testing; Psychopathology; Research Methods & Statistics; Social Psychology; Thinking & Cognition

MANUSCRIPT GUIDELINES/COMMENTS:

Emotion publishes significant contributions to the study of emotion from a wide range of theoretical traditions and research domains. *Emotion* includes articles that advance knowledge and theory about all aspects of emotional processes, including reports of substantial empirical studies, scholarly reviews, and major theoretical articles. Submissions from all domains of emotion research are encouraged, including studies focusing on cultural, social, temperament and personality, cognitive, development, health, or biological variables that affect or are affected by emotional processes. Studies of psychopathology contributing to the understanding of the role of emotional processes in affective and behavioral disorders are also welcome. Reports of work at the animal and molecular levels will be considered if they help to elucidate fundamental mechanisms of emotion. Most of the articles published in *Emotion* will be reports of original research, but other types of articles are acceptable. Case studies from either a clinical setting or a laboratory will be considered if they raise or illustrate important questions that go beyond the single case and have heuristic value. Articles that present or discuss theoretical perspectives on the basis of published data, may also be accepted. Comprehensive reviews of the empirical literature in an area of study are acceptable if they contain a meta-analysis and/or present novel theoretical or methodological perspectives. Comments on articles published in the journal will be considered.

All submissions, electronic and mail, must be accompanied by a cover letter confirming compliance with APA ethical principles as stated at the following website:
   http://www.apa.org/journals/emo/#principles.

Manuscript submission guidelines. New and revised manuscripts may be submitted electronically at **http://www.jbo.com/jb3/submissions/dsp_jbo.cfm?journal_code=emo** in Rich Text Format (RTF). All **tables and figures** should be included in the manuscript file that is submitted.

Mail submission. Please submit *one* hard copy of the manuscript along with a complete disk copy (text, tables, and figures) to the Co-Editor,

   Richard J. Davidson, PhD
   Emotion Journal Office
   Department of Psychology and Waisman Center
   University of Wisconsin—Madison
   1500 Highland Avenue
   Madison, Wisconsin 53705-2280

General correspondence may be directed to the Editor's Office **Hermann@waisman.wisc.edu**

All copies should be clear, readable, and on paper of good quality. In addition to the hard copy of the manuscript, a complete disk copy (text and tables, and figures if possible) must be provided, with a clear notation of the file names and the word processing and graphics software used. Figures may submitted on a separate disk or on a Zip disk. In addition to addresses and phone numbers, authors should supply electronic mail addresses and fax numbers for use by the editorial office and later by the production office. The majority of correspondence between the editorial office and authors is handled by e-mail, so a valid e-mail address is important to the timely flow of communication during the editorial process. Authors should provide electronic mail addresses in their cover letters and should keep a copy of the manuscript to guard against loss. Manuscripts are not returned.

Brief reports. *Emotion* also publishes brief reports. Manuscripts submitted as Brief Reports should not exceed 3,400 words, exclusive of references and figure captions. There should be no more than 2 figures or tables and no more than 30 references.

Theoretical notes. *Emotion* publishes articles that make important theoretical contributions to research areas that are of major importance for the study of emotion and affect. Preference is given to manuscripts that advance theory by integrating prior work and by suggesting concrete avenues for the empirical investigation of the theoretical predictions. Extensive, systematic evaluation of alternative theories is expected. Manuscripts devoted to surveys of the literature are acceptable only if they can be considered as a major contribution to the field, documenting cumulative evidence and highlighting central theoretical and/or methodological issues of scientific debate. *Emotion* also publishes, as Theoretical Notes, commentary that contributes to progress in a given subfield of emotion or affect. Such notes include, but are not limited to, discussions of alternative theoretical approaches, and metatheoretical commentary on theory testing and related topics. Manuscripts submitted as Theoretical Notes should not exceed 5,000 words (exclusive of references). There should be no more than 50 references.

Masked reviews are optional, and authors who wish masked reviews must specifically request them when they submit their manuscripts. For masked reviews, each copy of the manuscript must include a separate title page with the authors' names and affiliations, and these ought not to appear anywhere else in the manuscript. Footnotes that identify the authors must be typed on a separate page. Authors are to make every effort to see that the manuscript itself contains no clues to their identities. If authors elect a masked review, they must also supply a second clearly labeled disk that contains the masked version of the manuscript with all clues to their identities eliminated, including any document summary information created by word processing software.

Manuscripts for *Emotion* can vary in length; typically they will range from 15 to 40 double-spaced manuscript pages. Manuscripts should be of sufficient length to ensure theoretical and methodological competence. Most of the articles to be published in *Emotion* will be reports of original research, but other types of articles are acceptable. Case studies from either a clinical setting or a laboratory will be considered if they raise or illustrate important questions that go beyond the single case and have heuristic value. Manuscripts that present or discuss theoretical formulations of emotion and related affective phenomena, or that evaluate competing theoretical perspectives on the basis of published data, may also be accepted. Comprehensive reviews of the empirical literature in an area of study are acceptable if they contain a meta- analysis and/or present novel theoretical or methodological perspectives. Comments on articles published in the journal will be considered.

Authors should prepare manuscripts according to the *Publication Manual of the American Psychological Association* (5th ed.). All manuscripts must include an abstract containing a maximum of 120 words typed on a separate page. Formatting instructions (all copy must be double- spaced) and instructions on the preparation of tables, figures, references, metrics, and abstracts appear in the *Manual*. All **tables** and **figures** should be included in the manuscript file that is submitted. Also, all manuscripts are copyedited for bias-free language (see chap. 2 of the *Publication Manual*). Original color figures can be printed in color at the editor's discretion and provided the author agrees to pay half of the associated production costs; an estimate of these costs is available from the APA production office on request.

Authors are required to obtain and provide to APA prior to production all necessary permissions to reproduce in print and electronic form any copyrighted work, including, for example, test materials (or portions thereof) and photographs of people. Final files for production should be prepared as outlined in Preparing Your Electronic Files for Production at http://www.apa.org/journals/preparing_electronic_files.html.

APA can now place supplementary materials online, which will be available via the journal's Web page as noted above. To submit such materials, please see
www.apa.org/journals/supplementalmaterial.html

APA Ethical Principles

APA policy prohibits an author from submitting the same manuscript for concurrent consideration by two or more publications. In addition, it is a violation of APA Ethical Principles to publish "as original data, data that have been previously published" (Standard 8.13). As this journal is a primary journal that publishes original material only, APA policy prohibits as well publication of any manuscript that has already been published in whole or substantial part elsewhere.

Authors have an obligation to inform journal editors in their e-mail message or cover letter that the manuscript is not under review elsewhere, that the primary data have not been published previously or accepted for publication, and that the appropriate ethical guidelines were followed in the conduct of the research.

In addition, APA Ethical Principles specify that "after research results are published, psychologists do not withhold the data on which their conclusions are based from other competent professionals who seek to verify the substantive claims through reanalysis and who intend to use such data only for that purpose, provided that the confidentiality of the participants can be protected and unless legal rights concerning proprietary data preclude their release" (Standard 8.14). APA expects authors submitting to this journal to adhere to these standards. Specifically, authors of manuscripts submitted to APA journals are expected to have available their data throughout the editorial review process and for at least 5 years after the date of publication.

Authors will be required to state in writing that they have complied with APA ethical standards in the treatment of their sample, human or animal, or to describe the details of treatment. A copy of the APA Ethical Principles may be obtained electronically at http://www.apa.org/ethics/ or by writing the APA Ethics Office, 750 First Street, NE, Washington, DC 20002-4242.

APA requires authors to reveal any possible conflict of interest in the conduct and reporting of research (e.g., financial interests in a test or procedure, funding by pharmaceutical companies for drug research).

Environment & Behavior

ADDRESS FOR SUBMISSION:

Robert Bechtel, Editor
Environment & Behavior
University of Arizona
Environmental Psychology Program
Tucson, AZ 85721
USA
Phone: 520-621-7430
Fax: 520-621-9306
E-Mail: bechtel@u.arizona.edu
Web: www.sagepub.co.uk/journals
Address May Change: 1/7/2006

PUBLICATION GUIDELINES:

Manuscript Length: 16-20
Copies Required: Three
Computer Submission: No
Format: N/A
Fees to Review: 0.00 US$

Manuscript Style:
    American Psychological Association

CIRCULATION DATA:

Reader: Academics, Practitioners
Frequency of Issue: Bi-Monthly
Copies per Issue: 1,001 - 2,000
Sponsor/Publisher: Environmental Research
    Design Association/Sage Publications
Subscribe Price: 119.00 US$ Individual
    504.00 US$ Library/Institution

REVIEW INFORMATION:

Type of Review: Blind Review
No. of External Reviewers: 2
No. of In House Reviewers: 1
Acceptance Rate: 21-30%
Time to Review: 4 - 6 Months
Reviewers Comments: Yes
Invited Articles: 0-5%
Fees to Publish: 0.00 US$

MANUSCRIPT TOPICS:
Culture & Personality; Environment and Behavior; Group Dynamics

MANUSCRIPT GUIDELINES/COMMENTS:

About the Journal
Environment and Behavior is published in cooperation with the Environmental Design Research Association (EDRA). For more than three decades, *Environment & Behavior* has explored current experimental and theoretical work that examines the impact of the physical environment on human behavior.

Published bimonthly, *Environment and Behavior* brings you current research and theories as they develop. The articles are always fresh, the information consistently at the forefront of the discipline. *Environment and Behavior* analyses and records the influence of environment on individuals, groups and institutions. Feature articles, discussions and book reviews explore such topics as:

- Beliefs, meanings, values and attitudes of individuals or groups concerning various environments such as neighbourhoods, cities, transport routes and devices, or recreational areas

- Evaluation and effectiveness of environments designed to accomplish specific objectives
- Interrelationships between human environments and behavioural systems
- Planning, policy and political action aimed at controlling environments and behaviour.

Interdisciplinary Views

Environment and Behavior explores the concepts and theories of specialists from a variety of disciplines, including: Anthropology, Architecture, Design, Education, Geography, Political, Science, Psychology, Sociology, and Urban Planning.

Thematic Discussions

Occasionally, *Environment and Behavior* supplements its broad coverage with single-theme Special Issues devoted to topics of particular concern and guest-edited by leading scholars. Previous Special Issues have included: Litter Control and Recycling, Relations Between Environmental Psychology and Allied Fields, Design Review: Public Participation in the Evaluation of Design, Environmental Design and Evaluation in Museums.

Notes for Authors

Articles are sought in the following areas:

1. Theoretical work on the interrelationships between human environments and behavioral systems. Methodological papers will be considered provided the primary focus concerns the environment-behavior relationship.

2. Reports on research relating to evaluation of environments designed to accomplish specific objectives e g., the social effects of different kinds of living accommodations or the effectiveness of hospital treatment areas.

3. Studies relating to the beliefs, meanings, values, and attitudes of individuals or groups concerning various environments e.g., the meanings and values attached to neighborhoods, cities, transport routes and devices, or recreational areas.

4. Studies concerning physical environments whose human mission is largely implicit or socially underdeveloped.

5. Studies of planning, policy, or political action aimed at controlling environments or behavior.

Manuscripts of approximately 1 6 typed double-spaced pages should be submitted in triplicate (one original and two clear copies) to Robert Bechtel Editor, Environment And Behavior, Environmental Psychology Program, University of Arizona, Tucson, AZ 85721. Each copy should include a 100-150 word abstract, tables and figures should be presented on separate pages and with sufficient clarity so that they can be photographed directly.

Manuscripts will not be returned unless return postage is enclosed. Follow the *Publication Manual of the American Psychological Association* (fourth edition) for journal style. A copy of the final revised manuscript saved on an IBM-compatible disk should be included with the final revised hard copy. Submission of a manuscript implies commitment to publish in the journal. Authors submitting manuscripts to the journal should not simultaneously submit them to another journal, nor should manuscripts have been published elsewhere in substantially similar form or with substantially similar content. Authors in doubt about what constitutes prior publication should consult the editor.

Ethics & Behavior

ADDRESS FOR SUBMISSION:

Gerald P. Koocher, Editor
Ethics & Behavior
ELECTRONIC SUBMISSION
Phone: 617-521-2313
Fax: 617-327-7725
E-Mail: koocher@simmons.edu
Web: http://www.leaonline.com/loi/eb
Address May Change: 12/31/2006

CIRCULATION DATA:

Reader: Academics, Mental Health
   Practitioners
Frequency of Issue: Quarterly
Copies per Issue: Less than 1,000
Sponsor/Publisher:
Subscribe Price: 40.00 US$

PUBLICATION GUIDELINES:

Manuscript Length: 1-30+
Copies Required: Electronic
Computer Submission: Yes Email preferred
Format: Microsoft Word
Fees to Review: 0.00 US$

Manuscript Style:
   American Psychological Association

REVIEW INFORMATION:

Type of Review: Blind Review
No. of External Reviewers: 2
No. of In House Reviewers: 1
Acceptance Rate: 40%
Time to Review: 1 - 2 Months
Reviewers Comments: Yes
Invited Articles: 6-10%
Fees to Publish: 0.00 US$

MANUSCRIPT TOPICS:
Ethics; Experimental Psychology; Psychological Testing

MANUSCRIPT GUIDELINES/COMMENTS:

Editorial Scope
This compelling journal publishes articles on an array of topics pertaining to various moral issues and conduct. These matters may include but are not restricted to: the exercise of social and ethical responsibility in human behaviors; ethical dilemmas or professional misconduct in health and human service delivery; the conduct of research involving human and animal participants; fraudulence in the management or reporting of scientific research; and public policy issues involving ethical problems. Data based, theoretical, and particularly instructive case analyses, as well as brief summaries of problem cases are also published. An editorial board consisting of specialists in ethics with backgrounds in law, medicine, pediatrics, psychiatry, psychology, public health, sociology, and theology allows for a wide spectrum of perspectives toward ethical issues.

Audience. Professionals driven by an interest in moral issues and conduct--and their impact on individuals and society.

Instructions To Contributors

Manuscript Submission. Submit three manuscript copies to the Editor, Gerald P. Koocher, Graduate School for Health Studies, Simmons College, 300 The Fenway, Boston, MA 02115. Prepare manuscripts according to the *Publication Manual of the American Psychological Association* (5th ed.). Type all components of the manuscript double-spaced, including title page, abstract, text, quotes, acknowledgments, references, appendixes, tables, figure captions, and footnotes. Except for brief case submissions, please include an abstract of 100-150 words with each manuscript. List three to five "key words" for database indexing at the bottom of the abstract page. Unaccepted manuscripts ordinarily will not be returned.

Blind Review. To facilitate anonymous review, only the article title should appear on the first page of the manuscript. An attached cover page must contain the title, authorship, and an introductory footnote with professional titles and mailing addresses of the authors and any statements of credit or research support. Every effort should be made by the authors to see that the manuscript itself contains no clues to their identities.

Permissions. Authors are responsible for all statements made in their work and for obtaining permission from copyright owners to reprint or adapt a table or figure or to reprint a quotation of 500 words or more. Authors should write to original author(s) and publisher to request nonexclusive world rights in all languages to use the material in the article and in future editions. Provide copies of all permissions and credit lines obtained.

Regulations. In a cover letter, authors should state that the findings reported in the manuscript have not been published previously and that the manuscript is not simultaneously under consideration elsewhere. Authors should also state that they have complied with appropriate ethical standards in the treatment of any participants in the work being reported.

Production Notes. Authors are responsible for reviewing page proofs to correct errors and answer editors' queries. Prompt return of page proofs is mandatory. Reprints may be ordered at the time page proofs are returned.

European Journal of Cognitive Psychology

ADDRESS FOR SUBMISSION:

Editor
European Journal of Cognitive Psychology
c/o Journals Editorial Assistant
Psychology Press Ltd.
27 Church Road
Hove, East Sussex, BN3 2FA
UK
Phone: (0) 1273 225007
Fax: (0) 1273 205612
E-Mail: reviews@psypress.co.uk
Web: http://www.tandf.co.uk/journals
Address May Change:

PUBLICATION GUIDELINES:

Manuscript Length: 10-30+
Copies Required: Two
Computer Submission: Yes
Format: MS Word, RTF or PDF
Fees to Review: 0.00 US$

Manuscript Style:
   American Psychological Association

CIRCULATION DATA:

Reader: Academics
Frequency of Issue: Bi-Monthly
Copies per Issue:
Sponsor/Publisher: European Society for
   Cognitive Psychology / Taylor & Francis
Subscribe Price: 360.00 US$ Individual
   717.00 US$ Institution

REVIEW INFORMATION:

Type of Review: Editorial Review
No. of External Reviewers: 2-3
No. of In House Reviewers: 0
Acceptance Rate: 35%
Time to Review: 2 - 3 Months
Reviewers Comments: Yes
Invited Articles: 21-30%
Fees to Publish: 0.00 US$

MANUSCRIPT TOPICS:
Cognitive Psychology; Experimental Psychology; Learning & Conditioning; Sensation & Perception; Thinking & Cognition

MANUSCRIPT GUIDELINES/COMMENTS:

Aims and Scope
The *European Journal of Cognitive Psychology* is the official journal of the European Society for Cognitive Psychology, which aims to encourage the exchange and integration of ideas, research and training in cognitive psychology throughout Europe. The journal publishes reports of empirical work, theoretical contributions and reviews of the literature in all areas of cognitive psychology including applied cognitive psychology. Peer commentaries sometimes accompany theoretical papers in an attempt to stimulate lively debate about controversial issues within cognitive psychology. The *European Journal of Cognitive Psychology* is an international journal, with increasing numbers of subscriptions from outside Europe, especially North America and Japan. The Editor is anxious to publish high quality papers from authors both within and outside Europe.

Readership
European Journal of Cognitive Psychology is of interest to experimental cognitive psychologists, applied psychologists, psycholinguists, computer scientists, cognitive neuropsychologists and those working in allied disciplines.

Instructions For Authors
Note to Authors. Please make sure your contact address information is clearly visible on the outside of all packages you are sending to Editors.

General. Submission of an article is taken as acceptance by the author that the publisher will hold copyright on all material published in the journal, including printed, electronic, and other publication formats, in all languages. It is the author's responsibility to ensure that the article contains nothing that is libelous or infringes copyright.

Please note that the publisher would actively encourage authors to submit papers electronically to expedite the peer review process. Please email your paper saved in a standard document format type such as Word (PC format), Rich Text Format, or PDF to **reviews@psypress.co.uk**.

If you are unable to supply a version of your paper by email, please send **two hard copies** of the manuscript and **a disk version** (Microsoft Word in PC format or PDF format) to: The Editor, Professor Claus Bundesen, c/o Psychology Press Ltd, 27 Church Road, Hove, East Sussex, BN3 2FA, UK. Email: **reviews@psypress.co.uk**.

Journal Production Editor: **kate.moysen@psypress.co.uk**

Typescripts. The style and format of the typescripts should conform to the specifications given in the *Publication Manual of the American Psychological Association*. Typescripts should be double spaced on one side only of A4 paper, with adequate margins, and numbered throughout. The title page of an article should contain only (1) the title of the paper, the name(s) and address(es) of the author(s); (2) a short title not exceeding 40 letters and spaces, which will be used for page headlines; (3) name, full contact address, telephone, fax, and email details of the author to whom correspondence and proofs should be sent.

Figures and tables. Each of these should be on a separate page, not integrated with the text. Clear citations should indicate where they are to be inserted in the manuscript. Figures will be reproduced directly from originals supplied by the author(s). These must be of good quality, clearly and completely lettered. Maximum printed size of figures is 11.4 x 17cm. Photocopies will reproduce poorly, as will pale or broken originals. Dense tones should be avoided, and never combined with lettering. Half-tone figures should be clear, highly-contrasted black and white glossy prints.

References. A list of references quoted in the text should be given at the end of the paper, in alphabetical order of author's names. Titles of journals and books should be given in full, as exemplified below:

Baddeley, A. D. (1999). *Essentials of human memory.* Hove, UK: Psychology Press.

Bundesen, C. (2002). A general theory of visual attention. In L. Bäckman & C. von Hofsten (Eds.), *Psychology at the turn of the millennium: Vol. 1. Cognitive, biological, and health perspectives* (pp. 179-200). Hove, UK: Psychology Press.

Rayner, K., & Juhasz, B. J. (2004). Eye movements in reading: Old questions and new directions. *European Journal of Cognitive Psychology, 16,* 340-352.

Submission of Accepted Manuscripts on Disk. The publishers strongly encourage the submission of final, accepted manuscripts on disk (accompanied by hard copy). Guidelines for presentation of final manuscripts on disk see website.

Manuscripts will not normally be reviewed blind. If an author wishes to have his or her manuscript reviewed blind, the manuscript should be prepared in such a way that after detachment of the title page no clues as to the identity of the author remain. Additionally, the request for blind review should be included in a covering letter.

Specified corresponding authors will receive their article by email as a complete PDF. This allows the author to print up to 50 copies, free of charge, and disseminate them to colleagues. One copy of the journal issue in which their paper appears will be sent by post to all specified corresponding authors free after print publication. Paper offprints can be purchased by authors if they complete and return an offprint order form which will be enclosed with their proofs.

European Journal of Developmental Psychology

ADDRESS FOR SUBMISSION:

Willem Koops, Editor
European Journal of Developmental
 Psychology
c/o Journals Editorial Assistant
Psychology Press Ltd.
27 Church Road
Hove, East Sussex, BN3 2FA
UK
Phone: (0) 1273 225007
Fax: (0) 1273 205612
E-Mail: w.koops@fss.uu.nl
Web: http://www.tandf.co.uk/journals
Address May Change:

PUBLICATION GUIDELINES:

Manuscript Length:
Copies Required: One
Computer Submission: Yes Disk, Email
Format: MS Word, RTF, PDF
Fees to Review: 0.00 US$

Manuscript Style:
 American Psychological Association

CIRCULATION DATA:

Reader: Academics
Frequency of Issue: Quarterly
Copies per Issue:
Sponsor/Publisher: Taylor & Francis
Subscribe Price: 118.00 US$ Individual
 243.00 US$ Institution

REVIEW INFORMATION:

Type of Review:
No. of External Reviewers: 2-3
No. of In House Reviewers:
Acceptance Rate:
Time to Review: 2-6 Months
Reviewers Comments: Yes
Invited Articles:
Fees to Publish: 0.00 US$

MANUSCRIPT TOPICS:
Developmental Psychology; Social Psychology; Thinking & Cognition

MANUSCRIPT GUIDELINES/COMMENTS:

Note to Authors. Please make sure your contact address information is clearly visible on the outside of all packages you are sending to Journals Editorial Assistant.

Manuscript Submission
Manuscripts are invited for submission. Please note that authors are encouraged to submit papers electronically to expedite the peer review process. Please email your paper, saved in a standard document format type such as Word, Rich Text Format, or PDF, to **reviews@psypress.co.uk**. Alternatively, if you wish to submit a hard copy, please send one copy of the manuscript AND a disk version to: Journals Editorial Assistant, Psychology Press Ltd, 27 Church Road, Hove, East Sussex, BN3 2FA, UK. Tel: (0)1273 225007, Fax: (0)1273 205612.

Your covering email/letter must include full contact details (including email), the title of the journal to which you are submitting, and the title of your article.

All manuscripts should be submitted in American Psychological Association (APA) format following the latest edition of *Publication Manual of the APA* (currently 5th edition).

Copyright. It is a condition of publication that authors vest or license copyright in their articles, including abstracts, in Psychology Press Ltd. This enables us to ensure full copyright protection and to disseminate the article, and the journal, to the widest possible readership in print and electronic formats as appropriate. Authors may, of course, use the material elsewhere after publication providing that prior permission is obtained from Taylor & Francis Ltd. Authors are themselves responsible for obtaining permission to reproduce copyright material from other sources. To view the 'Copyright Transfer Frequently Asked Questions' please visit www.tandf.co.uk/journals/copyright.asp.

Fast-Track Reviewing. Fast-track reviewing is offered for papers with a particular time-critical focus. Papers reviewed under this program will be reviewed by the editor and one member of the editorial board only. Reviews will be brief, and will result in a "yes/no" decision without any further feedback. Accepted papers will be initially published on the journal's website. Authors who receive a "no" decision may wish to re-submit articles for a fuller review process, and the opportunity to revise and re-submit in line with the reviewers comments. The decision regarding which papers will be offered fast-track reviewing rests with the editor, and authors wishing to apply for this must send a covering letter with the manuscript, explaining what the time-critical focus is, and why the article needs to be in the fast-track program.

Ethics Statement. In preparing manuscripts, authors shall adhere to local ethics guidelines. Where these are not applicable or available, authors shall adhere to the ethics guidelines for the conduct of research and the preparation of manuscripts as laid out by the APA (American Psychological Association).

Format

Typescripts. The style and format of the typescripts should conform to the specifications given in the *Publication Manual of the American Psychological Association* (5th ed.). Typescripts should be double spaced on one side only of A4 paper, with adequate margins, and numbered throughout. The title page of an article should contain only:
1. the title of the paper, the name(s) and address(es) of the author(s);
2. a short title not exceeding 40 letters and spaces, which will be used for page headlines;
3. name and address of the author to whom correspondence and proofs should be sent;
4. your telephone and fax numbers, and e-mail address, as this helps speed of processing considerably;
5. up to six keywords.

Abstract. An abstract of 50-200 words should follow the title page on a separate sheet.

Headings. Indicate headings and subheadings for different sections of the paper clearly. Do not number headings.

412

Acknowledgements. These should be as brief as possible and typed on a separate sheet at the beginning of the text.

Permission to quote. Any direct quotation, regardless of length, must be accompanied by a reference citation that includes a page number. Any quote over six manuscript lines should have formal written permission to quote from the copyright owner. It is the author's responsibility to determine whether permission is required from the copyright owner and, if so, to obtain it. (See the bottom of the page for a template of a letter seeking copyright permission.)

Footnotes. These should be avoided unless absolutely necessary. Essential footnotes should be indicated by superscript figures in the text and collected on a separate sheet at the end of the manuscript.

Reference citations within the text. Use authors' last names, with the year of publication in parentheses after the last author's name, e.g., "Jones and Smith (1987)"; alternatively, "(Brown, 1982; Jones & Smith, 1987; White, Johnson, & Thomas, 1990)". On first citation of references with three to six authors, give all names in full, thereafter use first author "et al.". If more than one article by the same author(s) in the same year is cited, the letters a, b, c etc. should follow the year.

Reference list. A full list of references quoted in the text should be given at the end of the paper in alphabetical order of authors' surnames (or chronologically for a group of references by the same authors), commencing as a new sheet, typed double spaced. Titles of journals and books should be given in full, e.g.:

Books
Hobson, P. (2002). *The cradle of thought: Exploring the origins of thinking*. Oxford: Macmillan.

Chapter in edited book
Koops, W. (2003). Imaging childhood. In W. Koops & M. Zuckerman (Eds.), *Beyond the century of the child: Cultural history and developmental psychology* (pp. 1-21). Philadelphia: University of Pennsylvania Press.

Journal article
Orobio de Castro, B., Veerman, J. W., Koops, W., Bosch, J. D., & Monshouwer, H. J. (2002). Hostile attribution of intent and aggressive behavior: A meta-analysis. *Child Development, 73,* 916-934.

Tables. These should be kept to the minimum. Each table should be typed double spaced on a separate sheet, giving the heading, e.g., "Table 2", in Arabic numerals, followed by the legend, followed by the table. Make sure that appropriate units are given. Instructions for placing the table should be given in parentheses in the text, e.g., "(Table 2 about here)".

Figures should only be used when essential. The same data should not be presented both as a figure and in a table. Where possible, related diagrams should be grouped together to form a single figure. Figures should be drawn to professional standards and it is recommended that the linear dimensions of figures be approximately twice those intended for the final printed version. Each of these should be on a separate page, not integrated with the text. Figures will be reproduced directly from originals supplied by the author(s). These must be of good quality, clearly and completely lettered. Make sure that axes of graphs are properly labelled, and that appropriate units are given. Photocopies will reproduce poorly, as will pale or broken originals. Dense tones should be avoided, and never combined with lettering. Half-tone figures should be clear, highly-contrasted black and white glossy prints.

Black and white figures are included free of charge. Colour figures are not normally acceptable for publication in print -- however, it may be possible both to print in black and white and to publish online in colour. Colour figures will only be printed by prior arrangement between the editor(s), publisher and author(s); and authors may be asked to share the costs of inclusion of such figures. The figure captions should be typed in a separate section, headed, e.g., "Figure 2", in Arabic numerals. Instructions for placing the figure should be given in parentheses in the text, e.g., "(Figure 2 about here)". More detailed Guidelines for the Preparation of Figure Artwork are available from the publisher: Psychology Press Ltd, 27 Church Road, Hove, East Sussex BN3 2FA, UK (Email: deborah.maloney@psypress.co.uk).

Statistics. Results of statistical tests should be given in the following form:

"... results showed an effect of group, $F(2, 21) = 13.74$, $MSE = 451.98$, $p < .001$, but there was no effect of repeated trials, $F(5, 105) = 1.44$, $MSE = 17.70$, and no interaction, $F(10, 105) = 1.34$, $MSE = 17.70$."

Other tests should be reported in a similar manner to the above example of an F-ratio. For a fuller explanation of statistical presentation, see pages 136-147 of the *APA Publication Manual* (5th ed.). For guidelines on presenting statistical significance, see pages 24-25.

Abbreviations that are specific to a particular manuscript or to a very specific area of research should be avoided, and authors will be asked to spell out in full any such abbreviations throughout the text. Standard abbreviations such as RT for reaction time, SOA for stimulus onset asynchrony or other standard abbreviations that will be readily understood by readers of the journal are acceptable. Experimental conditions should be named in full, except in tables and figures.

After Acceptance of Publication in the Journal
Proofs. Page proofs will be emailed to the corresponding author as a PDF attachment to check for typesetting accuracy. No changes to the original typescript will be permitted at this stage. A list of queries raised by the copy editor will also be emailed. Proofs should be returned promptly with the original copy-edited manuscript and query sheet.

Early electronic offprints(e-prints). Specified corresponding authors will receive their article by email as a complete PDF. This allows the author to print up to 50 copies, free of charge, and disseminate them to colleagues. In many cases, this facility will be available up to two weeks prior to print publication of the article. One copy of the journal issue in which their paper appears will be sent by post to all specified corresponding authors free after print publication. Paper offprints can still be purchased by authors if they complete the enclosed offprint order form and return with payment together with their corrected proofs.

Copyright Permission

Contributors are required to secure permission for the reproduction of any figure, table, or extensive (more than six manuscript lines) extract from the text, from a source which is copyrighted -- or owned -- by a party other than Psychology Press Ltd or the contributor. This applies both to direct reproduction or "derivative reproduction" -- when the contributor has created a new figure or table which derives **substantially** from a copyrighted source. The following form of words can be used in seeking permission:

Dear [COPYRIGHT HOLDER]

I/we are preparing for publication an article entitled
[STATE TITLE]
to be published by Psychology Press Ltd in The *European Journal of Developmental Psychology.*

I/we should be grateful if you would grant us permission to include the following materials:
[STATE FIGURE NUMBER AND ORIGINAL SOURCE]

We are requesting non-exclusive rights in this edition and in all forms. It is understood, of course, that full acknowledgement will be given to the source.

Please note that Psychology Press Ltd are signatories of and respect the spirit of the STM Agreement regarding the free sharing and dissemination of scholarly information.

Your prompt consideration of this request would be greatly appreciated.

Yours faithfully

Volume contents and author index. The list of contents and the author index for the whole of the year's issues are published in the last issue of the year of each journal. For the *European Journal of Development Psychology,* this is issue 4 (December).

European Journal of Personality

ADDRESS FOR SUBMISSION:

Ivan Mervielde, Editor
European Journal of Personality
University of Ghent
Department of Developmental Personality
and Social Psychology
Henri Dunantlaan 2, B-9000 Ghent
Belgium
Phone: +31 9 264 64 17
Fax: +31 9 264 64 99
E-Mail: ivan.mervielde@ugent.be
Web: www.interscience.wiley.com
Address May Change:

PUBLICATION GUIDELINES:

Manuscript Length: 26-30
Copies Required: Five
Computer Submission: Yes
Format: N/A
Fees to Review: 0.00 US$

Manuscript Style:
    American Psychological Association

CIRCULATION DATA:

Reader: Academics
Frequency of Issue: Bi-Monthly Plus 1
    Special Issue
Copies per Issue: Less than 1,000
Sponsor/Publisher: John Wiley & Sons
Subscribe Price: 345.00 US$ Individual
    1055.00 US$ Institution

REVIEW INFORMATION:

Type of Review: Editorial Review
No. of External Reviewers: 3
No. of In House Reviewers: 0
Acceptance Rate: No Reply
Time to Review: 2 - 3 Months
Reviewers Comments: Yes
Invited Articles: 11-20%
Fees to Publish: 0.00 US$

MANUSCRIPT TOPICS:
Personality

MANUSCRIPT GUIDELINES/COMMENTS:

Aims and Scope
The *European Journal of Personality* is the official journal of the European Association of Personality Psychology, and is published by John Wiley & Sons. The *Journal* will promote the development of empirical and theoretical personality psychology within Europe and elsewhere, by reporting and reviewing original research, theoretical issues, methodological advances and current experience.

It is intended that the journal will reflect all areas of current personality psychology.

The *Journal* will emphasize (1) *human individuality* as manifested in cognitive processes, emotional and motivational functioning, and personal ways of interacting with the environment, (2) *individual differences* in personality structure and dynamics, and (3) *studies of intelligence* and interindividual differences in cognitive functioning.

Instructions To Authors

Note: from 01/01/2005 the *European Journal of Personality* will switch to electronic submission. For the latest information consult Wiley's website URL:

http://www.interscience.wiley.com/jpages/0890-2070/

Initial Manuscript Submission. Submit five copies of the manuscript (including copies of tables and illustrations), proposals for special issues:

Prof. Ivan Mervielde, Editor of *European Journal of Personality*,
Department of Psychology, Ghent University, Henri Dunantlaan 2, B-9000 Gent, Belgium

Authors **must** also supply:

- an electronic copy of the final version (see section below);
- a *Copyright Transfer Agreement* with original signature(s) - without this we are unable to accept the submission; and
- permission grants - if the manuscript contains extracts, including illustrations, from other copyright works (including material from on-line or intranet sources) it is the author's responsibility to obtain written permission from the owners of the publishing rights to reproduce such extracts using the Wiley *Permission Request Form*. Permission grants should be submitted with the manuscript.

Submission of a manuscript will be held to imply that it contains original unpublished work and is not being submitted for publication elsewhere at the same time. Submitted material will not be returned to the author, unless specifically requested.

Electronic submission. The electronic copy of the final, revised manuscript **must** be sent to the Editor **together with** the paper copy. Disks should be PC or Mac formatted; write on the disk the software package used, the name of the author and the name of the journal. We are able to use most word processing packages, but prefer Word or WordPerfect [and TeX or one of its derivatives].

Illustrations must be submitted in electronic format where possible. Save each figure as a separate file, in **TIFF** or **EPS** format preferably, and include the source file. Write on the disk the software package used to create them; we favor dedicated illustration packages over tools such as Excel or PowerPoint.

Manuscript style. The language of the journal is English. All submissions including book reviews must have a title, be printed on one side of the paper, be double-line spaced and have a margin of 3cm all round. Illustrations and tables must be printed on separate sheets, and not be incorporated into the text.

- The **title page** must list the full title, a short title of up to 70 characters, and names and affiliations of all authors. Give the full address, including e-mail, telephone and fax, of the author who is to check the proofs.
- Include the name(s) of any **sponsor(s)** of the research contained in the paper, along with **grant number(s)**.

- Supply an **abstract** of approximately 120 words for all articles, except book reviews. An abstract is a concise summary of the whole paper, not just the conclusions, and is understandable without reference to the rest of the paper. It should contain no citation to other published work.

Papers should normally be between 4000 to 8000 words, with longer review articles by arrangement with the Editor.

Reference style. The APA system of citing sources indicates the author's last name and the date, in parentheses, within the text of the paper.

A. A typical citation of an entire work consists of the author's name and the year of publication.
Example: Charlotte and Emily Bronte were polar opposites, not only in their personalities but in their sources of inspiration for writing (Taylor, 1990). Use the last name only in both first and subsequent citations, except when there is more than one author with the same last name. In that case, use the last name and the first initial.

B. If the author is named in the text, only the year is cited.
Example: According to Irene Taylor (1990), the personalities of Charlotte. . .

C. If both the name of the author and the date are used in the text, parenthetical reference is not necessary.
Example: In a 1989 article, Gould explains Darwin's most successful. . .

D. Specific citations of pages or chapters follow the year.
Example: Emily Bronte "expressed increasing hostility for the world of human relationships, whether sexual or social" (Taylor, 1988, p. 11).

E. When the reference is to a work by two authors, cite both names each time the reference appears.
Example: Sexual-selection theory often has been used to explore patters of various insect matings (Alcock & Thornhill, 1983) . . . Alcock and Thornhill (1983) also demonstrate. . .

F. When the reference is to a work by three to five authors, cite all the authors the first time the reference appears. In a subsequent reference, use the first author's last name followed by *et al.* (meaning "and others").
Example: Patterns of byzantine intrigue have long plagued the internal politics of community college administration in Texas (Douglas *et al.*, 1997) When the reference is to a work by six or more authors, use only the first author's name followed by *et al.* in the first and all subsequent references. The only exceptions to this rule are when some confusion might result because of similar names or the same author being cited. In that case, cite enough authors so that the distinction is clear.

G. When the reference is to a work by a corporate author, use the name of the organization as the author.

Example: Retired officers retain access to all of the university's educational and recreational facilities (Columbia University, 1987, p. 54).

H. **Personal letters, telephone calls, and other** material that cannot be retrieved are not listed in References but are cited in the text.
Example: Jesse Moore (telephone conversation, April 17, 1989) confirmed that the ideas. . .

I. **Parenthetical references** may mention more than one work, particularly when ideas have been summarized after drawing from several sources. Multiple citations should be arranged as follows.
Examples:
- List two or more works by the same author in order of the date of publication: (Gould, 1987, 1989)
- Differentiate works by the same author and with the same publication date by adding an identifying letter to each date: (Bloom, 1987a, 1987b)
- List works by different authors in alphabetical order by last name, and use semicolons to separate the references: (Gould, 1989; Smith, 1983; Tutwiler, 1989).

All references must be complete and accurate. Online citations should include date of access. If necessary, cite unpublished or personal work in the text but do not include it in the reference list. References should be listed in the following style:

Journal Article
Murzynski, J., & Degelman, D. (1996). Body language of women and judgments of vulnerability to sexual assault. *Journal of Applied Social Psychology, 26*, 1617-1626.

Book
Paloutzian, R. F. (1996). *Invitation to the psychology of religion* (2nd ed.). Boston: Allyn and Bacon.

Book with More than One Author
Natarajan, R., & Chaturvedi, R. (1983). *Geology of the Indian Ocean.* Hartford, CT: University of Hartford Press.

Hesen, J., Carpenter, K., Moriber, H., & Milsop, A. (1983). *Computers in the business world.* Hartford, CT: Capital Press. and so on.

The abbreviation *et al.* is not used in the reference list, regardless of the number of authors, although it can be used in the text citation of material with three to five authors (after the initial citation, when all are listed) and in all parenthetical citations of material with six or more authors.

Web Document on University Program or Department Web Site
Degelman, D., & Harris, M. L. (2000). *APA style essentials.* Retrieved May 18, 2000, from Vanguard University, Department of Psychology Website: http://www.vanguard.edu/faculty/ddegelman/index.cfm?doc_id=796

Stand-alone Web Document (no date)
Nielsen, M. E. (n.d.). *Notable people in psychology of religion.* Retrieved August 3, 2001, from http://www.psywww.com/psyrelig/psyrelpr.htm

Journal Article from Database
Hien, D., & Honeyman, T. (2000). A closer look at the drug abuse-maternal aggression link. *Journal of Interpersonal Violence, 15,* 503-522. Retrieved May 20, 2000, from ProQuest database.

Abstract from Secondary Database
Garrity, K., & Degelman, D. (1990). Effect of server introduction on restaurant tipping. *Journal of Applied Social Psychology, 20,* 168-172. Abstract retrieved July 23, 2001, from PsycINFO database.

Article or Chapter in an Edited Book
Shea, J. D. (1992). Religion and sexual adjustment. In J. F. Schumaker (Ed.), *Religion and mental health* (pp. 70-84). New York: Oxford University Press.

Illustrations. Supply each illustration on a separate sheet, with the lead author's name and the figure number, with the top of the figure indicated, on the reverse. Supply original **photographs**; photocopies or previously printed material will not be used. Line artwork must be high-quality laser output (not photocopies). Grey shading (tints) are not acceptable; lettering must be of a reasonable size that would still be clearly legible upon reduction, and consistent within each figure and set of figures. Supply artwork at the intended size for printing, which must not exceed 125mm × 200mm. There is a charge for printing **colour** illustrations of approximately £ 500 per page. If colour illustrations are supplied electronically in either **TIFF** or **EPS** format, they **may** be used in the PDF of the article at no cost to the author, even if this illustration was printed in black and white in the journal. The PDF will appear on the *Wiley InterScience* site.

Copyright. To enable the publisher to disseminate the author's work to the fullest extent, the author must sign a Copyright Transfer Agreement, transferring copyright in the article from the author to the publisher, and submit the original signed agreement with the article accepted for publication. A copy of the agreement to be used (which may be photocopied or printed from the website) can be found in *European Journal of Personality* and on the *Wiley InterScience* website at www.interscience.wiley.com. Copies may also be obtained from the journal editor or publisher.

Further Information. Proofs will be sent to the author for checking. This stage is to be used only to correct errors that may have been introduced during the production process. Prompt return of the corrected proofs, preferably within two days of receipt, will minimize the risk of the paper being held over to a later issue. 25 complimentary offprints will be provided to the author who checked the proofs, unless otherwise indicated. Further offprints and copies of the journal may be ordered. There is no page charge to authors.

European Journal of Psychological Assessment

ADDRESS FOR SUBMISSION:

R Fernandez-Ballesteros, Editor-in-Chief
European Journal of Psychological
    Assessment
Univiersidad Autonoma de Madrid
Facultad de Psicologia
Campus Cantoblanco
Madrid, E-28049
Spain
Phone: 34913975181
Fax: 34913975215
E-Mail: See Guidelines
Web: See Guidelines
Address May Change:

PUBLICATION GUIDELINES:

Manuscript Length: 20 pp.
Copies Required: Four
Computer Submission: Yes
Format: MS Word, RTF
Fees to Review: 0.00 US$

Manuscript Style:
    American Psychological Association

CIRCULATION DATA:

Reader: Academics, Practitioners
Frequency of Issue: Quarterly
Copies per Issue: Less than 1,000
Sponsor/Publisher: European Association of
    Psychological Assessment (EAPA)
Subscribe Price: 98.00 US$ Individual
    169.00 US$ Institution

REVIEW INFORMATION:

Type of Review: Editorial Review
No. of External Reviewers: 3
No. of In House Reviewers: 0
Acceptance Rate: 39%
Time to Review: 4 Months
Reviewers Comments: Yes
Invited Articles: 0-5%
Fees to Publish: 0.00 US$

MANUSCRIPT TOPICS:
Assessment; Evaluation; Research Methods & Statistics

MANUSCRIPT GUIDELINES/COMMENTS:

For English version of 'Advice for Authors' see:
    http://www.hhpub.com/journals/ejpa/journals.html

About the journal
The main purpose of the *EJPA* is to present important articles which provide seminal information on both theoretical and applied developments in this field. The journal is directed to practitioners as well as to academicians. The conviction of its editors is that the discipline of psychological assessment should, necessarily and firmly, be attached to the roots of psychological science, while going deeply into all the consequences of its applied, practice-oriented development.

Psychological assessment is experiencing a period of renewal and expansion, attracting more and more attention from both academic and applied psychology, as well as from political, corporate, and social organizations. The *EJPA* provides a meeting point for this movement, contributing to the scientific development of psychological assessment and to communication between professionals and researchers in Europe and worldwide.

The journal presents clearly written original papers, reviews, and commentaries dealing with such areas as:

- Concept and methodology
- Legal, ethical, professional, training issues
- Health and clinical, educational and organizational assessment
- Psychophysiological and neuropsychological assessment
- Psychological assessment and evaluation research

Editors-in-Chief
Rocío Fernández-Ballesteros, Universidad Autónoma de Madrid, Facultad de Psicología, Campus Cantoblanco, 28049- Madrid, SPAIN
Tel. +34 91 397-5181; Fax +34 91 397-5215; Email: **r.fballesteros@uam.es**

Hans Westmeyer, Editor-in-Chief, Dept. of Psychology, Freie Universität Berlin, Habelschwedter Allee, 45, D-14195 Berlin, GERMANY
Phone:49.30.8385-5602/04; Fax: 49.30.8385-5647; E-Mail: **hawest@zedat.fu-berlin.de**

Advice for Authors
The *European Journal of Psychological Assessment* publishes full-length papers on original research, test adaptations and test review. All submitted materials should not been submitted for publication elsewhere. Also, *EJPA* publishes book reviews and information on up-coming meetings, congresses and other professional events. The *Journal* appears four times a year.

Language. All contributions must be in English.

Manuscripts. Authors should consult a recent issue of the *Journal* for general style and layout. Please arrange and type manuscripts accordingly APA style.

The title page should contain, in addition to the title, the name(s) and complete address(es) of the author(s) (if different from the address of the institution) and institution(s) where the work was carried out. The text should be written 20 pages (Test adaptation no more than 15pp, including references tables and figures) double-spaced with a margin of 5 cm (2") on the left. It should normally be divided into *Summary* (not exceeding 200 words), *Keywords* (no more than five), *Introduction, Materials and Methods, Results, Discussion, Acknowledgments* (optional), and *References. Nonstandard abbreviations* should be defined in a footnote written on a separate page. Otherwise, footnotes should be avoided.

The delivery of manuscripts on diskette (5.25" or 3.5", preferably IBM MS-DOS compatible or Macintosh) or by e-mail are desirable.

Figures and Tables. The number of figures and tables should be kept to a minimum and only be included to facilitate understanding of the text. The same information should not appear in both a figure and a table. Tables must carry a title and should be typed on separate sheets and be intelligible without reference to the text. One set of figures with lettering should be suitable for reproduction, i.e., sharp glossy prints or drawings in black ink or good quality computer print-outs. Legends to figures should be typed on a separate sheet. Please indicate in the manuscript where figures and tables are to be placed.

References. References must include all and only works cited in the text and are to be arranged alphabetically. Works cited in the text within the same parentheses should be listed chronologically. The following formats are to be used:

Journal article. Crisp, A.H., Plamer, R.L. & Kalucy, R.S. (1976). How common is anorexia nervosa? A prevalence study. British Journal of Psychiatry, 128, 549-554. (Please note: the abbreviation et al. is not to be used in the reference section. Journal names are to be written out in full. In the text, this work is referred to as Crisp et al., 1976).

Entire book. Author (date). Book title. City (State and/or Country if city is relatively unknown): Publisher.

Article or chapter in edited book. Corbett, J.A. & Turpin, G. (1985). Tics and Tourette's syndrome In M. Rutter & L. Hersov (Eds.), Child and adolescent psychiatry. Modern approaches (2nd ed.)(pp. 516-5225). Oxford: Blackwell Scientific Publications.

Galley proofs and reprints. At the end of the manuscript, the postal address of the chief authors should be given. This person receives galley proofs of the paper in due course, and these must be sent back to the publisher *by return mail*. Changes in the style of content of the galleys can be made only in exceptional instances.

Instead of royalties, the authors receive 25 complimentary reprints of their article. Additional reprints may be ordered for a fee: this order must be placed simultaneously with the returning of the galleys to the publisher.

European Journal of Work and Organizational Psychology

ADDRESS FOR SUBMISSION:

Fred R. H. Zijlstra, Editor
European Journal of Work and
   Organizational Psychology
c/o Journals Editorial Assistant
Psychology Press Ltd.
27 Church Road
Hove, East Sussex, BN3 2FA
UK
Phone: (0) 1273 225007
Fax: (0) 1273 205612
E-Mail: f.zijlstra@surrey.ac.uk
Web: http://www.tandf.co.uk/journals
Address May Change:

PUBLICATION GUIDELINES:

Manuscript Length:
Copies Required: One
Computer Submission: Yes Disk, Email
Format: MS Word, RTF, PDF
Fees to Review: 0.00 US$

Manuscript Style:
   American Psychological Association

CIRCULATION DATA:

Reader: Academics
Frequency of Issue: Quarterly
Copies per Issue:
Sponsor/Publisher: European Association of
   Work and Organizational Psychology /
   Taylor & Francis
Subscribe Price: 231.00 US$ Individual
   502.00 US$ Institution

REVIEW INFORMATION:

Type of Review:
No. of External Reviewers: 2-3
No. of In House Reviewers:
Acceptance Rate:
Time to Review: 2-6 Months
Reviewers Comments: Yes
Invited Articles:
Fees to Publish: 0.00 US$

MANUSCRIPT TOPICS:
Occupational & Organizational Psychology; Social Psychology

MANUSCRIPT GUIDELINES/COMMENTS:

Note to Authors. Please make sure your contact address information is clearly visible on the outside of all packages you are sending to Editors.

The *European Journal of Work and Organizational Psychology* is the official journal of the European Association of Work and Organizational Psychology (EAWOP), and is published by Psychology Press Ltd, in association with the International Association of Applied Psychology (IAAP).

Manuscript Submission
Manuscripts are invited for submission. Please note that authors are encouraged to submit papers electronically to expedite the peer review process. Please email your paper, saved in a standard document format type such as Word, Rich Text Format, or PDF, to

424

Your covering email/letter must include full contact details (including email), the title of the journal to which you are submitting, and the title of your article.

All manuscripts should be submitted in American Psychological Association (APA) format following the latest edition of *Publication Manual of the APA* (currently 5th edition).

Submitted papers are usually subject to a double blind academic peer review process.

The publisher **strongly encourages** the submission of final, accepted manuscripts on disk (accompanied by one hard copy of text and figures). For guidelines for presentation of final manuscripts on disk including text, tables, and figure artwork please see http://tandf.co.uk/journals/authors/electronic.asp.

Journal Production Editor: **kate.moysen@psypress.co.uk**

Format
Typescripts. The style and format of the typescripts should conform to the specifications given in the *Publication Manual of the American Psychological Association* (5th ed.). Typescripts should be **double spaced** on **one side** only of A4 paper, with adequate margins, and numbered throughout. The title page of an article should contain only:
(1) the title of the paper, the name(s) and address(es) of the author(s);
(2) a short title not exceeding 40 letters and spaces, which will be used for page headlines;
(3) name and full contact address of the author to whom correspondence and proofs should be sent;
(4) your telephone, fax and email details, as this helps speed of processing considerably.

Abstract. An abstract of 50-200 words should follow the title page on a separate sheet.

Headings. Indicate headings and subheadings for different sections of the paper clearly. Do not number headings.

Acknowledgements. These should be as brief as possible and typed on a separate sheet at the beginning of the text.

Permission to quote. Any direct quotation, regardless of length, must be accompanied by a reference citation that includes a page number. Any quote over six manuscript lines should have formal written permission to quote from the copyright owner. It is the author's responsibility to determine whether permission is required from the copyright owner and, if so, to obtain it. (See the bottom of the page for a template of a letter seeking copyright permission.).

Footnotes. These should be avoided unless absolutely necessary. Essential footnotes should be indicated by superscript figures in the text and collected on a separate sheet at the end of the manuscript.

Reference citations within the text. Use authors' last names, with the year of publication in parentheses after the last author's name, e.g., "Jones and Smith (1987)"; alternatively, "(Brown, 1982; Jones & Smith, 1987; White, Johnson, & Thomas, 1990)". On first citation of references with three to six authors, give all names in full, thereafter use first author "et al.". If more than one article by the same author(s) in the same year is cited, the letters a, b, c etc. should follow the year.

Reference list. A full list of references quoted in the text should be given at the end of the paper in alphabetical order of authors' surnames (or chronologically for a group of references by the same authors), commencing as a new sheet, typed double spaced. Titles of journals and books should be given in full, e.g.:

Books
Baddeley, A. D. (1999). *Essentials of human memory*. Hove, UK: Psychology Press.

Chapter in edited book
Plomin, R., & Dale, P. S. (2000). Genetics and early language development: A UK study of twins. In D. V. M. Bishop & L. B. Leonard (Eds.), *Speech and language impairments in children: Causes, characteristics, intervention and outcome* (pp. 35-51). Hove, UK: Psychology Press.

Journal article
Schwartz, M. F., & Hodgson, C. (2002). A new multiword naming deficit: Evidence and interpretation. *Cognitive Neuropsychology*, 19, 263-288.

Tables. These should be kept to the minimum. Each table should be typed double spaced on a separate sheet, giving the heading, e.g., "Table 2", in Arabic numerals, followed by the legend, followed by the table. Make sure that appropriate units are given. Instructions for placing the table should be given in parentheses in the text, e.g., "(Table 2 about here)".

Figures. Figures should only be used when essential. The same data should not be presented both as a figure and in a table. Where possible, related diagrams should be grouped together to form a single figure. Figures should be drawn to professional standards and it is recommended that the linear dimensions of figures be approximately twice those intended for the final printed version. Each of these should be on a separate page, not integrated with the text.

Figures will be reproduced directly from originals supplied by the author(s). These must be of good quality, clearly and completely lettered. Make sure that axes of graphs are properly labelled, and that appropriate units are given. Photocopies will reproduce poorly, as will pale or broken originals. Dense tones should be avoided, and never combined with lettering. Half-tone figures should be clear, highly-contrasted black and white glossy prints.

Black and white figures are included free of charge. Colour figures are not normally acceptable for publication in print -- however, it may be possible both to **print** in black and white and to **publish online** in colour. Colour figures will only be printed by prior arrangement between the editor(s), publisher and author(s); and authors may be asked to share the costs of inclusion of such figures.

The figure captions should be typed in a separate section, headed, e.g., "Figure 2", in Arabic numerals. Instructions for placing the figure should be given in parentheses in the text, e.g., "(Figure 2 about here)". More detailed *Guidelines for the preparation of figure artwork* are available from the publisher: Psychology Press Ltd, 27 Church Road, Hove, East Sussex BN3 2FA, UK (Email: **kate.moysen@psypress.co.uk**).

Statistics. Results of statistical tests should be given in the following form:

"... results showed an effect of group, $F(2, 21) = 13.74$, $MSE = 451.98$, $p < .001$, but there was no effect of repeated trials, $F(5, 105) = 1.44$, $MSE = 17.70$, and no interaction, $F(10, 105) = 1.34$, $MSE = 17.70$."

Other tests should be reported in a similar manner to the above example of an F-ratio. For a fuller explanation of statistical presentation, see pages 136-147 of the *APA Publication Manual* (5th ed.). For guidelines on presenting statistical significance, see pages 24-25.

Abbreviations. Abbreviations that are specific to a particular manuscript or to a very specific area of research should be avoided, and authors will be asked to spell out in full any such abbreviations throughout the text. Standard abbreviations such as RT for reaction time, SOA for stimulus onset asynchrony or other standard abbreviations that will be readily understood by readers of the journal are acceptable. Experimental conditions should be named in full, except in tables and figures.

After Acceptance of Publication in the Journal
Proofs. Page proofs will be emailed to the corresponding author as a PDF attachment to check for typesetting accuracy. No changes to the original typescript will be permitted at this stage. A list of queries raised by the copy editor will also be emailed. Proofs should be returned promptly with the original copy-edited manuscript and query sheet.

Early electronic offprints (e-prints). Specified corresponding authors will receive their article by email as a complete PDF. This allows the author to print up to 50 copies, free of charge, and disseminate them to colleagues. In many cases, this facility will be available up to two weeks prior to print publication of the article. One copy of the journal issue in which their paper appears will be sent by post to all specified corresponding authors free after print publication. Paper offprints can still be purchased by authors if they complete the enclosed offprint order form and return with payment together with their corrected proofs.

Copyright Permission
Contributors are required to secure permission for the reproduction of any figure, table, or extensive (more than six manuscript lines) extract from the text, from a source which is copyrighted -- or owned -- by a party other than Psychology Press Ltd or the contributor.

This applies both to direct reproduction or "derivative reproduction" -- when the contributor has created a new figure or table which derives substantially from a copyrighted source.

The following form of words can be used in seeking permission:

Dear [COPYRIGHT HOLDER]

I/we are preparing for publication an article entitled
[STATE TITLE]
to be published by Psychology Press Ltd in the *European Journal of Work and Organizational Psychology.*

I/we should be grateful if you would grant us permission to include the following materials:
[STATE FIGURE NUMBER AND ORIGINAL SOURCE]
We are requesting non-exclusive rights in this edition and in all forms. It is understood, of course, that full acknowledgement will be given to the source.

Please note that Psychology Press Ltd are signatories of and respect the spirit of the STM Agreement regarding the free sharing and dissemination of scholarly information.

Your prompt consideration of this request would be greatly appreciated.

Yours faithfully

Volume contents and author index. The list of contents and the author index for the whole of the year's issues are published in the last issue of the year of each journal. For the *European Journal of Work and Organizational Psychology*, this is issue 4 (December).

European Psychologist

ADDRESS FOR SUBMISSION:

Verona Christmas-Best, Managing Editor
European Psychologist
  ONLINE SUBMISSIONS ONLY
University of Jena
Department of Psychology I
AmSteiger 3/1
Jena, D-07743
Germany
Phone: +49 3641 945201
Fax: +49 3641 945202
E-Mail: verona.christmas@uni-jena.de
Web: www.hhpub.com/journals/ep
Address May Change:

PUBLICATION GUIDELINES:

Manuscript Length: 21-25
Copies Required: Electronic
Computer Submission: Yes via web page
Format: MS Word; rtf
Fees to Review: 0.00 US$

Manuscript Style:
    American Psychological Association

CIRCULATION DATA:

Reader: Academics, Practitioners
Frequency of Issue: Quarterly
Copies per Issue: 1,001 - 2,000
Sponsor/Publisher: Hogrefe & Huber
  Publishers
Subscribe Price: 49.00 US$ Individual
    130.00 US$ Institution
    39.00 US$ Member Supporting Socities

REVIEW INFORMATION:

Type of Review: Editorial Review
No. of External Reviewers: 3+
No. of In House Reviewers:
Acceptance Rate: 35%
Time to Review: 2 - 3 Months
Reviewers Comments: Yes
Invited Articles: 6-10%
Fees to Publish: 0.00 US$

MANUSCRIPT TOPICS:
Abnormal Psychology; Adolescent Psychology; Adulthood; Alcoholism & Drug Addiction; Behavior Modification; Child Psychology; Counseling Process; Developmental Psychology; Educational Psychology; Exceptional Child; Experimental Psychology; Family Counseling & Therapy; General Psychology; Gerontology; History of Psychology; Learning & Conditioning; Neuropsychology; Personality; Physiological Psychology; Psychiatry; Psychobiology; Psychopathology; Research Methods & Statistics; Sensation & Perception; Social Psychology; Thinking & Cognition

MANUSCRIPT GUIDELINES/COMMENTS:

About the journal
The *European Psychologist*
- is a direct source of information regarding both applied and research psychology throughout Europe;
- provides both reviews of specific fields and original papers of seminal importance;

- integrates across subfields and provides easy access to essential state-of-the-art information in all areas within psychology;
- provides a European perspective on many dimensions of new work being done elsewhere in psychology;
- makes European psychology visible globally;
- promotes scientific and professional cooperation among European Psychologists;
- develops the mutual contribution of psychological theory and practice.

The *European Psychologist*, the English language voice of psychology in Europe, seeks to integrate across all specializations in psychology and to provide a general platform for communication and cooperation among psychologists throughout Europe and worldwide. The Journal accepts four kinds of contribution:

1. **Original articles** (peer reviewed) form an essential section of the journal. Not necessarily focused on European aspects, these present important new findings and ideas, and are written for a non-specialist, general readership in psychology.

2. **Contemporary reviews** (peer reviewed) provide carefully written state-of-the art papers on trends and developments within psychology, with possible reference to European perceptions or fields of specialization.

3. **Reports** inform readers about the work of major research and on psychology-related activities of European institutions and on scientific trends in member countries. Articles on legal and regulatory developments and on trends within respective fields and the political realm that will impact on any aspect of psychology may also be included here. These contributions can be presented in a lively manner, and may involve such formats as discussions, interviews, debates, or conventional articles.

4. **News and announcements**. The Journal will act as a central source of information on important legal, regulatory, ethical, and administrative events of interest to psychologists working throughout Europe. Such items include: Reports on major congresses, Calendar of forthcoming meetings, Information on key symposia and seminars, European funding information about major projects, Current data on academic and other major vacancies. Book reviews will also be published from time to time.

Advice for authors

The *European Psychologist* integrates across all specializations, providing a general platform for communication and cooperation among psychologists throughout Europe and worldwide. Each annual volume consists of four regular issues, with occasional supplements. Only papers that have not previously appeared in or been submitted elsewhere can be considered for publication. Submitted manuscripts are subject to peer review and may be returned to authors for revision.

The journal contains the following sections: original articles, reviews (of a broader field or topical context), reports, commentaries and news, book and journal reviews.

Submission of papers and articles. Manuscripts should be submitted online via the journal's website at: **http://www.hhpub.com/journals/ep/**

430

By submitting an article, the author confirms and guarantees on behalf of him-/herself and any co-authors that the manuscript has not been submitted or published elsewhere, and that he or she holds all copyright in and titles to the submitted contribution, including any figures, photographs, line drawings, plans, maps, sketches, and tables, and that the article and its contents do not infringe in any way on the rights of third parties.

The author agrees, upon acceptance of the article for publication, to transfer to the publisher the exclusive right to reproduce and distribute the article and its contents, both physically and in nonphysical, electronic, or other form, in the journal to which it has been submitted and in other independent publications, with no limitations on the number of copies or on the form or the extent of distribution. These rights are transferred for the duration of copyright as defined by international law. Authors will be asked to complete, sign, and return a Copyright Agreement form upon acceptance of their article.

The **title page** of each paper or article should include, in the following order: Title of the article; Author name(s) (preceded by first names, but with no academic titles given); Name of the institute or clinic (if there is more than one author or institution, affiliations should be indicated using superscript arabic numerals); and an Address for correspondence (including the name of the corresponding author with fax and phone numbers).

A **summary** (maximum length 250 words) should be printed on a separate sheet for original papers, reviews, and reports. A maximum of 5 key reference terms should be given after the summary.

Reference citations in the text and in the reference list proper should follow conventions listed in the *Publication Manual of the American Psychological Association* 4th ed., referred to hereinafter as the *APA Manual*. For example:

Bezchlibnyk-Butler, K.Z., Jr., & Jeffries, J.J. (1995). *Clinical handbook of psychotropic drugs* (5th ed.). Göttingen: Hogrefe & Huber.

Czigler, I., Csibra, G.,&Ambró, Á. (1994). Event-related potentials and aging: Identification of deviant visual stimuli. *Journal of Psychophysiology*, 8, 193–210.

O'Malley, S. (in press). Psychosocial treatments for drug abuse. In C. Stefanis, H. Hippius,&D. Naber (Eds.), *Psychiatry in progress:Vol. 2.*

Research in addiction: An update (pp. 129–136). Göttingen: Hogrefe & Huber.

Tables should be numbered using Arabic numerals. Tables must be cited in the text (e.g., "As shown in Table 1,..."). Each table should be printed on a separate sheet. Below the table number, a brief descriptive title should be given; this should then be followed by the body of the table. It is recommended that each table should also include a brief explanatory legend.

Figures should be numbered using Arabic numerals. Each figure must be cited in the text (e.g., "As illustrated in Figure 1,..."). Two originals in a form suitable for reproduction (high-resolution (300 dpi) graphics files, unscreened original photographs, glossy black-and-white prints, original drawings, slides) should be submitted, along with a good copy. Each figure must be accompanied by a legend. The legends should be printed on a separate sheet. Figures will normally be reproduced in black and white only. While it is possible to reproduce color illustrations, authors are reminded that they will be invoiced for the extra costs involved.

If figures or tables are taken from another source, a letter from the respective copyright holders granting permission to reproduce them must be submitted with the manuscript.

Length of articles
Original Papers & Reviews: ca. 8–10 printed pages; ca. 5500 words of main text plus ca. 40 references (not including summary & title page; if figures or tables are included, the word count should be adjusted accordingly).

Reports: ca. 2–4 printed pages; ca. 1500–2500 words plus up to 15 references.

If the reference list does not conform to APA style, the manuscript will have to be returned to the author for correction.

Scientific nomenclature and style
Authors should follow the guidelines of the *APA Manual* regarding style and nomenclature. Manuscripts that do not conform to these guidelines may have to be returned to the authors for correction.

Language
It is recommended that authors who are not native speakers of English have their papers checked and corrected by a native-speaker colleague before submission. The Editor-in-Chief may have to return manuscripts for correction if the English is inadequate. Standard US American spelling and punctuation as given in *Webster's New Collegiate Dictionary* should be followed.

Proofs
Pdf proofs will be sent to the corresponding author. Changes of content or stylistic changes may only be made in exceptional cases in the proofs. Corrections that exceed 5% of the typesetting costs may be invoiced to the authors.

Complimentary copies
In consideration of the transfer of copyright to the publisher, each author of a review, report, or original article will receive two complimentary copies of the issue in which the article appeared. In addition, offprints can be ordered at cost price, provided that the request is sent in at the same time as the proofs are returned.

Submission of News and Announcements
Items for inclusion in this section should be sent as a file attachment via e-mail direct to the News Editor, Dr. Katharina Althaus, **katharina.althaus@psychologie.ch**. For further information, please refer to the inside front cover.

European Review of Social Psychology

ADDRESS FOR SUBMISSION:

M. Hewstone & W. Stroebe, Editors
European Review of Social Psychology
University of Oxford
Department of Experimental Psychology
South Parks Road
Oxford, OX1 3UD
UK
Phone:
Fax:
E-Mail: miles.hewstone@psy.ox.ac.uk
Web: http://www.tandf.co.uk/journals
Address May Change:

PUBLICATION GUIDELINES:

Manuscript Length:
Copies Required:
Computer Submission: Yes Email
Format: MS Word, RTF, PDF
Fees to Review: 0.00 US$

Manuscript Style:
    American Psychological Association

CIRCULATION DATA:

Reader: Academics
Frequency of Issue: Online
Copies per Issue:
Sponsor/Publisher: Association of
    Experimental Social Psychology / Taylor
    & Francis
Subscribe Price: 150.00 US$

REVIEW INFORMATION:

Type of Review:
No. of External Reviewers:
No. of In House Reviewers:
Acceptance Rate:
Time to Review:
Reviewers Comments:
Invited Articles:
Fees to Publish: 0.00 US$

MANUSCRIPT TOPICS:
Social Psychology

MANUSCRIPT GUIDELINES/COMMENTS:

Note to Authors. Please make sure your contact address information is clearly visible on the outside of all packages you are sending to Editors.

The *European Review of Social Psychology* is an international journal that publishes outstanding work of authors from all nations, rather than restricting it to Europeans. However, even though the *European Review of Social Psychology* is worldwide in terms of the nationality to the authors, it is European in terms of the nationality of the editors who select the contributions and shape the editorial policies, with the help of an editorial board consisting of senior scholars from various European countries, Australasia, and North America. The emphasis of contributions to the *European Review* should be on critical assessment of major areas of research and of substantial individual programmes of research as well as on topics and initiatives of contemporary interest and originality.

Volumes contain three types of contributions:

(1) Reviews of the field in some specific area of social psychology, typically one in which European researchers have made some special contribution.

(2) Reports of extended research programmes that contribute to knowledge of a particular phenomenon or process.

(3) Contributions to a contemporary theoretical issue or debate.

Thus, the *European Review of Social Psychology* is not an outlet for the publication of primary data.

Manuscript Submission
Most manuscripts are commissioned by the Editors, who invite contributions based on the author's recent publication of data in leading peer-reviewed journals that publish original empirical articles. However, the Editors welcome suggestions either direct from the authors, or indirectly from other scholars. Authors with a concrete proposal should provide a ca. 5-page outline, with a full listing of their own prior primary publications which will form the basis of the proposed submission. These outlines should be submitted electronically to Miles Hewstone (Email: **miles.hewstone@psy.ox.ac.uk**). In addition, please send **three paper copies** of these outlines to Miles Hewstone, European Review of Social Psychology, Department of Experimental Psychology, University of Oxford, South Parks Road, Oxford OX1 3UD, UK. Authors should wait for an editorial decision before starting work on the manuscript proper.

As a rule, manuscripts should not exceed 40 pages (**double spaced**, inclusive of references. Authors should submit their manuscripts electronically to the editorial office (email: **miles.hewstone@psy.ox.ac.uk**). In addition, please send five copies of each manuscript, in APA format, to Miles Hewstone, *European Review of Social Psychology*, Department of Experimental Psychology, University of Oxford, South Parks Road, Oxford OX1 3UD, UK.

Copyright. It is a condition of publication that authors vest or license copyright in their articles, including abstracts, in the European Association of Experimental Social Psychology. This enables us to ensure full copyright protection and to disseminate the article, and the journal, to the widest possible readership in print and electronic formats as appropriate. Authors may, of course, use the material elsewhere after publication providing that prior permission is obtained from Taylor & Francis Ltd. Authors are themselves responsible for obtaining permission to reproduce copyright material from other sources. To view the 'Copyright Transfer Frequently Asked Questions' please visit
www.tandf.co.uk/journals/copyright.asp.

Review process. Invitation to submit a manuscript to the *European Review of Social Psychology* does not imply that the manuscript will ultimately be accepted for publication. All manuscripts will be externally reviewed. As a result, some manuscripts will be rejected and others have to undergo more or less extensive reviews.

The publishers require the submission of final, accepted manuscripts on disk (Microsoft Word in PC format), accompanied by hard copy. For guidelines for presentation of final manuscripts on disk please see http://www.tandf.co.uk/journals/authors/electronic.asp.

Preparation of Manuscript

Manuscripts should be **double-spaced** throughout on **one side** of A4 white paper. Manuscripts should be prepared in accord with the format and style specified by the American Psychological Association. For full details of this format, please see the *Publication Manual of the APA* (5th edition).

Title Page. This should be as concise as possible, and typed on a separate sheet, containing only the following:
1. the title of the paper, the name(s) and address(es) of the author(s);
2. a short title not exceeding 40 letters and spaces, which will be used for page headlines;
3. name and address of the author to whom correspondence and proofs should be sent;
4. your telephone, fax and e-mail numbers, as this helps speed of processing considerably.

Abstract. (p. 2) An abstract of 100-150 words should follow the title page on a separate sheet.

Headings. Indicate headings and sub-headings for different sections of the paper clearly. Do not number headings.

Acknowledgements. These should be as brief as possible and typed on a separate sheet at the beginning of the text.

Permission to quote. Any direct quotation, regardless of length, must be accompanied by a reference citation that includes a page number. Any quote over six manuscript lines should have formal written permission to quote from the copyright owner. It is the author's responsibility to determine whether permission is required from the copyright owner, and if so, to obtain it. (See sample copyright request letter at the bottom of this page.)

Authors are responsible for obtaining permission to reprint previously published figures, tables, and other material. Letters of permission should accompany the final submission.

Footnotes. These should be avoided unless absolutely necessary. Essential footnotes should be indicated by superscript figures in the text and collected on a separate sheet at the end of the manuscript.

Reference citations within the text. Use authors' last names, with the year of publication in parentheses after the last author's name, e.g., "Jones and Smith (1987)"; alternatively: "(Brown, 1982; Jones & Smith, 1987; White, Johnson, & Thomas, 1990)". On first citation of references with three or more authors, give all names in full, thereafter use first author "et al.". If more than one article by the same author(s) in the same year is cited, the letters a, b, c, etc., should follow the year.

References. A full list of references quoted in the text should be given at the end of the paper in alphabetical order of authors' surnames (chronologically for a group of references by the same authors) as specified in the *Publication Manual of the APA* (5th edition). Personal communications should be cited as such in the text (with a full date) and should not be included in the reference list.

Titles of journals and books should be given in full, as in the following examples:

Books
Baddeley, A. D. (1999). *Essentials of human memory*. Hove, UK: Psychology Press.

Chapter in edited book
Plomin, R., & Dale, P. S. (2000). Genetics and early language development: A UK study of twins. In D. V. M. Bishop & L. B. Leonard (Eds.), *Speech and language impairments in children: Causes, characteristics, intervention and outcome* (pp. 35-51). Hove, UK: Psychology Press.

Journal article
Schwartz, M. F., & Hodgson, C. (2002). A new multiword naming deficit: Evidence and interpretation. *Cognitive Neuropsychology*, 19, 263-288.

Tables. As a rule, tables should summarize findings of several studies. The number of tables included in manuscripts should not normally exceed 5-6. Each table should be typed double spaced on a separate sheet, giving the heading, for example, "Table 2", in Arabic numerals, followed by the legend, followed by the table. Make sure that appropriate units are given. Instructions for placing the table should be given in parentheses in the text, for example "(Table 2 about here)".

Figures. Figures should normally be limited to 3-5 . Where possible, related diagrams should be grouped together to form a single figure. Figures should be drawn to professional standards, and it is recommended that the linear dimensions of figures be approximately twice those intended for the final printed version. (Maximum printed figure size 181 mm x 114 mm, including caption.) Make sure that axes of graphs are properly labelled, and that appropriate units are given. The figure captions should be typed in a separate section, headed, for example, "Figure 2", in Arabic numerals. Do not use graphics that present two-dimensional data in quasi-three-dimensional form (i.e., histograms). Instructions for placing the figure should be given in parentheses in the text, for example: "(Figure 2 about here)".

Statistics. Since the empirical findings on which the papers published by the *European Review of Social Psychology* are based will already have been published in other (senior) international journals, statistics for significance levels of p-values will not be included in these manuscripts.

Abbreviations. Abbreviations that are specific to a particular manuscript or to a very specific area of research should be avoided, and authors will be asked to spell out in full any such abbreviations throughout the text. Standard abbreviations such as RT for reaction time, SOA for stimulus onset asynchrony or other standard abbreviations that will be readily understood by readers of the journal are acceptable. Experimental conditions should be named in full, except in tables and figures.

After Acceptance of Publication in the Journal
Proofs. Page proofs will be emailed to the corresponding author as a PDF attachment to check for typesetting accuracy. No changes to the original typescript will be permitted at this stage. A list of queries raised by the copy editor will also be emailed. Proofs should be returned promptly with the original copy-edited manuscript and query sheet.

Early electronic offprints (e-prints). Corresponding authors can now receive their article by e-mail as a complete PDF. This allows the author to print up to 50 copies, free of charge, and disseminate them to colleagues. At the end of the year, the online articles are bound together and sold as a hardback book.

Copyright Permission
Contributors are required to secure permission for the reproduction of any figure, table, or extensive (more than six manuscript lines) extract from the text, from a source which is copyrighted -- or owned -- by a party other than Psychology Press Ltd or the contributor. This applies both to direct reproduction or "derivative reproduction" -- when the contributor has created a new figure or table which derives **substantially** from a copyrighted source.

The following form of words can be used in seeking permission:

Dear [COPYRIGHT HOLDER]

I/we are preparing for publication an article entitled:
[STATE TITLE]
to be published by Psychology Press Ltd in the *European Review of Social Psychology*.

I/we should be grateful if you would grant us permission to include the following materials:
[STATE FIGURE NUMBER AND ORIGINAL SOURCE]
We are requesting non-exclusive rights in this edition and in all forms. It is understood, of course, that full acknowledgement will be given to the source.

Please note that Psychology Press Ltd are signatories of and respect the spirit of the STM Agreement regarding the free sharing and dissemination of scholarly information.

Your prompt consideration of this request would be greatly appreciated.

Yours faithfully

Evolution and Human Behavior

ADDRESS FOR SUBMISSION:

Martin Daly & Margo Wilson, Editors
Evolution and Human Behavior
McMaster University
Department of Psychology
  ELECTRONIC SUBMISSIONS
Hamilton
Ontario, L8S 4K1
Canada
Phone: 905-525-9140 x 23033, x 23018
Fax:
E-Mail: ehb-eds@mcmaster.ca
Web: See Guidelines
Address May Change:

PUBLICATION GUIDELINES:

Manuscript Length: 1 - 30+
Copies Required: 1 Electronic + 1 Hard
Computer Submission: Yes Email Required
Format: Word 2000
Fees to Review: 0.00 US$

Manuscript Style:
  See Manuscript Guidelines

CIRCULATION DATA:

Reader: Academics, Psychologists,
  Anthropologists
Frequency of Issue: 6 Times/Year
Copies per Issue: 1,001 - 2,000
Sponsor/Publisher: Human Behavior &
  Evolution Society/Elsevier Science
  Publishing Co.
Subscribe Price: 60.00 US$ Individual
  30.00 US$ Student

REVIEW INFORMATION:

Type of Review: Editorial Review
No. of External Reviewers: 1-2
No. of In House Reviewers: 0-1
Acceptance Rate: 21-30%
Time to Review: 1 - 2 Months
Reviewers Comments: No Reply
Invited Articles: 0-5%
Fees to Publish: 0.00 US$

MANUSCRIPT TOPICS:
Culture & Personality; Evolution & Human Behavior

MANUSCRIPT GUIDELINES/COMMENTS:

Website. **www.science.mcmaster.ca/psychology/ehb/ehb.htm**

Aims and Scope
Evolution and Human Behavior is an interdisciplinary journal, presenting research reports and theory in which evolutionary perspectives are brought to bear on the study of human behavior. It is primarily a scientific journal, but submissions from scholars in the humanities are also encouraged. Papers reporting on theoretical and empirical work on other species will be welcome if their relevance to the human animal is apparent.

Audience. Ethologist, Sociobiologists, Animal Behaviorists, Zoologists, Psychologists, Anthropologists and Sociologists.

438

Guide for Authors

All manuscripts should be submitted to Martin Daly or Margo Wilson, Department of Psychology, McMaster University, Hamilton, Ontario, Canada L8S 4K1. *Evolution and Human Behavior* publishes primary research reports, theoretical contributions, and critical synthetic review papers. Books reviews are solicited by the editors; suggestions concerning books warranting review are welcome. Brief letters to the Editors and comments on material previously published in the journal may be considered. Manuscripts are submitted with the understanding that they are original, unpublished work and are not being submitted elsewhere.

Manuscript. Submit the manuscript, typed double-spaced on 8.5 x 11 in. Bond paper. On the title page include names and addresses of authors, academic or professional affiliations, and the complete address of the author to whom proofs and reprint requests should be sent. Also provide a running title of less than 45 characters and spaces, which will appear on alternate pages in the journal. Include an Abstract of not more than 200 words (less than 50 words for Short Communications) on the following page. Below the Abstract list Key Words that best code the contents of the article for indexing purposes. The text proper begins on the following page and ends with a citation of acknowledgments, whenever appropriate. References, tabular material, figure captions, and footnotes follow, each section beginning a new page. Table and figures are numbered in order of their appearance with Arabic numerals and each should have a brief descriptive title. Footnotes to the text are numbered consecutively with superior Arabic numerals.

Electronic Submissions. Authors are required to submit an electronic version of the manuscript to the editorial office along with the hard copy submission. The electronic version should be emailed to **ehb-eds@mcmaster.ca**. Please observe the following criteria. Make certain that the electronic version and hard copy match exactly. Send either a .doc or .pdf file and specify the software used, including the specific release, e.g. Word 97 or WordPerfect 6.1. The article file should include all textual material (text, references, tables, figure captions, etc.) and separate illustration files, if available. The file should follow the general instructions on style/arrangement and, in particular, the reference style of this journal as given in the Information for Authors. The file should be single-spaced and should use the wrap-around end-of-line feature, i.e., returns at the end of the paragraphs only. Place two returns after every element, such as title, headings, paragraphs, figures and table callouts. Be sure to keep a back-up disk for reference and safety.

Mathematical Notation. Use typewritten letters, numbers, and symbols whenever possible. Identify boldface, script letters, etc. at their first occurrence. Distinguish between one and the letter "l" and between zero and the letter "o" whenever confusion might result.

References. References should be prepared according to the *Publication Manual of the American Psychological Association*, Fourth Edition. Examples follow:

Journal. Wittingham, L.A., Taylor, P.D., & Robertson, R.J. (1992). Confidence of paternity and male parental care. *American Naturalist, 139,* 1115-1125.

Book. Williams, G.C. (1966). *Adaptation and natural selection.* Princeton: Princeton University Press.

Chapter. Dickemann, M. (1981). Paternal confidence and dowry competition: a biocultural analysis of purdah. In R.D. Alexander & D.W. Tinkle (Eds.), *Natural selection and social behavior,* (pp.417-438). New York: Chiron Press.

Illustrations. Unmounted, glossy, black and white photographs or India ink drawings on white paper should accompany the original copy of the manuscript. Photocopies are suitable for the other three copies of the manuscript. To facilitate identification and processing, on the back of each figure write the number, first author's name, and indicate which side is top. Illustrations should be mounted on white bond paper with rubber cement or glue used sparingly. Captions appear on a separate page.

Proofs and Reprints. The corresponding author will receive proofs, which should be corrected and returned within 48 hours of receipt or the article will be published without author corrections. The author is responsible for proofreading the manuscript; the publisher is not responsible for any error not marked by the author on proof. Corrections in proof are limited to printer's error; no substantial author changes are allowed at this state. Reprints may be ordered prior to publication; consult the price list accompanying proofs.

Page Charges. No page charges are applied in the journal.

Copyright. Upon acceptance of an article by the journal, the author(s) will be asked to transfer copyright of the article to the publisher. This transfer will insure the widest possible dissemination of information under the U.S. Copyright Law.

Experimental Aging Research

ADDRESS FOR SUBMISSION:

Jeffrey W. Elias, Editor
Experimental Aging Research
Phone:
Fax:
E-Mail: Elias_Treland@Earthlink.net
Web: http://www.tandf.co.uk/journals
Address May Change:

CIRCULATION DATA:

Reader:
Frequency of Issue:
Copies per Issue:
Sponsor/Publisher: Taylor & Francis
Subscribe Price: 0.00 US$

PUBLICATION GUIDELINES:

Manuscript Length:
Copies Required:
Computer Submission:
Format:
Fees to Review: 0.00 US$

Manuscript Style:

REVIEW INFORMATION:

Type of Review:
No. of External Reviewers:
No. of In House Reviewers:
Acceptance Rate:
Time to Review:
Reviewers Comments:
Invited Articles:
Fees to Publish: 0.00 US$

MANUSCRIPT TOPICS:
Gerontology

MANUSCRIPT GUIDELINES/COMMENTS:

Aims and Scope
Experimental Aging Research is a life span developmental and aging journal dealing with research on the aging process from a psychological and psychobiological perspective. It meets the need for a scholarly journal with refereed scientific papers dealing with age differences and age changes at any point in the adult life span. Areas of major focus include experimental psychology, neuropsychology, psychobiology, work research, ergonomics, and behavioral medicine. Original research, book reviews, monographs, and papers covering special topics are published.

The Institute of Scientific Information Journal Citations Report for 2002 ranks *Experimental Aging Research* 57th out of 61 journals in Psychology (Social Science) and 24th out of 27 journals in Geriatrics & Gerontology (Social Science), with an impact factor of 0.667.

Readership
Life span developmental psychologists and psychobiologists, gerontologists, behavioral and life span methodologists, ergonomists, health psychologists, and health care professionals.

Submission of Manuscripts

It is suggested that authors send their manuscript via e-mail attachment to Jeffrey W. Elias, Ph.D. Editor-in-Chief, Experimental Aging Research at the following e-mail address:**Elias_Treland@earthlink.net**. If manuscripts cannot be sent this way, please contact the editor via e-mail to make arrangements to send a diskette or typewritten manuscript to: Jeffrey W. Elias, Editor-in-Chief, *Experimental Aging Research*, P.O. Box 83429, Gaithersburg, Maryland 20883-3429. Typewritten manuscripts and all other correspondence can be sent to the above P.O. Box. A separate letter of transmittal should accompany each transmission or mailing that includes a telephone and fax number, and an e-mail address where the author can be reached during office hours. The names, institutions, and e-mail addresses of four persons should be supplied who might be considered qualified reviewers for the submitted manuscript. This does not guarantee that one of the suggested might be used. Books (2 copies) can be sent to Dr. Julia Treland at: Experimental Aging Research, P.O. Box 83429, Gaithersburg, Maryland 20883-3429. Dr. Treland can be reached via e-mail at **Elias_Treland@earthlink.net**.

Each manuscript must be accompanied by a statement that it has not been published elsewhere and that it has not been submitted simultaneously for publication elsewhere. Authors are responsible for obtaining permission to reproduce copyrighted material from other sources and are required to sign an agreement for the transfer of copyright to the publisher. All accepted manuscripts, artwork, and photographs become the property of the publisher. All parts of the manuscript should be typewritten, double-spaced, with margins of at least one inch on all sides. Number manuscript pages consecutively throughout the paper. Authors should also supply a shortened version of the title suitable for the running head, not exceeding 50 character spaces. Each article should be summarized in an abstract of not more than 100 words. Avoid abbreviations, diagrams, and reference to the text. (The average paper is from 20 to 30 typed pages. Brief reports are acceptable. Papers longer than 35 pages should be approved by the Editor-in- Chief.)

The journal employs the style and format used by the American Psychological Association. Please use the most current publication manual: *The Publication Manual of the American Psychological Association* (4th ed., 1994). This may be ordered from the Publication Department, American Psychological Association, 750 First Street, NE, Washington, D.C. 20002-4242, USA, phone (202) 336-5500, fax (202) 336-5502. A useful URL for the APA style manual and for referencing electronic media and URLs is: www.apastyle.org/elecmedia.html. Authors should consult the first issue of each volume for editorial policy. Further instructions and an author template can be obtained from the journal's web page at www.taylorandfrancis.com.

Tables and Figures

Tables and figures/illustrations (line drawings, halftones, photos, photomicrographs, etc.) should not be embedded in the text but should be included as separate sheets or files. A short descriptive title should appear above each table with a clear legend and any footnotes suitably identified below. All units must be included. Figures should be completely labeled, taking into account necessary size reduction. Captions should be typed, double-spaced, on a separate sheet. All original figures should be clearly marked in pencil on the reverse side with the number, author's name, and top edge indicated, and should be clean originals or digital files.

Digital files are recommended for highest quality reproduction and should follow these guidelines:
- 300 dpi or higher
- sized to fit on journal page
- EPS, TIFF, or PSD format only
- submitted as separate files, not embedded in text files

Color illustrations will be considered for publication; however, the author will be required to bear the full cost involved in their printing and publication. The charge for the first figure is $1,200.00. Subsequent figures, totaling no more than 4 text pages, are $500.00 each. Good quality color prints should be provided in their final size. Figures needing reduction or enlargement will be charged an additional 25 percent. The publisher has the right to refuse publication of any artwork deemed unacceptable.

References
Cite in the text by author and date (Smith, 1983). Prepare reference list in accordance with the *APA Publication Manual*, 4th ed. Examples:

Journal
Pellegrino, J. W, & Battig, W. E. (1974). Relationships among high order organisational measures and free recall. *Journal of Experimental Psychology*, 102, 463-472.

Book
Underwood, B. J. (1983). *Attributes of memory*. Glenview, IL: Scott, Foresman.

Contribution to a book
Craik E I.M. & Byrd, M. (1982). Aging and cognitive deficits: The role of attentional resources. In EI.M. Craik & S. E. Trehub (Eds.), *Advances in the study of communication and affect: Aging and cognitive processes* (pp. 191-211). New York: Plenum Press.

Proofs
Page proofs are sent to the designated author. They must be carefully checked and returned within 48 hours of receipt.

Reprints
The corresponding author of each article will receive one complete copy of the issue in which the article appears. Reprints of an individual article may be ordered from Taylor & Francis. Use the reprint order form included with page proofs.

Families in Society

ADDRESS FOR SUBMISSION:

William E. Powell, Editor
Families in Society
11700 West Lake Park Drive
Milwaukee, WI 53224-3099
USA
Phone: 414-359-1040
Fax: 414-359-1074
E-Mail: See Guidelines
Web: www.familiesinsociety.org
Address May Change:

PUBLICATION GUIDELINES:

Manuscript Length: 16-20 (body text)
Copies Required: Two
Computer Submission: Yes
Format: MS Word, (Mac & PC)
Fees to Review: 0.00 US$

Manuscript Style:
   American Psychological Association

CIRCULATION DATA:

Reader: Academics, Practitioners and
   Students
Frequency of Issue: Quarterly
Copies per Issue: 3,000
Sponsor/Publisher: Alliance for Children
   and Families
Subscribe Price: 44.00 US$ Individual
   286.00 US$ Institution
   60.00 US$ Nonprofit / $41 Student

REVIEW INFORMATION:

Type of Review: Blind Review
No. of External Reviewers: 50
No. of In House Reviewers: 0
Acceptance Rate: 34%
Time to Review: 3-6 Months
Reviewers Comments: Yes
Invited Articles: 0-5%
Fees to Publish: 0.00 US$

MANUSCRIPT TOPICS:

Behavior Modification; Culture & Personality; Developmental Psychology; Environment and Behavior; Gender Roles; Group Dynamics; Human Relations; Human Sexuality; Psychology of Women; Social Work; Treatment; Worker-Client Relationships

MANUSCRIPT GUIDELINES/COMMENTS:

Editorial Mission
One of the most respected professional peer-reviewed journals in the human services field, *Families in Society*, now in its 85th year, is a forum for addressing the interests, activities, and concerns of professionals in direct practice, as well as associates in supervision, administration, policy and planning, research, and education.

Article Types
Because of social work's unique concern with the person-in-the-situation, across the life span and across generations, *FIS* articles typically reflect the broad array of issues, conditions, and problems that are pertinent to personal, interpersonal, familial, community, and societal problems of living. In this regard, articles might be informative, instructive, reflective, and controversial. More specifically, the journal welcomes articles concerned with:

Issues in direct practice. Examples include practice with special populations, innovations, preparation for practice, unmet needs, dealing with involuntary clients, obstacles to helping, private practice and agency practice, the place of values, culture, and diversity.

Reflections on and analysis of practice. FIS is particularly interested in critical and controversial essays that examine the state of the art, the strengths and failings of professional practice, the adequacy of professional education, the limitations of social policy, future needs, and personal reflections on what it means to be a social worker, the philosophy of practice.

The role of theory and other foundations for practice. Among other issues is the question about how the integration of theory and practice might be achieved. What theories are particularly relevant to social work education and practice?

Research reports. FIS is receptive to many forms of inquiry including quantitative and qualitative. Beyond the relevance of the study itself, a major criterion for publication is the study's applicability to practice concerns and its accessibility to practitioner-readers.

Agency/profession. Articles dealing with the context of practice including training and supervision, the agency and the community, legal and ethical issues, administration, funding, and interagency alliances are welcome.

Other formats. FIS also invites literary formats other than the standard manuscript that readily capture the humanistic qualities of practice. Such formats might include brief commentaries, reports of experiences, reflections on practice, personal essays, narratives, and critical discussions.

Author Guidelines/Manuscript Preparation
Manuscripts must follow the guidelines set by the *Publication Manual of the American Psychological Association*. If you don't have ready access to the manual, you can obtain information on the APA style at any of the following Web sites: www.apastyle.org and www.nutsandbolts.washcoll.edu/apa.html.

Standard-format journal articles should be created using any popular word processing software. Microsoft Word is the preferred application. We accept files from both PCs and Macintoshes. Files can also be saved as Rich Text Format (RTF) files.

When submitting your initial manuscript, please print out and mail two copies. to the address below, along with an electronic version of the file. *The electronic version of your file should be sent to us via e-mail at* **manuscripts@familiesinsociety.org**.

Articles should be no more than 20 pages in length, double-spaced, excluding references and accompanying figures and tables. Each copy should include a cover sheet with the name, title and the /affiliation of each author. The next page should include the title and abstract, followed by the main body of the article, but this page and those following should not include indication of authorship. The cover letter should identify the corresponding author with contact information, including an e-mail address.

Please pay particular attention to the writing of the abstract as it is often used by index services in lieu of or in addition to the actual article. Many indexers, including PsychInfo, limit abstracts to 120 words, and we highly recommend this limit to prevent indexers from truncating or rewriting the abstract. For more information on what constitutes a well-written abstract, visit www.apa.org/journals.

Literature citations in text should follow the author–date style. Web sources in the reference list require the exact date the information was retrieved or accessed.

Tables and figures should be included with the manuscript, but not within the body copy. Instead, insert placeholders in the copy to indicate where the table or figure should be placed. Include tables and figures as separate, properly labeled files.

Queries regarding the suitability of potential articles are welcome. William Powell, the editor, can be reached at: Families in Society, 11700 West Lake Park Drive, Milwaukee, WI 53224-3099 Tel: 414-359-1040 Fax: 414-359-1074 E-mail: **manuscripts@familiesinsociety.org**

The Manuscript Peer Review Process

Manuscripts submitted to *Families in Society* are double-blind peer reviewed. When a manuscript is received in the journal's Milwaukee editorial headquarters, it is logged in and forwarded to the editor who identifies two to three potential reviewers. These consulting editors/reviewers are then contacted to determine availability to review the manuscript within a specified period of time. If they are available to do the review, they are typically given 30 days to complete a review, provide comments, and recommend acceptance or rejection. In some cases, it may be necessary to query more than three reviewers.

Manuscript Review Criteria

Consulting editors/reviewers critique manuscript using a review guide provided by Families in Society. Key review criteria include:

- Relevancy to the social work environment
- Appropriateness for inclusion in Families in Society
- Quality of writing and adherence to the style standards established by the APA
- Thoroughness and relevancy of the literature search
- Soundness of research methods or ideas
- Conclusions that are in keeping with the scope of the manuscript
- Findings that are applicable to practice, policy, or other use
- Articles that are relevant to practice should include implications for practice

Manuscript Reviewer Recommendations

When each review is completed, the reviewers select one of the following recommendations:

- Accept
- Accept with minor revisions
- Accept with substantial revisions
- Reject, but may reconsider if substantially revised or rewritten
- Refer to another journal
- Reject

Reviewer recommendations are then reviewed by the journal's editor. Once the editor determines that a manuscript has been properly and thoroughly considered, the editor makes a disposition which is conveyed to the author or authors.

Initial Manuscript Disposition

The Families in Society accepted-for-publication rate is approximately 34% of all manuscripts reviewed. Most of these manuscripts are accepted conditionally, pending revisions suggested by the reviewers, editor, or both. To aid the author(s) revising their manuscripts, comments provided by the consulting editors are often provided along with the initial disposition. When a request that a manuscript be revised is received by an author, the author may elect to challenge the some of the suggestions through a letter to the editor when the manuscript is resubmitted. Authors with questions about provided comments may send these questions to the journal (preferably by e-mail) and they will be forwarded to the editor.

Determining Manuscript Publication Date

Manuscripts accepted for publication typically appear 12 to 18 months after being submitted for consideration. Manuscripts are not scheduled for publication in the order in which they are accepted. Instead, the editor selects manuscripts based on ocus or topic, and a desired editorial balance within an issue.

Special Issues or Issues with a Special Focus

Every year *Families in Society* produces within the context of its quarterly publication schedule at least one special issue, or issue with a special focus. Typically, these consist of an entire issue or a large segment of an issue devoted to a singular focus. For example, recent special issues or focus sections featured the strengths perspective, program outcomes, and social welfare. Most special issues have a "guest editor," who works with the *Families in Society* editor to prepare the content. More information on upcoming special issues is available on our Web site and suggestions for special issues and focus sections are welcome.

Copyright and Permissions

All material published in *Families in Society,* except advertising, is copyrighted by the Alliance for Children and Families.

No material from the publication may be reproduced, reprinted or excerpted without written permission from the Alliance for Children and Families.

All permission requests should be entered via the Copyright Clearance Center (www.copyright.com) for *Families in Society* material.

Permissions and fees are waived for *Families in Society* authors wishing to reproduce their own material for personal use; fees only are waived for authors who wish to use more than a single table or figure of their own material commercially (but for use in edited books, fees are waived only if the author is serving as the book editor).

Family Process

ADDRESS FOR SUBMISSION:

Evan Imber-Black, Editor
Family Process
c/o Ackerman Institute for the Family
149 E. 78th Street
New York, NY 10021
USA
Phone: 212-879-4900 ext.153
Fax: 914-699-1548
E-Mail: evanft@verizon.net
Web: www.familyprocess.org
Address May Change:

PUBLICATION GUIDELINES:

Manuscript Length: 21-25 6000 words
Copies Required: Five
Computer Submission: Yes Hard copy +
   Disk
Format: MS Word
Fees to Review: 0.00 US$

Manuscript Style:
   American Psychological Association

CIRCULATION DATA:

Reader: Academics, Practitioners
Frequency of Issue: Quarterly
Copies per Issue: 3,001 - 4,000
Sponsor/Publisher: Blackwell Publishers,
   Inc.
Subscribe Price: 54.00 US$ Individual
   108.00 US$ Institution /$24 Student
   See Website - more details

REVIEW INFORMATION:

Type of Review: Blind Review
No. of External Reviewers: 3
No. of In House Reviewers: 1
Acceptance Rate: 11-20%
Time to Review: 2 - 3 Months
Reviewers Comments: Yes
Invited Articles: 0-5%
Fees to Publish: 0.00 US$

MANUSCRIPT TOPICS:
Adolescent Psychology; Child Psychology; Family Counseling & Therapy; Family Dynamics

MANUSCRIPT GUIDELINES/COMMENTS:

Website. **www.blackwellpublishing.com**   Email: **subscrip@bos.blackwellpublishing.com**

Topics Include. Family Systems; Family and Marital Interaction Research; Children and Adolescents in the Context of the Family; Family Therapy Training; Philosophical Underpinnings of Family Systems Approaches; Qualitative and Quantitative Clinical Research; Family Relationships to Larger Systems and Networks.

About *Family Process*
Family Process is a multidisciplinary international journal that publishes research, training, and theoretical contributions in the broad area of family therapy. Founded in 1962, it is widely considered to be the pre-eminent publication of its kind in the family therapy field. Since its inception, almost 40 years ago, the journal has become a major resource for mental health and social service professionals who are looking for cutting edge research and clinical ideas about family and systems theory and practice.

When *Family Process* was first published, family therapy was in its infancy. Now this discipline is recognized as one of the most important approaches to a wide range of psychological and behavioral problems. The exciting history of the family therapy field is all contained in our searchable online archive, where over the years the most important conceptual ideas and treatment advances have been documented.

We welcome you to browse through samples of the articles we have published this past year, and become a member of our family by subscribing to the journal and website or by purchasing our CD-ROM containing all the articles from the first 38 years of the journal's publication. We also invite you to send us your own work for possible publication in the journal.

INSTRUCTIONS FOR AUTHORS
Manuscripts should be sent to:
    Evan Imber-Black, Ph.D., Editor, c/o Ackerman Institute for the Family, 149 East 78th St., NY, NY 10021, E-mail: **editor@FamilyProcess.org**

General Requirements
In a cover letter, please include the word count of the article, and the address, phone number, and if possible, fax and e-mail address of the principle author. Authors will be advised of the decision about their manuscripts as rapidly as possible. Manuscripts are received with the understanding that they are not being submitted simultaneously to another publication.

Authors are requested to prepare their articles in conformity with *Family Process* style (refer to pervious issues for reference). Papers should be written clearly and concisely, using gender-neutral language and a minimum of jargon. Brevity is also desirable. All case reports should protect patient confidentiality.

Typing
Manuscripts (original and 4 copies) should be on white bond paper, double-spaced throughout, and with 1 ½ inch margins. A copy of the manuscript on an IBM compatible disk in text only format (.txt) should be included with the initial submission. Files submitted in WordPerfect or Microsoft Word format are encouraged. In either case, the author is advised to keep a copy for checking against page proofs. Upon acceptance, authors will be expected to provide the final manuscript on disk.

Authors
Because *Family Process* uses a blind review system, a separate cover page should be used to provide identifying information about the authors. The authors' names should not be included on subsequent pages. For each author, give professional degree/title, and name and location of the principal institutional affiliation, and complete mailing address of the principal author; the latter will appear in a footnote on page 1 of the article if accepted. Upon acceptance, the principal author will receive a copyright transfer form and an off-print order form. These must be returned immediately upon receipt. In addition to the principal author's address, also include the address for all other authors to receive complimentary copies of the issue.

Acknowledgements
Any listing of grant support or special appreciation that the authors wish to include should be included on the cover page. If the article is accepted for publication, this information will appear in another footnote on page 1.

Opening Summary
For full-length articles, the author should include an abstract of approximately 200-250 words. Research articles should use the standard categories of introduction, methods, results and discussion. In articles describing theory, training or clinical interventions, the abstract should make it possible for the reader to have a brief overview of all relevant aspects of the work, including the intent, scope, general procedures, and principal conclusions. For brief reports, these summaries should be similar in content, but limited to 100 words.

References
An important responsibility of the author is the preparation of a correct reference list, double spaced and located at the end of the article. References should be checked against original sources.

References in Text
First citation may include up to 4 names (NB: et al. = "and others"); more than 4, cite first 3, et al., date. Subsequent citations: include dual authors; more than 2, cite first surname et al., date. Serial listings: alphabetize by surname of first author.

Reference List. Alphabetize by surname; list *all* authors; spell out journal names: abbreviations for journals and shortcuts (ibid., op. Cit.) are not acceptable. (See following examples.)

Articles. Ackerman, N.W.(1971). The growing edge of family therapy. Family Process 10:143-156.//Smith, N., Smith, A., & Jones, P. (1968)....

Chapters. Goldstein, M.J., & Strachan, A.M. (1987). The family and schizophrenia (pp. 481-509). In T. Jacob (ed.), Family interaction and psychopathology: Theories, methods, and findings. New York: Plenum Press.

Edited Books. Wynne, L.C., McDaniel, S.H., & Weber, T.T. (eds.). (1986). Systems consultation: A new perspective for family therapy. New York: Guilford Press.

Quotations
Page number(s) must be provided.

Footnotes
A superior number at the appropriate place in the text should indicate the appearance of a footnote. The numbered list of footnotes, typed double space, should be located after the reference listing.

450

Headings

The journal uses a bi-column format; headings must be short. Within the text, three levels of headings are used: major heads are centered, boldface capitals, thus:

METHOD

Major subheads are flushed left, boldface, with initial capitals, thus:

Family Constellation

Minor subheads are flushed left, italicized, with initial capitals, thus:

Case Example

Tables

Use a separate sheet of paper for each table.

Figures

The author must supply High-contrast glossy prints or camera-ready copies; legends are typed on a separate page. See current issues of the Journal for models. Indicate in the text where tables/figures are to be placed, thus:

/Table (Figure) 1 above here/

Copy Editing, Proofs, and Off-print/Reprint Orders

After an article has been accepted for publication, it is copy-edited for literary style, conformity to the style of this journal, clarity of presentation, coherence, punctuation, standard usage of terms, spelling, etc. After the article is typeset authors may be charged for any changes they wish to make. The author will receive page-proofs from the printer, together with an Off-Print/Reprint order form that must be returned within 10 days of receipt.

Occasionally, and with the author's permission, an article that has been accepted will be followed by an invited commentary to which the author may submit a rejoinder. The author's unwillingness to participate in this process will in no way affect the publication of an accepted article.

Books for listing or review, as well as articles on professional publications in the field, should be sent to carol Anderson, Ph.D., Editor, Family Process, UPMC Health System, Room 441, 3811 O'Hara St., Pittsburgh, PA 15213 USA.

Family Relations: Interdisciplinary Journal of Applied Family Studies

ADDRESS FOR SUBMISSION:

Joyce A. Arditti, Editor
Family Relations: Interdisciplinary Journal
of Applied Family Studies
Virginia Tech
Human Development
ONLINE SUBMISSIONS ONLY
359 Wallace Hall
Blacksburg, VA 24061
USA
Phone: 540-231-1646
Fax: 540-231-7012
E-Mail: frjourn@vt.edu
Web: www.ncfr.org
Address May Change: 12/31/2008

PUBLICATION GUIDELINES:

Manuscript Length: 26-30
Copies Required: Five
Computer Submission: Yes
Format:
Fees to Review: 15.00 US$

Manuscript Style:
American Psychological Association

CIRCULATION DATA:

Reader: Academics
Frequency of Issue: 5 Times/Year
Copies per Issue: 4,001 - 5,000
Sponsor/Publisher: National Council on
Family Relations
Subscribe Price: 109.00 US$ Individual
551.00 US$ Institution
See Webiste - more details

REVIEW INFORMATION:

Type of Review: Blind Review
No. of External Reviewers: 3
No. of In House Reviewers: 1
Acceptance Rate: 11-20%
Time to Review: 2 - 3 Months
Reviewers Comments: Yes
Invited Articles: 0-5%
Fees to Publish: 0.00 US$

MANUSCRIPT TOPICS:
Adolescent Psychology; Adulthood; Child Psychology; Family Counseling & Therapy;
Family Studies; Gerontology; Social Psychology

MANUSCRIPT GUIDELINES/COMMENTS:

Family Relations publishes applied articles that are original, innovative and interdisciplinary and that focus on diverse families and family issues. Audiences include family life educators in academic and community settings, researchers with an applied or evaluation focus, family practitioners who utilize prevention or therapeutic models and techniques, and family policy specialists. Examples of appropriate articles include those dealing with applied research, educational philosophies or practices, syntheses of substantive areas, program evaluations, and curriculum development and assessment. Articles should be conceived and written with implications for practice and/or policy in mind.

452

General. Manuscripts must be submitted online. For complete detailed instructions on uploading your manuscript, please visit the *Family Relations* online submission site (**http://mc.manuscriptcentral.com/fr**) and log on. If you need assistance select "get help". Once logged on select author center, and then select "submit a new manuscript." If you do not have a user ID, click the "create an account" icon and follow the online instructions. Any major word processing software may be used, and both DOS-based and Macintosh operating systems are acceptable. Authors with no Internet connection should contact the Editorial Office. The author checklists must be completed during the submission process. Copyright assignment is a condition of publication, and papers will not be passed to the Publisher unless copyright has been assigned. A link to the appropriate copyright form can be found online during the submission process. However, authors should not submit a copyright form until their manuscript has been accepted for publication.

Complete instructions for preparing and submitting manuscripts online are provided at the submission site and at **http://www.ncfr.com/fr/authors/index.htm**. There also is an online tutorial available at **Scholar One Online Users Guide**.

If you need further assistance, please contact the editorial office by phone at 540-231-1646 or via e-mail at **frjourn@vt.edu**.

Please follow the appropriate *APA* 5th edition format when submitting manuscripts online. In addition, it is vital that manuscripts submitted online are prepared for blind review. A \$15 processing fee also will be collected at the time of submission.

Tables. Formatting for tables must follow the guidelines listed at:
   http://oregonstate.edu/~acock/tables

Feminism & Psychology

ADDRESS FOR SUBMISSION:

Sue Wilkinson, Editor
Feminism & Psychology
Loughborough University
Department of Social Sciences
Leicestershire, LE11 3TU
UK
Phone: +44 0 1509 223364
Fax: +44 0 1509 223944
E-Mail: s.wilkinson@lboro.ac.uk
Web: www.sagepub.co.uk/journals
Address May Change:

PUBLICATION GUIDELINES:

Manuscript Length: 21-30
Copies Required: Six
Computer Submission: No
Format: N/A
Fees to Review: 0.00 US$

Manuscript Style:
   See Manuscript Guidelines

CIRCULATION DATA:

Reader: Academics, Practitioners
Frequency of Issue: Quarterly
Copies per Issue: Less than 1,000
Sponsor/Publisher: Sage Publications
Subscribe Price: 78.00 US$ Individual
   579.84 US$ Institution
   See Website - more details

REVIEW INFORMATION:

Type of Review: Blind Review
No. of External Reviewers: 3+
No. of In House Reviewers: 0
Acceptance Rate: 11-20%
Time to Review: 4 - 6 Months
Reviewers Comments: Yes
Invited Articles: 0-5%
Fees to Publish: 0.00 US$

MANUSCRIPT TOPICS:
Feminism; Gender Roles; Psychological Effects of Gender; Psychology of Women

MANUSCRIPT GUIDELINES/COMMENTS:

Aims and Scope
Feminism & Psychology aims to provide an international forum for debate at the interface between feminism and psychology. The principal aim of the journal is to foster the development of feminist theory and practice in - and beyond - psychology, and to represent the concerns of women in a wide range of contexts across the academic-applied 'divide'. It publishes high-quality, original research and debates that acknowledge gender and other social inequalities and consider their psychological effects; studies of sex differences are published only when set in this critical context. Contributions should consider the implications of 'race', class, sexuality and other social inequalities where relevant. The journal seeks to maintain a balance of theoretical and empirical papers, and to integrate research, practice and broader social concerns.

Feminism & Psychology encourages contributions from members of groups which are generally underrepresented in psychology journals, and individuals at all stages of their 'careers'. The journal has a policy of not publishing sexist, racist or heterosexist material. The journal encourages positive reviewing, which aims to provide supportive and constructive feedback to authors.

Feminism & Psychology publishes:
- Theoretical and empirical articles
- Research reviews
- Reports and reviews of issues relevant to practice
- Book reviews
- Observations and Commentaries
- Special Features
- A 'Spoken Word' section

'Observations and Commentaries' takes shorter pieces (between 500 and 2000 words).

'Special features' are designed to highlight the views of women who are the clients, students, survivors or general users of psychology, and to present debate on a wide range of contemporary issues surrounding feminism and psychology. The Spoken Word features topical contributions (discussions, interviews, profiles) which rely primarily on the spoken rather than the written word.

Notes for Authors
1. All submissions will be peer reviewed. *Papers* written in English are invited for consideration, provided they have not been published, nor are currently under consideration, elsewhere. The journal also aims to include translated pieces which have been published previously elsewhere, in languages other than English.

2. *Manuscripts* should be typewritten, double-spaced throughout, on A4, or 8.5" x 11", paper with generous margins, and not right-justified. References should be Harvard system, and in the following style:

Caplan, P.J. (1989) *Don't Blame Mother*. New York: Harper & Row.

Woolsey, L.K. and McBain, L. (1987) 'Issues of Power and Powerlessness in All-woman Groups', *Women's Studies International Forum* 10 (2): 579-88.

Griffith, A.I. and Smith, D.E. (1987) 'Constructing Cultural Knowledge: Mothering as Discourse', pp. 27-44 in J. Gaskell and A. McLaren (eds) *Women and Education*. Calgary: Detselig Press.

All figures should be of a reproducible standard. Footnotes should be kept to a minimum, and presented as End Notes. Papers should normally be between 5000 and 8000 words, but exceptionally up to 10,000 words for theoretical and empirical articles, research reviews and reports of practice; and between 500 and 2000 words for observations and commentaries. Please provide a word count. A variety of formats will be welcomed.

3. Extracts of qualitative data containing transcription notation should be prepared in the *exact* format you wish them to appear, especially as regards punctuation, spacing, underlining, etc. Each line should contain no more than 80 characters in 10pt including numbering and the speakers name.

4. Authors should avoid the use of *sexist, racist* and *heterosexist language.* Manuscripts that do not conform to these specifications will not be considered. Authors are encouraged to use clear language which avoids unnecessary jargon.

5. An *abstract* of approximately 150 words, plus 5-10 key words, should be included with each submission; but need not be supplied for observations or commentaries.

6. *Authors'* names, titles and affiliations, with complete postal and email addresses and telephone/fax numbers, should appear on a separate cover page. Authors are invited to provide any biographical information they would wish reviewers to take into account on a separate sheet. The aim of this information is to avoid discrimination against those without standard academic backgrounds or institutional support. All submitted articles will be reviewed anonymously.

7. Submissions are welcomed for Special Features and The Spoken Word. These will normally be developed in conjunction with a member of the Editorial Group. In the first instance, suggestions should be sent to the Special Features Coordinator of the Editorial Group.

8. **Twenty-five offprints** of the article, plus a copy of the journal, will be supplied to article authors on publication.

9. **Book reviews** will normally be commissioned by the Book Review Editor although unsolicited reviews will be considered, and the journal will also review other media and relevant fiction.

10. **Six copies** of all manuscript submissions, including the original, and a copy on disk (in any PC-compatible format) should be sent to the Editorial Office: c/o Celia Kitzinger, Associate Editor F&P, Department of Sociology, University of York, heslington, York, YO10 5DD, UK.

A further disk copy, containing the final version, abstract, key words, notes, references, biographical note and full contact details, will be required before publication. Further information may be sought from the Editorial Assistant.

11. **Copyright**. Before publication authors are requested to assign copyright to SAGE Publications, subject to retaining their right to reuse the material in other publications written or edited by themselves and due to be published at least one year after initial publication in the journal.

Genetic, Social, and General Psychology Monographs

ADDRESS FOR SUBMISSION:

Sarah C. Yauss, Managing Editor
Genetic, Social, and General Psychology
   Monographs
1319 Eighteenth Street, NW
Washington, DC 20036-1802
USA
Phone: 202-296-6267 ext. 1257
Fax: 202-296-5149
E-Mail: mono@heldref.org
Web: www.heldref.org
Address May Change:

PUBLICATION GUIDELINES:

Manuscript Length: 35+ pp
Copies Required: Three
Computer Submission: Yes
Format: MS Word
Fees to Review: 0.00 US$

Manuscript Style:
   American Psychological Association

CIRCULATION DATA:

Reader: Academics
Frequency of Issue: Quarterly
Copies per Issue: Less than 1,000
Sponsor/Publisher: Heldref Publications,
   Inc.
Subscribe Price: 166.00 US$ Individual
   176.00 US$ Institution

REVIEW INFORMATION:

Type of Review: Editorial Review
No. of External Reviewers: 2+
No. of In House Reviewers: 1
Acceptance Rate: 10%
Time to Review: 2 - 3 Months
Reviewers Comments: Yes
Invited Articles: 0-5%
Fees to Publish: 0.00 US$

MANUSCRIPT TOPICS:
Abnormal Psychology; Adolescent Psychology; Adulthood; Alcoholism & Drug Addiction;
Behavior Modification; Child Psychology; Counseling Process; Developmental Psychology;
Educational Psychology; Exceptional Child; Experimental Psychology; Family Counseling &
Therapy; Gerontology; History of Psychology; Learning & Conditioning; Neuropsychology;
Personality; Physiological Psychology; Psychiatry; Psychobiology; Psychological Testing;
Psychopathology; Research Methods & Statistics; Sensation & Perception; Social Psychology;
Thinking & Cognition; To a certain extent all topics in Psychology.

MANUSCRIPT GUIDELINES/COMMENTS:

Topics Include. Behavior disorders; Career development; Cognitive development; Cross-
cultural studies; Depression; Divorce; Eating disorders; Emotional development; Gender
identities; Intelligence; Parenting; Piagetian theory; Relationship quality; Self-esteem; Stress
and coping; Values.

Every issue of *Genetic, Social, and General Psychology Monographs* provides a variety of
new insights into human development through integrative reviews of psychology studies and
original theory development.

Guidelines for Authors

Genetic, Social, and General Psychology Monographs accepts articles of monograph length that are devoted to both clinical and developmental psychological research and theory. Typically a *Monographs* article exceeds thirty-five typed pages and may present a series of research studies or an in-depth criticism of an existing theory. Innovative research and unique approaches are particularly encouraged. Articles deal with the biological as well as the behavioral and social aspects of psychology and are based on either developmental or clinical research. Past topics include cognitive, social, and emotional development; metacognition; gender identity and roles; moral judgment and values; relationships; and personality traits.

Type all manuscripts on 8 ½ X 11 in. (22 X 28 cm) paper, double-space *all* lines, and leave 1 ½ in. (4-cm) margins on each side for editorial work. Submit the original version and two copies. Retain an additional copy for proofing. Do not fold manuscripts. Enclose a submission letter, with a statement that the manuscript is not under concurrent consideration elsewhere. Each manuscript is reviewed by at least two readers, a process ordinarily requiring 3 months.

Manuscripts must adhere to the conventions of style and format described in the *Publication Manual of the American Psychological Association* (4th ed., 1994). The checklist in Appendix B of the *Manual* is especially helpful in preparing manuscripts for submission. Include a separate title page that lists the departmental affiliations of all authors. Type the author identification notes on a separate page; include a complete mailing address for reprint requests. Glossy prints must be supplied for all figures once the manuscript is accepted for publication. Accepted manuscripts will be edited for clarity and adherence to APA and Heldref style rules.

Each author receives two complimentary copies of the issue in which his or her article appears and permission to reproduce additional copies of that article. Contributors may order reprints at their own expense through Heldref Publications.

Submit all manuscripts to the Managing Editor,
Genetic, Social and General Psychology Monographs
1319 Eighteenth Street, NW, Washington, DC 20036-1802
Phone: 202-296-6267, Fax: 202-296-5149

After an article has been accepted, it should be submitted electronically as a double-spaced Word file, with minimal formatting, in Times or Times New Roman. Do not use electronic style sheets, forced section or page breaks, or automatic footnotes. E-mail tables in a separate file, and figures in another file.

Gerontology & Geriatrics Education

ADDRESS FOR SUBMISSION:

Judy Ainlay, Managing Editor
Gerontology & Geriatrics Education
Consortium Gerontology Studies Program
484 Main Street, Suite 500
Worcester, MA 01608
USA
Phone: 508-754-6829
Fax: 508-797-0069
E-Mail: pmosherashley@worcester.edu
Web: www.haworthpressinc.com
Address May Change:

PUBLICATION GUIDELINES:

Manuscript Length: 16-20
Copies Required: Three
Computer Submission: Yes
Format: MS Word for Windows
Fees to Review: 0.00 US$

Manuscript Style:
    American Psychological Association

CIRCULATION DATA:

Reader: Academics, Practitioners
Frequency of Issue: Quarterly
Copies per Issue: Less than 1,000
Sponsor/Publisher: Haworth Press, Inc.
Subscribe Price: 75.00 US$ Individual
    200.00 US$ Institution
    445.00 US$ Library

REVIEW INFORMATION:

Type of Review: Blind Review
No. of External Reviewers: 2
No. of In House Reviewers: 2
Acceptance Rate: No Reply
Time to Review: 2-4 Months
Reviewers Comments: Yes
Invited Articles: 11-20%
Fees to Publish: 0.00 US$

MANUSCRIPT TOPICS:
Educational Issues; Geriatric Training; Gerontology

MANUSCRIPT GUIDELINES/COMMENTS:

About the Journal
Gerontology & Geriatrics Education is dedicated to improving the quality and quantity of education and services available to the elderly by providing information to a broad range of students, teachers, practitioners, administrators, and policymakers. It is the prime source journal for those who teach others about older adults or how to work with the elderly and those who serve the elderly themselves.

The journal provides for the exchange of information related to research, curriculum development, course and program evaluation, classroom and practice innovation, and other topics with educational implication for gerontology and geriatrics. *Gerontology & Geriatrics Education* is a useful resource for anyone concerned with keeping informed about the critical educational issues related to aging and the aged.

Articles in this highly regarded journal cover research results, observations, evaluations, theoretical discussions, and recommendations related to gerontology and geriatrics course work, practice placements, and curriculum design and implementation. The journal also

- reports innovations in the teaching of gerontology and geriatrics at the undergraduate, graduate, and postgraduate levels and in paraprofessional and public education
- discusses issues, methods, and materials in the training and supervision of gerontology and geriatrics educators, researchers, and practitioners in all levels of health care, including long-term care settings
- explores new roles for gerontology and geriatrics educators in public and private programs and in community and academic institutions, including corporate and industrial settings
- communicates new methods for developing gerontology and geriatrics educational programs in both academic and applied settings and new approaches for supporting such educational programs
- reports on research and evaluation that has been carried out concerning the development and assessment of individual courses, concentrations, majors, or degree and certificate programs in gerontology and geriatrics in any discipline
- includes research and discussion on aging-related issues that have relevance for gerontological and geriatrics educators
- publishes full-length articles which provide information, evaluations, or reviews of new educational materials and innovative teaching methods in the field of aging

A special feature of the journal is the occasional "theme" issue which allows for a more concentrated coverage of aging-related educational information on a single discipline, provides a discussion of a particular topic of interest across disciplines, and enables a wider distribution of information from gerontology and geriatrics education conferences, symposia, or debates.

Instructions for Authors
1. **Original Articles Only**. Submission of a manuscript to this Journal represents a certification on the part of the author(s) that it is an original work, and that neither this manuscript nor a version of it has been published elsewhere nor is being considered for publication elsewhere.

2. **Manuscript Length**. Your manuscript may be approximately 15-18 pages. Sentences should be double-spaced (including references and abstract). Lengthier manuscripts may be considered, but only at the discretion of the Editor. Sometimes, lengthier manuscripts may be considered if they can be divided up into sections for publications in successive Journal issues.

3. **Manuscript Style**. References, citations, and general style of manuscripts for this Journal should follow the APA style (as outlined in the latest edition of the *Publication Manual of the American Psychological Association*). References should be double-spaced and placed in alphabetical order. Attention should be given to avoid sexist language.

If an author wishes to submit a paper that has been already prepared in another style, he or she may do so. However, if the paper is accepted (with or without reviewer's alterations), the author is fully responsible for retyping the manuscript in the correct style as indicated above. Neither the Editor nor the Publisher is responsible for re-preparing manuscript copy to adhere to the Journal's style.

4. Manuscript Preparation

Margins. Leave at least a one-inch margin on all four sides.

Paper. Use clean, white 8 ½" x 11" bond paper.

Number of copies. 4 (the original plus three photocopies).

Cover page. Important—staple a cover page to the manuscript, indicating only the article title (this is used for anonymous refereeing).

Second "title page". Enclose a regular title page but do not staple it to the manuscript. Include the title again, plus:

- full authorship
- an ABSTRACT of about 100 words. (Below the abstract provide 3–10 key words for index purposes).
- a header or footer on each page with abbreviated title and pg number of total (e.g., pg 2 of 7)
- an introductory footnote with authors' academic degrees, professional titles, affiliations, mailing and e-mail addresses, and any desired acknowledgment of research support or other credit.

5. Return Envelopes. When you submit your four manuscript copies, also include:

- a 9" x 12" envelope, self-addressed and stamped (with sufficient postage to ensure return of your manuscript);
- a regular envelope, stamped and self-addressed. This is for the Editor to send you an "acknowledgement of receipt" letter.

6. Spelling, Grammar, and Punctuation. You are responsible for preparing manuscript copy which is clearly written in acceptable, scholarly English and which contains no errors of spelling, grammar, or punctuation. Neither the Editor nor the Publisher is responsible for correcting errors of spelling and grammar. The manuscript, after acceptance by the Editor, must be immediately ready for typesetting as it is finally submitted by the author(s). Check your paper for the following common errors:

- dangling modifiers
- misplaced modifiers
- unclear antecedents
- incorrect or inconsistent abbreviations

Also, check the accuracy of all arithmetic calculations, statistics, numerical data, text citations, and references.

7. Inconsistencies Must Be Avoided. Be sure you are consistent in your use of abbreviations, terminology, and in citing references, from one part of your paper to another.

8. Preparation of Tables, Figures, and Illustrations. Any material that is not textual is considered artwork. This includes tables, figures, diagrams, charts, graphs, illustrations,

appendices, screen captures, and photos. Tables and figures (including legend, notes, and sources) should be no larger than 4 ½ X 6 ½ inches. Type styles should be Helvetica (or Helvetica narrow if necessary) and no smaller than 8 point. We request that computer-generated figures be in black and white and/or shades of gray (preferably no color, for it does not reproduce well). Camera-ready art must contain no grammatical, typographical, or format errors and must reproduce sharply and clearly in the dimensions of the final printed page (4 ½ x 6 ½ inches). Photos and screen captures must be on disk as a TIF file, or other graphic file format such as JPEG or BMP. For rapid publication we must receive black-and-white glossy or matte positives (white background with black images and/or wording) in addition to files on disk. Tables should be created in the text document file using the software's Table feature.

9. **Submitting Art**. Both a printed hard copy and a disk copy of the art must be provided. We request that each piece of art be sent in its own file, on a disk separate from the disk containing the manuscript text file(s), and be clearly labeled. We reserve the right to (if necessary) request new art, alter art, or if all else has failed in achieving art that is presentable, delete art. If submitted art cannot be used, the Publisher reserves the right to redo the art and to change the author for a fee of $35.00 per hour for this service. The Haworth Press, Inc. is not responsible for errors incurred in the preparation of new artwork. Camera-ready artwork must be prepared on separate sheets of paper. Always use black ink and professional drawing instruments. On the back of these items, write your article title and the journal title lightly in soft-lead pencil (please do not write on the face of art). In the text file, skip extra lines and indicate where these figures are placed. Photos are considered part of the acceptable manuscript and remain with the Publisher for use in additional printings.

10. **Electronic Media**. Haworth's in-house typesetting unit is able to utilize your final manuscript material as prepared on most personal computers and word processors. This will minimize typographical errors and decrease overall production time. Please send the first draft and final draft copies of your manuscript to the journal Editor in print format for his/her final review and approval. After approval of your final manuscript, please submit the final approved version both on printed format ("hard copy") and floppy diskette. On the outside of the diskette package write:
1) the brand name of your computer or word processor
2) the word processing program and version that you used
3) the title of your article, and
4) the file name.

Note: Disk and hard copy must agree. In case of discrepancies, it is The Haworth Press' policy to follow hard copy. Authors are advised that no revisions of the manuscript can be made after acceptance by the Editor for publication. The benefits of this procedure are many with speed and accuracy being the most obvious. We look forward to working with your electronic submission which will allow us to serve you more efficiently.

11. **Alterations Required by Referees and Reviewers**. Many times a paper is accepted by the Editor contingent upon changes that are mandated by anonymous specialist referees and members of the Editorial Board. If the Editor returns your manuscript for revisions, you are responsible for retyping any sections of the paper to incorporate these revisions (if applicable, revisions should also be put on disk).

12. **Typesetting**. You will not be receiving galley proofs of your article. Editorial revisions, if any, must therefore be made while your article is still in manuscript. The final version of the manuscript will be the version you see published. Typesetter's errors will be corrected by the production staff of The Haworth Press. Authors are expected to submit manuscripts, disks, and art that are free from error.

13. **Reprints**. The senior author will receive two copies of the journal issue and 25 complimentary reprints of his or her article. The junior author will receive two copies of the journal issue. These are sent several weeks after the journal issue is published and in circulation. An order form for the purchase of additional reprints will also be sent to all authors at this time. (Approximately 4-6 weeks is necessary for the preparation of reprints.) Please do not query the Journal's Editor about reprints. All such questions should be sent directly to The Haworth Press, Inc., Production Department, 37 West Broad Street, West Hazleton, PA 18202. To order additional reprints (minimum: 50 copies), please contact The Haworth Document Delivery Center, 10 Alice Street, Binghamton, NY 13904-1580; 1-800-342-9678 or Fax (607) 722-6362.

14. **Copyright**. Copyright ownership of your manuscript must be transferred officially to The Haworth Press, Inc. before we can begin the peer-review process. The Editor's letter acknowledging receipt of the manuscript will be accompanied by a form fully explaining this. All authors must sign the form and return the original to the Editor as soon as possible. Failure to return the copyright form in a timely fashion will result in a delay in review and subsequent publication.

Group Dynamics: Theory, Research, and Practice

ADDRESS FOR SUBMISSION:

Dennis M. Kivlighan, Jr., Editor
Group Dynamics: Theory, Research, and
   Practice
University of Maryland
3214 Benjamin Blvd.
College Park, MD 20742
USA
Phone:
Fax: 804-828-2237
E-Mail: dennisk@wam.umd.edu
Web: www.apa.org/journals/gdn
Address May Change:

PUBLICATION GUIDELINES:

Manuscript Length: 21-25
Copies Required: Four
Computer Submission: Yes
Format: MS Word or WordPerfect
Fees to Review: 0.00 US$

Manuscript Style:
   American Psychological Association

CIRCULATION DATA:

Reader: Academics, Practitioners
Frequency of Issue: Quarterly
Copies per Issue: 1,001 - 2,000
Sponsor/Publisher: APA - American
   Psychological Association
Subscribe Price:

REVIEW INFORMATION:

Type of Review: Editorial Review
No. of External Reviewers: 3
No. of In House Reviewers: 0
Acceptance Rate: 50%
Time to Review: 4 - 6 Months
Reviewers Comments: Yes
Invited Articles: 6-10%
Fees to Publish: 0.00 US$

MANUSCRIPT TOPICS:
Group Dynamics; Human Relations

MANUSCRIPT GUIDELINES/COMMENTS:

Group Dynamics: Theory, Research, and Practice publishes original empirical articles, theoretical analyses, literature reviews, and brief reports dealing with basic and applied topics in the field of group research and application. We construe the phrase *group dynamics* in the broadest sense—the scientific study of all aspects of groups—and publish work by investigators in such fields as psychology, psychiatry, sociology, education, communication, and business. The journal publishes articles examining groups in a range of contexts, including ad hoc groups in experimental settings, therapy groups, naturally forming friendship groups and cliques, organizational units, self-help groups, and learning groups. Theoretically driven empirical studies of hypotheses that have implications for understanding and improving groups in organizational, educational, and therapeutic settings are particularly encouraged.

Manuscript submission. Authors should submit their papers via e-mail by attaching the document to an e-mail sent to Dennis M. Kivlighan Jr.

464

(see **http://www.vcu.edu/hasweb/group/gd.html for details**). Alternatively, four copies of the manuscript should be sent to

Dennis M. Kivlighan Jr.
Counseling and Personnel Services
3214 Benjamin Building
University of Maryland
College Park, Maryland 20742

Authors must provide an electronic copy of the manuscript in the format used by their word-processing software (preferably WordPerfect or Word). Please note that tables should be prepared using the table-creating features of word processor. The first page of the manuscript should include the corresponding author's contact information, including addresses, telephone number, FAX number, and e-mail address. Authors should keep a copy of their manuscript in case of loss.

Group Dynamics: Theory, Research, and Practice publishes original empirical articles, theoretical analyses, literature reviews, and brief reports dealing with basic and applied topics in the field of group research and application. We construe the phrase group dynamics in the broadest sense—the scientific study of all aspects of groups—and publish work by investigators in such fields as psychology, psychiatry, sociology, education, communication, and business. The journal publishes articles examining groups in a range of contexts, including ad hoc groups in experimental settings, therapy groups, naturally forming friendship groups and cliques, organizational units, self-help groups, and learning groups. Theoretically driven empirical studies of hypotheses that have implications for understanding and improving groups in organizational, educational, and therapeutic settings are particularly encouraged.

Types of manuscripts. *Group Dynamics* is the forum for empirical research on all aspects of groups, and so primarily publishes data-based papers that test hypotheses about groups. Theory papers and literature reviews will be published, provided they meet the standards set by such journals as *Psychological Review* and *Psychological Bulletin*. Other types of papers, such as manuscripts that describe innovations and applications in group contexts that do not include evaluative data pertaining to the effectiveness of the intervention, will be reviewed for publication, but such papers should be submitted in the form of brief reports (defined below). All papers to be accepted for publication must make a definitive contribution to theory, research, or practice.

Manuscript preparation. Authors are responsible for the content and style of their work, and they should follow the guidelines of the *Publication Manual of the American Psychological Association* (5th ed.) when preparing manuscripts. Manuscripts must include an abstract containing a maximum of 120 words typed on a separate page and should not exceed 25 pages, including references. (Authors must justify any exceptions to the length restriction when they submit their work.) Manuscripts must be double-spaced throughout, and all copies should be clear and on paper of good quality. Manuscripts printed with an unusual typeface will be accepted only if easily readable; faxed manuscripts will not be accepted. Authors should avoid using abbreviations, symbols, and footnotes. Also, all manuscripts are copyedited for bias-free language (see chap. 2 of the *Publication Manual*). Original color figures can be printed in color at the editor's discretion and provided the author agrees to pay half of the associated production costs; an estimate of these costs is available from the APA production office on request. Authors should include a copy of the manuscript on a computer disk. Manuscripts that do not conform to the *Publication Manual's* standards will be returned unreviewed to authors.

Brief reports. The Journal publishes brief reports, such as single-experiment studies that do not require extensive theoretical introduction, case studies, reports of therapeutic innovations, and theoretical commentaries about specific issues. When possible, qualitative or quantitative evidence of the impact and effectiveness of therapeutic techniques should be included in reports of such interventions. Brief reports must conform to the *Publication Manual* standards, but the manuscript itself cannot exceed 18 pages, including references, tables, and figures. Unsolicited book reviews will not be accepted.

Masked reviews. Masked reviews are optional, and authors who wish such reviews must request them when submitting their work. They must also prepare their manuscript so that they cannot be identified: A separate title page with authors' names and affiliations must be provided, and any identifying footnotes or self-citations should be removed.

Permissions. Authors are required to obtain and provide to APA prior to production all necessary permissions to reproduce in print and electronic form any copyrighted work, including, for example, test materials (or portions thereof) and photographs of people. Final files for production should be prepared as outlined in Preparing Your Electronic Files for Production at http://www.apa.org/journals/preparing_electronic_files.html.

Ethical standards. APA policy prohibits an author from submitting the same manuscript for concurrent consideration by two or more publications. In addition, it is a violation of APA Ethical Principles to publish "as original data, data that have been previously published" (Standard 8.13). As this journal is a primary journal that publishes original material only, APA policy prohibits as well publication of any manuscript that has already been published in whole or substantial part elsewhere. Authors have an obligation to consult the editor concerning prior publication of any data upon which their article depends.

In addition, APA Ethical Principles specify that "after research results are published, psychologists do not withhold the data on which their conclusions are based from other competent professionals who seek to verify the substantive claims through reanalysis and who intend to use such data only for that purpose, provided that the confidentiality of the participants can be protected and unless legal rights concerning proprietary data preclude their release" (Standard 8.14). APA expects authors submitting to this journal to adhere to these standards. Specifically, authors of manuscripts submitted to APA journals are expected to have available their data throughout the editorial review process and for at least 5 years after the date of publication.

Manuscript review. The Editor and Associate Editors, in consultation with members of the Journal's Editorial Review Board and ad hoc reviewers, will determine which manuscripts are accepted for publication in the journal. The primary criterion for acceptance will be the work's impact on understanding groups. The introduction should be theoretically coherent and compelling, and any relevant literatures should be reviewed. The methods and measures used should be appropriate, the findings should be interpretable and statistically meaningful, and conclusions drawn should be suitable ones given the results obtained. Authors of manuscripts examining basic theory and research should identify implications of their work for more applied areas, and authors of manuscripts dealing with more applied topics should draw conclusions that are relevant to basic research and theory. When possible, manuscripts dealing with applied topics will be critiqued by a basic researcher, and basic research studies will be reviewed by a practitioner. In some cases these critiques will be published with the original article.

Group Processes & Intergroup Relations

ADDRESS FOR SUBMISSION:

Dominic Abrams, Editor
Group Processes & Intergroup Relations
University of Kent
Department of Psychology
Cantebury, CT2 7NP
UK
Phone: +44 0 1227 827475
Fax: +44 0 1227 827030
E-Mail: gpir@kent.ac.uk
Web: www.sagepub.com
Address May Change:

PUBLICATION GUIDELINES:

Manuscript Length: 26-30
Copies Required: Five
Computer Submission: Yes Email +
    Hardcopy
Format: Prefer Word
Fees to Review: 0.00 US$

Manuscript Style:
    American Psychological Association

CIRCULATION DATA:

Reader: Academics
Frequency of Issue: Quarterly
Copies per Issue: No Reply
Sponsor/Publisher: Sage Publications, Ltd.
Subscribe Price:

REVIEW INFORMATION:

Type of Review: Editorial Review
No. of External Reviewers: 3
No. of In House Reviewers: No Reply
Acceptance Rate: 21-30%
Time to Review: 4 - 6 Months
Reviewers Comments: Yes
Invited Articles: 0-5%
Fees to Publish: 0.00 US$

MANUSCRIPT TOPICS:
Group Dynamics; Group Processes; Intergroup Relations

MANUSCRIPT GUIDELINES/COMMENTS:

Aims and Scope
Group Processes & Intergroup Relations is a mainstream social psychology journal dedicated to social psychological research into group processes and intergroup relations.

Targeted at social psychologists and researchers in intersecting disciplines, it publishes empirical, theoretical, and review articles on basic and applied aspects of the social psychology of groups: this includes group phenomena and phenomena influenced by group membership, ranging from small interactive groups to large scale social categories, and from basic social cognition and the analysis of interaction to the macrosocial study of intergroup relations. *GPIR* thus provides a scientific forum for basic and applied social psychological research into many areas of critical social concern including: prejudice, discrimination, stereotyping, social categorization, minority and majority influence, conformity, group decision-making, leadership, group structure, group socialization, bargaining and negotiation, intergroup conflict and cooperation, collective action and cognition, social identity, language and identity, ethnic and cultural relations, and social dilemmas.

GPIR is also strongly committed to the international nature of research on group processes and intergroup relations. The editorial team comprises a broad range of scholars and researchers from around the world.

Together, these experts are committed to ensuring the journal represents the very best research on group and intergroup phenomena from a social psychological perspective, as well as other related disciplines such as sociology, organizational psychology, cross-cultural psychology, language and communication.

Submission Manuscript Guidelines

Manuscripts should be prepared strictly in accordance with APA publication guidelines as described in the *Publication Manual of the American Psychological Association* (5th ed.). Manuscripts that do not conform to these guidelines will be returned unreviewed.

Suggested target for word length is 5000-8000 words and text should be clearly organized with a clear hierarchy of headings and subheadings. Quotations exceeding 40 words should be displayed, indented in the text.

Tables and figures should have short descriptive titles, and camera-ready artwork or b/w glossy prints should be supplied for all figures. Authors are responsible for obtaining copyright permission for reproducing any illustrations, tables, figures or lengthy quotations previously published elsewhere. Authors should avoid using abbreviations, symbols and footnotes.

Authors are expected to have complied with APA guidelines concerning ethical publication and research practices. By submitting the manuscript to the journal the authors are agreeing that the work is not concurrently under review elsewhere and that the findings presented have not been published elsewhere. They are also agreeing that they have conformed to ethical guidelines and that authorship order accurately reflects relative contributions. Because English is the recognized international language for academic psychology, the journal accepts manuscripts and publishes articles in English only.

Authors should send an email or disk (PC) version of the article together with one printed copy and covering letter, single sided.

Manuscripts should provide a title page with an abstract of no more than 150 words that succinctly summarizes the key points and two to five key words to identify the contents of the article.

Full name of each author with current affiliation and full address/phone/fax/email details plus short biographical note should also be supplied. All manuscripts will be refereed but if blind refereeing is preferred, these author details should be supplied on a separate sheet.

Before publication, authors are requested to assign copyright to SAGE Publications, subject to retaining their right to reuse the material in other publications written or edited by themselves and due to be published at least one year after initial publication in the journal.

On acceptance of their manuscript, authors will be asked to submit a copy of the final version of their manuscript on a computer disc in either PC or Mac format.

Authors will receive proofs of their articles and be asked to send corrections to SAGE Publications within 3 weeks. They will receive a complimentary copy of the journal and 25 offprints of their article.

Contributions should be submitted to the Editorial Office:

Dominic Abrams, Group Processes & Intergroup Relations, Dept of Psychology, University of Kent, Canterbury CT2 7NP, UK Tel: +44 1227 827475. Fax: +44 1227 827030; Email: **gpir@kent.ac.uk**

Harvard Review of Psychiatry

ADDRESS FOR SUBMISSION:

S.F. Greenfield, J.T. Coyle, Co-Editors
Harvard Review of Psychiatry
Elizabeth Schmidt, Managing Editor
McLean Hospital
115 Mill Street
Belmont, MA 02478
USA
Phone: 617-855-3123 (Dr. Greenfield)
Fax: 617-855-3740 (Editorial office)
E-Mail: shelly_greenfield@hms.harvard.ed
Web: http://www.tandf.co.uk/journals
Address May Change:

PUBLICATION GUIDELINES:

Manuscript Length: 26-30
Copies Required: Seven
Computer Submission: No
Format: N/A
Fees to Review: 0.00 US$

Manuscript Style:
, AMA Manual of Style, Words into
Type/Chicago

CIRCULATION DATA:

Reader: Academics, Practitioners
Frequency of Issue: Bi-Monthly
Copies per Issue:
Sponsor/Publisher: Taylor & Francis
Subscribe Price:

REVIEW INFORMATION:

Type of Review: Blind Review
No. of External Reviewers: 3
No. of In House Reviewers: 2
Acceptance Rate: 40%
Time to Review: 1 - 2 Months
Reviewers Comments: Yes
Invited Articles: 31-50%
Fees to Publish: 0.00 US$

MANUSCRIPT TOPICS:
Psychiatry

MANUSCRIPT GUIDELINES/COMMENTS:

Aims and Scope
The *Harvard Review of Psychiatry* is the authoritative source for scholarly reviews and perspectives on important topics in psychiatry. Founded by the Harvard Medical School's Department of Psychiatry, the *Harvard Review of Psychiatry* features review papers that summarize and synthesize the key literature in a scholarly and clinically relevant manner.

Topics covered include:
- Schizophrenia and related disorders
- Mood disorders
- Personality disorders
- Substance use disorders
- Anxiety
- Neuroscience

- Psychosocial aspects of psychiatry
- Ethics
- Psychiatric education
- and much more

In addition, a Clinical Challenges section presents a case with discussion from a panel of experts. Brief reviews are presented in topic-specific columns that include Cross-Cultural Psychiatry, History of Psychiatry, Ethics, and others.

Instructions For Authors

Scope of Manuscripts. The *Harvard Review of Psychiatry* is a bimonthly journal that publishes scholarly papers on a wide variety of topics of interest to clinicians. It includes the following types of articles:

Reviews. Reviews summarize and synthesize the literature on various topics in a rigorous, scholarly, and clinically relevant fashion. These topics may include psychotic disorders, mood disorders, personality disorders, substance use disorders, anxiety disorders, neuroscience, child psychiatry, geriatric psychiatry, psychological aspects of psychiatry, legal and policy issues in psychiatry, and other subjects relevant to clinicians.

Perspectives. Perspectives provide an overview of an area of interest to clinicians and in which there is controversy or only limited literature. Authors should be experts who can provide both a synthetic review of the existing literature and a particular clinical perspective derived from their expertise.

Columns. Columns present a well-argued, thoughtful point of view on a focused topic. They should cite relevant literature that supports the author's viewpoint, as well as literature that may conflict with it. Columns may include clinical case material.

Clinical challenges. Clinical challenges present a clinical case report and are followed by expert discussion of the case from multiple perspectives. These cases present diagnostic or treatment challenges, or highlight a current debate in the field. Prospective authors should contact David Brendel, MD, PhD, Deputy Editor (email: **dbrendel@partners.org**; telephone: 617-855-3498).

Original reports. Original reports present data from empirical studies. The findings should be discussed in a clinically relevant manner.

Letters to the editor. Letters that comment on articles published in the *Harvard Review of Psychiatry* will be considered for publication.

Length. Reviews, perspectives, and clinical challenges should range between 25 and 40 manuscript pages, including the abstract, references, tables, and figures. Original reports should be approximately 25 manuscript pages long, including the abstract, references, tables, and figures. Columns should be approximately 15 pages long. Letters should not exceed three manuscript pages, including references, and should include no tables or figures.

Submission of Manuscripts
Consideration of proposed manuscripts. Authors considering a topic for submission to the Review are encouraged to submit a one-page description of the proposed manuscript. Proposals should include the title and author(s), a brief outline, and a description of the submission's clinical relevance. They should be sent by email or fax to Shelly F. Greenfield, MD, MPH, Editor-in-Chief, Harvard Review of Psychiatry
(email: **shelly_greenfield@hms.harvard.edu**; fax: 617-855-3740).

General information. Manuscripts should be submitted electronically or by mail to William B. Jaffee, Ph.D, McLean Hospital, Proctor House, third floor, 115 Mill Street, Belmont, MA 02478, USA (email: **wjaffee@mclean.harvard.edu**; telephone: (617) 855-3123. Authors submitting their manuscripts by mail are required to include an electronic version, preferably in Microsoft Word for Windows. Manuscripts may be reviewed using either the hard copies or electronic versions. A cover letter accompanying the manuscript should identify the section for which the manuscript is submitted (e.g., Reviews, Perspectives, etc.) and include the names and institutional affiliations of all authors, as well as the name, address, telephone and fax numbers, and email address of the corresponding author.

Letters of permission to reproduce previously published material. All material reproduced intact or modified from previously published or copyrighted material must be accompanied by a letter of permission from the original author and copyright holder. All such material should also provide a full credit line (e.g., in the figure or table legend) acknowledging the original source. The credit line should be worded according to the copyright holder's specifications.

Peer review. All manuscripts are peer reviewed, and letters commenting on published articles are sent to the author(s) for response. The Editors notify the corresponding author when a decision regarding acceptance has been made. Accepted manuscripts and letters are edited for clarity and for conformity to the Review's style. The journal uses a masked reviewing system. Therefore, the title page of the manuscript should omit the authors' names and affiliations, but should include the title of the manuscript and its date of submission. Authors should make every effort to ensure that neither the manuscript text nor the electronic file contains clues to their identities.

Preparation of Manuscripts
General information. Manuscript and other requirements conform to the "Uniform Requirements for Manuscripts Submitted to Biomedical Journals" established by the International Committee of Medical Journal Editors (N Engl J Med 1991;324:424–8). Submitting the materials in the correct format will expedite the review process and prevent unnecessary delay in publication. All major parts of the manuscript (title page, abstract, text, acknowledgments, references, tables, and legends for illustrations) must be typed double-spaced in 12-point type. All four margins must be at least 1 inch, and the right-hand margin should be unjustified (ragged). The manuscript should be arranged in the following order: title page, abstract and key words, text, references, figures, figure legends, and tables. Start each section on a new page. All pages must be numbered, beginning with the title page. If a running head is used, it must not include authors' names.

Title page. The title page should include: (1) the article title, which should be concise but informative; (2) the authors' first and last names, academic degrees, and primary institutional affiliation(s); (3) the full address, telephone number, and fax number of the author who is to receive reprint requests (email address optional); (4) acknowledgments, including grant support (granting agency and grant number) and drug company support of any kind; and (5) the name, location, and date of any meetings at which the submitted manuscript has been presented.

Abstract. The abstract should not exceed 200 words. Below the abstract provide three to ten key words or phrases to assist indexers. The words or phrases should preferably be taken from the MeSH headings used for indexing articles in PubMed.

Text. For review articles, the text should begin with an introductory section, include a brief description of the methods used to select the articles reviewed (database, terms searched, limitations imposed), and end with a discussion section. The use of subheadings is encouraged. For original reports, the text should use the standard format of an introduction, methods, results, and discussion.

References. Identify references in the text, tables, and legends by Arabic numbers as superscripts, and number references in the order in which they first occur in the text. (Do not arrange them alphabetically by author.) Key in the subscripts and the reference list at the end of the text; do not use your word processor's footnote or endnote feature for this purpose. Double-space the reference list. Use the style of the examples below, abbreviating journal titles according to Index Medicus. List all authors, but if the number exceeds six, give the first six names followed by "et al." Unpublished observations, unpublished manuscripts, and personal communications may not be included in the reference list. However, references to written, not oral, communications may be inserted in parentheses in the text. Articles in press may be cited in the reference list, with the name of the publication included. Authors of submitted manuscripts are responsible for verifying references against the original documents.

Reference examples:

1. Black DW, Noyes R Jr, Goldstein RB, Blum N. A family study of obsessive compulsive disorder. Arch Gen Psychiatry 1992;49:362–8.

2. Mavissakalian M. Differential efficacy between tricyclic antidepressants and behavior therapy of panic disorder. In: Ballenger JC, ed. Clinical aspects of panic disorder. New York: Wiley-Liss, 1990:211–8.

3. Talbott JA, Hales RE, Yudofsky SC, eds. The American Psychiatric Press textbook of psychiatry. Washington, DC: American Psychiatric Press, 1988.

Tables and figures. Include tables and high-quality prints of all figures with each copy of the manuscript. Tables and figures should not duplicate text material. They should be cited in the text and numbered sequentially in the order that they are mentioned in the text. Type each table double-spaced on a separate sheet, preferably using Microsoft Excel. Supply a brief title for each table and a short heading for each column. Use footnotes for explanatory matter, including explanations of abbreviations in the tables. Figures should be professionally prepared and should consist of glossy or other camera-ready black-and-white prints. Half-tone illustrations (gray-toned photographs) should be no larger than 5 x 7 inches. Letters, numbers, and symbols should be clearly legible and of sufficient size that, when reduced for publication, each item will still be legible. The font should preferably be Times New Roman. All figures for the same article should be prepared using the same typeface and approximately the same type size. Each figure should have a label pasted on its back indicating the first author's name, the figure number, and the top of the figure. Avoid writing on the backs of figures. Do not bend or otherwise damage figures, mount them on cardboard, or attach paper clips or staples to them. The heading for the vertical axis of a graph should run along the axis, and headings for the horizontal axis should appear below that axis, not at the top of the graph. Do not extend the vertical or horizontal axis of a graph beyond the point needed for the data shown. Place the key, if used, within or above the figure so that it does not widen the figure. Numerical data that can be expressed more succinctly in tabular form should be converted to tables.

Illustrations. Illustrations (line drawings, halftones, photos, photomicrographs, etc.) should be clean originals or digital files. Digital files are recommended for highest quality reproduction and should follow these guidelines: a) 300 dpi or higher, b) sized to fit on journal page, c) EPS, TIFF, or PSD format only, d) submitted as separate files, not embedded in text files. Color illustrations will be considered for publication; however, the author will be required to bear the full cost involved in their printing and publication. The charge for the first page with color is $900.00. The next three pages with color are $450.00 each. A custom quote will be provided for color art totaling more than 4 journal pages. Good-quality color prints or files should be provided in their final size. The publisher has the right to refuse publication of color prints deemed unacceptable.

Legends. Titles, detailed explanations for figures (in the form of footnotes), and explanations of any superscript letters or abbreviations used in figures belong in the legend, not on the illustrations themselves. Legends for figures should be typed double-spaced on a separate page.

Abbreviations. Abbreviations may be used but (1) should be employed only for terms appearing repeatedly throughout the manuscript, (2) must be spelled out the first time they appear in the text, and (3) must be consistent throughout the manuscript. Abbreviations may not be used in the title and should be avoided, if possible, in the abstract. Employ standard abbreviations if they exist.

Drug names. Generic rather than trade names of drugs should be used, although trade names may be mentioned in parentheses in the first text reference to the drug.

Other Requirements
Transfer of copyright. For a manuscript to be published in the *Harvard Review of Psychiatry*, copyright must be assigned to the President and Fellows of Harvard College. An Assignment of Copyright form will be sent to the corresponding author once a manuscript has been accepted; all authors must sign the form.

Affirmation of authorship. All persons designated as authors must qualify for authorship. Authorship credit should be based only on substantial contributions to (1) conception and design, or analysis and interpretation of data, (2) drafting the article or revising it critically for important intellectual content, and (3) final approval of the submitted version. All three conditions must all be met. General supervision of the research group or participation solely in the acquisition of funding or the collection of data does not justify authorship. Each author should have participated sufficiently in the work to take public responsibility for the content, and the authors are responsible for all statements made in their work, including any changes made by the editorial office that have been approved by the corresponding author. Individuals who contribute to the manuscript but who do not meet authorship requirements may be cited in an acknowledgment if their permission for such citation is obtained.

Disclosure of commercial interests. Prior to publication, authors will be required to disclose any affiliations with. or financial involvement (e.g., employment, consultancies, stock ownership, honoraria, expert testimony) in, any organization or entity with a direct financial interest in the subject matter or materials discussed in the manuscript. A Disclosure of Commercial Interests form will be sent to the corresponding author once a manuscript has been accepted; all authors must complete and sign it. In addition, any relevant financial support of the authors' research must be identified in an acknowledgment in the manuscript.

Prior and duplicate publication. When a manuscript is submitted, the cover letter must include a statement indicating that the manuscript represents original material, has not been previously published, and is not under consideration for publication elsewhere. Except for abstracts of less than 400 words, any form of publication, including components of symposia, proceedings, books or book chapters, or reports of any kind, constitutes prior publication. Press reports of meetings will not usually be considered a breach of this rule, but such reports should not be amplified with additional data or with copies of tables or illustrations. Authors should notify the Editors if the manuscript contains data that have been used in published articles, in articles that are in press, or in manuscripts that have been or will soon be submitted for publication. The authors should include copies of such material with the submitted manuscript and should explain the differences between the manuscripts.

Reproduction. Authors retain the right to use the work that they have submitted in other publications written or edited by them, in any medium, provided that the *Harvard Review of Psychiatry* is acknowledged as the original place of publication, that the President and Fellows of Harvard College are acknowledged as the owners of the copyright, and that the publisher, Taylor & Francis, is notified of any republication.

Informed consent. Manuscripts must include a statement that informed consent was obtained from human subjects. Authors should protect patient anonymity by avoiding the use of patients' names or initials, hospital number, or other identifying information.

Reprints. Authors may order reprints of their articles directly from the publisher, Taylor & Francis, 325 Chestnut St., Suite 800, Philadelphia, PA 19106. An order form and schedule of prices will be sent with the galley proofs to the corresponding author. Individual reprints of articles must be obtained from the author.

Health Communication

ADDRESS FOR SUBMISSION:

Teresa L. Thompson, Editor
Health Communication
University of Dayton
Department of Communication
Dayton, OH 45469
USA
Phone: 937-229-2379
Fax: 937-229-2055
E-Mail: thompson@udayton.edu
Web: www.erlbaum.com/journals
Address May Change:

PUBLICATION GUIDELINES:

Manuscript Length: 21-25
Copies Required: Three
Computer Submission: Yes
Format: MS Word or WordPerfect
Fees to Review: 0.00 US$

Manuscript Style:
American Psychological Association

CIRCULATION DATA:

Reader: Academics
Frequency of Issue: 6 Times/Year
Copies per Issue: Less than 1,000
Sponsor/Publisher: Lawrence Erlbaum
  Associates, Inc.
Subscribe Price: 45.00 US$ Individual
  365.00 US$ Institution
  40.50 US$ Indv,328.50 Inst Electronic

REVIEW INFORMATION:

Type of Review: Blind Review
No. of External Reviewers: 2
No. of In House Reviewers: 2
Acceptance Rate: 11-20%
Time to Review: 2 - 3 Months
Reviewers Comments: Yes
Invited Articles: 0-5%
Fees to Publish: 0.00 US$

MANUSCRIPT TOPICS:
Group Dynamics; Health Communication; Psycholinguistics; Social Psychology

MANUSCRIPT GUIDELINES/COMMENTS:

Editorial Scope
As an outlet for scholarly intercourse between medical and social sciences, this noteworthy journal seeks to improve practical communication between caregivers and patients and between institutions and the public. Outstanding editorial board members and contributors from both medical and social science arenas collaborate to meet the challenges inherent in this goal. Although most inclusions are data-based, the journal also publishes pedagogical, methodological, theoretical, and applied articles using either quantitative or qualitative methods. Topics covered include provider-patient (or family) interaction, communication and cooperation, health information, promotion, interviewing, and public relations.

Audience
Scholars and practitioners in communication, psychology, sociology, public health, medicine, nursing, dentistry, physical therapy, dietetics, pharmacy, and the allied health professions.

Instructions To Contributors

Manuscript Submission. Submit three manuscript copies to Teresa L. Thompson, Editor, *Health Communication,* Department of Communication, University of Dayton, Dayton, OH 45469. Only original manuscripts submitted to *Health Communication* will be considered for publication. The cover letter should include a statement that the manuscript is not being submitted elsewhere. The cover letter should also indicate the address and telephone number of the person to whom editorial correspondence is to be addressed. Include a self-addressed postcard for notification of receipt. Manuscripts will be reviewed by at least two reviewers besides the Editor. Authors will be notified of the disposition of their manuscripts expeditiously. Manuscripts will not be returned. Electronic submissions are also encouraged, and should be sent as attachments to **thompson@udayton.edu** in Word or WordPerfect.

Book Reviews. Send to Bryan B. Whaley, Department of Communication, University of San Francisco, 2130 Fulton Street, San Francisco, CA 94117–1080.

Format and Organization. Manuscripts should be prepared according to the guidelines in the *Publication Manual of the American Psychological Association* (5th ed.) and should be no longer than 25 pages. Double-space all text, including references, figure captions, footnotes, and tables. Prepare manuscripts for blind review—author identification removed, detachable title page with author(s) and affiliation(s). The title page should also include the name and address of the person to whom reprint requests are to be sent and a shortened version of the title of the manuscript for use as a running head (40 characters or fewer, including spaces).

Permissions. Authors are responsible for all statements made in their work and for obtaining permission from copyright owners to use a lengthy quotation (500 words or more) or to reprint or adapt a table or figure published elsewhere. Authors should write to both author(s) and publisher of such material to request nonexclusive world rights in all languages for use in the article and in future editions of it.

Content. Do not use new technical words, psychological jargon or slang, or terminology not consistent with the style guidelines in the *Publication Manual of the APA* (5th edition). Define any abbreviations or acronyms the first time they are used.

Figures and Tables. All figures and tables should be numbered separately using Arabic numerals and should be grouped at the end of the manuscript. Clearly visible notes within the text should indicate approximate placement of figures and tables. Figures must be professionally prepared and must be camera-ready. Type figure captions on a separate sheet. Write the article title and figure number lightly in pencil on the back of each piece of artwork. Refer to the *Publication Manual of the APA* for format of tables. Double-space.

References. Double-space. Compile references alphabetically (see the *Publication Manual of the APA* for multiple-author citations and references). Spell out names of journals. Provide page numbers of chapters in edited books. Text citations must correspond accurately to the references in the reference list.

Page Proofs. Authors are sent page proofs of their manuscripts and are asked to proofread them for printer's errors and other defects. Correction of typographical errors will be made without charge; other alterations will be charged to the author.

Reprints. Authors may order reprints of their articles when they receive page proofs. Printing considerations do not permit the ordering of reprints after authors have returned proofs.

Health Education Research

ADDRESS FOR SUBMISSION:

Michael Eriksen, Editor-in-Chief
Health Education Research
Georgia State University
Institute of Public Health
P.O. Box 3995
Atlanta, GA 30302-3995
USA
Phone: 404-651-4135
Fax: 404-651-1559
E-Mail: her@gsu.edu
Web: http://her.oupjournals.org
Address May Change:

PUBLICATION GUIDELINES:

Manuscript Length: 2000-4000 Words
Copies Required: One Electronic
Computer Submission: Yes Email, Online
Format: MS Word or WordPerfect
Fees to Review: 0.00 US$

Manuscript Style:
    American Psychological Association

CIRCULATION DATA:

Reader: Academics, Practitioners
Frequency of Issue: 6 Times/Year
Copies per Issue: Less than 1,000
Sponsor/Publisher: International Union for
    Public Health Education / Oxford
    University Press
Subscribe Price:

REVIEW INFORMATION:

Type of Review: Blind Review
No. of External Reviewers: 3
No. of In House Reviewers: 0
Acceptance Rate: 15-25%
Time to Review: 2 - 3 Months
Reviewers Comments: Yes
Invited Articles: 0-5%
Fees to Publish: 0.00 US$

MANUSCRIPT TOPICS:
Adolescent Psychology; Alcoholism & Drug Addiction; Behavior Medicine; Behavior Modification; Gerontology; Health Psychology; Psychiatry; Psychopathology; Social Psychology

MANUSCRIPT GUIDELINES/COMMENTS:

About the Journal
Publishing original, refereed papers, *Health Education Research* deals with all the vital issues involved in health education and promotion worldwide -providing a valuable link between the researcher and the results obtained by practising health educators and communicators.

Information for Authors
Please read these instructions carefully and follow them strictly. In this way you will help ensure that the review and publication of your paper is as efficient and quick as possible. The editors reserve the right to return manuscripts that are not in accordance with these instructions.

Papers must be clearly and concisely written in English. In the interests of speed, manuscripts are not extensively copy-edited, and authors are requested to check their texts carefully before submitting them. Papers should be intelligible to as wide an audience as possible; particular attention should be paid to the Introduction and Discussion sections, which should clearly draw attention to the novelty and significance of the data reported, and to the implications for future developments. Failure to do this may result in publication delays or rejection of the paper.

Scope
Health Education Research: Theory & Practice invites original contributions in any area of research in health education and educational aspects of health promotion. The perspective is international, and the journal publishes material on both theoretical processes and models, and on their practical implementation. Articles may be data-based or theoretical, and are welcome from academics or practitioners working in any health-related field.

Submission and Review of Manuscripts
Contributors in The Americas should submit their manuscript electronically.

To submit new manuscript for consideration by *HER*:
1. Please email, as an attachment, your manuscript (saved as a .doc or .rtf file) and figures to **her@gsu.edu**. Please indicate the corresponding author's name in the filename (AuthorName.doc).
2. In the body of your email message, include the text of your cover letter to the Editor-in-Chief, Dr. M. Eriksen.
3. See additional instructions for authors below.

To submit a revised manuscript that previously has been reviewed by *HER*:
1. Please email, as an attachment, your revised manuscript (saved as a .doc or .rtf file) and figures to **her@gsu.edu**. Please use a filename such as "MS 12 34 56 v 2.doc".
2. In the body of your email message, include the text of your cover letter to the editor assigned to your manuscript.
3. Attach a second document that contains your response to the reviewers' comments and lists the revisions that you have made to your manuscript. All identifying information will be removed before this document is shared with the reviewers. Please use a filename such as "MS 12 34 56 response.doc".

To submit the final version of manuscript that has been accepted for publication in *HER*:
1. Please email, as an attachment, the final version of your manuscript (saved as a .doc or .rtf file) and figures to **her@gsu.edu**. Please use a filename such as "MS 12 34 56 final.doc". On the title page, please include separate word counts for the abstract, body text (not including tables), and reference sections.
2. In the body of your email message, include the text of your cover letter to the editor assigned to your manuscript. Include your response to the reviewers' comments and list the revisions that you have made to your manuscript.
3. Mail the License to Publish form and any high-resolution figures (please send both electronic and hard copies of the figures) to: Kate Wellsby, Production Editor, Journals

Department, Oxford University Press, Great Clarendon Street, Oxford OX2 6DP, United Kingdom.
4. Send any Reviewer Information Forms *to Health Education Research*, Institute of Public Health, Georgia State University, PO Box 3995, Atlanta, GA 30302-3995, USA.

All other contributors should submit their manuscript (the original and three copies) directly to the Executive Editor: Prof. K. Tones, 42 Moseley Wood Lane, Leeds LS16 7EP, UK (e-mail address: **keith.tones@virgin.net**).

A covering letter should identify the person (with address, postal/zip code, telephone number, fax number and e-mail address) responsible for correspondence relating to manuscripts. This letter should include a statement indicating that the research or intervention project was approved (or judged exempt) by an institutional review board. (In the manuscript, authors should cite methods employed for protection of participants, including informed consent and assurances of confidentiality or anonymity.) Please refer to the section titled Preparation of manuscripts for submission for additional information about the preferred format and style of manuscripts. Authors are advised to keep a further copy of their manuscript.

Submission of a paper implies that it reports unpublished work and that it is not under consideration for publication elsewhere. If previously published tables, illustrations or more than 200 words of text are to be included, the copyright holder's permission must be obtained. Copies of any such permission letters should be enclosed with the paper.

The highest editorial scientific standards are maintained throughout the journal. To this end, all papers are refereed by at least three authorities of acknowledged expertise in the paper's subject area.

Word-processor disks/diskettes can be used for setting accepted articles. (Contributors considering the submission of a disk with their final, accepted manuscript should refer to the separate information for submission of disks.)

Conflicts of interest. *Health Education Research* would not wish you or your co-authors to be embarrassed if any undeclared conflicts of interest were to emerge after publication. Potential conflicts of interest must therefore be disclosed to the Editor in the form of a statement in the covering letter. This statement will be published and/or shared with the reviewers at the Editor's discretion. Contributors should declare any commercial interests, such as directorships, share holdings, grants, fees, gifts or travel expenses received, by the individual author or their associated department/organization, from organizations whose service/product, or whose competitors' service/product, is a subject of discussion or evaluation in a scientific study, Editorial, Review or Letter. Any other connections, direct or indirect, that might raise the question of bias in the work reported or the conclusions, implications or opinions stated, including personal relationships or academic competition, must be declared. All sources of funding must be disclosed as an acknowledgement in the text.

Books for review. Publishers wishing to submit their books for review should submit them to: Mr J. K. Davies, Faculty of Health, University of Brighton, Falmer, Brighton BN1 9PH, UK.

Speed of publication. The journal aims to publish papers as soon as is reasonably possible. At all stages, in order to avoid delays, maximum use is made of the telephone, fax and e-mail. Help us by providing the telephone number, fax number and e-mail address of the corresponding author.

HER **Advance Access** is the journal's system for the early online publication of articles ahead of the printed issue. Papers are published online via Advance Access once a week, in typeset and proof-read format. *HER* Advance Access significantly reduces the time from acceptance to publication for *HER* articles (to approximately 8 weeks). If you are a subscriber to the journal you can view the Advance Access papers by visiting http://her.oupjournals.org/ and clicking the Advance Access link. Appearance in Advance Access constitutes official publication, and the Advance Access version can be cited by a unique DOI (Digital Object Identifier).

Preparation of manuscripts. Manuscripts should be in their final form when they are submitted so that proofs require only correction of typographical errors.

If English is not your first language, please have your manuscript reviewed by a native English speaker or a University level teacher of English language. We regret that any papers showing no evidence of proof-reading before submission will be returned immediately.

Types of manuscript. *Health Education Research* accepts manuscripts of four different formats: Research Papers, Programme Papers, Research Notes and Points of View papers.

Research Papers. Research Papers may follow the standard research format, or they may present theoretical discussions and implications for health education research and practice. Review articles are also included in this category.

Data-based research articles, including review articles, should be divided into the following sections: Title page, Abstract, Introduction, Method, Results, Discussion, Acknowledgements, References, Tables, Legends to figures. Theoretical articles should follow the above basic structure but should replace the Method, Results and Discussion sections with appropriate headings. In both cases, authors who wish to write extensive Introduction and Discussion sections may use additional subheadings in these sections if this seems helpful. It is expected that qualitative research studies will provide concise details of the data generation and analytic processes used and will show how the validity and trustworthiness of findings were established.

Contributions that exceed 4000 words (for the main text, excluding the abstract, tables, figures and references) normally are not considered unless agreed in advance with the appropriate Editor, but even then publication may be subject to delay. The length of papers which include a qualitative research study may be extended by a maximum of 1500 words to allow for the use of quotations. This does not require the prior agreement of the Editor.

Programme Papers are designed to meet the practical and applied needs of readers. They may include descriptions of intervention programmes and should address important aspects of programme planning and delivery, and they should not exceed 4000 words in length. They differ from standard articles in that they do not have a clear research element, e.g. survey, pre-test or proper evaluation. They should, however, discuss implications for monitoring and evaluation along with other substantive issues of programme development and implementation. Invited experts will comment on the research and evaluation implications of selected papers. Programme papers are encouraged from health education practitioners and policy makers.

Research Notes describe ongoing research which might be of interest to readers. They also may provide comments on research being conducted by others. These papers may be structured as for longer papers, as appropriate, and they should not exceed 2000 words in length.

Points of View papers present an author's opinions about a particular health education topic, especially a controversial issue or an issue that an author feels has been neglected and should be addressed by health education researchers and the Journal. The structure for these papers may vary, but they should not exceed 2000 words in length.

Research participants. Authors are asked to refer to participants in research as 'participants', 'respondents', 'individuals', or by a more specific word ('children', 'students', etc.), rather than as 'subjects'.

General format. All manuscripts presenting data or evaluation results from human subjects should include a statement describing the review process followed by the research or intervention project to safeguard the rights of human subjects.

An original and four copies of the manuscript must be submitted. They should be legibly typed on A4 or American quarto paper (8.5 x 11 inch bond paper). All sections of the manuscript must be double-spaced (space between the lines of type not less than 6 mm). Margins of 25 mm (1 inch) should be left at the sides, top and bottom of each page. Number each page top right (Title page is 1). Manuscripts produced by dot matrix printers should have type that is large and dark, have clear punctuation and have 'descenders' of the letters p, q, y and g below the line. Please avoid footnotes; use instead, and as sparingly as possible, parenthesis within brackets. Underline only words or letters to appear in italics. Clearly identify unusual or handwritten symbols and Greek letters. Differentiate between the letter O and zero, and the letters I and l and number 1. Mark the position of each figure and table in the margin.

Title page. The title should be short, specific and informative, and printed on a separate page. Serial titles are not accepted. The surname and initials of each author should be followed by his or her department, institution, city with postal code, and country. Any changes of address may be given in numbered footnotes. Please provide a running title of not more than 50 characters and include four to five key words or short phrases to assist us in the review process. Indicate the word count for the main text (excluding the abstract, tables, figures and references) at the bottom of the title page.

Abstract. The second page of every manuscript must contain only the Abstract, which should be a single paragraph not exceeding 200 words. Please abide strictly by this limitation of length. The Abstract should be comprehensible to readers before they have read the paper, and abbreviations and reference citations should be avoided.

Acknowledgements. These should be included on a separate page at the end of the text and not in footnotes. Please do not include references to specific institutions or funding agencies in the text of the manuscript. Personal acknowledgements should precede those of institutions or agencies.

References. Authors are responsible for the accuracy of the References. Published articles and those in press (state the journal which has accepted them) may be included. In the text a reference should be cited by author and date as 'Reports by Author (Author, 1989) have confirmed...' or '...as reported earlier (Author and Author, 1985; Author et al., 19860.' Do not place text other than the author and date within the parentheses. In the text no more than two authors may be cited per reference; if there are more than two authors use et al. At the end of the manuscript the citations should be typed in alphabetical order, listing all authors' names, with the authors' surnames and initials inverted. References should include, in the following order: authors' names, year, paper title, journal title, volume number, inclusive page numbers, and name and address of publisher (for books only). The name of the journal should be given in full. References should therefore be listed as follows:

Roberts, M. M., French, K. and Duffy, J. (1984) Breast cancer and breast self-examination: what do Scottish women know? Social Science and Medicine, 18, 791-797.

Fynn, A. (1981) Cigarette advertising and health education: use and abuse of media. In Leathar, D. S., Hastings, G. B. and Davies, J. K. (eds), Health Education and the Media. Pergamon Press, Oxford, p. 129.

Bergler, R. (1981) Advertising and Cigarette Smoking: a Psychological Study. Hans Huber, Bern.

Personal communications (J. Smith, personal communication) should be authorized by those involved in writing, and unpublished data should be cited as (unpublished data). Both should be used as sparingly as possible and only when the unpublished data referred to is peripheral rather than central to the discussion. References to manuscripts in preparation, or submitted, but not yet accepted, should be cited in the text as (Smith and Jones, in preparation) and should NOT be included in the list of references.

Tables. Tables should be typed on separate sheets and numbered consecutively with Roman numerals. Tables should be self-explanatory and include a brief descriptive title. Footnotes to tables indicated by lower case letters are acceptable, but they should not include extensive experimental detail. An arrow in the text margin should be used to indicate where a table should be inserted in the text. Do not submit tables as photographs.

Illustrations. All illustrations (line drawings and photographs) should be referred to in the text as Figure 1 etc., which should be abbreviated to 'Fig. 1' only in the figure legend. On the manuscript indicate with an arrow in the margin the most appropriate position for the figure.

Photographs. Photographs should be of sufficiently high quality with respect to detail, contrast and fineness of grain to withstand the inevitable loss of contrast and detail inherent in the printing process. Photographs must be submitted in the desired final size so that reduction can be avoided. The type area of a page is 192 x 149 mm and photographs, including their legends, must not exceed this area. A single column is 72 mm wide; a double column is 149 mm wide. Ideally, photographs should fit either a single or a double column.

Colour plates. Inclusion of colour plates is subject to a special charge.

Line drawings. Please provide these as clear, sharp prints, suitable for reproduction as submitted. No additional artwork, redrawing or typesetting will be done. Therefore, all labelling should be made with a lettering set. Freestyle hand lettering or drawing is not acceptable. Ensure that the size of lettering is in proportion with the overall dimensions of the drawing. Ideally, line drawings should be submitted in the desired final size to avoid reduction (maximum dimensions 192 x 149 mm including legends) and should fit either a single (72 mm) or a double column width (149 mm). If submitting line drawings which require reduction, please check that the lettering will be clearly legible after the drawing has been reduced to the size at which it will be printed. After reduction, letters should not be smaller than 1.5 mm in height.

Figure legends. These should be on a separate, numbered manuscript sheet. Define all symbols and abbreviations used in the figure. Common abbreviations and others in the preceding text should not be redefined in the legend.

Page charges are NOT levied.

Format For Accepted Manuscripts
Disk submission. After the manuscript has gone through all the review and editing stages, copy the data onto a clean, newly formatted disk. The data should be saved in the word processor's native format and also in Rich Text Format (.rtf file). To avoid confusion do not copy any irrelevant files and/or back-up files onto the disk. Apple Mac users should ensure the disk wastebasket is empty before submitting the disk.

Use the first-named author's name or manuscript number for the file name.

To avoid loss or damage in transit ensure that the disk is adequately protected and always keep a copy of the data on your computer and/or back-up disk. Include two hard copies of the manuscript with the disk.

Guide for authors preparing electronic documents for disk submittal
- Prepare your manuscript using a word processing program (save as .doc or .rtf) and create your figures using software capable of generating high-resolution figures.
- Enter headings, text and references in the style and order of the journal.
- Insert figure captions and tables at the end of the file. Note that on acceptance Production requires high resolution versions of figures.

- Avoid the use of footnotes; use instead, and as sparingly as possible, parentheses within brackets.
- Check the final copy of your paper carefully as any errors will be faithfully translated into the typeset version. In the case of a mismatch between disk and hard copy, the disk copy will be taken as the definitive version.

Figure submission. Images on disk can be accepted in Adobe PhotoShop compatible formats. Images should be saved in TIFF format.

Colour figures should be saved as CMYK colour rather than RGB.

Image resolution should be a minimum of 300 dpi.

Publication quality hard copies of all figures should still be submitted and will be used for reproduction if the electronic files cannot be used. Write the title of your paper, the name of the first author and the figure number on an adhesive label, which should be pasted on the back of each figure. On the label also indicate clearly the top margin of each figure.

Photographs. These must be submitted in the desired final size so that reduction can be avoided. The type area of a page is 192 x 149 mm and photographs, including their legends, must not exceed this area. A single column is 72 mm wide; a double column is 149 mm wide. Ideally, photographs should fit either a single or a double column. Photographs should be of sufficiently high quality with respect to detail, contrast and fineness of grain to withstand the inevitable loss of contrast and detail inherent in the printing process. Please indicate the magnification by a rule on the photograph. When several prints of varying quality of the same figure are provided, please indicate which print should be used for reproduction in the journal. Be sure that all mounted prints are aligned at exact right angles.

Line drawings. Ideally, line drawings should be submitted in the desired final size to avoid reduction (maximum dimensions 192 x 149 mm including legends) and should fit either a single (72 mm) or a double column width (149 mm). If submitting line drawings that require reduction, please check that the lettering will be clearly legible after the drawing has been reduced to the size at which it will be printed. After reduction, letters should not be smaller than 1.5 mm in height.

Licence to publish. It is a condition of publication in the Journal that authors grant an exclusive licence to publish to Oxford University Press. This ensures that requests from third parties to reproduce articles are handled efficiently and consistently and will also allow the article to be as widely disseminated as possible. In granting an exclusive licence, Authors may use their own material in publications provided that the Journal is acknowledged as the original place of publication, and Oxford University Press is notified in writing and in advance.

Proofs. Authors are sent page proofs. Please provide an e-mail address to enable page proofs to be sent as PDF files via e-mail. To avoid delays in publication, proofs should be checked immediately for typographic errors and returned to the publishers by express (special delivery) post. Alternatively, to save time, corrections may be sent by fax to Oxford University Press, fax number +44 (0)1865 3533773. Essential changes of an extensive nature may be made only by insertion of a Note added in proof. A charge is made to authors who insist on amendment within the text at the page-proof stage.

Online access/offprints. The publisher will provide free online access to your article. Order forms are sent out with the proofs, and must be returned with the proofs to Oxford University Press. Printed offprints may be purchased (late orders submitted after the journal is printed are subject to a 50 per cent surcharge to cover the additional printing cost).

Health Psychology

ADDRESS FOR SUBMISSION:

Robert M. Kaplan, Editor-in-Chief
Health Psychology
UCLA School of Public Health
Department of Health Services
PO Box 951772
Room 31-293C CHS
Los Angeles, CA 90025-1772
USA
Phone:
Fax:
E-Mail: rmkaplan@ucla.edu
Web: http://www.apa.org/journals/hea
Address May Change: 12/31/2010

PUBLICATION GUIDELINES:

Manuscript Length: 25-30
Copies Required: One
Computer Submission: Yes
Format: MS Word or WordPerfect
Fees to Review: 0.00 US$

Manuscript Style:
    American Psychological Association

CIRCULATION DATA:

Reader: Academics, Practitioners
Frequency of Issue: Bi-Monthly
Copies per Issue: 5,001 - 10,000
Sponsor/Publisher: American Psychological
    Association
Subscribe Price:
    See Website for Details

REVIEW INFORMATION:

Type of Review: Editorial Review
No. of External Reviewers: 3
No. of In House Reviewers: 0
Acceptance Rate: 30%
Time to Review: 2 - 3 Months
Reviewers Comments: Yes
Invited Articles: 0-5%
Fees to Publish: 0.00 US$

MANUSCRIPT TOPICS:
Psychobiology

MANUSCRIPT GUIDELINES/COMMENTS:

Journal Description
Health Psychology is a scholarly journal devoted to furthering an understanding of scientific relationships between behavioral principles on the one hand and physical health and illness on the other. The readership has a broad range of backgrounds, interests, and specializations, often interdisciplinary in nature. The major type of paper being solicited for *Health Psychology* is the report of empirical research. Such papers should have significant theoretical or practical import for an understanding of relationships between behavior and physical health. Integrative papers that address themselves to a broad constituency are particularly welcome. Suitable topics for submission include, but are not restricted to, the role of environmental, psychosocial, or sociocultural factors that may contribute to disease or its prevention; behavioral methods used in the diagnosis, treatment, or rehabilitation of individuals having physical disorders; and techniques that could reduce disease risk by

modifying health beliefs, attitudes, or behaviors including decisions about using professional services. Interventions used may be at the individual, group, multicenter, or community level.

Effective in January 2005, the Incoming Editor is receiving all new submissions to the journal. Submissions that are accepted will be published beginning in the 2006 volume. Submit manuscripts electronically (.rtf, PDF, or .doc). via the website at:
http://www.jbo.com/jbo3/submissions/dsp_jbo.cfm?journal_code=hea

General correspondence may be directed to Robert M. Kaplan, Incoming Editor, Department of Health Services, UCLA School of Public Health, P.O. Box 951772, Room 31-293C, Los Angeles, CA 90025-1772, and mail two copies of the manuscript and a disk with an electronic version of the paper (MS Word or WordPerfect word processing formats are fine) to Robert M. Kaplan, Incoming Editor, Department of Health Services, UCLA School of Public Health, P.O. Box 951772, Room 31-293C, Los Angeles, CA 90025-1772.

General correspondence may be directed to the Editor's Office (**rmkaplan@ucla.edu**)

The preferred length of manuscripts is 25-30 double-spaced pages, including references, notes, tables, captions, and figures. All copies should be clear, readable, and on paper of good quality. An unusual typeface is acceptable only if it is clear and legible. In addition to addresses and phone numbers, authors should supply electronic mail addresses and fax numbers, if available, for potential use by the editorial office and later by the production office. Authors should keep a copy of the manuscript to guard against loss. Supplementary materials. APA can now place supplementary materials online, which will be available via the journal's Web page as noted above. To submit such materials, please see www.apa.org/journals/supplementalmaterial.html for details.

Authors may submit a list of suggested reviewers for the manuscript; suggested reviewers should not, of course, have any conflict of interest regarding the review. Masked review policy. Masked review may be requested by the author. Authors requesting masked review should include a cover sheet, which shows the title of the manuscript, the authors' names and institutional affiliations, and the date the manuscript is submitted. The first page of the manuscript should omit the authors' names and affiliations but should include the title of the manuscript and the date it is submitted.

Manuscript Preparation
Authors should prepare manuscripts according to the *Publication Manual of the American Psychological Association* (5th ed.). Manuscripts may be copyedited for bias-free language (see chap. 2 of the *Publication Manual*). Formatting instructions (all copy must be double-spaced) and instructions on the preparation of tables, figures, references, metrics, and abstracts appear in the *Manual*. For APA's Checklist for Manuscript Submission, see www.apa.org/journals.

Abstract and keywords. All manuscripts must include an abstract containing a maximum of 120 words typed on a separate page. After the abstract, please supply up to five keywords or brief phrases.

References. References should be listed in alphabetical order. References should be cited in text as follows: "The results replicated those of a previous study (Knoth & Mair, 1991)," or "The procedure was a modification of Krettek and Price (1989) and Smith et al. (1977)." Multiple references should be cited in alphabetical order: Earlier investigations (Abbott, 1988; Hunt & Aggleton, 1983; Winocur, 1985). . . . Each listed reference should be cited in text, and each text citation should be listed in the References. Basic formats are as follows:

Barnett, R. C., Davidson, H., & Marshall, N. L. (1991). Physical symptoms and the interplay of work and family roles. *Health Psychology, 10*, 94–101.

Cohen, J., & Cohen, P. (1975). *Applied multiple regression/correlation analysis for the behavioral sciences.* Hillsdale, NJ: Erlbaum.

Haynes, S. G., Eaker, E. D., & Feinleib, M. (1984). The effect of employment, family, and job stress on coronary heart disease. In E. B. Gold (Ed.), *The changing risk of disease in women: An epidemiologic approach* (pp. 37–48). Lexington, MA: Heath.

All statistical tests should include an indication of *effect size* whenever possible (estimates of effect size for some statistical tests have not been fully developed). All randomized controlled trials must include a diagram indicating participant flow into the study and a completed CONSORT checklist (see "The CONSORT Statement: Revised Recommendations for Improving the Quality of Reports of Parallel-Group Randomized Trials," by M. Moher, K. F. Schulz, and D. Altman, for the CONSORT Group, 2001, *Journal of the American Medical Association*, 285, pp. 1987-1991).

Figures. Graphics files are welcome if supplied as Tiff, EPS, or Powerpoint. High-quality printouts or glossies are needed for all figures. The minimum line weight for line art is 0.5 point for optimal printing. When possible, please place symbol legends below the figure image instead of to the side. Original color figures can be printed in color at the editor's and publisher's discretion provided the author agrees to pay half of the associated production costs; an estimate of these costs is available from the APA production office on request.

Submission Letter

Authors are required to include the following in their submission letter:
1. a statement of compliance with APA ethical standards in the treatment of their sample, human or animal, or a description of the details of the treatment (see below);

2. a statement that the manuscript or data have not been published previously and that they are not under consideration for publication elsewhere;

3. a statement to reflect that all listed authors have contributed significantly to the manuscript and consent to their names on the manuscript; and

4. a brief statement of how the article content is relevant to the domain of *Health Psychology* as described in the journal inside cover (see Content).

Failure to include any of the requirements above may result in a delay of the review process.

Brief Reports
Health Psychology accepts Brief Reports of soundly designed research studies that are of specialized interest or limited importance—reports that cannot be accepted as regular articles due to lack of space. An author who submits a Brief Report must agree not to submit the full report to another journal. To ensure that a Brief Report does not exceed the available journal pages (approximately 4 pages), set your computer so that (a) the approximate number of characters per line is 90 (use 12-point Times Roman type with 1-inch [2.54-cm] side margins), (b) the number of double-spaced lines per page is about 25, and (c) the total number of lines in the report is about 400. Count all lines, including headings and references but excluding title, author name(s), affiliation(s), and abstract; figure 27 lines for each 1/4 journal page required for tables and figures (visual estimation necessary).

Letters to the Editor
Health Psychology will now consider letters concerning articles previously published in the journal. Letters should be no more than 500 words in length and have a maximum of five references. Letters may be sent electronically to the journal's editorial assistant, Dianne Pagani (email: **HAS_Health_Psychology@notes.cc.sunysb.edu**). Authors will be notified of the decision to publish the letter and will be sent an edited version. Authors of the original article will be offered an opportunity to reply to the letter. No additional letters on the topic will be accepted.

Permissions
Authors are required to obtain and provide to the editor on final acceptance all necessary permissions to reproduce in print and electronic form any copyrighted work, including, for example, test materials (or portions thereof) and photographs of people.

Ethical Principles
APA policy prohibits an author from submitting the same manuscript for concurrent consideration by two or more publications. APA's policy regarding posting articles on the Internet may be found at www.apa.org/journals. In addition, it is a violation of APA Ethical Principles to publish "as original data, data that have been previously published" (Standard 8.13). As this journal is a primary journal that publishes original material only, APA policy prohibits as well publication of any manuscript that has already been published in whole or in substantial part elsewhere. Authors have an obligation to consult journal editors concerning prior publication of any data upon which their article depends.

In addition, APA Ethical Principles specify that "after research results are published, psychologists do not withhold the data on which their conclusions are based from other competent professionals who seek to verify the substantive claims through reanalysis and who intend to use such data only for that purpose, provided that the confidentiality of the participants can be protected and unless legal rights concerning proprietary data preclude their release" (Standard 8.14). APA expects authors submitting to this journal to adhere to these standards. Specifically, authors of manuscripts submitted to APA journals are expected to have available their data throughout the editorial review process and for at least 5 years after the date of publication. A copy of the APA Ethical Principles may be obtained electronically at http://www.apa.org/ethics/ or by writing the APA Ethics Office, 750 First Street, NE, Washington, DC 20002-4242.

APA requires authors to reveal any possible conflict of interest in the conduct and reporting of research (e.g., financial interests in a test procedure, funding by pharmaceutical companies for drug research).

Authors of accepted manuscripts will be required to transfer copyright to APA.

Preparing files for production
If your manuscript is accepted for publication, please follow the guidelines for file formats and naming provided at www.apa.org/journals/preparing_electronic_files.html. If your manuscript was mask reviewed, please ensure that the final version for production includes a byline and full author note for typesetting.

History of Psychology

ADDRESS FOR SUBMISSION:

James H. Capshew, Editor
History of Psychology
Indiana University
Dept. of History & Philosophy of Science
1011 East Third Street
Goodbody Hall 130
Bloomington, IN 47405
USA
Phone: 812-855-3655
Fax: 812-855-3631
E-Mail: jcapshew@indiana.edu
Web: www.apa.org
Address May Change:

PUBLICATION GUIDELINES:

Manuscript Length: 30+
Copies Required: Four
Computer Submission: Yes Disk
Format: English/MS Word
Fees to Review: 0.00 US$

Manuscript Style:
  American Psychological Association

CIRCULATION DATA:

Reader: Academics
Frequency of Issue: Quarterly
Copies per Issue: 1,001 - 2,000
Sponsor/Publisher:
Subscribe Price: 73.00 US$ Individual
  250.00 US$ Institution
  51.00 US$ Member

REVIEW INFORMATION:

Type of Review: Blind Review
No. of External Reviewers: 2
No. of In House Reviewers: 0
Acceptance Rate: 11-20%
Time to Review: 2 - 3 Months
Reviewers Comments: Yes
Invited Articles: 0-5%
Fees to Publish: 0.00 US$

MANUSCRIPT TOPICS:
History of Psychology

MANUSCRIPT GUIDELINES/COMMENTS:

History of Psychology features refereed articles addressing all aspects of psychology's past and of its interrelationship with the many contexts within which it has emerged and has been practiced. It also publishes scholarly work in closely related areas, such as historical psychology (the history of consciousness and behavior), psychohistory, theory in psychology as it pertains to history, historiography, biography and autobiography, and the teaching of the history of psychology.

Because *History of Psychology* publishes manuscripts submitted by psychologists, by historians, and by other scholars, authors may choose for their manuscript style the form specified either in the *Publication Manual of the American Psychological Association* (5th ed.) or in *The Chicago Manual of Style* (14th ed., University of Chicago Press). If the latter style is chosen, reference lists should be eliminated or incorporated into endnotes.

Authors are required to obtain and provide to APA prior to production all necessary permissions to reproduce in print and electronic form any copyrighted work, including, for example, test materials (or portions thereof) and photographs of people. Final files for production should be prepared as outlined in Preparing Your Electronic Files for Production.

Manuscripts will receive a masked review. Authors are requested to include with each copy of the manuscript a cover sheet, which shows the title of the manuscript, the authors' names and institutional affiliations, and the date the manuscript is submitted. The first page of the manuscript should omit the authors' names, and affiliations but should include the title of the manuscript and the submission date. Footnotes containing information pertaining to the authors' identity or affiliations should be on separate pages. Every effort should be made to see that the manuscript itself contains no clues to the authors' identity.

Authors are required to obtain and provide to APA prior to production all necessary permissions to reproduce in print and electronic form any copyrighted work, including, for example, test materials (or portions thereof) and photographs of people.

APA policy prohibits an author from submitting the same manuscript for concurrent consideration by two or more publications. In addition, it is a violation of APA Ethical Principles to publish "as original data, data that have been previously published" (Standard 8.13). Authors have an obligation to consult journal editors concerning prior publication of any data upon which their article depends. In addition, APA Ethical principles specify that "after research results are published, psychologists do not withhold the data on which their conclusions are based from other competent professionals who seek to verify the substantive claims through reanalysis and who intend to use such data only for that purpose, provided that the confidentiality of the participants can be protected and unless legal rights concerning proprietary data preclude their release" (Standard 8.14). APA expects authors of manuscripts submitted to APA journals to have their data available throughout the editorial review process and for at least 5 years after the date of publication. APA requires authors to reveal any possible conflict of interest in the conduct and reporting of research (e.g., financial interests in a test or procedure, financing by pharmaceutical companies for drug research).

History of Psychology seeks to publish essay reviews of thematically related sets of books and other media addressing issues important to an understanding of psychology past. Scholars who have identified such sets of books and other media and wish to prepare such essays should discuss their proposed reviews with the editor before beginning to write them.

Submit four copies of each manuscript, with phone number, fax number, and electronic mail address, if available, included on the cover sheet of each copy. All copies should be clear, readable, and on paper of good quality. A dot matrix or unusual typeface is acceptable only if it is clear and legible. Do not submit manuscripts electronically. Authors should keep a copy of the manuscript to guard against loss. Mail manuscripts to the Editor, James H. Capshew, *History of Psychology*, Department of History and Philosophy of Science, 1011 East Third Street, Goodbody Hall 130, Indiana University, Bloomington, IN 47405. .Phone: 812-855-36555712; Fax 812-855-363; General correspondence may be directed to the Editor's Office.

Human Development

ADDRESS FOR SUBMISSION:

Geoffrey Saxe, Editor
Human Development
University of California, Berkeley
Institute of Human Development
1211 Tolman Hall
Berkeley, CA 94720-1690
USA
Phone: 510-642-3705
Fax: 510-642-7969
E-Mail: humdev@berkeley.edu
Web: See Guidelines
Address May Change:

PUBLICATION GUIDELINES:

Manuscript Length: 26-30
Copies Required: Four
Computer Submission: Yes Email
Format: English, Microsoft Word
Fees to Review: 0.00 US$

Manuscript Style:
    American Psychological Association

CIRCULATION DATA:

Reader: Academics
Frequency of Issue: 6 Times/Year
Copies per Issue: 1,001 - 2,000
Sponsor/Publisher: Karger Publishers
Subscribe Price: 116.00 US$ Personal
    464.00 US$ Institution
    149.00 US$ Personal Print + Online

REVIEW INFORMATION:

Type of Review: Editorial Review
No. of External Reviewers: 3+
No. of In House Reviewers: 1
Acceptance Rate:
Time to Review: 2 - 3 Months
Reviewers Comments: Yes
Invited Articles: 6-10%
Fees to Publish: 0.00 US$

MANUSCRIPT TOPICS:
Adulthood; Child Psychology; Family Counseling & Therapy; Gerontology; Social
Psychology

MANUSCRIPT GUIDELINES/COMMENTS:

Website. **http://www.karger.com/journals/hde/hde_jh.htm**

The Editors and Editorial Board welcome manuscripts for review that address important
issues related to human development from varied disciplinary perspectives, including
psychology, anthropology, education, biology, and related disciplines. Manuscripts favored
are conceptual in nature, drawing upon empirical findings and observations for illustrative
purposes. Observations and findings are often used to raise theoretical issues, flesh out
interesting and potentially powerful ideas, and differentiate key constructs. Scholars who are
considering submitting a manuscript should consult current issues of the journal for examples
of style, format, and content of published papers.

Submission

Only original papers written in English are considered and should be sent to the Editor:

Dr. Geoffrey B. Saxe, *Human Development,* Institute of Human Development, University of California, Berkeley, 1211 Tolman Hall, Berkeley, CA 94720-1690 (USA),
E-Mail: **humdev@uclink.berkeley.edu**

Potential contributors may contact the Associate Editor, as well as the Editor, in seeking information or advice about possible submissions. The Associate Editor is:

Dr. Melanie Killen, Department of Human Development, 3304 Benjamin Building, University of Maryland, College Park, MD 20742-1131 (USA),
E-Mail: **Melanie_A_Killen@umail.umd.edu**

Please address other submission inquiries to the Editorial Assistant, at the first address above, phone 510-642-3705.

Manuscripts of 25–45 pages should be submitted in quadruplicate (with four sets of illustrations of which one is an original), typewritten double-spaced on one side of the paper, with a wide margin. Manuscripts should be formatted in accordance with the *Publication Manual of the American Psychological Association*, 5th Edition.

Conditions

All manuscripts are subject to editorial review. Manuscripts are received with the explicit understanding that they are not under simultaneous consideration by any other publication. Submission of an article for publication implies the transfer of the copyright from the author to the publisher upon acceptance. Accepted papers become the permanent property of 'Human Development' and may not be reproduced by any means, in whole or in part, without the written consent of the publisher. It is the author's responsibility to obtain permission to reproduce illustrations, tables, etc. from other publications. A statement of editorial policy appeared in Vol. 46, No. 1, 2003, pp. 1–2.

The journal consists of the following types of publications:
1. Papers
2. Commentaries on Papers*
3. Replies to Commentaries by Authors*
4. Essay Reviews of Books*
* by invitation only.

Arrangement

Presentation and citation of references, statistics, punctuation and abbreviations, construction of tables, selection of headings, and indentation must be in the APA style, 5th ed., as established by the American Psychological Association and adopted as our standard. It is important that authors whose first language is not English have the paper checked by a native English speaker before submission.

Title page. The first page of each paper should indicate the title, the authors' names, the institute where the work was conducted, and a short title for use as running head.

Full address on title page. The exact postal address of the corresponding author complete with postal code must be given at the bottom of the title page. Please also supply phone and fax numbers, as well as the e-mail address for the corresponding author.

Key words on title page. For indexing purposes, a list of 3–10 key words is essential.

Abstract. Each paper needs an abstract of up to 10 lines and no more than 150 words.

Footnotes. Include only when essential. Number them consecutively and type them at the foot of the appropriate page.

Tables and illustrations. Tables and illustrations (both numbered in Arabic numerals) should be prepared on separate sheets, using APA, 5th ed., format. Tables require a heading and figures a legend, also prepared on a separate sheet. For the reproduction of illustrations, only good drawings and original photographs can be accepted; negatives or photocopies cannot be used. Due to technical reasons, figures with a screen background should not be submitted. When possible, group several illustrations on one block for reproduction (max. size 144 x 196 mm) or provide crop marks. On the back of each illustration, indicate its number, the author's name, and 'top' with a soft pencil. Electronically submitted b/w half-tone and color illustrations must have a final resolution of 300 dpi after scaling, line drawings one of 800–1200 dpi.

Color Illustrations
Up to 6 color illustrations per page can be integrated with the text at the special price of CHF 660.-/USD 545.00 per page. Color illustrations are reproduced at the author's expense.

References
The list of references should include only those publications which are cited in the text. References should be listed alphabetically according to the last name of the first author. Please refer to the *Publication Manual of the APA* for formats required for reference citations in the text and the preparation of a reference list.

Digital Object Identifier (DOI)
S. Karger Publishers supports DOIs as unique identifiers for articles. A DOI number will be printed on the title page of each article. DOIs can be useful in the future for identifying and citing articles published online without volume or issue information. More information can be found at www.doi.org

Examples of APA Required Formats for References:

(a) *Papers published in periodicals.* Wertsch, J.V., & Youniss, J. (1987). Contextualizing the investigator: The case of developmental psychology. *Human Development*, 30, 18–31.

(b) *Books.* Matthews, D.E., & Farewell, V.T. (1985). *Using and understanding medical statistics.* Basel: Karger.

(c) *Chapters in edited books.* Hatano, G. & Inagaki, K. (1989). Sharing cognition through collective comprehension activity. In L.B. Resnick, J.M. Levine, & S.D. Teasley (Eds.) *Socially Shared Cognition* (pp. 331–348). Washington, D.C.: American Psychological Association.

For other examples, see the current issue. For further details, consult the *Publication Manual of the American Psychological Association*, 5th Edition.

Galley Proofs
Unless indicated otherwise, galley proofs are sent to the first-named author and should be returned with the least possible delay. Alterations made in galley proofs, other than the correction of printer's errors, are charged to the author. No page proofs are supplied.

Reprints
Order forms and a price list are sent with the galley proofs. Orders submitted after the issue is printed are subject to considerably higher prices.

Human Relations

ADDRESS FOR SUBMISSION:

Paul Willman, Editor
Human Relations
 ONLINE SUBMISSIONS ONLY
The Tavistock Institute
30 Tabernacle Street
London, EC2A 4UE
England
Phone: +44 0 2074 573946
Fax: +44 0 2074 170566
E-Mail: a.gilbertson@tavinstitute.org
Web: www.tavinstitute.org/hrindex.html
Address May Change:

PUBLICATION GUIDELINES:

Manuscript Length: 5,000 Words
Copies Required: Electronic
Computer Submission: Yes via website
Format:
Fees to Review: 0.00 US$

Manuscript Style:
  See Manuscript Guidelines

CIRCULATION DATA:

Reader: Academics
Frequency of Issue: Monthly
Copies per Issue: 1,001 - 2,000
Sponsor/Publisher: Sage Publications
Subscribe Price: 83.00 US$ Individual
  778.00 US$ Institution

REVIEW INFORMATION:

Type of Review: Blind Review
No. of External Reviewers: 3
No. of In House Reviewers: 0
Acceptance Rate: 25%
Time to Review: 4 Months
Reviewers Comments: Yes
Invited Articles: 0-5%
Fees to Publish: 0.00 US$

MANUSCRIPT TOPICS:

Decision Making Theory; Gender Roles; Group Dynamics; Human Relations; Industry & Organization; Motivation; Negotiating Process; Psychology of Women; Sports & Leisure

MANUSCRIPT GUIDELINES/COMMENTS:

About the Journal. The first issue of *Human Relations* appeared in June 1947 when the aim of its founders was to use social science for the purposes of understanding the complexity of human problems, translating understanding into social action and, as Thomas Fairley, the first Editor of the journal, wrote in the introductory note to the first issue, striving 'to relate social theory to social practice', including 'studies of intra-personal, inter-personal and inter-group relations'. Over fifty years later these are still the projects to which the journal devotes itself, along with attending to developments in organisational theory and action research. The link between social theory and practice forms the core subject of the journal. The journal holds it true that such linkages increase the likelihood of relevance and of innovative research in emerging fields of work, taking the social scientist outside traditional areas and approaches. The journal is open to such thinking and experimentation, and actively welcomes submissions which cross disciplinary boundaries.

Today, as fifty years ago, the objective of the journal is to reflect a broad spectrum of problems and approaches to their solution, aiming toward 'the integration of the social sciences'.

Guidelines for submission

1. Authors present, in the text of their papers, explanations of the significance and relevance of their research and/or scholarship. They couch these explanations in clear English and in a manner comprehensible to readers, including those outside the authors' area of specialism.

2. Papers must advance knowledge in the sense that both the subject and method of investigation address an arena of wider interest than that which might be contained in 'old saws', narrow long-standing debates on matters of little consequence outside a particular specialism. Authors are requested to indicate to the Editors how the paper meets their requirement in a covering letter (see Submission of Manuscripts below).

3. Authors and reviewers pay attention to the relevance of cited works and to the degree to which the concepts discussed in the cited works are used in the article. A superfluity of citations, with little or no explanation of why these citations were chosen, creates noise and redundancy of information.

4. While a description of the theoretical frame adopted by an author necessarily includes some consideration of methodology, such consideration does not normally provide more than a small proportion of the paper's content. An overly long explanation of why particular norms and standards have been chosen detracts from discussion of substance. Exceptions are made where the underlying philosophical conventions of technical standards are being challenged in the name of innovation.

5. Papers whose conclusions merely offer scores along, or describe relationships between chosen empirical measures, with commentary on the efficaciousness of techniques adopted in measurement, are not suitable for publication in this journal. Exceptions are made where authors present a technical or methodological critique of a particular tool of analysis, thus carrying forward an important debate which engages more than one area of scientific interest.

6. Studies based on laboratory experiments are normally unacceptable unless presented with confirmatory field data. Studies referring to simulation exercises involving students or others without experiential knowledge of the simulated context are particularly discouraged.

7. Field-study results are more likely to be accepted if they use more than a single technique of data collection and analysis. Further, authors strengthen the validity of, for example, questionnaire scales or constructs tracked over time and space by considering multiple influences in the context of the field study.

8. Papers which simply report the findings of studies which use cross-sectional designs and self-report questionnaire measures are discouraged although where a study is particularly innovative or novel such a design may, in exceptional circumstances, be justified. Authors are encouraged to indicate how this requirement is met in their covering letter.

9. Success in publication rests on how well the paper contributes in both social and conceptual relevance. Authors indicate the implications of their findings for the readers' intelligent understanding of the social issue being studied. In their conclusions, authors also assert a conceptual contribution made to the theoretical framework in which their work is couched.

Submission of manuscripts

1. All manuscripts must be accompanied by a completed *Human Relations* Manuscript Submission Form, in which potential contributors will indicate how their manuscript meets the Editorial Guidelines and, in particular, how the content of the manuscript meets the conditions set out in point 2 of the Editorial Guidelines

2. Contributors should also indicate on the Manuscript Submission Form the similarities and key differences between the submitted manuscript and their previously published or submitted manuscripts, where the material in the submitted manuscript and other work is similar or overlaps in some way. Copies of such material should be submitted with the manuscript. This is particularly important where the same or similar data are being used as the basis for more than one manuscript.

3. Contributors should submit their manuscripts online via **www.humanrelationsjournal.org**.

4. Contributors must attest on the Manuscript Submission Form that the manuscript submitted has not been published previously and is not currently under consideration for publication elsewhere. A statement transferring copyright from the authors (or their employers, if they hold the copyright) to The Tavistock Institute will be required before the manuscript can be accepted for publication. The Editors will supply the necessary forms for this transfer. Such a written transfer of copyright, which previously was assumed to be implicit in the act of submitting a manuscript, is necessary under the U.S. Copyright Law in order for the publisher to carry through the dissemination of research results and reviews as widely and effectively as possible.

5. After a manuscript has been accepted, all correspondence should be addressed to the Editors, Human Relations, The Tavistock Institute, 30 Tabernacle Street, London, EC2A 4UE, England (except page proofs and reprint order forms, which should be returned to the publisher).

6. Submitted manuscripts should be typed, double-spaced, on one side of the paper only, and with generous margins. Authors are advised to retain a copy themselves as protection against loss in the post. Manuscripts may be of any length consistent with their content. However, most papers can be presented effectively without exceeding 6000 words (30 manuscript pages) and papers over 8000 words, inclusive of references and all text in tables and footnotes, will not be considered.

7. A 100- to 150-word *abstract* describing the aims, methods, findings, and conclusions of the study should be included as a separate manuscript page. A list of 4-6 key words, in alphabetical order, should be provided directly below the abstract. Key words should express the precise content of the manuscript, as they are used for indexing purposes.

8. Submitted manuscripts are subject to blind-review process. Therefore, omit the author's name from all manuscript pages, including the title page. Language within the text that suggests the identity of the author(s) should be avoided. A brief biographical note describing the authors' qualifications, experience and current interests, should be included on a separate manuscript page.

9. Authors must provide high-quality artwork for all figures. Poor-definition reproductions are not suitable. Each table and figure should be given a title and should be presented on a separate manuscript page at the end of the paper. Diagrams and tables reproduced from already published work must be accompanied by permission of the original publisher (or copyright holder, if not the publisher). Please indicate the position of figures and tables in the text as follows:

INSERT TABLE 1 ABOUT HERE

10. In the text, reference citations should appear as follows:
Trist (1973) shows; Miller & Rice (1967) agree.
    or
Recent studies (Mintzberg, 1989; Ishikawa, 1990) show.

11. References should be listed in alphabetical order at the end of the manuscript.

12. Journal references should be listed as follows:

TUSHMAN, M. L., & ANDERSON, P. Technological discontinuities and organizational environments. Administrative Science Quarterly, 1986, 31, 590-613.

Note that the journal title is given in full and that the author(s)' entire last name(s) and initials are capitalized. Underlining can be used to indicate that italic type is required.

13. Book references should be listed as follows:

MARROW, A. J. The practical theorist. The life and work of Kurt Lewin. New York: Basic Books, 1969.
Note that lowercase letters are used for the book title.

14. Throughout the paper, the use of footnotes, italics, and quote marks should be avoided where possible.

15. Quotations should be kept to a minimum. Authors are asked, where possible, to keep quotations to 100 words or less. Where these quotations exceed 400 words, the permission of the publisher (or copyright holder, if not the publisher) must be obtained and acknowledged.

16. Authors are encouraged to seek colleagues' comments on a manuscript before submitting it.

Processing of manuscripts and production

1. Upon submission, the Editors make an initial judgment about the suitability of the manuscript for publication in this journal. Suitable manuscripts are then sent to a minimum of three reviews. After these reviewers make their recommendations on a manuscript, the editors reach a final judgment. Every effort is made to complete the review process within four months of receipt of a manuscript.

2. Once accepted, manuscripts are copyedited and scheduled for publication. Authors are notified of the year and issue number as soon as it is known.

3. One set of page proofs is sent to the designated corresponding author. The corrected page proofs should be returned to the publisher within the scheduled time given by the publisher. Corrections should be restricted to typographical errors. The publisher reserves the right to disallow any other changes, as these may involve expensive resetting of type and delay.

Humor: International Journal of Humor Research

ADDRESS FOR SUBMISSION:

Salvatore Attardo, Editor-in-Chief
Humor: International Journal of Humor
    Research
Youngstown State University
English Department
Youngstown, OH 44555
USA
Phone: 330-941-1649
Fax: 330-941-1782
E-Mail: humor@cc.ysu.edu
Web: www.humorstudies.org
Address May Change:

PUBLICATION GUIDELINES:

Manuscript Length: 21-30
Copies Required: Four
Computer Submission: Yes
Format: MS Word, rtf
Fees to Review: 0.00 US$

Manuscript Style:
    Chicago Manual of Style

CIRCULATION DATA:

Reader: Academics
Frequency of Issue: Quarterly
Copies per Issue: Less than 1,000
Sponsor/Publisher: International Society for
    Humor Studies and Art Gliner Center for
    Humor Studies
Subscribe Price: 0.00 US$ ISHS Member
    153.00 US$ Institution

REVIEW INFORMATION:

Type of Review: Editorial Review
No. of External Reviewers: 3
No. of In House Reviewers: No Reply
Acceptance Rate: 6-10%
Time to Review: 4 - 6 Months
Reviewers Comments: Yes
Invited Articles: 0-5%
Fees to Publish: 0.00 US$

MANUSCRIPT TOPICS:

Abnormal Psychology; Adolescent Psychology; Child Psychology; Educational Psychology;
Experimental Psychology; Humor Behavior; Personality; Psychiatry; Research Methods &
Statistics; Social Psychology; Thinking & Cognition

MANUSCRIPT GUIDELINES/COMMENTS:

Contributors are invited to submit articles pertaining to humor research to the Editors:
Editor-in-chief: Salvatore Attardo, English Department, Youngstown State University,
Youngstown, OH 44555, USA; E-mail: **humor@cc.ysu.edu**

Book review editor: Peter Derks, Emeritus Professor of Psychology, College of William and
Mary, Williamsburg, VA 23187-8795, USA; E-mail: **plderk@facstaff.wm.edu**

Newsletter editor: Amy Carrell, Department of English, University of Central Oklahoma, 100
North University Drive, Edmond, OK 73034-5209, USA; E-mail: **acarrell@ucok.edu**

Contributions should be in English. Contributors whose native language is not English are asked to have their article carefully checked by a native speaker. Each article must include an **abstract** of up to 200 words and a list of up to six **keywords**. Please submit articles as electronic files (e-mail attachments), ideally MS Word. Electronic files must be typed double-spaced in 12 point font, with wide margins and page numbers (top right). Please avoid using automatic running heads/feet, and turn off any automatic formatting, especially numbering. There is also no need to justify the text.

Manuscripts should be divided into sections and, if necessary, subsections with numbered headings. The title of the article should appear at the top of the first page, followed by the author's full name and affiliation. Emphasized and foreign words should be italicized. Please avoid the use of boldface in running text. Use double quotation marks throughout (quoted material within quotations must be enclosed in single quotation marks).

Line drawings ("Figures") and **photographs** ("Plates") must be submitted as electronic graphic files, ideally gif or jpeg. Figures should be placed in separate files to the text files and clearly labeled. They should be referred to in the text and their approximate position indicated. Captions should be typed on a separate page and placed at the end of the article. Original artwork may be required if the electronic files are poor quality.

Tables should be placed at the end of the article, numbered consecutively and given titles. Reference to the tables must be made in the text and their approximate position indicated.

Endnotes should be kept to an absolute minimum. They should be marked consecutively throughout the text by a raised number following a punctuation mark. All endnotes should be listed on a separate page entitled "Notes" and should be included after the main body of the article (following any appendixes), before the reference section. Notes should not be placed at the foot of the relevant page.

References are cited in the text by giving the name of the author/editor, year of publication and the page reference, all in parentheses, for example (Davies 1990a: 32). Use "et al." in cases of more than two authors. Please note that "et al." should not be italicized.

The reference section should contain all works referred to in the text, and only those. They must be listed fully in alphabetical order of author/editor, with complete bibliographical details (including publisher). Journal and book titles must be given in full and must be italicized. Page references must be given for articles in books and journals. References should conform to the following examples:

Davies, Christie
  1990a *Ethnic Humor Around the World: A Comparative Analysis.* Bloomington: Indiana University Press.
  1990b An explanation of Jewish jokes about Jewish women. *Humor: International Journal of Humor Research* 3 (4), 363–378.

Goldstein, Jeffrey H., and Paul E. McGhee (eds.)
  1972 *The Psychology of Humor.* New York: Academic Press.

506

Martin, Rod A.
    1998   Approaches to the sense of humor: A historical review. In Ruch, Willibald (ed.), *The Sense of Humor: Explorations of a Personality Characteristic.* Berlin/New York: Mouton de Gruyter, 15–60.

Morreall, John
    1991   Humor works. Paper presented at the Ninth International Conference on Humour and Laughter, St. Catherine's, Ontario.

Raskin, Victor
    1985   *Semantic Mechanisms of Humor* (Synthese Language Library 24). Dordrecht: D. Reidel.

Schopenhauer, Arthur
    1957   [1819] *The World as Will and Idea*, vol. 1. London: Routledge and Kegan Paul.

Authors are requested to check their manuscript very carefully before submission. Authors will receive page proofs for correction, which must be returned by dates determined by the publication schedule. 30 offprints of each article will be sent free of charge. (When there is more than one author, the offprints will be sent to the first-named author for distribution.) It is not possible to order additional offprints. Contributors to special issues also receive one complimentary copy of the issue.

Infant Behavior and Development

ADDRESS FOR SUBMISSION:

Geert Savelsbergh, Editor
Infant Behavior and Development
Vrije Universiteit - Institute of
  Fundamental Clnc. Human Mvmt.
  Sciences
The Perceptual - Motor Development Group
Van de Boecherstraat 7-9
1081 BT Amsterdam,
The Netherlands
Phone: +31 0204448461
Fax:
E-Mail: ibad@fbw.vu.nl
Web: www.elsevier.com/locate/inbede
Address May Change:

PUBLICATION GUIDELINES:

Manuscript Length: 16-25
Copies Required: Four
Computer Submission: Yes Disk
Format: IBM Compatible Disk
Fees to Review: 0.00 US$

Manuscript Style:
  American Psychological Association

CIRCULATION DATA:

Reader: Academics
Frequency of Issue: Quarterly
Copies per Issue: Less than 1,000
Sponsor/Publisher: Elsevier Science
Subscribe Price: 123.00 US$ Individual
  362.00 US$ Institution

REVIEW INFORMATION:

Type of Review: Editorial Review
No. of External Reviewers: 2
No. of In House Reviewers: 1
Acceptance Rate: 21-30%
Time to Review: 2 - 3 Months
Reviewers Comments: Yes
Invited Articles: 6-10%
Fees to Publish: 0.00 US$

MANUSCRIPT TOPICS:
Child Psychology; Infant Studies; Sensation & Perception; Social Psychology

MANUSCRIPT GUIDELINES/COMMENTS:

Description
Infant Behavior & Development publishes empirical (fundamental and clinical), theoretical, methodological and review papers. Brief reports dealing with behavioral development during infancy (up to 3 years) will also be considered. Papers of an inter- and multidisciplinary nature, for example neuroscience, non-linear dynamics and modeling approaches, are particularly encouraged. Areas covered by the journal include cognitive development, emotional development, perception, perception-action coupling, motor development and socialization.

508

Guide for Authors

Infant Behavior and Development is an archival journal that publishes reports of research, both human and animal, that contribute significantly to our understanding of behavior through the second year of life. Theoretical articles, attempts to replicate, and commentaries are occasionally considered, but preference is given to original research articles. Submit manuscripts in *quadruplicate* to the Editor, Dr. Geert Savelsbergh, The Perceptual-Motor Development Group, Institute for Fundamental Clinical Human Movement Sciences, Vrije University, Van de Boecherstraat 7-9, 1081 BT Amsterdam, The Netherlands. Submissions must be accompanied by a statement that the research was conducted in accordance with APA ethical standards in the treatment of the study sample, both animal and human. Do *not* submit original artwork until requested. Manuscripts in excess of 25 pages (total) must be accompanied by a statement from the author justifying why. Authors are invited to submit the names, addresses, and particular areas of expertise of individuals who would be appropriate reviewers. The relation of the individual to the author should be specified (former colleague, student, co-author, professional acquaintance, etc.).

1. **Manuscript Preparation.** Submissions must conform in all respects to the format specified in the *Publication Manual of the American Psychological Association* (5th Edition, 1994), or they will be returned without review. (Copies may be ordered from APA Order Dept., P.O. Box 2710, Hyattsville, MD 20784.) This requirement applies to the format for tables and figures. (Exceptions for a Brief Report appear below.) Four to six key words must be listed on a separate line following the abstract. Authors are responsible for obtaining permissions-to-publish both from copyright holders and authors for illustrations, tables, or lengthy quotes published elsewhere. All submissions must be double-spaced in 10- or 12-point type with 1-inch margins on all sides of 8 ½ x 11-inch bond paper. On the title page (p. 1), list the current address of the leading author. The corresponding author must also provide a complete postal address, e-mail, fax number, and telephone number on the bottom left of the title page. Information concerning research and acknowledgments should be listed in a paragraph titled, "Acknowledgments." This will appear at the end of the text. The abstract (p. 2) may not exceed 150 words. Chapters cited in references *must include page numbers;* presentations at meetings *must include year and month.* Do *not* cite unpublished or submitted manuscripts in References (cite in text as "personal communication" with complete date), and do not use titles (e.g., Dr., RN) when acknowledging individuals. Use American spelling and standard international units (e.g., cm, kg); avoid jargon. All measures of central tendency must be accompanied by *SD*s or *SE*s. Notes should be used sparingly and indicated by consecutive superscript numbers in the text. Notes should be typed separately at the end of the document before the References.

2. **Brief Reports.** A Brief Report is simply a short paper; pilot studies and articles of lesser quality are not acceptable. It should be prepared in the same format as a full-size manuscript except that it has only a 45-word abstract, no special headings (Method, Participants, Apparatus, Procedure, Results, Discussion), and must not exceed 8 typed pages *including* references, tables, and figures but *excluding* abstract and title pages. Authors must state that a fuller report will be provided upon request in "Acknowledgments."

3. **Policy on Multiple Publications.** (*IBAD*, 1994, Vol. 17, No. 1). Multiple or piecemeal publication of data from the same study are not acceptable. Authors must inform the Editor if

data in a submitted manuscript have been reported elsewhere and how the present study is different. Authors must also submit, in quadruplicate, copies of closely related manuscripts that are published, in press, or under review by another journal and that report data from the same study.

4. Policy on Sample Information. (*IBAD*, 1997, Vol. 20, No. 1). Authors must report complete information about their study sample composition, including sex, race/ethnicity, occupational status, and educational attainment. Minimally, this requires use of current and codable occupational categories (e.g., Nakao, K., & Treas, J., 1992, The 1989 Socioeconomic Index of Occupations: Construction from the 1989 Occupational Prestige Scores. General Social Survey Methodological Reports, #74. Chicago, IL: NORC), four educational attainment categories (without H.S. diploma, H.S. graduate without college education, some college education, degree from 4-year college or more), and five race/ethnicity categories (e.g., U.S. Bureau of Census). The reference person for this information must be specified. The study-sampling strategy must also be specified.

5. Submission of Disks. All final manuscripts must be accompanied by an IBM-compatible disk with all text files spell-checked and stripped of any and all embedded graphics (equations, graphs, charts, line drawings, or illustrations). This text file must be marked as to the placement of all graphics. All text files must be saved as either Word-perfect 5.1-6.1, or MS Word 4.0-7.0. Camera-ready copy for graphics (graphs, charts, line drawings, or illustrations) must be sent separately and in a separate graphics file as either eps (encapsulated postscript), tiff (tagged image file format), or ps (postscript file).

6. References. Contributors should refer to the APA Publication Manual for the correct listing of references in the text and reference list. References in text and reference section must be checked for consistency of spelling and dates. Chapters in books must be accompanied by page number per APA format.

Atkinson, R. C., & Shiffrin, R. M. (1971). The control of short-term memory. *Scientific American, 225,* 82?90.

Quinn, P. C., & Eimas, P. D. (1996). Perceptual organization and categorization in young infants. In C. Rovee-Collier & L. P. Lipsitt (Eds.), *Advances in infancy research* (Vol. 10, pp. 1?36). Norwood, NJ: Ablex.

7. Corrections Policy. Authors will be sent page proofs prior to publication (along with their copy-edited manuscript) and are expected to return them as immediately as possible to the Editor, Geert Savelsbergh (address listed above), who will review and finalize corrections before returning them to the publisher.

8. Complimentary Copies and Offprints. The lead author will receive 25 free offprints. Additional off-prints can be ordered when page proofs are returned (an offprint order form will be included with instructions for correction of proofs).

Infant Mental Health Journal

ADDRESS FOR SUBMISSION:

Joy Osofsky, Editor
Infant Mental Health Journal
Louisiana State University
Health Science Center
Department of Psychiatry
1542 Tulane Avenue
New Orleans, LA 70112
USA
Phone: 504-568-6004
Fax: 504-568-6246
E-Mail: imhj@lsuhsc.edu
Web:
Address May Change:

PUBLICATION GUIDELINES:

Manuscript Length: 20-25
Copies Required: Three
Computer Submission: No
Format: N/A
Fees to Review: 0.00 US$

Manuscript Style:
       American Psychological Association

CIRCULATION DATA:

Reader: Academics, Counselors, Social
   Workers
Frequency of Issue: 6 Times/Year
Copies per Issue: Less than 1,000
Sponsor/Publisher:
Subscribe Price: 95.00 US$ Individual
   107.00 US$ Outside North America

REVIEW INFORMATION:

Type of Review: Blind Review
No. of External Reviewers: 2
No. of In House Reviewers: 0
Acceptance Rate: 50%
Time to Review: 4 - 6 Months
Reviewers Comments: Yes
Invited Articles: No Reply
Fees to Publish: 0.00 US$

MANUSCRIPT TOPICS:
Child Psychology; Developmental Psychology; Infant Mental Health; Infant Studies;
Prevention and Intervention

MANUSCRIPT GUIDELINES/COMMENTS:

Reader. Counselors, Early Childhood Education Specialists, Nurses, Physicians,
Psychologists, and Public Health Workers

The *IMHJ* publishes research articles, literature reviews, program descriptions/evaluations,
clinical studies, and book reviews that focus on infant social-emotional development, care
giver-infant interactions, contextual and cultural influences on infant and family development,
and all conditions that place infants and/or their families at-risk for less than optimal
development. The *IMHJ* is dedicated to an interdisciplinary approach to the optimal
development of infants and their families, and, therefore, welcomes submissions from all
disciplinary perspectives.

Manuscripts (An original and three copies) should be submitted to the Editor typed, with double spacing throughout and ample margins. Blind reviewing will be used. Each copy of the paper should include a cover sheet with the following information: Title of manuscript, name of author(s), and author(s) affiliation. The title should appear on the abstract and on the first page of text. Information about the identity of the author(s) contained in footnotes should appear on the title page only. The title page is not included when the manuscript is sent out for review. A cover letter to the Editor should accompany the paper: it should request a review and indicate that the manuscript has not been published previously or submitted elsewhere.

An abstract of approximately 150 words must be included. Tables and figures must be sufficiently clear so that they can be photographed directly. (Black and white glossy prints are acceptable.) Letter quality or near letter-quality print must be used for computer-prepared manuscripts.

Style must conform to that described by the *American Psychological Association Publication Manual*, Fourth Edition, 1994 revision (American Psychological Association, 1200 Seventeenth Street, N.W., Washington, D.C. 20036). Authors are responsible for final preparation of manuscripts to conform to the *APA* style.

Manuscripts are reviewed by the Editor, Associate Editor(s), members of the Editorial Board, and invited reviewers with special knowledge of the topic addressed in the manuscript. The Editor retains the right to reject articles that do not conform to conventional clinical or scientific ethical standards. Normally, the review process is completed in 3 months. Nearly all manuscripts accepted for publication require some degree of revision. There is no charge for publication of papers in the *Infant Mental Health Journal*. The publisher may levy additional charges for changes in proof other than correction of printers errors. Proof will be sent to the corresponding author and must be read carefully because final responsibility for accuracy rests with the author(s). Author(s) must return corrected proof to the publisher in a timely manner. If the publisher does not receive corrected proof from the author(s), publication will still proceed as scheduled.

Additional questions with regard to style and submission of manuscripts should be directed to the Editor.

International Forum for Logotherapy: Journal of Search for Meaning

ADDRESS FOR SUBMISSION:

R.R. Hutzell, Editor
International Forum for Logotherapy:
    Journal of Search for Meaning
PO Box 112
Knoxville, IA 50138-0112
USA
Phone: 641-842-2415
Fax:
E-Mail: hutzells@lisco.net
Web:
Address May Change:

PUBLICATION GUIDELINES:

Manuscript Length: 5-8
Copies Required: Two
Computer Submission: Yes Disk
Format: MS Word, WordPerfect
Fees to Review: 0.00 US$

Manuscript Style:
    American Psychological Association

CIRCULATION DATA:

Reader: Practitioners
Frequency of Issue: 2 Times/Year
Copies per Issue: Less than 1,000
Sponsor/Publisher: Viktor Frankl Institute
    of Logotherapy
Subscribe Price: 60.00 US$

REVIEW INFORMATION:

Type of Review: Blind Review
No. of External Reviewers: 1
No. of In House Reviewers: 2
Acceptance Rate: 40-50%
Time to Review: 2 - 3 Months
Reviewers Comments: Yes
Invited Articles: 0-5%
Fees to Publish: 0.00 US$

MANUSCRIPT TOPICS:
Behavior Modification; Counseling Process; Family Counseling & Therapy; Logotherapy; Social Psychology

MANUSCRIPT GUIDELINES/COMMENTS:

The *International Forum for Logotherapy: Journal of Search for Meaning* is the official publication of the Viktor Frankl Institute of Logotherapy. It presents the meaning-oriented existential philosophy and therapy developed by Dr. Viktor Frankl and expanded by logotherapists throughout the world, working in counseling, education, medicine, nursing, psychiatry, psychology, social work, theology and other fields where the question of meaning becomes pertinent.

The *Forum* publishes experiential reports, theoretical papers, personal essays, original research studies, tests and questionnaires, literature reviews, innovative logotherapeutic techniques for individuals and groups, and book reviews. It is abstracted in *Index Medicus, Psychological* Abstracts, and other major international retrieval sources.

There are no costs for publishing articles in the *Forum*. The journal is published semi-annually in the Spring and Fall.

It is preferred that manuscripts be prepared according to the guidelines of the *Publication Manual of the American Psychological Association*. However, there are no set hard-and-fast guidelines for manuscript preparation - manuscripts are edited to fit the style of the journal if necessary.

Abstracts are published with original research articles. Author photographs and biographical sketches are published with all articles.

Typical article length is 1500 to 2500 words. This is roughly 5 to 8 double-spaced pages, with one-inch margins, of elite type or 10-point font, on 8.5 x 11 inch paper.

Manuscripts are generally refereed by the journal editors. Research articles are peer reviewed by other experts in the field of logotherapy.

Manuscripts (two clear copies) should be submitted to Robert Hutzell, Ph.D., Editor, The International Forum for Logotherapy, P.O. Box 112, Knoxville, Iowa 50138-0112 USA. Or, preferably, submit by email to **hutzells@lisco.net**.

International Journal for the Psychology of Religion

ADDRESS FOR SUBMISSION:

Raymond F. Paloutzian, Editor
International Journal for the Psychology of
   Religion
Westmont College
Department of Psychology
955 La Paz Road
Santa Barbara, CA 93108-1099
USA
Phone: 805-565-6233
Fax: 805-565-6116
E-Mail: dwulff@wheatonma.edu
Web: www.LEAonline.com
Address May Change:

PUBLICATION GUIDELINES:

Manuscript Length: 21-32
Copies Required: Five
Computer Submission: No
Format: N/A
Fees to Review: 0.00 US$

Manuscript Style:
   American Psychological Association

CIRCULATION DATA:

Reader: Academics
Frequency of Issue: Quarterly
Copies per Issue: Less than 1,000
Sponsor/Publisher: Lawrence Erlbaum
   Associates, Inc.
Subscribe Price:
   50.00 US$ Indv Print + Online US/Can
   80.00 US$ Indv Print + Online Foreign

REVIEW INFORMATION:

Type of Review: Blind Review
No. of External Reviewers: 3
No. of In House Reviewers: 0
Acceptance Rate: 6-10%
Time to Review: 2 - 3 Months
Reviewers Comments: Yes
Invited Articles: 0-5%
Fees to Publish: 0.00 US$

MANUSCRIPT TOPICS:
Culture & Personality; Group Dynamics; Psychological Studies; Religious
Processes/Phenomena

MANUSCRIPT GUIDELINES/COMMENTS:

Editorial Scope
IJPR is devoted to psychological studies of religious processes and phenomena in all religious
traditions--the only international publication concerned exclusively with the psychology of
religion. This journal provides a means for sustained discussion of psychologically relevant
issues that can be examined empirically and concern religion in the most general sense. It
presents articles covering a variety of important topics, such as the social psychology of
religion, religious development, conversion, religious experience, religion and social attitudes
and behavior, religion and mental health, and psychoanalytic and other theoretical
interpretations of religion. The issues also include a major essay and commentary, plus
perspective papers and articles on the field in a specific country.

Audience
Psychologists, theologians, philosophers, religious leaders, neuroscientists, and social scientists.

Instructions To Contributors
Manuscript Submission. Submit five manuscript copies (one with and four without author identification) to Dr. Raymond F. Paloutzian, Department of Psychology, Westmont College, 955 La Paz Road, Santa Barbara, CA 93108-1099, USA; phone (805) 565-6233, fax (805) 565-6116. In a cover letter, state that the findings reported in the manuscript have not been published previously and that the manuscript is not being simultaneously submitted elsewhere.

Prepare manuscripts according to the *Publication Manual of the American Psychological Association* (5th ed.). Use 8½ x 11-in. nonsmear paper; set all margins at 1 in.; type all components of the manuscript double-spaced, including title page, abstract (1,000 characters or fewer, counting spaces between words), text, quotes, acknowledgments, references, appendices, tables, figure captions, and footnotes; indent all paragraphs; single-spaced material is not accepted.

Major articles (including references) should be no more than 32 manuscript pages in length, accounts of the psychology of religion in a region or within a tradition no more than 16 pages, and empirical and theoretical reports no more than 25 pages. All manuscripts must include an abstract. If possible, submit a 3½" Macintosh or IBM-compatible computer disk in Microsoft Word, WordPerfect, or other popular word-processing formats, plus an ASCII or RTF copy of the file. A computer disk will be required upon acceptance of the manuscript.

References. Provide complete, APA-formatted references and text citations and make sure that the two correspond exactly. *The APA Manual* provides (a) detailed guidelines on preparing references and citations and (b) many excellent sample references and citations. The manual includes the requirement that, when typing a reference for a chapter in an edited book, the inclusive page numbers of the chapter must be added.

Figures. Submit (a) professionally prepared black-and-white originals or camera-ready glossy reproductions and (b) photocopies of all figures. Please note that figures in your article will only look as good as what you provide. Make sure lettering and details are crisp, clear, and large enough so that they will be legible upon reduction. (Figures are reduced in size in order to conserve space on the printed page.) Make sure each figure is identified. Assess whether textual information appearing on a piece of artwork might be presented as part of the caption; if so, alter artwork and caption accordingly.

Statistics. See *APA Manual* regarding presentation.

Acronyms. Define on first mention.

Tests, Scales, Subscales, Factors, Variables, Effects. See *APA Manual* regarding capitalization.

516

Book Reviews. The book review editor is Dr. David M. Wulff, Psychology Department, Wheaton College, Norton, MA 02766-2322, USA; Phone (508) 286-3691, Fax (508) 286-3640, E-mail: **dwulff@wheatonma.edu**.

Books are generally reviewed by invitation only. Persons interested in writing reviews are encouraged to contact the book review editor, indicating their areas of special competence and interest and providing a vita and sample of their writing, preferably a book review or other publication. Reviewers are sent detailed instructions at the time the reviews are commissioned. Electronic versions of reviews may be submitted by e-mail and hard copies by regular mail or fax.

Publishers should send book announcements and review copies directly to the book review editor. Two copies of each published review will be forwarded to the book's publisher.

Permissions. Authors are responsible for all statements made in their work and for obtaining permission from copyright owners to reprint or adapt a table or figure or to reprint a quotation of 500 words or more. Authors should write to original author(s) and publisher to request nonexclusive world rights in all languages to use the material in the article and in future editions. Provide copies of all permissions and credit lines obtained.

Production Notes. Accepted manuscripts are copyedited and typeset into page proofs. Authors are asked to read proofs to correct errors and answer editors' queries. Authors may order reprints of their articles when they receive proofs. Printing considerations do not permit ordering reprints after authors have returned proofs.

International Journal of Aging and Human Development

ADDRESS FOR SUBMISSION:

Bert Hayslip, Jr., Editor
International Journal of Aging and Human
   Development
University of North Texas
Department of Psychology
PO Box 311280
Denton, TX 76203-1280
USA
Phone: 940-565-2675
Fax: 940-565-4682
E-Mail: hayslipb@unt.edu
Web: baywood.com
Address May Change:

PUBLICATION GUIDELINES:

Manuscript Length: 21-25
Copies Required:
Computer Submission: No
Format:
Fees to Review: 0.00 US$

Manuscript Style:
   American Psychological Association

CIRCULATION DATA:

Reader: Academics
Frequency of Issue: 4 Times/Year
Copies per Issue:
Sponsor/Publisher: Baywood Publsihing
   Co.
Subscribe Price:
   87.00 US$ Indv for 8 Issues
   344.00 US$ Inst for 8 Issues

REVIEW INFORMATION:

Type of Review: Blind Review
No. of External Reviewers: 2
No. of In House Reviewers: 1
Acceptance Rate: 21-30%
Time to Review: 4 - 6 Months
Reviewers Comments: Yes
Invited Articles: 0-5%
Fees to Publish: 0.00 US$

MANUSCRIPT TOPICS:
Adulthood; Developmental Psychology; Gerontology

MANUSCRIPT GUIDELINES/COMMENTS:

Aims & Scope
Under what conditions does "development" end? Under what conditions does "aging" begin? Can these conditions themselves be modified by intervention at the psychological, social, or biological levels? To what extent are patterns of development and aging attributable to biological factors? To psychological factors? How can social and behavioral sciences contribute to the actualization of human potential throughout the entire life span? What are the implications of gerontological research for our understanding of the total development of human organism?

These are some of the broad questions with which *The International Journal of Aging & Human Development* is concerned. Emphasis is upon psychological and social studies of aging and the aged. However, the *Journal* also publishes research that introduces observations from other fields that illuminate the "human" side of gerontology, or utilizes gerontological observations to illuminate in other fields.

Instructions to Authors

Submit manuscript to: Dr. Bert Hayslip, University of North Texas, Department of Psychology, P.O. Box 311280, Denton, TX 76203

Originality. Only original articles are accepted for publication. Submission of a manuscript represents certification on the part of the authors(s) that neither the article submitted, nor a version of it has been published, or is being considered for publication elsewhere.

Manuscripts. Submit four copies. Retain one copy, as manuscript will not be returned. manuscript must be word processed or typewritten on 8 ½" x 11" white paper, one side only, double-spaced, with wide margins. Paginate consecutively starting with the title page. The organization of the paper should be indicated by the appropriate headings and subheadings. Authors should also submit the names and addresses of 2 individuals qualified to review their work.

Abstracts of 100 to 150 words are required to introduce each article.

Format. Prepare manuscripts according to the *Publication Manual of the American Psychological Association* (5th ed.). A synopsis of this manual is available from the American Psychological Society.

Style. Technical terms specific to a particular discipline should be defined. Write for clear comprehension by readers from a broad spectrum of scholarly and professional backgrounds. Avoid acronyms and footnoting, except for acknowledgements.

Permissions. Authors are responsible for all statements made in their manuscript and for obtaining from copyright owners to reprint or adapt a table or figures, or to reprint a quotation of 500 words or more. Authors should write to original authors(s) and publisher to request nonexclusive world rights in all languages to use the material in the article and in future editions. Provide copies of all permission and credit lines obtained at the time of manuscript submission.

Reprints. Authors will receive twenty complimentary reprints of their published article and a copy of the *Journal* issue. Additional reprints may be ordered, using the form provided when proofs are sent for correction.

International Journal of Behavioral Development

ADDRESS FOR SUBMISSION:

William M. Bukowski, Editor
International Journal of Behavioral
 Development
Concordia University
Dept - Psych & Ctr for Human
 Development
PY Building, Room 123-14
7141 Sherbrooke St. West
Montreal, Quebec, H4B 1R6
Canada
Phone: (514) 848-2424 ext. 2184
Fax: (514) 848-2424 ext. 7563
E-Mail: ijbd@alcor.concordia.ca
Web: http://www.tandf.co.uk/journals
Address May Change:

PUBLICATION GUIDELINES:

Manuscript Length: 35 pages
Copies Required: One
Computer Submission: Yes Email Preferred
Format: MS Word
Fees to Review: 0.00 US$

Manuscript Style:
 American Psychological Association

CIRCULATION DATA:

Reader: , Developmental Psychologists
Frequency of Issue: 6 Times/Year
Copies per Issue:
Sponsor/Publisher: International Society for
 the Study of Behavioural Development /
 Taylor & Francis
Subscribe Price: 245.00 US$ Individual
 986.00 Institution

REVIEW INFORMATION:

Type of Review: Blind Review
No. of External Reviewers: 2-3
No. of In House Reviewers: 0
Acceptance Rate: 45%
Time to Review: 60-75 Days
Reviewers Comments: Yes
Invited Articles: Rarely
Fees to Publish: 0.00 US$

MANUSCRIPT TOPICS:
Adolescent Psychology; Adulthood; Child Psychology; Developmental Psychology

MANUSCRIPT GUIDELINES/COMMENTS:

Aims and Scope
The *International Journal of Behavioral Development* is the official journal of the International Society for the Study of Behavioural Development. The journal is already the leading international outlet devoted to reporting interdisciplinary research on diversity in development. The *IJBD* promotes the discovery, dissemination and application of knowledge about developmental processes at all stages of the life span - infancy, childhood, adolescence, adulthood and old age. The *IJBD* is especially interested in scholarly reports and reviews of empirical studies of variations in developmental processes and outcomes within and across contexts. These contexts may be defined by culture, ethnicity, geographical region, economic conditions and practices, or history. In this way, the *IJBD* provides a truly world-wide

520

platform for researchers which can facilitate a greater integrated lifespan perspective. In addition to original empirical research, the Journal also publishes theoretical and review papers, as well as other work of scientific interest that represents a significant advance in the understanding of any aspect of behavioural development. Papers are considered from a wide range of disciplines, covering all aspects of the lifespan. Articles on topics of eminent current interest, such as research on the later life phases, biological processes in behaviour development, cross-national, and cross-cultural issues, and interdisciplinary research in general, are particularly welcome.

Manuscript Submission
An electronic version of the paper, in Word or WordPerfect, sent by email should be submitted in the format outlined in the *Publication Manual of the American Psychological Association* (5th ed.) to **ijbd@alcor.concordia.ca**

When submission via email is not possible, **two copies** of the paper version of the manuscript **plus an electronic version of the paper on disk** should be mailed to the Journal's Editor:

Professor William M. Bukowski, Editor, IJBD Office, c/o Department of Psychology, Concordia University, 7141 rue Sherbrooke Ouest, Montréal, Quebec, H4B 1R6, Canada.

The publishers strongly encourage the submission of final, accepted manuscripts on disk (accompanied by hard copy). For guidelines for presentation of final manuscripts on disk please see http://www.tandf.co.uk/journals/authors/electronic.asp.

Copyright. It is a condition of publication that authors vest or license copyright in their articles, including abstracts, in The International Society for the Study of Behavioural Development. This enables us to ensure full copyright protection and to disseminate the article, and the journal, to the widest possible readership in print and electronic formats as appropriate. Authors may, of course, use the material elsewhere after publication providing that prior permission is obtained from Taylor & Francis Ltd. Authors are themselves responsible for obtaining permission to reproduce copyright material from other sources. To view the 'Copyright Transfer Frequently Asked Questions please visit
www.tandf.co.uk/journals/copyright.asp.

Journal Production Editor: **kirsten.buchanan@psypress.co.uk**

Format
Typescripts. The title page of an article should contain only:
1. the title of the paper, the name(s) and address(es) of the author(s);
2. a short title not exceeding 40 letters and spaces, which will be used for page headlines;
3. name and address of the author to whom correspondence and proofs should be sent;
4. your telephone, fax and e-mail numbers, as this helps speed of processing considerably.

Abstract. An abstract of 50-200 words should follow the title page on a separate sheet.

Headings. Indicate headings and subheadings for different sections of the paper clearly. Do not number headings.

Acknowledgements. These should be as brief as possible and typed on a separate sheet at the beginning of the text.

Permission to quote. Any direct quotation, regardless of length, must be accompanied by a reference citation that includes a page number. Any quote over six manuscript lines should have formal written permission to quote from the copyright owner. It is the author's responsibility to determine whether permission is required from the copyright owner and, if so, to obtain it. (See the bottom of the page for a template of a letter seeking copyright permission.)

Footnotes. These should be avoided unless absolutely necessary. Essential footnotes should be indicated by superscript figures in the text and collected on a separate sheet at the end of the manuscript.

Reference citations within the text. Use authors' last names, with the year of publication in parentheses after the last author's name, e.g., "Jones and Smith (1987)"; alternatively, "(Brown, 1982; Jones & Smith, 1987; White, Johnson, & Thomas, 1990)". On first citation of references with three to six authors, give all names in full, thereafter use first author "et al.". If more than one article by the same author(s) in the same year is cited, the letters a, b, c etc. should follow the year.

Reference list. A full list of references quoted in the text should be given at the end of the paper in alphabetical order of authors' surnames (or chronologically for a group of references by the same authors), commencing as a new sheet, typed double spaced. Titles of journals and books should be given in full, e.g.:

Books
Baddeley, A. D. (1999). *Essentials of human memory*. Hove, UK: Psychology Press.

Chapter in edited book
Plomin, R., & Dale, P. S. (2000). Genetics and early language development: A UK study of twins. In D. V. M. Bishop & L. B. Leonard (Eds.), *Speech and language impairments in children: Causes, characteristics, intervention and outcome* (pp. 35-51). Hove, UK: Psychology Press.

Journal article
Schwartz, M. F., & Hodgson, C. (2002). A new multiword naming deficit: Evidence and interpretation. *Cognitive Neuropsychology*, 19, 263-288.

Tables. These should be kept to the minimum. Each table should be typed double spaced on a separate sheet, giving the heading, e.g., "Table 2", in Arabic numerals, followed by the legend, followed by the table. Make sure that appropriate units are given. Instructions for placing the table should be given in parentheses in the text, e.g., "(Table 2 about here)".

Figures. Figures should only be used when essential. The same data should not be presented both as a figure and in a table. Where possible, related diagrams should be grouped together to form a single figure. Figures should be drawn to professional standards and it is recommended that the linear dimensions of figures be approximately twice those intended for the final printed version. Each of these should be on a separate page, not integrated with the text. Figures will be reproduced directly from originals supplied by the author(s). These must be of good quality, clearly and completely lettered. Make sure that axes of graphs are properly labelled, and that appropriate units are given. Photocopies will reproduce poorly, as will pale or broken originals. Dense tones should be avoided, and never combined with lettering. Half-tone figures should be clear, highly-contrasted black and white glossy prints.

Black and white figures are included free of charge. Colour figures are not normally acceptable for publication in print -- however, it may be possible both to **print** in black and white and to **publish online** in colour. Colour figures will only be printed by prior arrangement between the editor(s), publisher and author(s); and authors may be asked to share the costs of inclusion of such figures.

The figure captions should be typed in a separate section, headed, e.g., "Figure 2", in Arabic numerals. Instructions for placing the figure should be given in parentheses in the text, e.g., "(Figure 2 about here)". More detailed Guidelines for the Preparation of Figure Artwork are available from the publisher: Psychology Press Ltd, 27 Church Road, Hove, East Sussex BN3 2FA, UK (Email: **kirsten.buchanan@psypress.co.uk**).

Statistics. Results of statistical tests should be given in the following form:

"... results showed an effect of group, $F(2, 21) = 13.74$, $MSE = 451.98$, $p < .001$, but there was no effect of repeated trials, $F(5, 105) = 1.44$, $MSE = 17.70$, and no interaction, $F(10, 105) = 1.34$, $MSE = 17.70$."

Other tests should be reported in a similar manner to the above example of an F-ratio. For a fuller explanation of statistical presentation, see pages 136-147 of the *APA Publication Manual* (5th ed.). For guidelines on presenting statistical significance, see pages 24-25.

Abbreviations. Abbreviations that are specific to a particular manuscript or to a very specific area of research should be avoided, and authors will be asked to spell out in full any such abbreviations throughout the text. Standard abbreviations such as RT for reaction time, SOA for stimulus onset asynchrony or other standard abbreviations that will be readily understood by readers of the journal are acceptable. Experimental conditions should be named in full, except in tables and figures.

After Acceptance of Publication in the Journal
Proofs. Page proofs will be sent to the specified corresponding author of the article to check for typesetting accuracy. No changes to the original typescript will be permitted at this stage. Proofs should be returned promptly with the original query sheet.

Early electronic offprints (e-prints). Specified corresponding authors will receive their article by email as a complete PDF. This allows the author to print up to 50 copies, free of charge, and disseminate them to colleagues. In many cases, this facility will be available up to two weeks prior to print publication of the article. One copy of the journal issue in which their paper appears will be sent by post to all specified corresponding authors free after print publication. Paper offprints can still be purchased by authors if they complete the enclosed offprint order form and return with payment together with their corrected proofs.

Copyright Permission

Contributors are required to secure permission for the reproduction of any figure, table, or extensive (more than six manuscript lines) extract from the text, from a source which is copyrighted -- or owned -- by a party other than Psychology Press Ltd or the contributor.

This applies both to direct reproduction or "derivative reproduction" -- when the contributor has created a new figure or table which derives **substantially** from a copyrighted source.

The following form of words can be used in seeking permission:

Dear [COPYRIGHT HOLDER]

I/we are preparing for publication an article entitled
[STATE TITLE]
to be published by Psychology Press Ltd in the *International Journal of Behavioral Development*.

I/we should be grateful if you would grant us permission to include the following materials:
[STATE FIGURE NUMBER AND ORIGINAL SOURCE]
We are requesting non-exclusive rights in this edition and in all forms. It is understood, of course, that full acknowledgement will be given to the source.

Please note that Psychology Press Ltd are signatories of and respect the spirit of the STM Agreement regarding the free sharing and dissemination of scholarly information.

Your prompt consideration of this request would be greatly appreciated.

Yours faithfully

Volume contents and author index. The list of contents and the author index for the whole of the year's issues are published in the last issue of the year of each journal. For the *International Journal of Behavioral Development*, this is issue 6 (November).

International Journal of Behavioral Medicine

ADDRESS FOR SUBMISSION:

Ulf Lundberg, Editor
International Journal of Behavioral
  Medicine
Stockholm University
Department of Psychology
S-106 91
Stockholm,
Sweden
Phone: +46 8 163 874
Fax: +46 8 167 847
E-Mail: ul@psychology.su.se
Web: www.psychology.su.se/
Address May Change:

PUBLICATION GUIDELINES:

Manuscript Length: 21-25
Copies Required: No Reply
Computer Submission: Yes
Format: MS Word, Powerpoint
Fees to Review: 0.00 US$

Manuscript Style:
  American Psychological Association

CIRCULATION DATA:

Reader: Academics
Frequency of Issue: Quarterly
Copies per Issue: 3,001 - 4,000Electronic
Sponsor/Publisher: Lawrence Erlbaum
  Associates, Inc.
Subscribe Price: 50.00 US$ Individual
  310.00 US$ Institution
  45.00 US$ Indv, $279 Inst. Electronic

REVIEW INFORMATION:

Type of Review: Editorial Review
No. of External Reviewers: 3
No. of In House Reviewers: 0
Acceptance Rate: 40%
Time to Review: 2 - 3 Months
Reviewers Comments: Yes
Invited Articles: 0-5%
Fees to Publish: 0.00 US$

MANUSCRIPT TOPICS:
Group Dynamics; Health and Behavior; Social Psychology

MANUSCRIPT GUIDELINES/COMMENTS:

Content
The *International Journal of Behavioral Medicine* is a scholarly journal devoted to furthering an understanding of scientific relations between sociocultural, psychosocial, and behavioral principles on the one hand and biological processes, physical health, and illness on the other. Our readership has a broad range of backgrounds, interests, and specializations that are interdisciplinary in nature. The journal emphasizes original research, although concise, well-integrated, authoritative reviews of empirical research are also published. All articles should have significant theoretical or practical import for an understanding of behavioral medicine. Articles that address a broad constituency are particularly welcome. Suitable topics for submission include, but are not restricted to, the role of environmental, psychosocial, or sociocultural factors that may contribute to disease or its prevention; animal behavior studies that provide insight into pathophysiological processes; psychophysiological investigations

having implications for the study of disease; behavioral methods used in the diagnosis, treatment, or rehabilitation of individuals having physical disorders; and techniques that could reduce disease risk by modifying health beliefs, attitudes, or behaviors. Interventions described may be at the individual, group, multicenter, or community level.

Audience
Scholars and professionals in psychology, medicine, nursing, and the allied health professions.

Instructions To Contributors
Manuscript Preparation. Prepare manuscripts according to the *Publication Manual of the American Psychological Association* (5th ed.; APA, 750 First Street, NE, Washington, DC 20002–4242). Follow "Guidelines for Nonsexist Language in APA Journals."

Strong preference is given to manuscripts of 20 pages or fewer, including references, tables, and figures. Use 1½-in. margins. Type all components double-spaced and in the following order: title page (p. 1), abstract and key words (p. 2), text (including quotes), acknowledgments, references, appendices, footnotes, tables, and figure captions. On page 1, type article title, author name(s) and affiliation(s), running head (abbreviated title, no more than 45 characters and spaces), and name and address of the person to whom requests for reprints should be addressed; on page 2, type an abstract of no more than 150 words and a list of no more than 6 key words; type author notes and acknowledgments at the end of the article (just before the References section). Attach photocopies of all figures.

Permissions. Authors are responsible for all statements made in their work and for obtaining permission from copyright owners to reprint or adapt a table or figure or to reprint a quotation of 500 words or more. Authors should write to original author(s) and publisher to request nonexclusive world rights in all languages to use the material in the article and in future editions. Provide copies of all permissions and credit lines.

Cover Letter. In a cover letter, include the contact author's address and telephone and fax numbers and state that the manuscript includes only original material that has not been published and that is not under review for publication elsewhere.

Manuscript Submission. Electronic submissions are preferred. Electronic manuscripts should be submitted as attachment files, preferably in MS Word format (PC or Mac) and figures as Powerpoint files to **ijbm@psychology.su.se**.

Manuscripts can also be submitted as paper copies. Submit five (5) high-quality manuscript printouts to the Editor, Prof. Ulf Lundberg, Department of Psychology, Stockholm University, S–106 91 Stockholm, Sweden. Fax: +46-8-167-847; Phone: +46-8-163-874; E-mail: **ul@psychology.su.se**.

Manuscripts are not returned to authors.

After manuscripts are accepted, they should be submitted as before (disc, paper copy, camera-ready figures).

Accepted Manuscripts and Computer Disks. After manuscripts are accepted, authors are asked to (a) submit a disk containing two files (word-processor and ASCII versions of the manuscript), (b) make sure the content of the files exactly matches that of the printed, accepted, finalized manuscript (provide revised printout if necessary), (c) submit camera-ready figures, and (d) sign and return a copyright-transfer agreement. It is the responsibility of the contact author to ascertain that all coauthors approve the accepted manuscript and concur with its publication in the journal.

Production Notes. Files of accepted manuscripts are copyedited and typeset into page proofs. Authors read proofs to correct errors and answer editors' queries. Authors may order reprints of their articles when they receive proofs.

International Journal of Clinical and Experimental Hypnosis

ADDRESS FOR SUBMISSION:

Arreed Barabasz, Editor
International Journal of Clinical and
   Experimental Hypnosis
Washington State University
Department of Educational Leadership
  and Counseling Psychology
PO Box 642136
Pullman, WA 99164-2136
USA
Phone:
Fax:
E-Mail: ijceh@pullman.com
Web: http://www.tandf.co.uk/journals
Address May Change:

PUBLICATION GUIDELINES:

Manuscript Length: 26-30
Copies Required: One
Computer Submission: Yes Email
Format:
Fees to Review: 0.00 US$

Manuscript Style:
   American Psychological Association

CIRCULATION DATA:

Reader: Academics, Practitioners
Frequency of Issue: 5 Times/Year
Copies per Issue: 4,001 - 5,000
Sponsor/Publisher: Soc for Clinical & Exp'l
  Hypnosis, Soc for Psych Hypnosis, Intl
  Soc of Hypnosis/Taylor & Francis
Subscribe Price: 103.00 US$
   55.00 US$

REVIEW INFORMATION:

Type of Review: Editorial Review
No. of External Reviewers: 3
No. of In House Reviewers: 1
Acceptance Rate: 21-30%
Time to Review: 1 - 2 Months
Reviewers Comments: Yes
Invited Articles: 6-10%
Fees to Publish: 0.00 US$

MANUSCRIPT TOPICS:
Counseling Process; Hypnosis; Psychiatry

MANUSCRIPT GUIDELINES/COMMENTS:

Aims and Scope. The *International Journal of Clinical and Experimental Hypnosis* publishes only original research and clinical papers dealing with hypnosis and psychology, psychiatry, the medical and mental specialties, and allied areas of science. Submissions include clinical and experimental studies, discussions of theory, significant historical and cultural material, and questions for inclusion in the Clinical Forum. It is the purpose of this journal to present in an integrated manner the best research in scientific hypnosis and to encourage support continued through inquiry.

Address manuscripts to the Editor: Dr. Arreed Barabasz. Email: **ijceh@pullman.com**. Mailing address: IJCEH, Washington State University, PO Box, 642136, Pullman, WA, 99164-2136.

Authors are strongly encouraged to submit manuscripts via email. The email should contain an attachment with the manuscript prepared using MS Word or WordPerfect. Each manuscript must be accompanied by a statement that it has not been published elsewhere and that it has not been submitted simultaneously for publication elsewhere. Authors are responsible for obtaining permission to reproduce copyrighted material from other sources and are required to sign an agreement for the transfer of copyright to the publisher. All accepted manuscripts, artwork, and photographs become the property of the publisher.

All parts of the manuscript should be typewritten, double-spaced, with margins of at least one inch on all sides. Number manuscript pages consecutively throughout the paper. Authors should also supply a shortened version of the title suitable for the running head, not exceeding 50 character spaces. Each article should be summarized in an abstract of not more than 140 words. Avoid abbreviations, diagrams, and reference to the text in the abstract.

References. Cite in the text by author and date (Smith, 1983). Prepare reference list in accordance with the *APA Publication Manual*, 5th ed. Examples:

Journal. Orne, M. T. (1951). The mechanisms of hypnotic age regression: An experimental study. *Journal of Abnormal and Social Psychology*, 46, 213-225.

Book. Gill, M. M., & Brenman, M. (1959). *Hypnosis and related states.* New York: International Universities Press.

Contribution to a Book. Norman, D. A., & Shallice, T. (1986). Attention to action: Willed and automatic control of behavior. In R. J. Davidson, G. E. Schwartz, & D. Shapiro (Eds.), *Conscious and self-regulation* (Vol. 4). New York: Plenum Press.

Illustrations. Illustrations submitted (line drawings, halftones, photos, photomicrographs, etc.) should be clean originals or digital files. Digital files are recommended for highest quality reproduction and should follow these guidelines:
- 300 dpi or higher
- Sized to fit on journal page
- EPS, TIFF, or PSD format only
- Submitted as separate files, not embedded in text files

Color illustrations will be considered for publication; however, the author will be required to bear the full cost involved in their printing and publication. The charge for the first page with color is $900.00. The pext three pages with color are $450.00 each. A custom quote will be provided for color art totaling more than 4 journal pages. Good-quality color prints should be provided in their final size. The publisher has the right to refuse publication of color prints deemed unacceptable.

Tables and Figures. Tables and figures (illustrations) should not be embedded in the text, but should be included as separate sheets or files in text format. A short descriptive title should appear above each table with a clear legend and any footnotes suitably identified below. All units must be included. Figures should be completely labeled, taking into account necessary size reduction. Captions should be typed, double-spaced, on a separate sheet. All original figures should be clearly marked in pencil on the reverse side with the number, author's name, and top edge indicated.

Proofs. Page proofs are sent to the designated author using Taylor & Francis' EProof system. They must be carefully checked and returned within 48 hours of receipt.

Offprints/Reprints. The corresponding author of each article will receive 25 complementary offprints and one complete copy of the issue in which the article appears and up to two copies if there are multiple authors. Offprints of an individual article may be ordered from Taylor & Francis. Use the offprint order form included with page proofs. Up to 10 additional issue copies may also be ordered. If offprints are not ordered by the required date, reprint pricing goes into effect, and issue copies may not be ordered.

International Journal of Conflict Management

ADDRESS FOR SUBMISSION:

Judi McLean Parks, Editor
International Journal of Conflict
   Management
Washington University
Campus Box 1133
One Brookings Drive
St. Louis, MO 63130
USA
Phone: 314-935-7451
Fax: 314-935-6359
E-Mail: ijcm-mcleanparks@olin.wustl.edu
Web: www.iacm-conflict.org/ijcm
Address May Change:

PUBLICATION GUIDELINES:

Manuscript Length: 35
Copies Required: Four
Computer Submission: Yes
Format: IBM, MS DOS
Fees to Review: 0.00 US$

Manuscript Style:
   American Psychological Association

CIRCULATION DATA:

Reader: Academics, Counsulltants,
   Interdisciplinary
Frequency of Issue:
Copies per Issue:
Sponsor/Publisher: Information Age
   Publishing
Subscribe Price: 60.00 US$ Student
   190.00 US$ Institution
   85.00 US$ Professional

REVIEW INFORMATION:

Type of Review: Blind Review
No. of External Reviewers: 3
No. of In House Reviewers: 1
Acceptance Rate: 15%
Time to Review: 2 - 3 Months
Reviewers Comments: Yes
Invited Articles: 0-5%
Fees to Publish: 0.00 US$

MANUSCRIPT TOPICS:
Group Dynamics; Industry & Organization; Social Psychology

MANUSCRIPT GUIDELINES/COMMENTS:

Website. **http://members.aol.com/mgt2000/ijcm.htm**

Manuscript Topics
1. Organizational conflict
2. Communication and conflict
3. Mediation
4. Arbitration
5. Negotiation
6. Bargaining and industrial relations
7. Law and procedural justice
8. Peace and international conflict
9. Conflict in the public sector
10. Social psychological conflict

Manuscripts
The *IJCM* publishes original theoretical and empirical articles, case studies, simulations, and book reviews on management. The journal is published 4 times a year. Manuscripts must be

prepared according to the 1994 edition of the *Publication Manual of the American Psychological Association* and will be reviewed by double-blind review process. Five hard copies of the manuscript and one in disk and requests for other details should be addressed to the Editor.

International Journal of Group Psychotherapy

ADDRESS FOR SUBMISSION:

Les R. Greene, Editor
International Journal of Group
  Psychotherapy
American Group Psychotherapy Assn.
25 East 21st Street, 6th Floor
New York, NY 10010
USA
Phone: 877-668-2472
Fax: 212-979-6627
E-Mail: info@agpa.org
Web: www.guilford.com
Address May Change:

PUBLICATION GUIDELINES:

Manuscript Length: 25
Copies Required: Six
Computer Submission: Yes
Format:
Fees to Review: 0.00 US$

Manuscript Style:
  American Psychological Association

CIRCULATION DATA:

Reader: Academics, Practitioners
Frequency of Issue: Quarterly
Copies per Issue: 4,000-5,000
Sponsor/Publisher: Guilford Publications
Subscribe Price: 75.00 US$ Individual
  250.00 US$ Institution
  103.00 US$, 278 US$ Canada/Foreign

REVIEW INFORMATION:

Type of Review: Blind Review
No. of External Reviewers: 3
No. of In House Reviewers: 0
Acceptance Rate: 45%
Time to Review: 4 Months
Reviewers Comments: Yes
Invited Articles: 20%
Fees to Publish: 0.00 US$

MANUSCRIPT TOPICS:
Group Dynamics; Group Psychotherapy

MANUSCRIPT GUIDELINES/COMMENTS:

Manuscripts. To submit manuscripts for consideration for publication, either mail 6 copies to the American Group Psychotherapy Association, 25 East 21st Street, 6th Floor, New York, NY 10010 or send an email attachment to **info@agpa.org**. The manuscript must be prepared according to the style outlined in the *Publication Manual of the American Psychological Association* (Fifth Edition, 2001). However, the names, highest degrees, titles, and professional affiliations of the authors, as well as the address of the corresponding author, should appear on the title (first) page of the manuscript. An abstract not to exceed 125 words comprises the second page of the manuscript. Regular articles should not exceed 25 pages inclusive of references, figures, and tables. Brief Reports should not exceed six pages. Manuscript material must be original, neither previously published nor to be published in another source. Manuscripts must not be simultaneously under consideration for publication by another source. Authors need to avoid sexist language and should ensure the confidentiality of information concerning their clients/patients and their groups by taking reasonable steps to avoid personally identifiable information and/or by obtaining the consent of these individuals or groups to publish such material. In the case of research manuscripts, investigators must have complied with contemporary standards of ethical behavior for human experimentation. Please refer to "Guidelines for Authors Submitting Manuscripts to the *International Journal of Group Psychotherapy*" which is found on pp. 503-515 of the October 1993 issue as well as the Editor's note in the October 2004 issue for more details on manuscript submission.

International Journal of Offender Therapy and Comparative Criminology

ADDRESS FOR SUBMISSION:

George B. Palermo, Editor
International Journal of Offender Therapy
and Comparative Criminology
925 East Wells
Milwaukee, WI 53202
USA
Phone: 414-271-2382
Fax: 414-277-2382
E-Mail: palermogb@juno.com
Web: www.sagepub.com
Address May Change:

PUBLICATION GUIDELINES:

Manuscript Length: 16-20
Copies Required: Three
Computer Submission: Yes Disk
Format: MS Word, WordPerfect
Fees to Review: 0.00 US$

Manuscript Style:
American Psychological Association

CIRCULATION DATA:

Reader: Academics
Frequency of Issue: Bi-Monthly
Copies per Issue: Less than 1,000
Sponsor/Publisher: Sage Publications
Subscribe Price: 76.00 US$ Individual
575.00 US$ Institution

REVIEW INFORMATION:

Type of Review: Blind Review
No. of External Reviewers: 0-2
No. of In House Reviewers: 2-3
Acceptance Rate: 60%
Time to Review: 1 - 2 Months
Reviewers Comments: Yes
Invited Articles: 0-5%
Fees to Publish: 0.00 US$

MANUSCRIPT TOPICS:
Abnormal Psychology; Behavior Modification; Criminology - Legal Issues; Experimental Psychology; Personality; Psychiatry; Psychobiology; Psychological Testing; Psychopathology; Research Methods & Statistics; Social Psychology

MANUSCRIPT GUIDELINES/COMMENTS:

About the Journal
For over four decades the *International Journal of Offender Therapy and Comparative Criminology* has provided therapists, counselors, researchers, policymakers and other professionals in the field of criminology with answers by focusing on the three key aspects of offender therapy - psychological, genetic/biological and environmental - and combining them into a treatment approach.

Putting Theory into Practice
Peer-reviewed and expertly edited, the *International Journal of Offender Therapy and Comparative Criminology* is a quarterly journal dedicated to providing a forum for research,

discussion and treatment of variables associated with crime and delinquency. It emphasizes treatment of the offender, both as it relates to theory and to clinical practice.

Providing a Comprehensive Forum

The *International Journal of Offender Therapy and Comparative Criminology* recognizes that many disciplines are involved in and inform this area of study and practice, and seeks to provide a comprehensive forum through which treatment practices can be improved. To that end, the journal contains submissions by experts in all fields that directly affect the treatment of prisoners and offenders. These fields include: psychology, psychiatry, social work, law and legal studies, medicine, criminology, criminal justice, corrections, sociology, health sciences.

Advancing Key Areas

Promoting a unique approach to the research and practice of prisoner and offender treatment, the *International Journal of Offender Therapy and Comparative Criminology* strives to grasp and advance the central aspects of the challenging phenomena of crime and delinquency.

Psychological... because some serious psychological disorders are strikingly common among prisoners and offenders, the journal works to shed new light on their derivations and treatments, providing researchers and practitioners with innovative avenues to explore.

Genetic/Biological... the profound effect that genetic and/or biological influences can have on prisoners and offenders is critical – so is the journal's mandate to provide works that help researchers and practitioners to recognize, treat and ultimately overcome these factors.

Environmental... the life history is central to understanding prisoners and offenders, and the *International Journal of Offender Therapy and Comparative Criminology* seeks to enhance the understanding of practitioners and researchers on how to address this aspect in their work. Taking these three aspects of crime and delinquency, the *International Journal of Offender Therapy and Comparative Criminology* combines them into a focused treatment approach through pertinent and credible research that can be applied to practice.

An International Perspective

Although societies around the world differ greatly, the phenomenon of crime and delinquency does not. The *International Journal of Offender Therapy and Comparative Criminology* expands the knowledge base of researchers and practitioners by reporting on international development, and provides the opportunity to learn from the experiences, policies, programmes and perspectives of their colleagues from around the world and to use that new information in their own work.

Notes for Authors

The *International Journal of Offender Therapy and Comparative Criminology* will consider for publication original manuscripts.

1. Submit one original and two copies of the manuscript, and one diskette copy. Manuscripts will not be returned.

2. Manuscripts should be typewritten, left-justified, double-spaced on one side of 8 ½ X 11 white paper. This includes not only the text, but also the notes, references, block quotations, tables and all other material. Manuscripts should be approximately 10-25 pages in length, including bibliography, tables, etc. Underlining should be used for italics. No bold should be used.

3. The title page should contain only the title, name of author(s) and a running head of three to five words. The running head (one-phrase description of the article) should comprise the article title or an abbreviated version thereof.

4. Include an abstract of no more than 150 words.

5. A list of 3-5 key words is to be provided directly below the abstract. Key words should express the precise content of the manuscript, as they are used for indexing purposes.

6. On a separate page following the references, include author(s) name, degree, position, affiliation, mailing address, e-mail address, tel./fax numbers.

7. Use endnotes rather than footnotes, grouped on a separate page, followed by acknowledgments (if any), followed by references.

8. Each element of the manuscript (title page, abstract, author's notes, appendix, endnotes, references, each table, and each figure) should begin on a new page.

9. The format and style of the manuscript must follow the guidelines of the *Publication Manual of the American Psychological Association* (4th ed.). References should be done with a hanging indent.

10. Tables and figures should be kept to a minimum, be self-explanatory, and supplement (not duplicate) the text. Tables and figures should appear on separate pages at the end of the manuscript. Figures must be clean, black-and-white, camera-ready copies (please do not send glossies). Tables should not have cells or lines dividing the different elements. Preferably, each element is separated by tabs. Do not use "graphic mode"; it cannot be translated.

11. Written permission has been obtained for (a) all quotations (usually those longer than six lines) from commercially copyrighted publications and (b) all tables or figures taken from other sources. Any quotes without permissions must be paraphrased or deleted before the journal goes to press.

12. Disks should be clearly labeled with the name of the first author, the name of the journal, the software and format used, and whether IBM (preferred) or Macintosh. Everything should be in one file (that is, it should not be broken into separate files for the abstract, text, references, etc.) The electronic file should be in the simplest form, with no embedded codes or footnotes and no special fonts or formatting. You are encouraged to run the spell-checking before submitting a disk. Elements in tables should be separated by tabs, not cells or lines.

Manuscripts are accepted for publication with the understanding that they have not been published elsewhere. Manuscripts will not be returned. The editorial staff does not hold itself responsible for statements made in its publication by contributors.

Send manuscripts to Dr. George B. Palermo, International Journal of Offender Therapy and Comparative Criminology, 925 East Wells Street, Milwaukee, WI 53202, USA.

International Journal of Psychiatry in Medicine

ADDRESS FOR SUBMISSION:

Harold G. Koenig, Editor
International Journal of Psychiatry in
  Medicine
Duke University
  ELECTRONIC SUBMISSIONS
Dept of Psychiatry & Behavioral Sciences
Box 3400 Duke University Medical Center
Durham, NC 27710
USA
Phone: 919-681-6633
Fax: 919-383-6962
E-Mail: koenig@geri.duke.edu
Web: www.baywood.com
Address May Change:

PUBLICATION GUIDELINES:

Manuscript Length:
Copies Required:
Computer Submission: Yes Email
Format:
Fees to Review: 0.00 US$

Manuscript Style:

CIRCULATION DATA:

Reader:
Frequency of Issue:
Copies per Issue:
Sponsor/Publisher:
Subscribe Price: 0.00 US$

REVIEW INFORMATION:

Type of Review:
No. of External Reviewers:
No. of In House Reviewers:
Acceptance Rate: 35-45%
Time to Review: 3-6 Months
Reviewers Comments:
Invited Articles:
Fees to Publish: 0.00 US$

MANUSCRIPT TOPICS:
Counseling Process; Ethics; Gerontology; Psychiatry; Psychobiology; Social Psychology

MANUSCRIPT GUIDELINES/COMMENTS:

The goal of the *International Journal of Psychiatry in Medicine* is to address the complex relationships among biological, psychological, social, religious and cultural systems in patient care. The aim of the journal is to provide a forum where researchers and clinicians in psychiatry, medicine, and surgery from around the world can educate each other and advance knowledge concerning biological, psychological, and social theory, methods, and treatment as they apply to patient care.

Topics of interest include, but are not limited to:
- psychobiological, psychological, social, religious, and cultural modifiers of illness
- the minor and moderate mental disorders seen and treated in medical and surgical practice

- doctor-patient interactions
- ethical issues in medicine
- biomedical etiologies of mental symptoms
- research from successful multi-disciplinary, collaborative models such as geriatrics
- health services research.

The *Journal* will publish original research, review articles, innovative educational programs, and illustrative case reports.

Submit Your Manuscript to:
Harold G. Koenig, M.D., M.H.Sc.
Department of Psychiatry and Behavioral Sciences
Box 3400, Duke University Medical Center
Durham, NC 27710
USA

Instructions are in accordance with the International Committee of Medical Journal Editors.For further details see: Uniform requirements for manuscripts submitted to biomedical journals. *JAMA* 1993;269:2282-2286.

Detailed Instructions
1. Limit submissions to biopsychosocial aspects of disease and patient care. The goal of the *International Journal of Psychiatry in Medicine* is to address the complex relationships among biological, psychological, social, religious and cultural systems in patient care. The aim of the journal is to provide a forum where researchers and clinicians in psychiatry, medicine, and surgery from around the world can educate each other and advance knowledge concerning biological, psychological, and social theory, methods, and treatment as they apply to patient care. Topics of interest include, but are not limited to: psychobiological, psychological, social, religious and cultural modifiers of illness; the minor and moderate mental disorders seen and treated in medical practice; doctor-patient interactions; ethical issues in medicine; biomedical etiologies of mental symptoms; research from successful collaborative, multidisciplinary models such as geriatrics; and, health services research. The journal will publish original research, review articles, innovative educational programs, and illustrative case reports.

2. Require all co-authors to read final submitted draft carefully and comprehensively. Preliminary review by senior colleagues and science editors is also strongly encouraged.

3. Send five (5) copies of submission with minimum of one inch margins. Place mailing address and e-mail address of corresponding author on title page of manuscript. Send five (5) copies of manuscript with minimum of one-inch margins, and retain a copy; include manuscript on diskette in Microsoft Word or Word Perfect word-processing format. Only original artwork may be returned.

Alternatively, and **preferably**, rather than submitting by mail, authors may e-mail cover letter and manuscript to **koenig@geri.duke.edu**. Soon, this method will be required for all submissions to facilitate the review process.

4. Type on one side of 8 ½" x 11" white paper. Double space everywhere. Number all pages starting with the title page.

5. Arrange in the following order with each item beginning a new page: Title Page, Abstract, Text, Acknowledgments, References, Tables / Figures.

6. The title page should have a title which is informative, declarative, and concise. Authors' first names, middle initials, and last names should be provided followed with the highest academic degree and institutional affiliation for each author. If the paper has been presented at a meeting, give the name of the meeting, the location, and the inclusive dates. Provide a full address for the author who is to receive correspondence about the manuscript and reprint requests.

7. Abstract should be a single paragraph no longer than 250 words, structured with headings: Objective-, Method-, Results-, Conclusions-. Authors of research articles should include: Objective -- question(s) addressed by the study; Method -- design of the study, setting (location and level of clinical care), patients or participants (basic manner of selection), interventions (if any), main outcome measures; Results -- main findings; and Conclusions -- principal conclusion emphasizing new and important aspects of study or observations, including direct clinical applications, if appropriate. Authors of review articles should include the following information, under the headings indicated: Objective -- the primary purpose of the review article; Method -- data sources, study selection (the number of studies selected for review and how there were selected), data extraction (primary rules for abstracting data and how they were applied); Results -- methods of data synthesis, key findings; and Conclusions -- including potential applications and research needs.

8. After abstract include 3 to 10 index words* and "(Int'l. J. Psychiatry in Medicine 200x; 30:000-000)". *(from MeSH list of *Index Medicus*)

9. The text should include four major sections with headings: Introduction, Method, Results, Discussion.

Introduction. The headings should be on a separate line next to the left margin. Where appropriate, additional subheadings and sub-subheadings can be used indented and underlined at the beginning of a paragraph, respectively.

Method
Subjects. The method section for research studies should provide a comprehensive description of the subjects. This includes the nature of the subject group, (including informed consent), methods of recruitment, the manner of selection and number who entered and completed the study.

Informed Consent. At the end of the description of the subjects, indicate whether the procedures followed were in accordance with the ethical standards of the responsible committee on human experimentation. In most cases, this should clearly state that after complete description of the study to the subjects, written informed consent was obtained.

Procedures. Procedures, interventions (if any), measurements used (including information about reliability as appropriate), and methods of data analysis (or synthesis for reviews) should be provided. Adequate description of statistical methods should be provided.

Analysis. Statistical tests that are not well known should be referenced. Standard deviations rather than standard errors of the mean are required. Spell out all abbreviations (other than those for units of measure) the first time they are used. Idiosyncratic abbreviations should not be used. Generic rather than trade names of drugs should be used.

Results. The Results should include all significant and important nonsignificant results. Include the test value, degree(s) of freedom, and probability. For example, "The analysis of variance indicated that those who received the interventions had significantly lower levels of depression than those assigned to the control condition (F=4.32, df=3, 37, p<0.05)." Present the results in a logical sequence in the text, tables and figures. Do not repeat in the text all the data in the tables. Emphasize or summarize only important observations.

Discussion. The Discussion should emphasize new and important aspects of the study and the conclusions that follow from them. Relate the findings to other relevant studies. Do not repeat in detail data or material given in the Introduction or Results. Link the conclusions with the goals of the study but avoid unqualified statements and conclusions not completely supported by the data or review. Include implications and limitations of the study. Include implications for future research.

10. In Acknowledgments, report grant or any other financial support in a separate paragraph and include the full name of the granting agency and grant number. Drug company support of any kind must be acknowledged.

11. References are to be cited in text in numerical order [1], with brackets [2]. The brackets should come before punctuation marks such as commas and periods, not after.

12. References are to be listed in numerical sequence at the end of the article. All authors, Article title. Journal Title (spelled out) Year; Volume Number: Pages inclusive. e.g. Journal Article - 1. Smith J, Jones RK. This is it. World Research Journal 1991;41:1-10. Book - 2. Jones RK, Smith J. Primary care. In: Well IM, editor. All we know. Amityville, NY: Baywood, 1996:18-50. Accuracy of each citation is the authors' responsibility. References should conform exactly to the original spelling, accents, punctuation, etc. Authors should be sure that all references listed have been cited in the text. Personal communications, unpublished manuscripts, manuscripts submitted but not yet accepted should not be included in the reference list. Manuscripts actually in press may be cited with journal or publisher/ location.

13. Figures should be referenced in text and appear in numerical sequence starting with Figure 1 (even if only one figure). Line art must be original drawings in black ink proportionate to our page size, and suitable for photographing. Indicate top and bottom of figure where confusion may exist. Labeling should be 8 point type. Clearly identify all figures. Figures should be drawn on separate pages and their placement noted by inserting: -- Insert Figure 1 here --

14. Tables must be cited in text in numbered sequence starting with Table 1 (even if only one table). Each table must have a descriptive title. Any footnotes to tables are indicated by super lower case letters. When tables include numbers and percent, the absolute number should be given first and the percent in parentheses (%). Tables should be typed on separate pages and their approximate placement indicated within text by inserting: -- Insert Table 1 here --. References in tables and figures are numbered as though the tables and figures were part of the text.

15. Footnotes are placed at the bottom of the page where referenced. They should be numbered with super Arabic numbers without parens or brackets. Footnotes should be brief with an average length of three lines.

16. Authors will be notified of the receipt of their paper and a number that has been assigned to it. This number should be included in all further correspondence. Reviewed manuscripts will not be returned except upon special request made in the original submission letter and if a self-addressed, postage-paid envelope is included.

17. Authors may suggest three potential unbiased reviewers, but their use is not guaranteed.

International Journal of Psychology

ADDRESS FOR SUBMISSION:

Laura Hernandez-Guzman, Editor
International Journal of Psychology
Indiana 260-608
Colonia Napoles
, 03710
Mexico D. F.
Phone: +525556665620
Fax: +525556655228
E-Mail: lher@servidor.unam.mx
Web: http://www.tandf.co.uk/journals
Address May Change:

PUBLICATION GUIDELINES:

Manuscript Length: 21-25
Copies Required: One
Computer Submission: Yes Disk; Email
Format: MS Word
Fees to Review: 0.00 US$

Manuscript Style:
    American Psychological Association

CIRCULATION DATA:

Reader: Academics
Frequency of Issue: Bi-Monthly
Copies per Issue:
Sponsor/Publisher: International Union of
    Psychological of Science/ Taylor &
    Francis
Subscribe Price: 146.00 US$ Individual
    625.00 US$ Institution

REVIEW INFORMATION:

Type of Review: Blind Review
No. of External Reviewers: 3
No. of In House Reviewers: 0
Acceptance Rate: 21-30%
Time to Review: Over 6 Months
Reviewers Comments: Yes
Invited Articles: 6-10%
Fees to Publish: 0.00 US$

MANUSCRIPT TOPICS:

Adolescent Psychology; Adulthood; Alcoholism & Drug Addiction; Child Psychology; Cross-Cultural Differences; Developmental Psychology; Experimental Psychology; History of Psychology; Learning & Conditioning; Neuropsychology; Personality; Physiological Psychology; Psychobiology; Psychological Testing; Research Methods & Statistics; Sensation & Perception; Social Psychology; Thinking & Cognition

MANUSCRIPT GUIDELINES/COMMENTS:

Aims and Scope

The *International Journal of Psychology* is the journal of the International Union of Psychological Science (IUPsyS) and is published under the auspices of the IUPsyS. Its purpose is to circulate, in an international framework, scientific information within and among subdisciplines of psychology and to foster the development of psychological science around the world. The journal emphasizes empirical research and theory in basic and applied psychology, especially with an international focus. It does not publish technical articles, validations of questionnaires and tests, or clinical case studies. Regular issues include two types of articles: empirical articles and review articles. Empirical articles report data from single or multiple studies in one of the major fields of scientific psychology. Review articles

544

provide overviews of the international literature on a particular topic; authors are especially encouraged to include in their review relevant publications from regions of the world not typically cited and/or in languages other than English or French. Special topical issues or sections are also published two or three times a year.

Many of *IJP*'s issues include a second section, the *International Platform for Psychologists*, which provides an opportunity to exchange news and opinions on psychology as an academic and applied profession. This section also contains information about the IUPsyS, about major international meetings, and about the activities of the National Psychological Societies. Finally it offers an opportunity to express opinions and to discuss internationally significant psychological issues. There is also a United Nations section with the *International Platform for Psychologists*.

The *Journal* occasionally publishes a special issue, guest edited by specialists, devoted to a single topic.

Instructions for Authors
Note to Authors. Please make sure your contact address information is clearly visible on the outside of all packages you are sending to Editors.

Our aim is to gradually increase the reach of the journal to even more geographical areas of the world and to extend the areas of scientific psychology covered by the journal. Authors from all fields within scientific psychology are encouraged to send their manuscripts to the journal.

From the beginning of 2001 the journal will be published in English instead of English and French, so from January 2001 submissions in French will no longer be accepted. Please note that authors are encouraged to submit papers electronically to expedite the peer review process. Please email your paper, saved in a standard document format type such as Word or Rich Text Format, to **lher@servidor.unam.mx**. Alternatively, if you wish to submit a hard copy, please send one copy of the manuscript AND a disk version to the Editor: Dra. Laura Hernández-Guzmán, President, The Mexican Psychological Society, Calle Indiana 260 Desp.608, Col. Napoles, 03710, Mexico City, Mexico. All manuscripts must include at least a 300-word abstract in English. The electronic version should not include complex formatting, such as Quark Xpress or Aldus PageMaker, and the "fast save" feature must be turned off. Your covering email/letter must include full contact details (including email), the title of the journal to which you are submitting, and the title of your article. All manuscripts should be submitted following the latest edition of *Publication Manual of the APA* (currently 5th edition).

International Quarterly of Community Health Education

ADDRESS FOR SUBMISSION:

George P. Cernada, Editor
International Quarterly of Community
    Health Education
P.O. Box 3585
Amherst, MA 01004-3585
USA
Phone:
Fax:
E-Mail: gcernada@schoolph.umass.edu
Web: www.baywood.com
Address May Change:

CIRCULATION DATA:

Reader: Academics, Practitioners
Frequency of Issue: Quarterly
Copies per Issue: Less than 1,000
Sponsor/Publisher: Baywood Publishing
    Co., Inc.
Subscribe Price: 64.00 US$ Individual
    225.00 US$ Institution

PUBLICATION GUIDELINES:

Manuscript Length: 6-30
Copies Required: Three
Computer Submission: No
Format: N/A
Fees to Review: 0.00 US$

Manuscript Style:
    See Manuscript Guidelines

REVIEW INFORMATION:

Type of Review: Blind Review
No. of External Reviewers: 2
No. of In House Reviewers: 0
Acceptance Rate: 35-50%
Time to Review: 6 Months or Less
Reviewers Comments: No
Invited Articles: 0-5%
Fees to Publish: 0.00 US$

MANUSCRIPT TOPICS:
Research Methods & Statistics; Social Psychology

MANUSCRIPT GUIDELINES/COMMENTS:

Topics Include. Health Education and Promotion: Applied Research; Program Evaluation; Case Studies; Annotated Bibliographies; Policy; Theory; Book Reviews

Aims & Scope
The *International Quarterly of Community Health Education* is committed to publishing applied research, policy and case studies dealing with community health education and its relationship to social change. Since 1981, this rigorously peer-referred *Journal* has contained a wide selection of material in readable style and format by contributors who are not only authorities in their field, but can also write with vigor, clarity, and occasionally with humor. Since its introduction the *Journal* has considered all manuscripts, especially encouraging stimulating articles which manage to combine maximum readability with scholarly standards. The *Journal* stresses systematic application of social science and health education theory and methodology to public health problems and consumer-directed approaches to control of

preventive and curative health services. Environmental and structural changes are emphasized and victim-blaming approaches are closely examined.

Instructions to Authors

Submit manuscript to: Dr. George P. Cernada, PO Box 3585, Amherst, MA 01004-3585.

Manuscripts are to be submitted in triplicate. Retain one copy, as manuscript will not be returned unless accompanied by a self-addressed, stamped envelope. Manuscript must be typewritten on 8-1/2" x 11" white paper, one side only, double-spaced, with wide margins. Paginate consecutively starting with the title page. The organization of the paper should be indicated by appropriate headings and subheadings.

Originality Authors should note that only original articles are accepted for publication. Submission of a manuscript represents certification on the part of the author(s) that neither the article submitted, nor a version of it has been published, or is being considered for publication elsewhere.

Abstracts of 100 to 150 words are required to introduce each article.

References should relate only to material cited within text and be listed in numerical order according to their appearance within text. State author's name, title of referenced work, editor's name, title of book or periodical, volume, issue, pages cited, and year of publication. Do not abbreviate titles. Please do not use ibid., op. cit., loc. cit., etc. In case of multiple citations, simply repeat the original numeral. Detailed specifications available from the editor upon request.

Footnotes are placed at the bottom of page where referenced. They should be numbered with superior Arabic numbers without parentheses or brackets. Footnotes should be brief with an average length of three lines.

Figures should be referenced in text and appear in numerical sequence starting with Figure 1. Line art must be original drawings in black ink proportionate to our page size, and suitable for photographing. Indicate top and bottom of figure where confusion may exist. Labeling should be 8 point type. Clearly identify all figures. Figures should be drawn on separate pages and their placement within the text indicated by inserting: —Insert Figure 1 here—.

Tables must be cited in text in numerical sequence starting with Table 1. Each table must have a descriptive title. Any footnotes to tables are indicated by superior lower case letters. Tables should be typed on separate pages and their approximate placement indicated within text by inserting: —Insert Table 1 here—

Authors will receive twenty complimentary reprints of their published article. Additional reprints may be ordered.

Issues in Mental Health Nursing

ADDRESS FOR SUBMISSION:

Sandra P. Thomas, Editor
Issues in Mental Health Nursing
University of Tennessee - Knoxville
College of Nursing
1200 Volunteer Blvd.
Knoxville, TN 37996
USA
Phone: 865-974-7581
Fax: 865-974-3569
E-Mail: sthomas@utk.edu
Web: http://www.tandf.co.uk/journals
Address May Change:

PUBLICATION GUIDELINES:

Manuscript Length: 26-30
Copies Required: Three
Computer Submission: Yes Disk, Email
Format: MS Word or WordPerfect
Fees to Review: 0.00 US$

Manuscript Style:
American Psychological Association

CIRCULATION DATA:

Reader: Academics, Practitioners
Frequency of Issue: 8 Times/Year
Copies per Issue:
Sponsor/Publisher: Taylor & Francis
Subscribe Price: 113.00 US$ Individual
354.00 US$ Institution

REVIEW INFORMATION:

Type of Review: Blind Review
No. of External Reviewers: 2
No. of In House Reviewers: 0
Acceptance Rate: 60%
Time to Review: 2 - 3 Months
Reviewers Comments: Yes
Invited Articles: 21-30%
Fees to Publish: 0.00 US$

MANUSCRIPT TOPICS:

Abnormal Psychology; Adolescent Psychology; Adulthood; Alcoholism & Drug Addiction; Child Psychology; Counseling Process; Developmental Psychology; Family Counseling & Therapy; Neuropsychology; Personality; Psychiatry; Psychopathology

MANUSCRIPT GUIDELINES/COMMENTS:

Aims and Scope

Issues in Mental Health Nursing is a refereed journal designed to expand psychiatric and mental health nursing knowledge. It deals with new, innovative approaches to client care, in-depth analysis of current issues, and empirical research. Because clinical research is the primary vehicle for the development of nursing science, the journal presents data-based articles on nursing care provision to clients of all ages in a variety of community and institutional settings. Additionally, the journal publishes theoretical papers and manuscripts addressing mental health promotion, public policy concerns, and educational preparation of mental health nurses. International contributions are welcomed.

Readership. Psychiatric-mental health nursing students, practitioners, educators, researchers, and administrators; psychologists; psychiatrists; sociologists; and social workers.

Instructions for Authors

Note to Authors: please make sure your contact address information is clearly visible on the outside of all packages you are sending to Editors.

Address manuscripts to the Editor, Sandra P. Thomas, University of Tennessee, 1200 Volunteer Blvd., Knoxville, TN 37996, USA. Authors are strongly encouraged to submit manuscripts on disk. The disk should be prepared using MS Word or WordPerfect and should be clearly labeled with the authors' names, file name, and software program. A hardcopy printout that exactly matches the disk must be supplied. Each manuscript must be accompanied by a statement that it has not been published elsewhere and that it has not been submitted simultaneously for publication elsewhere. Authors are responsible for obtaining permission to reproduce copyrighted material from other sources and are required to sign an agreement for the transfer of copyright to the publisher. All accepted manuscripts, artwork, and photographs become the property of the publisher.

All parts of the manuscript should be typewritten, double-spaced, with margins of at least one inch on all sides. Number manuscript pages consecutively throughout the paper. Authors should also supply a shortened version of the title suitable for the running head, not exceeding 50 character spaces. Each article should be summarized in an abstract of not more than 100 words. Avoid abbreviations, diagrams, and reference to the text. Further instructions and an author template can be obtained from the journal's web page at www.taylorandfrancis.com.

References

Cite in the text by author and date (Smith, 1983). Prepare reference list in accordance with the *APA Publication Manual*, 5th ed. Examples:

Journal. Tsai, M., & Wagner, N. N. (1978). Therapy groups for women sexually molested as children. Archives of Sexual Behaviour, 7(6), 417-427.

Book. Millman, M. (1980). Such a pretty face. New York: W. W. Norton.

Contribution to a Book. Hartley, J. T., & Walsh, D. A. (1980). Contemporary issues in adult development of learning. In L. W. Poon (ed.), Ageing in the 1980s (pp. 239-252). Washington, DC: American Psychological Association.

Illustrations

Illustrations submitted (line drawings, halftones, photos, photomicrographs, etc.) should be clean originals or digital files. Digital files are recommended for highest quality reproduction and should follow these guidelines:

- 300 dpi or higher
- sized to fit on journal page
- EPS, TIFF, or PSD format only
- submitted as separate files, not embedded in text files

Color illustrations will be considered for publication; however, the author will be required to bear the full cost involved in their printing and publication. The charge for the first figure is $1,200.00. Subsequent figures, totaling no more than 4 text pages, are $500.00 each. Good-quality color prints should be provided in their final size. Figures needing reduction or enlargement will be charged an additional 25 percent. The publisher has the right to refuse publication of any artwork deemed unacceptable.

Tables and Figures

Tables and figures (illustrations) should not be embedded in the text, but should be included as separate sheets or files. A short descriptive title should appear above each table with a clear legend and any footnotes suitably identified below. All units must be included. Figures should be completely labeled, taking into account necessary size reduction. Captions should be typed, double-spaced, on a separate sheet. All original figures should be clearly marked in pencil on the reverse side with the number, author's name, and top edge indicated.

Proofs

Page proofs are sent to the designated author. They must be carefully checked and returned within 48 hours of receipt.

Offprints

The corresponding author of each article will receive one complete copy of the issue in which the article appears. Offprints of an individual article may be ordered from Taylor & Francis. Use the offprint order form included with page proofs.

Journal for the Theory of Social Behavior

ADDRESS FOR SUBMISSION:

Charles W. Smith, Editor
Journal for the Theory of Social Behavior
Department of Sociology
Queens, College, CUNY
Flushing, NY 11367-1597
USA
Phone: 718-997-2840
Fax: 718-997-2820
E-Mail: charles_smith@qc.edu
Web: www.soc.qc.edu/jtsb
Address May Change:

PUBLICATION GUIDELINES:

Manuscript Length: Under 10,000 Words
Copies Required: See Guidelines
Computer Submission: Yes
Format: MS Word or Text
Fees to Review: 0.00 US$

Manuscript Style:
    American Psychological Association

CIRCULATION DATA:

Reader: Academics
Frequency of Issue: Quarterly
Copies per Issue: 1,001 - 2,000
Sponsor/Publisher: Blackwell Publishers,
    Inc.
Subscribe Price:

REVIEW INFORMATION:

Type of Review: Editorial Review
No. of External Reviewers: 3+
No. of In House Reviewers: 1
Acceptance Rate: 11-20%
Time to Review: 3-5 Months
Reviewers Comments: Yes
Invited Articles: 0-5%
Fees to Publish: 0.00 US$

MANUSCRIPT TOPICS:
Culture & Personality; Decision Making Theory; Psycholinguistics

MANUSCRIPT GUIDELINES/COMMENTS:

Aims and Scope
The Journal for the Theory of Social Behaviour publishes original theoretical and methodological articles that examine the links between social structures and human agency embedded in behavioural practices.

The *Journal* is truly unique in focusing first and foremost on social behaviour, over and above any disciplinary or local framing of such behaviour. In so doing, it embraces a range of theoretical orientations and, by requiring authors to write for a wide audience, the *Journal* is distinctively interdisciplinary and accessible to readers world-wide in the fields of psychology, sociology and philosophy.

Author Guidelines
Journal for the Theory of Social Behaviour seeks to publish original theoretical /methodological manuscripts of good quality bearing on social behaviour. As an

interdisciplinary journal, wide latitude is given to the manner in which this may be done including

(a) critiques of existing concepts and theories;
(b) proposals for innovative research methods;
(c) analysis of philosophic assumptions of the social sciences;
(d) presentation of new models of behaviour;
(e) discussions dealing with the relationship of everyday life behaviours with those situated within an experimental setting.

Though the primary focus of the *Journal* is theoretical, manuscripts should have potential applicability to the research process.

The *Journal* is not interested in publishing articles which focus solely upon non-social behaviour, which ignore individual agency, which are purely technical in orientation, or lack interdisciplinary relevance.

Submission of Manuscripts
Since *JTSB* now uses electronic communication in processing manuscripts, manuscripts of no more than 10,000 words and editorial queries should be sent as an email attachment in Word or common text format to Charles W. Smith at (**Charles_Smith@qc.edu**). Where necessary, manuscripts will also be accepted in hard copy (triplicate) accompanied by a disk containing the manuscript in the format noted above. Manuscript and disk should be sent to:

Charles W. Smith
Department of Sociology, Queens College
CUNY, Flushing
New York 11367
USA
Email: **Charles_Smith@qc.edu**

In all cases, please include your full address, including an email address and telephone/fax numbers where you may be reached.

Copyright Assignment Form. Authors will be required to assign copyright in their paper to The Executive Management Committee of *JTSB*. Copyright assignment is a condition of publication and papers will not be passed to the publisher for production unless copyright has been assigned. To assist authors an appropriate copyright assignment form will be supplied by the editorial office. Alternatively, authors may like to download a copy of the form at http://www.blackwellpublishing.com/pdf/jtsb_caf.pdf. (Government employees need to complete the Author Warranty sections, although copyright in such cases does not need to be assigned).

Journal Style
(a) Bibliographical references should be incorporated into the text, using the author-date system, with page numbers where necessary e.g. Smith (1980). All references should be listed alphabetically at the end of the article with the date appearing immediately after the author's name and initials. In the case of a journal article ((i) below) the reference should also include

the title of the article, the name in full of the journal in which it appears together with the volume and issue number and the inclusive page numbers. References to books and to chapters in books should be as follows ((ii) and (iii)): (i) GERGEN, K. J. (1985). The social constructionist movement in modern psychology. *American Psychologist*, **40**, (3), 266-275. (ii) HARRE, R. (1983). *Personal being: A theory of individual psychology*. Oxford: Blackwell. (iii) DEUTSCHER, I. (1984). Choosing ancestors: some consequences of the selection from intellectual traditions. In R. M. Farr and S. Moscovici (eds) *Social Representations*. Cambridge University Press, pp. 71-100.

(b) Avoid, wherever possible, the use of footnotes. When they are used they should be numbered consecutively throughout the article and typed separately at the end of the manuscript.

(c) Tables should be typed on a separate sheet and supplied at the end of the manuscript. Their location in the main text should be indicated by notes such as 'Table I here'.

(d) Figures should be supplied on separate sheets at the end of the typescript. Unless they are supplied in a quality suitable for reproduction they will be redrawn. Original artwork is preferred, drawn black on white, with lettering in pencil. Their position in the text should be indicated by notes such as 'Insert Figure I here'.

Journal of Abnormal Psychology

ADDRESS FOR SUBMISSION:

Timothy B. Baker, Editor
Journal of Abnormal Psychology
University of Wisconsin - Madison
Department of Psychology & CTRI
1202 West Johnson Street
Madison, WI 53706-1611
USA
Phone: 608-265-3939
Fax: 608-265-3102
E-Mail: abpsych@ctri.medicine.wisc.edu
Web: http://www.apa.org/journals/
Address May Change: 1/1/2006

PUBLICATION GUIDELINES:

Manuscript Length: 16-20
Copies Required: One
Computer Submission: Yes
Format: No Reply
Fees to Review: 0.00 US$

Manuscript Style:
    American Psychological Association

CIRCULATION DATA:

Reader: Academics, Practitioners
Frequency of Issue: Quarterly
Copies per Issue: No Reply
Sponsor/Publisher: American Psychological
    Association
Subscribe Price:

REVIEW INFORMATION:

Type of Review: Editorial Review
No. of External Reviewers: 2-3
No. of In House Reviewers: 1
Acceptance Rate: 11-20%
Time to Review: 2 - 3 Months
Reviewers Comments: Yes
Invited Articles: 6-10%
Fees to Publish: 0.00 US$

MANUSCRIPT TOPICS:

Abnormal Psychology; Alcoholism & Drug Addiction; Psychiatry; Psychological Testing;
Psychopathology

MANUSCRIPT GUIDELINES/COMMENTS:

The *Journal of Abnormal Psychology* publishes articles on basic research and theory in the broad field of abnormal behavior, its determinants, and its correlates. The following general topics fall within its area of major focus: (a) psychopathology—its etiology, development, symptomatology, and course; (b) normal processes in abnormal individuals; (c) pathological or atypical features of the behavior of normal persons; (d) experimental studies, with human or animal subjects, relating to disordered emotional behavior or pathology; (e) sociocultural effects on pathological processes, including the influence of gender and ethnicity; and (f) tests of hypotheses from psychological theories that relate to abnormal behavior. Thus, studies of patient populations, analyses of abnormal behavior and motivation in terms of modern behavior theories, case histories, and theoretical papers of scholarly substance on deviant personality and emotional abnormality would all fall within the boundaries of the journal's interests. Each article should represent an addition to knowledge and understanding of abnormal behavior in its etiology, description, or change. In order to improve the use of journal resources, it has been agreed by the two Editors concerned that the *Journal of Abnormal Psychology* will not consider articles dealing with diagnosis or treatment of abnormal behavior, and the *Journal of Consulting and Clinical Psychology* will not consider articles dealing with the etiology or descriptive pathology of abnormal behavior. Therefore, a study that focuses primarily on treatment efficacy should be submitted to the *Journal of Consulting and Clinical Psychology*. However, a longitudinal study focusing on developmental influences or origins of abnormal behavior should be submitted to the *Journal of Abnormal Psychology*.

Authors should ensure that their manuscripts and cover letters meet the criteria below and submit electronically using the Journal's online submission portal at
http://www.jbo.com/jbo3/submissions/dsp_jbo.cfm?journal_code=abn.

In addition, authors should mail one hard copy of their manuscript and a signed cover letter, prepared as detailed below, to the address below. Authors encountering difficulties submitting via the portal should e-mail the manuscript coordinator for assistance.

Timothy B. Baker, PhD
Editor, Journal of Abnormal Psychology
Department of Psychology
University of Wisconsin & CTRI
1202 West Johnson Street
Madison, WI 53706-1611
Manuscript Coordinator: **abpsych@ctri.medicine.wisc.edu**

General correspondence may be directed to the Editor's Office at
tbb@ctri.medicine.wisc.edu.

In addition to postal addresses and telephone numbers, authors are requested to supply electronic mail addresses and fax numbers, if available, for potential use by the editorial and production offices. Authors should keep a copy of the manuscript to guard against loss.

Masked reviews are *optional* and must be specifically requested in the cover letter accompanying the submission. For masked reviews, each copy of the manuscript must include a separate title page with the authors' names and affiliations, and these ought not to appear anywhere else in the manuscript. Footnotes that identify the authors must be typed on a separate page. Authors are to make every effort to see that the manuscript itself contains no clues to their identities.

Most of the articles published in the *Journal of Abnormal Psychology* are reports of original research, but other types of articles are acceptable. Short Reports of replications or of failures to replicate previously reported results are given serious consideration. Comments on articles published in the journal are also considered. Case studies from either a clinical setting or a laboratory will be considered if they raise or illustrate important questions that go beyond the single case and have heuristic value. Manuscripts that present or discuss theoretical formulations of psychopathology, or that evaluate competing theoretical formulations on the basis of published data, may also be accepted. Finally, the *Journal* will consider articles that present, explicate, or evaluate experimental or analytic methods of particular relevance to psychopathology. For further information on content, authors may refer to the *Journal* Description.

Authors must prepare manuscripts according to the *Publication Manual of the American Psychological Association* (5th ed.). All manuscripts must include an abstract that contains a maximum of 120 words typed on a separate sheet of paper. All copy must be double-spaced, and further typing instructions, especially in regard to tables, figures, references, metrics, and abstracts, appear in the *Manual*. Also, all manuscripts are copyedited for bias-free language (see chap. 2 of the *Publication Manual*). Original color figures can be printed in color provided the author agrees to pay half of the associated production costs; an estimate of these costs is available from the APA production office on request.

Articles will be published in six different sections of the *Journal:* Short Reports, Regular Articles, Extended Articles, Case Studies, Commentaries, and Theories and Methods. In preparing a Short Report, authors should to set the character–space limit at 60 characters per line and should not exceed 410 lines of text and references (exclusive of the title page, abstract, author note, footnotes, tables, and figures). There should be no more than two figures or tables. For Short Reports, the length limits are exact and must be strictly followed.

In preparing a **Short Report**, authors should use 12-point Times Roman type with 1-in. (2.54-cm) side margins and should not exceed 16 pages of text and references (exclusive of the title page, abstract, author note, footnotes, tables, and figures). There should be no more than two references, figures or tables. **Regular articles** addressing theories and methods should not exceed 36 manuscript pages (text and references). **Extended Articles** are published within regular issues of the *Journal* (they are not free-standing) and are reserved for manuscripts that require extended exposition (beyond what is possible in the 36-page limit for **Regular Articles**). Typically, **Extended Articles** will report multiple experiments, multifaceted longitudinal studies, transdisciplinary investigations, or studies that are extraordinarily complex in terms of methodology or analysis. **Case Studies** and **Commentaries** have the same length requirements as **Short Reports**.

Components of all cover letters, in addition to items 1—4 below, will contain the following: (a) the full postal and email address of the corresponding author; (b) the complete telephone and fax numbers of the same; (c) the proposed category under which the manuscript was submitted; and (d) a request for masked review, if desired, along with a statement ensuring that the manuscript was prepared in accordance with the guidelines above.

Authors are required to obtain and provide to APA all necessary permissions to reproduce any copyrighted work, including, for example, test instruments and other test materials or portions thereof. A statement addressing permissions should be included in the cover letter regarding any submitted work containing any of these listed (or similar) items. Final files for production should be prepared as outlined in Preparing Your Electronic Files for Production at http://www.apa.org/journals/preparing_electronic_files.html.

APA policy prohibits an author from submitting the same manuscript for concurrent consideration by two or more publications. In addition, it is a violation of APA Ethical Principles to publish "as original data, data that have been previously published" (Standard 8.13). As this journal is a primary journal that publishes original material only, APA policy also prohibits the publication of any manuscript that has already been published in whole or substantial part elsewhere. Authors have an obligation to consult journal editors about prior publication of any data on which their article depends. As such, corresponding authors need to clearly state in the cover letter that (a) the manuscript or date, in whole or substantial part, has not been previously published or presented; and (b) that the manuscript is not currently being considered by other journals nor will it be while it is under consideration of the *Journal of Abnormal Psychology*.

In addition, APA Ethical Principles specify that "after research results are published, psychologists do not withhold the data on which their conclusions are based from other competent professionals who seek to verify the substantive claims through reanalysis and who intend to use such data only for that purpose, provided that the confidentiality of the participants can be protected and unless legal rights concerning proprietary data preclude their release" (Standard 8.14). APA expects authors submitting to this journal to adhere to these standards. Specifically, authors of manuscripts submitted to APA journals are expected to ensure the availability of their data throughout the editorial review process and for at least 5 years after the date of publication. Authors should state in a signed cover letter that they have complied with APA ethical standards in the treatment of their sample, human or animal. A copy of the APA Ethical Principles may be obtained electronically on the website at http://www.apa.org/ethics/ or by writing the APA Ethics Office, 750 First Street, NE, Washington, DC 20002-4242. The cover letter should also indicate that no substantial portion of the article has appeared or is being considered for publication elsewhere.

Last, as the APA requires authors to reveal any possible conflict of interest in the conduct and reporting of research (e.g., financial interests in a test procedure, funding by pharmaceutical companies for drug research), authors must disclose the presence or absence of such conflicts in the cover letter.

Journal of Addictive Diseases

ADDRESS FOR SUBMISSION:

Barry Stimmel, Editor
Journal of Addictive Diseases
Mount Sinai School of Medicine
Dean for Graduate Medical Education
Annenberg 5102G
One Gustave L. Levy Place, Box 1193
New York, NY 10029
USA
Phone: 212-241-6694
Fax: 212-426-7748
E-Mail: bstimmel@smtplink.mssm.edu
Web:
Address May Change:

PUBLICATION GUIDELINES:

Manuscript Length: 11-15
Copies Required: Four
Computer Submission: No
Format: N/A
Fees to Review: 0.00 US$

Manuscript Style:
See Manuscript Guidelines

CIRCULATION DATA:

Reader: Practitioners
Frequency of Issue: Quarterly
Copies per Issue: 4,001 - 5,000
Sponsor/Publisher: American Society of
Addiction Medicine / Haworth Press, Inc.
Subscribe Price:

REVIEW INFORMATION:

Type of Review: Editorial Review
No. of External Reviewers: 2
No. of In House Reviewers: 0-1
Acceptance Rate: 40%
Time to Review: 1 - 2 Months
Reviewers Comments: Yes
Invited Articles: 11-20%
Fees to Publish: 0.00 US$

MANUSCRIPT TOPICS:
Alcoholism & Drug Addiction

MANUSCRIPT GUIDELINES/COMMENTS:

Journal of Addictive Diseases publishes original articles and topical review articles related to all areas of substance abuse. Each publication will be issue-oriented and may contain both basic science and clinical papers.

All submitted manuscripts are read by the editors. Many manuscripts may be further reviewed by consultants. Comments from reviewers will be returned with the rejected manuscripts when it is believed that this may be helpful to the author(s).

The content of *Journal of Addictive Diseases* is protected by copyright. Manuscripts are accepted for consideration with the understanding that their contents, all or in part, have not been published elsewhere and will not be published elsewhere except in abstract form or with

558

the express consent of the editor. Author(s) of accepted manuscripts will receive a form to sign for transfer of author's(s') copyright.

The editor reserves the right to make those revisions necessary to achieve maximum clarity and conciseness as well as uniformity to style. *Journal of Addictive Diseases* accepts no responsibility for statements made by contributing author(s).

Manuscript Preparation
A double-spaced original and three copies (including references, legends, and footnotes) should be submitted. The manuscript should have margins of at least 4 cm, with subheadings used at appropriate intervals to aid in presentation. There is no definite limitation on length, although a range of fifteen to twenty typed pages is desired.

A cover letter should accompany the manuscript containing the name, address, and phone number of the individual who will be specifically responsible for correspondence.

Electronic Media
Haworth's in-house typesetting unit is able to utilize your final manuscript material as prepared on most personal computers and word processors. This will minimize typographical errors and decrease overall production time. Please send the first draft and final draft copies of your manuscript to the journal Editor in print format for his/her final review and approval. After approval of your final manuscript, please submit the final approved version both on printed format ("hard copy") *and* floppy diskette. On the outside of the diskette package write: the brand name of your computer or word processor, the word processing program that you used, the title of your article, and the file name. NOTE: Disk and hard copy must agree. In case of discrepancies, it is The Haworth Press' policy to follow hard copy. Authors are advised that *no revisions* of the manuscript can be made after acceptance by the Editor for publication.

Title Page
The first page should include title, subtitle (if any), first name, and last name of each author, with the highest academic degree obtained. Each author's academic and program affiliation(s) should be noted, including the name of the department(s) and institution(s) to which the work should be attributed; disclaimers (if any); and the name and address of the author to whom correspondence should be addressed. Any acknowledgements of financial support should also be listed.

Abstracts
The second page should contain an abstract of not more than 150 words.

References
References should be typed double spaced on separate pages and arranged according to their order in the text. In the text the references should be in superscript Arabic numerals. The form of references should conform to the Index Medicus (National Library of Medicine) style. Sample references are illustrated below:

1. Brown MJ, Salamon D, Rendell M. Clonidine hallucinations. Ann Intern Med. 1980; 93:456-7.

2. Friedman HJ, Lester D. A critical review of progress towards an animal model of alcoholism. In: Blum K, ed. Alcohol and opiates: neurochemical and behavioral mechanisms. New York: Academic Press, 1977:1-19.

3. Berne E. Principles of group treatment. New York: Oxford University Press, 1966.

References to articles in press must state name of journal and, if possible, volume and year. References to unpublished material should be so indicated in parentheses in the text.

It is the responsibility of the author(s) to check references against the original source for accuracy both in manuscript and in galley proofs.

Tables and Figures
Tables and figures should be unquestionably clear so that their meaning is understandable without the text. Tables should be typed double spaced on separate sheets with number and title. Symbols for units should be confined to column headings. Internal, horizontal, and vertical lines may be omitted. The following footnote symbols should be used:* † ‡ § ¶. Tables must be camera ready. **Tables will be printed as is and will not be typeset**.

Figures should be submitted as glossy print photos, untrimmed and unmounted. The label pasted on the back of each illustration should contain the name(s) of author(s) and figure number, with top of figure being so indicated. Photomicrographs should have internal scale markers, with the original magnification as well as stain being used noted. If figures are of patients, the identities should be masked or a copy of permission for publication included. If the figure has been previously published, permission must be obtained from the previous author(s) and copyright holder(s). Color camera-ready art reproduction is available for a fee. Restrictions may apply. Please contact journal Editor prior to submission. Photographs are considered part of the acceptable manuscript and remain with the publisher for use in additional printings.

Manuscripts and other communications should be addressed to:

Barry Stimmel, MD
Mount Sinai School of Medicine
One Gustave L. Levy Place
Annenberg 5-02G, Box 1193
New York, New York 10029

Reprints
The senior author will receive two copies of the journal issue and 10 complimentary reprints of his or her article. The junior author will receive two copies of the journal issue. These are sent several weeks after the journal issue is published and in circulation. An order form for the purchase of additional reprints will also be sent to all authors at this time. (Approximately 4-6 weeks is necessary for the preparation of reprints.) Please do not query the Journal's Editor

about reprints. All such questions should be sent directly to The Haworth Press, Inc., Production Department, 21 East Broad Street, West Hazleton, PA 18201-3809 USA. To order additional reprints please contact Sample Copy Department, The Haworth Press, Inc. 10 Alice Street, Binghamton, NY 13904-1580 USA, 1-800-342-9678 or FAX 1-607-722-6362.

Copyright and Permissions

For permission to reprint articles that have appeared in Haworth journals, please contact: Copyright & Permissions Department, The Haworth Press, Inc., 10 Alice Street, Binghamton, NY 13904-1580 USA.

Copyright

Copyright ownership of your manuscript must be transferred officially to The Haworth Press, Inc. before we can begin the peer-review process. The Editor's letter acknowledging receipt of the manuscript will be accompanied by a form fully explaining this. All authors must sign the form and return the original to the Editor as soon as possible. Failure to return the copyright form in a timely fashion will result in delay in review and subsequent publication. [See following page.]

Journal of Adolescence

ADDRESS FOR SUBMISSION:

Ann Hagell, Editor
Journal of Adolescence
See Guidelines for Submission Addresses
Phone:
Fax:
E-Mail: joa@elsevier.com
Web: See Guidelines
Address May Change:

CIRCULATION DATA:

Reader: Academics
Frequency of Issue: 6 Times/Year
Copies per Issue:
Sponsor/Publisher: APSA (The Association
  for Professionals in Services for
  Adolescents)
Subscribe Price: 0.00 US$

PUBLICATION GUIDELINES:

Manuscript Length: 11-15
Copies Required: Four
Computer Submission: Yes Disk, Email
Format: Most, Word WordPerfect preferred
Fees to Review: 0.00 US$

Manuscript Style:

REVIEW INFORMATION:

Type of Review: Blind Review
No. of External Reviewers: 2
No. of In House Reviewers: 1
Acceptance Rate:
Time to Review:
Reviewers Comments:
Invited Articles:
Fees to Publish: 0.00 US$

MANUSCRIPT TOPICS:
Adolescent Psychology

MANUSCRIPT GUIDELINES/COMMENTS:

Guide for Authors
The *Journal* is an international, broadly based, cross-disciplinary journal that addresses itself to issues of professional and academic importance. The journal aims to enhance theory, research and clinical practice in adolescent psychology, psychiatry, sociology, social work, education and allied disciplines through the publication of papers concerned with the nature of adolescent development, interventions to promote successful functioning during adolescence, and the management and treatment of disorders occurring during adolescence. Its goal is to provide a forum for all who are concerned with the nature of adolescence, whether they are teaching, carrying out research, providing a service, or offering treatment, guidance or counseling. It is recognized that a variety of professions have an important contribution to make in furthering knowledge of adolescence, and the Editors welcome relevant contributions from all disciplinary areas. For the purposes of the *Journal*, adolescence is considered to be the developmental period between childhood and the attainment of adult status within a person's community and culture. The *Journal* publishes articles developed from a broad array of theoretical frameworks and diverse methodologies, including both quantitative and qualitative techniques. While the majority of the articles published in the Journal are reports of

562

empirical research studies, the *Journal* also publishes reviews of the literature, when such reviews provide the basis for extending knowledge in the field.

Submission to the Journal

Where possible, manuscripts should be submitted to the journal online, at the website http://ees.elsevier.com/yjado, where you will be guided through the process. Please submit the original source files, and not PDF files. You will be asked to select an editor from the list and a category designation for your manuscripts (article, brief report, book review etc.) Please send any queries about the submission process, your manuscript's status or journal procedures to the Editorial Office at **Joa@elsevier.com**. The system will generate an electronic (PDF) proof of manuscripts, which will be used for reviewing. All correspondence, including the editor's decision and request for revisions, will be by e-mail.

If online submission is not possible, manuscripts can be submitted by sending the source files on disk together with a matching hard copy (both text and figures and tables) by registered mail to either of the editors. (Please note that this is not the preferred way of submission and could cause a delay in publication of the article.)

Manuscripts (except those originating in North America) should be submitted to: *The Journal of Adolescence*, S&T Editorial Services, Elsevier Ltd, Stover Court, Bampfylde Street, Exeter, EX1 2AH; Email: **joa@elsevier.com**; Phone: +44 (0) 1392 285825

Manuscripts originating in North America should be submitted to: Dr. Alan Waterman, *Journal of Adolescence*, Department of Psychology, The College of New Jersey, PO Box 7718, Ewing, NJ 08628-0718, U.S.A.; Email: **water@tcnj.edu**

Book reviews and books for review should be submitted to either: Dr. Rachel Bromnick, Department of Psychology, University of Lincolnshire and Humberside, Brayford Pool, Lincoln LN6 7TS, UK or Dr. John Paul McKinney, 509 St. Andrew's Circle, Statesboro, GA 30458-3844, USA

Submissions should be accompanied by a covering letter or email. Revised submissions should be accompanied by a letter or email detailing the changes that have been made.

Submission of a manuscript implies that the work described has not been published previously (except in the form of an abstract or academic thesis), that it is not under consideration for publication elsewhere, that its publication is approved by all authors and tacitly or explicitly by the responsible authorities where the work was carried out, and that, if accepted, it will not be published elsewhere in the same form, in English or in any other language, without the written consent of the Publisher.

Electronic format requirements for accepted articles. An electronic version of the text should be submitted together with the final hardcopy of the manuscript. We accept most word processing formats, but Word, WordPerfect or LaTeX is preferred. The electronic version must match the hardcopy exactly. Always keep a backup copy of the electronic file for reference and safety. Label storage media with your name, journal title, and software used. Save your files using the default extension of the program used. No changes to the accepted version are permissible without the explicit approval of the Editor. Electronic files can be stored on 3? inch diskette, ZIP-disk or CD (either PC or Macintosh).

Presentation of manuscript. Please write your text in English (American or British usage is accepted, but not a mixture of these). Articles should not exceed 5000 words in length. Italics are not to be used for expressions of Latin origin, for example, in vivo, et al., per se. Use decimal points (not commas); use a space for thousands (10 000 and above).

Print the entire manuscript on one side of the paper only, using double spacing and wide (3 cm) margins. (Avoid full justification, i.e., do not use a constant right-hand margin.) Ensure that each new paragraph is clearly indicated. Present tables and figure legends on separate pages at the end of the manuscript. If possible, consult a recent issue of the journal to become familiar with layout and conventions. Number all pages consecutively.

Provide the following data on the title page (in the order given).

Title. Concise and informative. Titles are often used in information-retrieval systems. Avoid abbreviations and formulae where possible.

Author names and affiliations. Where the family name may be ambiguous (e.g., a double name), please indicate this clearly. Present the authors' affiliation addresses (where the actual work was done) below the names. Indicate all affiliations with a lower-case superscript letter immediately after the author's name and in front of the appropriate address. Provide the full postal address of each affiliation, including the country name, and, if available, the e-mail address of each author.

Corresponding author. Clearly indicate who is willing to handle correspondence at all stages of refereeing and publication, also post-publication. *Ensure that telephone and fax numbers (with country and area code) are provided in addition to the e-mail address and the complete postal address.*

Present/permanent address. If an author has moved since the work described in the article was done, or was visiting at the time, a 'Present address' (or 'Permanent address') may be indicated as a footnote to that author's name. The address at which the author actually did the work must be retained as the main, affiliation address. Superscript Arabic numerals are used for such footnotes.

Abstract. A concise and factual abstract is required (maximum length 150 words). The abstract should state briefly the purpose of the research, the principal results and major conclusions. An abstract is often presented separate from the article, so it must be able to stand alone. References should therefore be avoided, but if essential, they must be cited in full, without reference to the reference list.

Abbreviations. Define abbreviations that are not standard in this field at their first occurrence in the article: in the abstract but also in the main text after it. Ensure consistency of abbreviations throughout the article.

564

Keywords. It is recommended that you provide a list of keywords immediately following the abstract, which will be used for indexing purposes.

N.B. Acknowledgements. Collate acknowledgements in a separate section at the end of the article and do **not**, therefore, include them on the title page, as a footnote to the title or otherwise.

Brief Reports. The Editors will consider Brief Reports of between 1000 and 1500 words (three to five typewritten pages). This format should be used for reports of findings from the early stages of a program of research, replications (and failures to replicate) previously reported findings, results of studies with sampling or methodological problems that have yielded findings of sufficient interest to warrant publication, results of well designed studies in which important theoretical propositions have not been confirmed, case studies of individual adolescents in treatment, and creative theoretical contributions that have yet to be studied empirically. The title of the Brief Report should start with the words: "Brief Report:" A footnote should be included if a full-length report is available upon request from the author(s).

Arrangement of the article
Subdivision of the article. Divide your article into clearly defined sections. Any subsection may be given a brief heading. Each heading should appear on its own separate line.

Appendices. If there is more than one appendix, they should be identified as A, B, etc. Formulae and equations in appendices should be given separate numbering: (Eq. A.1), (Eq. A.2), etc.; in a subsequent appendix, (Eq. B.1) and so forth.

Acknowledgements. Place acknowledgements, including information on grants received, before the references, in a separate section, and not as a footnote on the title page.

Figure legends, tables, figures, schemes. Present these, in this order, at the end of the article. They are described in more detail below. High-resolution graphics files must always be provided separate from the main text file (see Preparation of illustrations).

Specific remarks
Tables. Number tables consecutively in accordance with their appearance in the text. Place footnotes to tables below the table body and indicate them with superscript lowercase letters. Avoid vertical rules. Be sparing in the use of tables and ensure that the data presented in tables do not duplicate results described elsewhere in the article.

Preparation of supplementary data. Elsevier now accepts electronic supplementary material to support and enhance your scientific research. Supplementary files offer the author additional possibilities to publish supporting applications, movies, animation sequences, high-resolution images, background datasets, sound clips and more. Supplementary files supplied will be published online alongside the electronic version of your article in Elsevier web products, including ScienceDirect: http://www.sciencedirect.com. In order to ensure that your submitted material is directly usable, please ensure that data is provided in one of our recommended file formats. Authors should submit the material in electronic format together with the article and supply a concise and descriptive caption for each file. For more detailed instructions please visit our Author Gateway at http://authors.elsevier.com. Files can be stored on 3? inch diskette, ZIP-disk or CD (either PC or Macintosh).

References

Responsibility for the accuracy of bibliographic citations lies entirely with the authors.

Citations in the text. Please ensure that every reference cited in the text is also present in the reference list (and vice versa). Any references cited in the abstract must be given in full. Unpublished results and personal communications should not be in the reference list, but may be mentioned in the text. Citation of a reference as 'in press' implies that the item has been accepted for publication.

Citing and listing of web references. As a minimum, the full URL should be given. Any further information, if known (author names, dates, reference to a source publication, etc.), should also be given. Web references can be listed separately (e.g., after the reference list) under a different heading if desired, or can be included in the reference list.

Citations should follow the referencing style used by the American Psychological Association. You are referred to the *Publication Manual of the American Psychological Association*, Fifth Edition, ISBN 1-55798-790-4, copies of which may be ordered from APA Order Dept., P.O.B. 2710, Hyattsville, MD 20784, USA or APA, 3 Henrietta Street, London, WC3E 8LU, UK. or http://www.apa.org/books/4200061.html Details concerning this referencing style can also be found at http://humanities.byu.edu/linguistics/Henrichsen/APA/APA01.html.

References should be arranged first alphabetically and then further sorted chronologically if necessary. More than one reference from the same author(s) in the same year must be identified by the letters "a", "b", "c", etc., placed after the year of publication.

Examples

Reference to a journal publication. Van der Geer, J., Hanraads, J. A. J., & Lupton R. A. (2000). The art of writing a scientific article. Journal of Scientific Communications, 163, 51-59.
Reference to a book. Strunk, W., Jr., & White, E. B. (1979). The elements of style. (3rd ed.). New York: Macmillan, (Chapter 4).

Reference to a chapter in an edited book. Mettam, G. R., & Adams, L. B. (1994). How to prepare an electronic version of your article. In B. S. Jones, & R. Z. Smith (Eds.), Introduction to the electronic age (pp. 281-304). New York: E-Publishing Inc.

Note that journal names are not to be abbreviated.

Preparation of illustrations Submitting your artwork in an electronic format helps us to produce your work to the best possible standards, ensuring accuracy, clarity and a high level of detail. Always supply high-quality printouts of your artwork, in case conversion of the electronic artwork is problematic. Save text in illustrations as "graphics" or enclose the font. Only use the following fonts in your illustrations: Arial, Courier, Helvetica, Times, Symbol. Number the illustrations according to their sequence in the text. Use a logical naming

566

convention for your artwork files, and supply a separate listing of the files and the software used. Provide all illustrations as separate files and as hardcopy printouts on separate sheets. Provide captions to illustrations separately. Produce images near to the desired size of the printed version. A detailed guide on electronic artwork is available on our website: http://authors.elsevier.com/artwork.You are urged to visit this site; some excerpts from the detailed information are given here.

Formats Regardless of the application used, when your electronic artwork is finalised, please "save as" or convert the images to one of the following formats (Note the resolution requirements for line drawings, halftones, and line/halftone combinations given below.):

- EPS: Vector drawings. Embed the font or save the text as "graphics".
- TIFF: Colour or greyscale photographs (halftones): always use a minimum of 300 dpi.
- TIFF: Bitmapped line drawings: use a minimum of 1000 dpi.
- TIFF: Combinations bitmapped line/half-tone (colour or greyscale): a minimum of 500 dpi is required.
- DOC, XLS or PPT: If your electronic artwork is created in any of these Microsoft Office applications please supply "as is".

Line drawings. Supply high-quality printouts on white paper produced with black ink. The lettering and symbols, as well as other details, should have proportionate dimensions, so as not to become illegible or unclear after possible reduction; in general, the figures should be designed for a reduction factor of two to three. The degree of reduction will be determined by the Publisher. Illustrations will not be enlarged. Consider the page format of the journal when designing the illustrations. Photocopies are not suitable for reproduction. Do not use any type of shading on computer-generated illustrations.

Photographs. (halftones) Please supply original photographs for reproduction, printed on glossy paper, very sharp and with good contrast. Remove non-essential areas of a photograph. Do not mount photographs unless they form part of a composite figure. Where necessary, insert a scale bar in the illustration (not below it), as opposed to giving a magnification factor in the legend.

Note that photocopies of photographs are not acceptable.

Copyright. Authors submitting a manuscript do so on the understanding that if it is accepted for publication, copyright of the article, including the right to reproduce the article in all forms and media, shall be assigned exclusively to The Association for Professional in Services for Adolescents. The written consent of the publisher must be obtained if any article is to be published elsewhere in any language. It is the policy of the publisher that authors need not obtain permission in the following cases: (1) to use their original figures or tables in their future work; (2) to make copies of their papers for use in their classroom teaching; and (3) to include their papers as part of their dissertation.

Proofs. When your manuscript is received by the Publisher it is considered to be in its final form. Proofs are not to be regarded as 'drafts'. One set of page proofs will be sent to the corresponding author, to be checked for typesetting/editing. No changes in, or additions to, the accepted (and subsequently edited) manuscript will be allowed at this stage. Proofreading is solely your responsibility. The Publisher reserves the right to proceed with publication if corrections are not communicated. Return corrections within 3 days of receipt of the proofs. Should there be no corrections, please confirm this.

Offprints. Twenty-five offprints will be supplied free of charge. Additional offprints and copies of the issue can be ordered at a specially reduced rate using the order form sent to the corresponding author after the manuscript has been accepted. Orders for reprints (produced after publication of an article) will incur a 50% surcharge.

Journal of Adolescent Research

ADDRESS FOR SUBMISSION:

Jeffrey Jensen Arnett, Editor
Journal of Adolescent Research
ELECTRONIC SUBMISSION ONLY
4409 Van Buren St.
University Park, MD 20782
Phone: 301-927-2886
Fax: 301-927-2886
E-Mail: arnett@jeffreyarnett.com
Web: www.sagepub.com
Address May Change:

PUBLICATION GUIDELINES:

Manuscript Length: 20-30 pages
Copies Required: Electronic
Computer Submission: Yes Email
Format: MS Word or WordPerfect
Fees to Review: 0.00 US$

Manuscript Style:
    American Psychological Association

CIRCULATION DATA:

Reader: Academics
Frequency of Issue: Bi-Monthly
Copies per Issue: 1,001 - 2,000
Sponsor/Publisher: Sage Publications, Inc.
Subscribe Price: 104.00 US$ Individual
    456.00 US$ Institution
    73.00 Pounds Indv., 319 Pounds Inst.

REVIEW INFORMATION:

Type of Review: Blind Review
No. of External Reviewers: 3
No. of In House Reviewers: 0
Acceptance Rate: 11-20%
Time to Review: 3 Months
Reviewers Comments: Yes
Invited Articles: 0-5%
Fees to Publish: 0.00 US$

MANUSCRIPT TOPICS:
Adolescent Psychology; Developmental Psychology; Educational Psychology; Family Studies; Personality; Psychiatry; Public Health; Social Psychology; Sociology

MANUSCRIPT GUIDELINES/COMMENTS:

About the Journal
The *Journal of Adolescent Research* is the primary source for the latest analysis on how adolescents and emerging adults develop, behave, and are influenced by societal and cultural factors from age 10 to 25.

Comprehensive Coverage
The *Journal of Adolescent Research* publishes empirical research and theoretical papers on all aspects of adolescent and emerging adult development. Each issue explores a range of diverse and relevant topics, such as: Sexual Behaviour, Drug and Alcohol Abuse, Affect and Emotion, Adolescent Medicine, Community and Environmental Contexts, Delinquency, Identity Formation, Rites of Passage, Parenting Styles, Coping Styles.

Interdisciplinary Views

The *Journal of Adolescent Research* uses an interdisciplinary approach to broaden the perspective on adolescent development. The editorial board and reviewers for the journal represent a wide range of disciplines, providing a unique and broad perspective on the nature of adolescent development. *JAR* brings peer-reviewed articles from a variety of fields, including: psychology, sociology, education, public health, family studies, criminology, social work, communication, counseling, health.

Submission Guidleines

The *Journal of Adolescent Research* publishes articles that increase understanding of development during adolescence and emerging adulthood. The emphasis of the journal is on publishing papers that meet at least one of the following criteria:

1. Combine quantitative and qualitative data.
2. Take a systematic qualitative or ethnographic approach.
3. Use an original and creative methodological approach.
4. Address an important but understudied topic. (This could include papers with strictly quantitative data).
5. Present new theoretical or conceptual ideas.

In addition, all articles must show an awareness of the cultural context of the research questions asked, the population studied, and the results of the study.

The journal accepts **electronic submissions only**. Manuscripts should be submitted via e-mail (in Word or Word Perfect format) to Jeffrey Jensen Arnett, Editor, *Journal Of Adolescent Research*, at **arnett@jeffreyarnett.com**. In general, manuscripts should not exceed 25 typed, double-spaced pages, including references, tables, and figures. Figures and tables should be included as part of the manuscript, not as separate files. Manuscripts should include an abstract of no more than 120 words following the title page. Five to six keywords, to be used in archival retrieval systems, should be indicated on the title page. The title page should also include contact information for the first author, including affiliation, mailing address, e-mail address, and phone and fax numbers. Text and references must conform to the *Publication Manual of the American Psychological Association* (Fourth Edition). Permission for reprint of the copyrighted material is the responsibility of the author. All artwork must be camera ready. Authors should include their name, affiliation, mailing address, and telephone number. Submission of a manuscript implies commitment to publish in the journal. Authors submitting manuscripts to the journal should not simultaneously submit them to another journal, nor should manuscripts have been published elsewhere in substantially similar form or with substantially similar content. Authors in doubt about what constitutes prior publication should consult the editor. Each manuscript should include an abstract.

Journal of Aging and Health

ADDRESS FOR SUBMISSION:

Kyriakos S. Markides, Editor
Journal of Aging and Health
University of Texas Medical Branch
Center on Ageing
Campus Mail Route 1153
Galveston, TX 77555-1153
USA
Phone: 409-772-2551
Fax: 409-772-2573
E-Mail: kmarkide@utmb.edu
Web: www.sagepub.com
Address May Change:

CIRCULATION DATA:

Reader: Academics
Frequency of Issue: Quarterly
Copies per Issue: 1,001 - 2,000
Sponsor/Publisher: Sage Publications, Inc.
Subscribe Price:

PUBLICATION GUIDELINES:

Manuscript Length: 21-25
Copies Required: Four
Computer Submission: No
Format: N/A
Fees to Review: 0.00 US$

Manuscript Style:
American Psychological Association

REVIEW INFORMATION:

Type of Review: Blind Review
No. of External Reviewers: 2
No. of In House Reviewers: 0
Acceptance Rate: 21-30%
Time to Review: 1 - 2 Months
Reviewers Comments: No Reply
Invited Articles: 0-5%
Fees to Publish: 0.00 US$

MANUSCRIPT TOPICS:
Gerontology

MANUSCRIPT GUIDELINES/COMMENTS:

Aims and Scope
The *Journal of Aging and Health* is an interdisciplinary forum for the presentation of research findings and scholarly exchange in the area of aging and health. Manuscripts are sought that deal with social and behavioral factors related to health and aging. Disciplines represented include the behavioral and social sciences, public health, epidemiology, demography, health services research, nursing, social work, medicine, and related disciplines. Although preference is given to manuscripts presenting the findings of original research, review and methodological pieces will also be considered.

Submission Manuscript Guidelines
Manuscripts should be prepared in accordance with the 4th edition of the *Publication Manual of the American Psychological Association*. Double space all manuscripts, including references, notes, abstracts, quotations, and tables, on 8 ½ x 11 paper. The title page should

include all authors' names and affiliations and highest professional degrees, the corresponding author's address and telephone number, and a brief running headline. Place acknowledgments on a separate page under the heading AUTHOR'S NOTE. This note should also include information on where to write to obtain reprints. The title page should be followed by an abstract of 100 to 150 words. On the abstract page include 3 to 5 words or short phrases for indexing purposes. The abstract page as well as the first page of the text should include the manuscript's title without the authors' names to facilitate blind review. Tables and references should follow APA style and be double spaced throughout. Ordinarily manuscripts will not exceed 30 pages (double-spaced) including tables, figures and references. Authors of accepted manuscripts will be asked to supply camera-ready figures. Supply four (4) copies of each manuscript and a copy of the final manuscript on an IBM-compatible disk to Kyriakos S. Markides, Ph.D., Editor, Journal of Aging and Health, Center on Ageing, University of Texas Medical Branch, Campus Mail Route 1153, Galveston, TX 77555-1153. Submission of a manuscript implies commitment to publish in the journal. Authors submitting manuscripts to the journal should not simultaneously submit them to another journal, nor should manuscripts have been published elsewhere in substantially similar form or with substantially similar content Authors in doubt about what constitutes prior publication should consult the editor.

Journal of Analytical Psychology

ADDRESS FOR SUBMISSION:

Pramila Bennett, Managing Editor
Journal of Analytical Psychology
1 Daleham Gardens
London, NW3 5BY
UK
Phone: +44-20-7794-3640
Fax: +44-20-7431-1495
E-Mail: journal.jap@btconnect.com
Web: jungian_analysis.org
Address May Change:

PUBLICATION GUIDELINES:

Manuscript Length: 8,000 words
Copies Required: Four
Computer Submission: Yes
Format: MS Word
Fees to Review: 0.00 US$

Manuscript Style:
   See Manuscript Guidelines

CIRCULATION DATA:

Reader: Academics, Practitioners, Trainees
Frequency of Issue: 5 Times/Year
Copies per Issue: 1,800-2,000
Sponsor/Publisher: The Society of
   Analytical Psychology / Blackwell
   Publishing, Oxford UK
Subscribe Price: 136.00 US$ Individual
   408.00 US$ Institution
   95.00 US$ IAAP Mem / $50 Trainee
   Mem

REVIEW INFORMATION:

Type of Review: Blind Review
No. of External Reviewers: 2+
No. of In House Reviewers: 2
Acceptance Rate: 65%
Time to Review: 4 - 6 Months
Reviewers Comments: Yes
Invited Articles: 0-5%
Fees to Publish: 0.00 US$

MANUSCRIPT TOPICS:
Adolescent Psychology; Child Psychology; History of Psychology; Neuropsychology; Personality; Psychiatry; Psychobiology; Psychopathology; Social Psychology

MANUSCRIPT GUIDELINES/COMMENTS:

Topics Include. Analytical Psychology; Attachment Theory; Child Analysis; History of Analytical Psychology and Psychoanalysis; Neurophysiology; Psychoanalysis

Co-Editors-in-Chief
Dr. Jean Knox, UK
Fax: +44 (0) 1865 515550
Email: **jm.knox@btinternet.com**

Dr. Joseph Cambray, US
Fax: +1 401 455 3741
Email: **cambrayj@ids.net**

Blackwell Publishing: www.blackwellpublishing.com/journal

About the Journal
The *Journal of Analytical Psychology* was launched in 1955 by a small and enthusiastic group of members of the Society of Analytical Psychology in London under the leadership and

editorship of Dr Michael Fordham. It is now the foremost international journal in the English language to focus on the clinical practice of Jungian analysis. With its clinical emphasis it has a special appeal for practitioners and those with clinical experience of analysis, but its readership also includes many scholars, historians, and students of analytical psychology.

The *Journal* continues to be enriched by its international connections. The addition of an American editor to join the UK team in 1990, and the developing rapprochement with the European societies, have brought the *Journal* closer to other Jungian groups, while the highly successful international conferences organized by the *Journal* in 1996, 1997, 1999, 2001 and 2003, in the US, Mexico and the Czech Republic have promoted a dialogue with the psychoanalytic community which is valued by both sides. A recent conference was held in Charleston, South Carolina in April 2003. The 50th Anniversary of Publication Conference is taking place in Oxford, England, from the 7th to the 10th April 2005. Further information can be obtained from the *Journal* email address above.

The *Journal* is renowned for its exploration of the relationship between analytical psychology and psychoanalysis. It also addresses issues on the leading edge of philosophy, science, religion, and an understanding of the arts. The articles demonstrate the continuing relevance and vitality of Jungian thought.

NOTES FOR CONTRIBUTORS
Address for correspondence
The Editors
The Journal of Analytical Psychology
1 Daleham Gardens, London NW3 5BY, UK

Submissions
Four copies of articles should be sent, typed in double-spacing and not more than 8,000 words in length, including footnotes and references. Articles should be accompanied by a word count, an abstract of not more than 200 words and 6 to 8 key words at the beginning of the paper, indicating the major argument of the article and its significance as an addition to existing knowledge or analysis. Articles should be original contributions and should not be submitted to another publication simultaneously. Authors of articles already published in foreign journals should communicate with the Editors before sending manuscripts. If the paper is accepted, the author will be required to supply it on disk, identical to the paper version. A brief autobiographical note containing relevant details about the author should be included on a separate sheet of paper. Manuscripts will not be returned.

Correspondence
The *Journal* welcomes responses to its published articles and aims to stimulate dialogue through correspondence. For brief communications, an abstract is not required.

Bibliographical references
All references cited should be listed alphabetically at the end of the article, using the house style. For this, please refer to a copy of the *Journal*.

Copyright
Copyright in all material published in the *Journal* is held by the Society. Authors will be required to sign a copyright assignment form.

It is the author's responsibility to obtain clearance for use of any material requiring copyright permission and to pay any fee which may be due. This applies to all verse quotations regardless of length, all prose quotations which exceed the fair dealing limits (i.e. more than 200 words for any one extract and more than 800 words for extracts from any one source), and for photographs and illustrations in copyright.

Confidentiality
Authors are warned to avoid any comment that might be deemed libelous or in breach of confidentiality.

Further clarifications on how to prepare manuscripts for submission to the *Journal* can be obtained from the above address or Tel: +44 (0) 207 794 3640; Fax: +44 (0) 207 431 1495 Email: **journal.jap@btconnect.com**

Authors are strongly advised to make use of this guidance, and also, if possible, to examine a Journal issue before beginning the final draft of their manuscript. Too great a departure from *Journal* requirements will necessitate resubmission in a retyped print-out in accordance with *Journal* style.

Journal of Applied Behavior Analysis

ADDRESS FOR SUBMISSION:

Patrick C. Friman, Editor
Journal of Applied Behavior Analysis
Clinical Services and Research
Youthcare Building
13603 Flanagan Blvd.
Boys Town, NE 68010
USA
Phone: 402-498-3353
Fax: 402-498-3375
E-Mail: frimanp@boystown.org
Web: seab.envmed.rochester.edu/jaba/
Address May Change:

CIRCULATION DATA:

Reader: Academics, Practitioners
Frequency of Issue: Quarterly
Copies per Issue: 3,001 - 4,000
Sponsor/Publisher:
Subscribe Price: 28.00 US$ Individual
    75.00 US$ Institution
    14.00 US$ Student

PUBLICATION GUIDELINES:

Manuscript Length: No Reply
Copies Required: Five
Computer Submission: Yes Disk
Format:
Fees to Review: 0.00 US$

Manuscript Style:
    American Psychological Association

REVIEW INFORMATION:

Type of Review: Blind Review
No. of External Reviewers: 3+
No. of In House Reviewers: 1
Acceptance Rate: 21-30%
Time to Review: Over 6 Months
Reviewers Comments: No Reply
Invited Articles: 0-5%
Fees to Publish: 0.00 US$

MANUSCRIPT TOPICS:
Behavior Analysis; Behavior Modification; Group Dynamics; Social Psychology

MANUSCRIPT GUIDELINES/COMMENTS:

The *Journal of Applied Behavior Analysis* is primarily for the original publication of reports of experimental research involving applications of the experimental analysis of behavior to problems of social importance. It will also publish technical articles relevant to such research and discussion of issues arising from behavioral applications. The *Journal* is published quarterly by the Society for the Experimental Analysis of Behavior, Inc., at Lawrence, Kansas.

PREPARATION OF MANUSCRIPTS FOR *JABA*
Masked Review
JABA will now routinely use masked review of manuscripts. Instructions for preparation of manuscripts for masked review appear in the *APA Publication Manual*. (They are on page 305 of the Fourth Edition.)

Authors are responsible for concealing their identities in manuscripts by placing the author's note on the manuscript's title page, which will be removed prior to sending the manuscript out for review. Authors who do not want a masked review should place the author's note in the body of the manuscript.

Types of Articles

Manuscripts submitted to *JABA* must be prepared according to the style described in the *Publication Manual of the American Psychological Association* (4th ed.). Manuscripts will be classified into the following categories for purposes of review:

Research Articles

The primary focus of *JABA* continues to be Research Articles of applied social importance. Both individual and group designs are appropriate, but in intervention studies, data on individual variation should be included. Further, the clinical significance of the effect on individuals should be discussed. In most cases, behavioral measures will be critical for acceptance, but in some instances, self-reports (e.g., headaches) will be acceptable, especially when such studies bear on issues relevant to types of interventions that might be used in applied behavior analysis.

Research Reports

Innovative pilot work, replications, controlled case studies, and studies that are primarily analogue in nature will be considered for publication as Research Reports. Because direct or systematic replication of research findings, as well as new areas of application having heuristic value, are crucial to the development of a field, such reports warrant special submission and review criteria.

Reports will undergo expedited peer review and will be judged according to the following criteria: (a) the subject matter has applied significance, (b) the information necessary to replicate the procedures is contained in the report or is readily available from the author, and (c) the data collection and analysis permit reasonable conclusions about the phenomenon. Less emphasis will be placed on methodological rigor for innovations (which contribute to our understanding of human behavior by encouraging further research) than for replications (particularly failures to replicate, which require demonstrating alternative controlling variables.

Studies appropriate as Reports will require less detailed descriptions of background, methodology, or findings than Research Articles, and must not exceed 100 typed lines with a 1/2 page table or figure. The author must agree not to publish an extended version of the Report in another journal.

Technical Articles

Manuscripts contributing primarily to research methodology, data analysis, or instrumentation may be accepted as Technical Articles. Such articles should report a complete experiment demonstrating a causal relationship. For cases in which experimental demonstration is not feasible, authors are expected to provide other suitable data or documentation supporting the utility of the methods, technique, or apparatus.

Technical Articles will be judged according to the following criteria: (a) the issue is of general importance to the future conduct of applied research, (b) the conclusions are unambiguous and are based on either sound experimentation or thorough analysis of current research practice, (c) the information necessary for implementation is contained in the report or is readily available from the author, and (d) publication of the manuscript is likely to produce significant improvement in applied behavior analysis methodology.

Discussion and Review Articles

Manuscripts surveying and critically evaluating particular areas of research or issues in applied behavior analysis may be accepted as Discussion or Review Articles. Such papers will be sent to several reviewers who will be asked whether they find the manuscript helpful in conducting, analyzing, or interpreting research in the field of applied behavior analysis. Accepted manuscripts will often be published with an accompanying commentary, which will be *solicited* by the Editor.

Book Reviews

Titles of books we receive, determined by the Editor to be of interest to some segment of our *JABA* readership, will be published occasionally. Anyone wishing to prepare a short review of a particular book should write to the editorial office indicating the book title and why he or she would be a particularly qualified reviewer. Reviews of approximately 500 to 700 words will be judged according to the following criteria: (a) the review is written in an interesting and engaging style, and (b) the evaluation of the book is determined to be fair, justified, and based on the book's purpose.

Comments from *JABA* Readers

Informal articles or letters to the Editor addressing topics deemed of general interest to *JABA* readers will be considered for publication as Comments from *JABA* Readers. Such "comments" can focus on conceptual and methodological issues in behavioral research or can suggest new lines of research, identify new sources of funding, discuss specific tools of the trade for researchers or practitioners, present current or historical issues and trivia, or address issues raised in previously published articles. Articles will typically be reviewed by the Editor and one Associate Editor. If the article is considered appropriate, it will be printed with only minor editing. Excerpts from reviewers' comments may occasionally be published as well. The final decision to accept or reject will rest with the Editor.

Manuscript Preparation Checklist

Submitted manuscripts must contain the following:

- Five high-quality copies of the entire manuscript.
- Copies of figures (with figure captions on a separate page) and tables for each manuscript being submitted; do not send letter-press, glossy prints, photographs, or original artwork. Figures should be numbered in pencil on the back and prepared according to the guidelines given on page 514 of Volume 32, Number 4 (Winter 2000) issue of *JABA*.
- A letter to the Editor containing the following:
  A. A request for review and possible publication of the manuscript.
  B. A statement indicating the manuscript has not been previously published and has not been nor will be submitted elsewhere during the *JABA* review process.
  C. A classification of article into type (see above, "Types of Articles").

D. The corresponding author's business address and telephone number as well as any upcoming address change. (This individual will receive copies of the editorial correspondence from the Editor and Associate Editor.)

- A title page including the following:
  A. The title of the paper.
  B. The first and surname of all authors.
  C. The affiliations of each author during the time the research was conducted. The names of the authors should not be listed on subsequent pages. (Refer to the *APA Manual* for appropriate affiliation listings for the title page and author notes.)
  D. The name, address, and telephone number of the corresponding author.

Five photocopies of each manuscript, prepared according to the format requirements of the *Publication Manual of the American Psychological Association*, Fourth Edition, should be submitted to:

Wayne Fisher, Editor
Marcus Institute
1920 Briarcliff Rd.
Atlanta, GA 30329.
Tel: (404) 419-4454
E-mail: **JABA@Marcus.ORG**

Questions regarding manuscript submission requirements or *Journal* reviewing practices are welcome.

Copyright and Permission Policy
Should you place your manuscript on your Web site? Please consult the American Psychological Association policy on Posting Articles on the Internet.

The Society for the Experimental Analysis of Behavior, Inc. adheres to the policy of the American Psychological Association in granting permission to reproduce its copyrighted material: Authors must secure from the Society and from the author of reproduced material written permission to reproduce a journal article in full or journal text of more than 500 words.

The Society typically grants permission contingent upon like permission of the author, inclusion of the Society copyright notice on the first page of the reproduced material, and payment of a fee of $20 per page. Permission from the Society and fees are waived for authors who wish to reproduce a single table or figure from a journal, provided the author's permission is obtained and full credit is given to the Society as copyright holder and to the author through a complete citation. (Requestors requiring written permission for commercial use of a single table or figure will be assessed a $20 service fee.)

Permission and fees are waived for authors who wish to reproduce their own material for personal use; fees only are waived for authors who wish to use more than a single table or figure of their own material commercially. Permission and fees are waived for library reserve use by instructors and educational institutions.

Requests for permission to reprint material appearing in JEAB should be sent to Devonia Stein, Business Manager, JEAB, Department of Psychology, Indiana University, Bloomington, IN 47405-1301. Requests concerning *JABA* should be addressed to Mary Louise Wright, Business Manager, JABA, Department of Human Development, University of Kansas, Lawrence, KS 66045-2133.

Journal of Applied Biobehavioral Research

ADDRESS FOR SUBMISSION:

Andrew Baum, Editor
Journal of Applied Biobehavioral Research
University of Pittsburgh Cancer Inst.
University of Pittsburgh Medical Center
Behavioral Medicine and Oncology
3600 Forbes Ave., Ste 405, Iroquois Bldg
Pittsburgh, PA 15213
USA
Phone: 412-647-4812
Fax: 412-647-1936
E-Mail: racantm@upmc.edu
Web: www.bellpub.com
Address May Change:

PUBLICATION GUIDELINES:

Manuscript Length: 30-40
Copies Required: Four
Computer Submission: Yes
Format: MS Word
Fees to Review: 0.00 US$

Manuscript Style:
    American Psychological Association

CIRCULATION DATA:

Reader: Academics
Frequency of Issue: Quarterly
Copies per Issue: More than 25,000
Sponsor/Publisher: Bellwether Publishing
Subscribe Price: 25.00 US$ Individual
    50.00 US$ Institution

REVIEW INFORMATION:

Type of Review: Blind Review
No. of External Reviewers: 2
No. of In House Reviewers: 0
Acceptance Rate: 40%
Time to Review: 2 - 3 Months
Reviewers Comments: Yes
Invited Articles: 0-5%
Fees to Publish: 0.00 US$

MANUSCRIPT TOPICS:
Abnormal Psychology; Adolescent Psychology; Alcoholism & Drug Addiction; Behavior
Modification; Experimental Psychology; Gerontology; Learning & Conditioning;
Neuropsychology; Personality; Physiological Psychology; Psychiatry; Psychobiology;
Psychological Testing; Research Methods & Statistics; Sensation & Perception; Social
Psychology; Thinking & Cognition

MANUSCRIPT GUIDELINES/COMMENTS:

Introduction
Semi-annual publication devoted to applications of experimental studies in psychology to
health hazards and related social issues (e.g., laboratory and field research in such areas as
health, population growth, crowding, eating or sleep disorders, pain, violence, poverty,
environmental stress, exercise, cross-cultural differences and gender differences in behavioral
and biological response to stimuli, drug abuse and addiction, workplace safety and health,
behavioral medicine, and environmental psychology). Published since 1993.

Information for Authors

The *Journal of Applied Biobehavioral Research* will disseminate findings of behavioral science research which have applications to current problems of society. By publishing relevant research and emphasizing the excellence of experimental design, as well as potential applicability of experimental results, the journal intends to bridge the theoretical and applied areas of biobehavioral research. The *Journal of Applied Biobehavioral Research* will serve as a means of communication among scientists, as well as between researchers and those engaged in the task of solving social and biomedical problems.

Preference is given to manuscripts reporting laboratory and field research in such areas as health, population growth, crowding, eating or sleep disorders, pain, violence, poverty, environmental stress, exercise, cross-cultural differences and gender differences in behavioral and biological response to stimuli, drug abuse and addiction, workplace safety and health, behavioral medicine, and environmental psychology. Reports of both laboratory and field research are accepted as are animal and human studies, meta-analyses, and occasional reviews. Suggestions for application of research findings should be included. Theoretical papers are acceptable in limited numbers. Papers of theoretical scope should whenever possible include some research data. Reviews of the pertinent literature should be made with applicability in mind. The journal will publish reviews of selected books on relevant topic areas.

The *Journal* will provide accelerated review and publication of manuscripts in areas related to behavioral medicine, psychobiology, social psychology, clinical psychology, health psychology, and other areas of behavioral sciences relevant to the interface between behavior and biology. Editorial decisions and reviews will be provided within 6 weeks of receipt of a manuscript and publication will follow within 3 months of acceptance. We will accomplish this by:

- asking authors to limit submission to 15 pages (text) or less,
- asking reviewers to limit their comments and suggestions to major methodological or conceptual problems, data analysis, and overall importance of the findings, and
- making greater use of fax and e-mail capacities in the review process.

By modifying the review process to assure shorter, more timely reviews, and by considering shorter, more focused papers, we intend to provide more timely publication of important work in these growing areas of investigation.

All manuscripts submitted to this journal should follow the style and method of presentation of American Psychological Association journals. Detailed instructions are given in the revised edition of the *Publication Manual of the American Psychological Association*. Manuscripts should be mailed in quadruplicate to Dr. Baum.

Managing Editor: Tina M. Mastro   **Editorial Associate**: Catherine L. McKeon

Books for review consideration should be submitted to Dr. Baum. Written permission must be obtained from the publishers to copy or reprint any table, figure, or part of text.

Journal of Applied Developmental Psychology

ADDRESS FOR SUBMISSION:

Ann McGillicuddy-DeLisi, Editor
Journal of Applied Developmental
    Psychology
c/o Editorial Office Manager
Lafayette College
Department of Psychology
Easton, PA 18042-1781
USA
Phone: 610-330-5859
Fax: 610-330-5349
E-Mail: jadp@lafayette.edu
Web: http://www.sciencedirect.com
Address May Change:

PUBLICATION GUIDELINES:

Manuscript Length: 30+
Copies Required: Three
Computer Submission: Yes Disk, Email
Format: MS Word
Fees to Review: 0.00 US$

Manuscript Style:
    American Psychological Association

CIRCULATION DATA:

Reader: Academics, Counselors
Frequency of Issue: Bi-Monthly
Copies per Issue:
Sponsor/Publisher:
Subscribe Price: 348.00 US$

REVIEW INFORMATION:

Type of Review: Blind Review
No. of External Reviewers: 2
No. of In House Reviewers: 0
Acceptance Rate:
Time to Review: 2 - 3 Months
Reviewers Comments: Yes
Invited Articles: 0-5%
Fees to Publish: 0.00 US$

MANUSCRIPT TOPICS:
Developmental Psychology

MANUSCRIPT GUIDELINES/COMMENTS:

This mission statement for the journal that is based on both historical context of the field when the journal was first founded in 1980 and on an analysis of future directions for applied developmental psychology. The journal itself has grown from the first volume of 4 issues per year totaling 300 pages per volume, to 750 pages per volume over 6 annual issues that now reflect a variety of different formats (e.g., special topic issues) to address increasingly diverse topics. This growth reflects the changes that have occurred in the field of developmental psychology. Students are now trained explicitly in applied developmental psychology in some graduate programs, and many developmental researchers who were trained in basic research currently train the next generation of scholars for careers in applied fields, and engage in research with an applied emphasis themselves. *The Journal of Applied Developmental Psychology* has adapted to these and other changes in the field and, we hope, has taken a leadership role in the evolution of this area of science.

583

Purpose

The purpose of The *Journal of Applied Developmental Psychology* is to disseminate knowledge of developmental phenomena that contribute to practices and policies that can be meaningfully applied to issues of behavioral science. As was the case at its inception, a broad definition of *development* is used and we continue to emphasize the synergistic relationship between research and application. Manuscripts that focus on a variety of developmental processes such as genetic, neuropsychological, perceptual, cognitive, communicative, social, contextual, and cultural variables at any point across the lifespan are welcomed. The journal remains committed to promoting the application of findings presented in published papers to real life social problems of infants, children, adolescents, and adults. The journal is committed to reporting basic and applied science that has broad impact.

Manuscripts Solicited

The journal primarily seeks papers that present theoretically based empirical studies that can have a meaningful impact. However, position papers, critical reviews, and theoretical analyses that can be translated into action are also considered. We seek submissions from a range of contributors who work in a variety of settings around the world. Papers should present well-designed research representing a variety of professional specializations (clinical, cognitive, social, biological, etc.) and applied dimensions (treatment and preventive interventions, social policy, program evaluation, training initiatives, etc.). In addition, the book review editor periodically selects relevant books to be reviewed in the journal.

Purposes and Procedures for Reviews

The identity of authors and of reviewers of the highest caliber will be held confidential in an effort to prevent discrimination based on professional status, gender, age, racial origin, culture, sexual preference, religious belief, language, disability, economic status, or political views. Reviews will be constructive with the goals of fostering the development of new questions and methodologies as well as providing critical feedback to authors.

In order to be responsive to a particular event or a salient social issue, a topic will be occasionally selected for a special article or as the focus of an entire issue. In some cases, special action editors will be appointed in order to ensure that the most relevant and innovative research ideas and methodologies are presented.

Audience

Developmental scientists, including psychologists, social workers, educators, social policy analysts, counselors and clinicians, medical practitioners, practitioner-researchers, academics, research and program evaluators, medical practitioners who work in pediatric and geriatric settings, those who evaluate disabilities, collaborate with schools, design interventions, interpret research findings and translate them into relevant policy, and who work in various capacities in policy and child advocacy organizations will find their needs and interests addressed by *The Journal of Applied Developmental Psychology.*

Summary

The Journal of Applied Developmental Psychology seeks to publish research of the highest quality in a manner that makes the findings and implications of basic research understandable and applicable without sacrificing the complexity of the relationships among involved constructs and variables. The journal will be a vehicle for promoting optimal human development by introducing provocative articles that enable readers to use the knowledge generated by the research to improve policy and practice.

Guide for Authors

The Journal of Applied Developmental Psychology is intended as a forum for communication between researchers and practitioners working in life-span human development fields. Articles describing application of empirical research from social and behavioral disciplines bearing on human development are appropriate. Conceptual and methodological reviews and position papers which facilitate application of research results to such settings as educational, clinical, and the like, are also welcome. Recommendations for intervention or for policy are appropriate when data based.

Review of manuscripts. Authors should remove any identifying information from the manuscript. All necessary information pertaining to identification, title, institutional affiliation, etc. should be on a cover page and only the title of the manuscript should appear on the first page of the manuscript. Authors should guarantee that the manuscript is an original submission and only to this journal.

Authors must follow the guidelines described in the fifth edition (1994) of the *Publication Manual of the American Psychological Association* (1200 Seventeenth St. NW, Washington, DC 20036). Instructions for typing, preparation of tables, figures, and references are all described in the manual. Manuscripts should conform to the conventions specified in the manual with the following advisements:

1. **Preparation of manuscript**. Please double space all material. Manuscripts should be typewritten on 8 ½ x 11 inches bond paper, leaving 1-in. margins on all sides. Number pages consecutively with the title page as page 1, and include a brief abstract from 100 to 150 words as page 2.

2. **Illustrations**. All illustrations and figures are to be submitted in a form suitable for reproduction without retouching or redrawing. The area of the typed page will be 4 ½ x 7 inches, and no illustration can exceed these margins. If photos are to be used, glossies should be submitted, no larger than 8 x 10. Original inked drawings reproduce best, and are preferable, but if these are not available, same-size matte photostats are acceptable. Do not enlarge or reduce art. This will be done by the printer.

3. **Numbering of figures and tables**. All tables and figures must be numbered consecutively using Arabic numbers. Ditto for tables. All tables and figures must be cited in text, and an indication for placement must be given. Every figure should be identified on the back or in a margin with a figure number, the name of the author, and the word "TOP." All figures must have captions, which should be typed on a separate sheet of paper. Each table should be typed on a separate sheet of paper, and should have a brief descriptive title. Tables should be clearly ruled horizontally to indicate levels of column headings. Vertical ruling is discouraged.

4. **Footnotes**. Footnotes should be used sparingly and indicated by consecutive superscript numbers in the text. Material to be footnoted should be typed separately and submitted with the manuscript following the figure legends.

5. **References**. Use the *APA Publication Manual* for the correct listing of references.

6. **Spelling, Terminology, Abbreviations**. Standard United States spelling and punctuation should be used throughout. Follow *Merriam Webster's Collegiate Dictionary* (10th ed.) for spelling and hyphenation of words. Please avoid jargon wherever possible. Avoid abbreviations that are not commonly accepted.

7. **Permissions**. Contributors are responsible for obtaining permission from copyright owners if they use an illustration, table, or lengthy quote from material that has been published elsewhere. Contributors should write to both the publisher and author of material they are seeking permission to reproduce.

8. **Affiliation**. Please include under your name on the title page the institution with which you are connected, your complete mailing address, and credits to any other institution where the work may have been done. Underneath your affiliation, please also include a shortened version of your title that can be used as a running head.

9. **Acceptance**. Upon acceptance, we request an IBM compatible disk, spell checked and stripped of all embedded graphics. Graphics are to be saved in a separate file, an eps, tiff, or ps file. The accuracy of the disk and page proofs is the authors' responsibility.

10. **Offprints**. The only opportunity contributors have to order offprints is when page proofs are returned.

11. **Three copies of ms. should be sent to**: Tanya Allison-Kewley, Office Manager, *Journal of Applied Developmental Psychology* Office, Psychology Department, Oechsle Hall, Lafayette College, Easton, PA 18042-1781 Phone: +1 610-330-5859 Fax: +1 610-330-5349 E-mail: **jadp@lafayette.edu**

Journal of Applied Psychology

ADDRESS FOR SUBMISSION:

Sheldon Zedeck, Editor
Journal of Applied Psychology
University of California
Department of Psychology
Berkeley, CA 94720-1650
USA
Phone: 510-642-5292
Fax: 510-642-7130
E-Mail: zedeck@socrates.berkeley.edu
Web: www.apa.org
Address May Change:

PUBLICATION GUIDELINES:

Manuscript Length: 26-30
Copies Required: Four
Computer Submission: No
Format: N/A
Fees to Review: 0.00 US$

Manuscript Style:
    American Psychological Association

CIRCULATION DATA:

Reader: Academics
Frequency of Issue: Bi-Monthly
Copies per Issue: 3,001 - 4,000
Sponsor/Publisher: American Psychological
    Association
Subscribe Price: 158.00 US$ Individual
    394.00 US$ Institution
    77.00 US$ APA Member

REVIEW INFORMATION:

Type of Review: Blind Review
No. of External Reviewers: 2
No. of In House Reviewers: 0
Acceptance Rate: 11-20%
Time to Review: 2 - 3 Months
Reviewers Comments: Yes
Invited Articles: 0-5%
Fees to Publish: 0.00 US$

MANUSCRIPT TOPICS:

Alcoholism & Drug Addiction; Behavior Modification; Consumer Psychology; Family Counseling & Therapy; Group Dynamics; Industry & Organization; Motivation; Tests, Measurement & Evaluation

MANUSCRIPT GUIDELINES/COMMENTS:

The *Journal of Applied Psychology* is devoted primarily to original investigations that contribute new knowledge and understanding to fields of applied psychology other than clinical and applied experimental or human factors. The journal considers quantitative investigations of interest to psychologists doing research or working in such settings as universities, industry, government, urban affairs, police and correctional systems, health and educational institutions, transportation and defense systems, labor unions, and consumer affairs. A theoretical or review article may be accepted if it represents a special contribution to an applied field. Topics appropriate for the *Journal of Applied Psychology* include personnel selection, performance measurement, training, work motivation, job attitudes, eyewitness accuracy, leadership, drug and alcohol abuse, career development, the conflict between job and family demands, work behavior, work stress, organizational design and interventions, technology, polygraph use, the utility of organizational interventions, consumer buying behavior, and cross-cultural differences in work behavior and attitudes. The specific topics addressed, however, change as a function of societal and organizational change; studies of human behavior in novel situations are also encouraged.

Mail manuscripts to:
Dr. Sheldon Zedeck
Editor, *Journal of Applied Psychology*
Department of Psychology
University of California
Berkeley, CA 94720-1650

Authors must submit five (5) copies of the manuscript. The copies should be clear, readable, and on paper of good quality. A dot matrix or unusual typeface is acceptable only if it is clear and legible. In addition to addresses and phone numbers, authors should supply electronic mail addresses and fax numbers, if available, for potential use by the editorial office and later by the production office. Authors should keep a copy of the manuscript to guard against loss.

The journal will accept submissions in masked (blind) review format only. Each copy of a manuscript should include a separate title page with author names and affiliations, and these should not appear anywhere else on the manuscript. Furthermore, author identification notes should be typed on the title page (see *Manual*). Authors should make every reasonable effort to see that the manuscript itself contains no clues to their identities. Manuscripts not in masked format will not be reviewed.

Articles submitted for publication in the *Journal of Applied Psychology* are evaluated according to the following criteria: (a) significance of contribution, (b) technical adequacy, (c) appropriateness for the journal, and (d) clarity of presentation. In addition, articles must be clearly written in concise and unambiguous language and must be logically organized. The goal of APA primary journals is to publish useful information that is accurate and clear.

Authors should prepare manuscripts according to the *Publication Manual of the American Psychological Association* (5th ed.). Articles not prepared according to the guidelines of the *Manual* will not be reviewed. All manuscripts must include an abstract containing a maximum of 960 characters and spaces (which is approximately 120 words) typed on a separate sheet of paper. Typing instructions (all copy must be double-spaced) and instructions on preparing tables, figures, references, metrics, and abstracts appear in the *Manual*. Also, all manuscripts are copyedited for bias-free language (see chap. 2 of the *Publication Manual*). Original color figures can be printed in color provided the author agrees to pay half of the associated production costs.

The journal will publish both regular articles, or Feature Articles, and Research Reports. Authors can refer to recent issues of the journal for approximate length of Feature Articles. (Total manuscript pages divided by 4 provides an estimate of total printed pages.) Longer articles will be considered for publication, but the contribution they make must justify the number of journal pages needed to present the research. Research Reports feature shorter manuscripts that make a distinct but relatively narrow contribution, such as important replications or studies that discuss specific applications of psychology. Authors may request

Research Report status at the time of submission, or the editor may suggest that a regular-length submission be pared down to Research Report length. Research Reports are limited to no more than 17 pages of text proper; these limits do not include the title page, abstract, references, tables, or figures. Different printers, fonts, spacing, margins, and so forth can substantially alter the amount of text that can be fit on a page. In determining the length limits of Research Reports, authors should count 25–26 lines of text (60 characters per line) as the equivalent of one page.

Authors are required to obtain and provide to APA all necessary permissions to reproduce any copyrighted work, including, for example, test instruments and other test materials or portions thereof.

APA policy prohibits an author from submitting the same manuscript for concurrent consideration by two or more publications. In addition, it is a violation of APA Ethical Principles to publish "as original data, data that have been previously published" (Standard 6.24). As this journal is a primary journal that publishes original material only, APA policy prohibits as well publication of any manuscript that has already been published in whole or substantial part elsewhere. Authors have an obligation to consult journal editors concerning prior publication of any data upon which their article depends.

In addition, APA Ethical Principles specify that "after research results are published, psychologists do not withhold the data on which their conclusions are based from other competent professionals who seek to verify the substantive claims through reanalysis and who intend to use such data only for that purpose, provided that the confidentiality of the participants can be protected and unless legal rights concerning proprietary data preclude their release" (Standard 6.25). APA expects authors submitting to this journal to adhere to these standards. Specifically, authors of manuscripts submitted to APA journals are expected to have their data available throughout the editorial review process and for at least 5 years after the date of publication.

Authors will be required to state in writing that they have complied with APA ethical standards in the treatment of their sample, human or animal, or to describe the details of treatment. A copy of the APA Ethical Principles may be obtained by writing the APA Ethics Office, 750 First Street, NE, Washington, DC 20002-4242 (or see "Ethical Principles," December 1992, *American Psychologist,* Vol. 47, pp. 1597-1611).

APA requires authors to reveal any possible conflict of interest in the conduct and reporting of research (e.g., financial interests in a test procedure, funding by pharmaceutical companies for drug research).

Journal of Applied Social Psychology

ADDRESS FOR SUBMISSION:

Andrew Baum, Editor
Journal of Applied Social Psychology
University of Pittsburgh Medical Center
Behavioral Medicine and Oncology
Suite 405, Iroquois Building
3600 Forbes Avenue
Pittsburgh, PA 15213
USA
Phone: 412-647-4812
Fax:
E-Mail: racantm@msx.upmc.edu
Web: http://www.bellpub.com
Address May Change:

PUBLICATION GUIDELINES:

Manuscript Length: 26-30
Copies Required: Four
Computer Submission: Yes
Format: MS Word
Fees to Review: 0.00 US$

Manuscript Style:
American Psychological Association

CIRCULATION DATA:

Reader: Academics
Frequency of Issue: Bi-Monthly
Copies per Issue: More than 25,000
Sponsor/Publisher:
Subscribe Price: 95.00 US$ Individual
779.00 US$ Institution

REVIEW INFORMATION:

Type of Review: Blind Review
No. of External Reviewers: 2
No. of In House Reviewers: 0
Acceptance Rate: 21-30%
Time to Review: 4 - 6 Months
Reviewers Comments: Yes
Invited Articles: No Reply
Fees to Publish: 0.00 US$

MANUSCRIPT TOPICS:

Abnormal Psychology; Adolescent Psychology; Alcoholism & Drug Addiction; Behavior Modification; Child Psychology; Counseling Process; Developmental Psychology; Educational Psychology; Experimental Psychology; Family Counseling & Therapy; Gerontology; Learning & Conditioning; Personality; Physiological Psychology; Psychiatry; Psychological Testing; Psychopathology; Research Methods & Statistics; Sensation & Perception; Social Psychology; Thinking & Cognition

MANUSCRIPT GUIDELINES/COMMENTS:

The *Journal of Applied Social Psychology* will disseminate findings from behavioral science research that have applications to current problems of society. By publishing relevant research and emphasizing excellence of experimental design, as well as potential applicability of experimental results, the journal intends to bridge the theoretical and applied areas of social research. The *Journal of Applied Social Psychology* will serve as a means of communication among scientists, as well as between researchers and those engaged in the task of solving social problems.

Preference is given to manuscripts reporting laboratory and field research in areas such as health, race relations, discrimination, group processes, population growth, crowding, accelerated cultural change, violence, poverty, environmental stress, helping behavior, effects of the legal system on society and the individual, political participation and extremism, cross-cultural differences, communication, cooperative problem solving, negotiations among nations, socioeconomics, social aspects of drug action and use, organizational and industrial issues, behavioral medicine, and environmental psychology.

Reports of both laboratory and field research are accepted. Suggestions for application of research findings should be included. Theoretical papers are acceptable in limited numbers. Papers of theoretical scope should, whenever possible, include some data research. Reviews of the pertinent literature should be made with applicability in mind.

All manuscripts submitted to this journal should follow the style and method of presentation of American Psychological Association journals. Detailed instructions are given in the revised edition of the *Publication Manual of the American Psychological Association*. Alternatively, you may wish to use the American Psychological Association's APA-Style Helper software which was developed as a companion to the *Publication Manual* for new writers in the behavioral and social sciences who need to produce manuscripts and documents written according to APA style. Manuscripts should be mailed in quadruplicate to Dr. Baum:

Editor
Andrew Baum, Behavioral Medicine and Oncology
University of Pittsburgh Cancer Institute, University of Pittsburgh Medical Center
3600 Forbes Avenue, Suite 405, Pittsburgh, PA 15213

Managing Editors
Martha M. Gisriel
Tina M. Mastro

Editorial Associate
Catherine L. McKeon

Books for review consideration should be submitted to Dr. Baum.

Written permission must be obtained from the publishers to copy or reprint any table, figure, or part of text.

Journal of Applied Sport Psychology

ADDRESS FOR SUBMISSION:

Vicki Ebbeck, Editor
Journal of Applied Sport Psychology
Oregon State University
Department of Exercise & Sport Science
Corvallis, OR 97331
USA
Phone: 541-737-6800
Fax: 541-737-2788
E-Mail: vicki.ebbeck@oregonstate.edu
Web: http://www.tandf.co.uk/journals
Address May Change:

PUBLICATION GUIDELINES:

Manuscript Length: 26-30
Copies Required: Electronic
Computer Submission: Yes Email
Format: MS Word
Fees to Review: 0.00 US$

Manuscript Style:
American Psychological Association

CIRCULATION DATA:

Reader: Academics, Practitioners
Frequency of Issue: Quarterly
Copies per Issue:
Sponsor/Publisher: Association for
Advancement of Applied Sport
Psychology / Taylor & Francis
Subscribe Price: 65.00 US$ Individual
169.00 US$ Institution

REVIEW INFORMATION:

Type of Review: Blind Review
No. of External Reviewers: 3
No. of In House Reviewers: 0
Acceptance Rate: 21-30%
Time to Review: 2 - 3 Months
Reviewers Comments: No Reply
Invited Articles: 0-5%
Fees to Publish: 0.00 US$

MANUSCRIPT TOPICS:
Group Dynamics; Motivation; Sports & Leisure

MANUSCRIPT GUIDELINES/COMMENTS:

Editorial Statement
The *Journal of Applied Sport Psychology* is a nonproprietary journal that is operated by the Association for the Advancement of Applied Sport Psychology for the promotion of quality research in the field of applied sport psychology. The publisher of the *JASP* is Taylor and Francis, Inc. of Philadelphia, PA. The *JASP* is published four times a year, and is a refereed publication with all submissions reviewed by three peers via blind review process. The editor of the journal is selected by the Executive Board of AAASP by a formal vote. He/She is appointed to a three-year term with one consecutive renewal possible if so voted by the Executive Board. Associate Editors are appointed by the Editor representing each of the sections within AAASP (Health Psychology, Intervention/Performance Enhancement, Social Psychology, Clinical/Counseling Psychology). The Associate Editors are approved by the Executive Board of the Association and serve staggered terms ranging from three to five years. An individual holding an AAASP Executive Board office as a Section Chair cannot serve as an Associate Editor. Editorial Board members are appointed to three, four or five-

year terms as determined by the Editorial staff of the *JASP*. Editorial Board members may be reappointed to one consecutive term or may be asked to retire their seat on the Board at the discretion of the Editorial staff. The journal is a direct benefit of membership in AAASP and is received by student and professional members.

Instructions To Authors

The *JASP* is designed to advance thought, theory and research on applied aspects of sport psychology. Submissions such as position papers, reviews, theoretical developments specific to sport and/or exercise and applied research conducted in these settings or having significant applied implications to sport and exercise are appropriate content for the *JASP*.

Submission of Manuscripts

Manuscripts should be submitted electronically to the editor, Vicki Ebbeck, Department of Exercise and Sport Science, Oregon State University, Corvallis, OR 97331; phone: 541-737-6800; fax: 541-737-2788; e-mail: **Vicki.Ebbeck@oregonstate.edu**. Files should be prepared using MS Word or WordPerfect and attached to an email message. Each manuscript must be accompanied by a statement that it has not been published elsewhere and that it has not been submitted simultaneously for publication elsewhere. Authors are responsible for obtaining permission to reproduce copyrighted material from other sources and are required to sign an agreement for the transfer of copyright to the publisher. All accepted manuscripts, artwork, and photographs become the property of the publisher.

All parts of the manuscript should be typewritten, double-spaced, with margins of at least one inch on all sides. Articles will normally be no more than 30 pages in length (including tables and figures). They should include a title page with author names, institutional affiliations, and contact information of the corresponding author, as well as a 150-word abstract and complete references. The title of the manuscript should reappear on the first page of the text. Authors should also supply a shortened version of the title suitable for the running head, not exceeding 50 character spaces. Research notes (12 pages including references, tables, and figures; omit abstract) are welcomed submissions.

Manuscripts, including tables, figures, and references, should be prepared in accordance with the *Publication Manual of the American Psychology Association* (Fifth Edition, 2001). Copies of the manual can be obtained from the Publication Department, American Psychological Association, 750 First Street NE, Washington, DC 20002-4242; phone (202) 336-5500.

Authors are encouraged to avoid the use of sexist, racist, and otherwise offensive language. Manuscript copies should be clear and legible and all figures must be camera ready. All reviews are blind and conducted by two reviewers and a Section Editor with the review process taking 8-10 weeks. Authors will receive typed feedback regarding the editorial decisions made on their manuscript and any suggested revision recommendations. Authors should be prepared to provide their raw data if requested during the review process. A file copy of the manuscript should be kept by the author.

Illustrations
Illustrations submitted (line drawings, halftones, photos, photomicrographs, etc.) should be clean originals or digital files. Digital files are recommended for highest quality reproduction and should follow these guidelines:

- 300 dpi or higher
- sized to fit on journal page
- EPS, TIFF, or PSD format only
- submitted as separate files, not embedded in text files

Color illustrations will be considered for publication; however, the author will be required to bear the full cost involved in their printing and publication. The charge for the first figure is $900.00. Subsequent figures, totaling no more than 4 text pages, are $450.00 each. Good quality color prints should be provided in their final size. Figures needing reduction or enlargement will be charged an additional 25 percent. The publisher has the right to refuse publication of any artwork deemed unacceptable.

Tables and Figures
Tables and figures should not be embedded in the text, but should be included as separate sheets or files. A short descriptive title should appear above each table with a clear legend and any footnotes suitably identified below. All units must be included. Figures should be completely labeled, taking into account necessary size reduction. Captions should be typed, double-spaced, on a separate sheet. All original figures should be clearly marked in pencil on the reverse side with the number, author's name, and top edge indicated.

Proofs
One set of page proofs is sent to the designated author. Proofs should be checked and returned within 48 hours.

Reprints
The corresponding author of each article will receive three complete copies of the issue in which the article appears. Reprints of individual articles may be ordered from Taylor & Francis. Use the reprint order form included with page proofs.

Journal of Autism and Developmental Disorders

ADDRESS FOR SUBMISSION:

Gary B. Mesibov, Editor
Journal of Autism and Developmental
  Disorders
Univ. of North Carolina, Chapel Hill
Division TEACCH
Campus Box 7180
100 Renee Lynn Drive
Carrboro, NC 27510-7180
USA
Phone: 919-966-8189
Fax: 919-966-4127
E-Mail: gary_mesibov@unc.edu
Web: www.wkap.nl
Address May Change:

PUBLICATION GUIDELINES:

Manuscript Length: 16-20
Copies Required: Three
Computer Submission: Yes
Format: N/A
Fees to Review: 0.00 US$

Manuscript Style:
  American Psychological Association,
  4th or 5th Edition

CIRCULATION DATA:

Reader: Academics, Practitioners, Parents
Frequency of Issue: 6 Times/Year
Copies per Issue: 2,001 - 3,000
Sponsor/Publisher: Kluwer Academic
  Publishers
Subscribe Price: 93.00 US$ Individual
    93.00 Euro Individual
    See Website - more info

REVIEW INFORMATION:

Type of Review: Editorial Review
No. of External Reviewers: 4
No. of In House Reviewers: 1
Acceptance Rate: 35%
Time to Review: 2 - 3 Months
Reviewers Comments: Yes
Invited Articles: No Reply
Fees to Publish: 0.00 US$

MANUSCRIPT TOPICS:
Autism; Behavior Modification; Developmental Disorders; Developmental Psychology;
Exceptional Child; Neuropsychology

MANUSCRIPT GUIDELINES/COMMENTS:

Topics Include. Subjects related to autism and other developmental disorders:
Communication; diagnosis-assessment/characteristics of disability, testing or screening
instruments; Epidemiology; Family/parents, siblings; Genetics; Medical/intervention or
therapy/physical conditions or attributes; Methodology; Neurobiology/brain function, face
processing-eye movement; Psychosocial-behavioral interventions, Social Development/joint
attention, play, imitation; Other.

Aims and Scope
Journal of Autism and Developmental Disorders covers all the severe psychopathologies in
childhood, including autism and childhood schizophrenia. Original articles discuss

experimental studies on the biochemical, neurological, and genetic aspects of a particular disorder; the implications of normal development for deviant processes; and interaction between disordered behavior of individuals and social or group factors. The *Journal* also features research and case studies involving the entire spectrum of interventions (including behavioral, biological, educational, and community aspects) and advances in the diagnosis and classification of disorders.

This *Journal* is devoted to all severe psychopathologies in childhood and is not necessarily limited to autism and childhood schizophrenia. The following topics fall within its scope: (1) experimental studies on the biochemical, neurological, and genetic aspects of the disorder; (2) the implications of normal development for deviant processes; (3) interaction between disordered behavior of individuals and social or group factors; (4) research and case studies involving the entire spectrum of interventions, including behavioral, biological, educational, and community aspects; (5) diagnosis and classification of disorders reflecting new knowledge.

Topics may be explored in several forms: (1) experimental studies of original research; (2) theoretical papers based on scholarly review of relevant topics; (3) critical reviews of important research or treatment activity; (4) case studies in which new insights for the individual are demonstrated and implications for other children or research are discussed. Papers, or substantial parts of such papers, that have already been published or committed elsewhere will not be accepted for publication in this *Journal*.

Guidelines for Submission
1. Manuscripts should be submitted to the Editor:
   Gary B. Mesibov
   Division of TEACCH
   100 Renee Lynn Drive
   Campus Box 7180
   University of North Carolina
   Carrboro, North Carolina 27510-7180

The *Journal* will operate a dual system until all paper manuscripts have been reviewed. The new electronic system will be activated in June 2004. Information regarding this can be found in Author Instructions at **http://www,kluweronline.com/issn/0162-3257**.

Please direct all inquiries concerning manuscripts to Kathie Barron at
   Kathie barron@med.unc.edu (919) 966-8182.

2. Submission is a representation that the manuscript has not been published previously and is not currently under consideration for publication elsewhere. This statement should be included in the cover letter. Also, a statement transferring copyright from the authors (or their employers, if they hold the copyright) to Kluwer Academic Publishing Corporation will be required before the manuscript can be accepted for publication. The Editor will supply the necessary forms for this transfer. Such a written transfer of copyright, which previously was assumed to be implicit in the act of submitting a manuscript, is necessary under the U.S. Copyright Law in order for the publisher to carry through the dissemination of research results

and reviews as widely and effectively as possible. Note: The new electronic system requires this form at the time of submission.

3. Type double-spaced, and submit the original and three copies (including copies of all illustrations and tables). Academic affiliations of all authors and the full mailing address of the one author who will review the proofs should be included.

4. A 120-word abstract is to be provided for articles and brief reports. It is not needed for a letter to the editor.

5. Tables should be numbered and referred to by number in the text. Each table should be typed on a separate sheet of paper and should have a descriptive title. Tables appear after the Reference section. The manuscript text should contain "call outs" in brackets to indicate the placement of tables and figures. Example: [place Table 1 about here].

6. Figures must be preceded by a Figure Caption sheet listing all captions for figures. Figures (photographs, drawings, diagrams, and charts) are to be numbered in one consecutive series of Arabic numerals. Photographs should be large, glossy prints, showing high contrast. Drawings should be prepared with india ink. Either the original drawings or good-quality photographic prints are acceptable. Identify figures on the back with author's name and number of the illustration. Electronic artwork submitted on disk should be in the TIFF or EPS format (1200 dpi for line and 300 dpi for half-tones and gray-scale art). Color art should be in the CYMK color space. Artwork should be on a separate disk from the text, and hard copy **must** accompany the disk. The manuscript text should contain "call outs" in brackets to indicate the placement of tables and figures. Example: [place Table 1 about here].

7. The 1994 fourth edition of the *Publication Manual of the American Psychological Association* should be used as the style guide for the preparation of manuscripts, particularly with respect to such matters as the citing of references and the use of abbreviations, numbers, and symbols. Transition will be made to APA – Fifth Edition in 2005. At present, either 4th or 5th guidelines are acceptable.

8. Instructions will be provided by the electronic system to be activated in June 2004. For manuscript presented under the former print system: after all revisions have been incorporated, manuscripts should be submitted to the Editor's Office as hard copy accompanied by electronic files on disk. Label the disk with identifying information-- software, journal name, and first author's last name. **The disk must be the one from which the accompanying manuscript (finalized version) was printed out.** The Editor's Office cannot accept a disk without its accompanying, matching hard-copy manuscript.

9. The journal makes no page charges. Reprints are available to authors, and order forms with the current prices schedule are sent with proofs. Complementary copies are not provided to authors.

Notes

Notes

Notes

Notes

Notes

Notes

Notes

Cabell's Directories
of Publishing Opportunities in
Business

NINTH EDITION 2004-2005

Accounting
Economics & Finance
Management
Marketing

To order Hardcopy or On-line versions - visit
www.cabells.com